W9-DDP-246

DISTRICT HEATING
HANDBOOK

FOURTH EDITION
Vol. 1

A Design Guide

Published in the interest of the
District Heating and Cooling Industry by
International District Heating Association
1735 "Eye" St. N.W., Washington, D.C. 20006

Copyright, 1983
International District Hearing Association
Washington, D.C.

ISBN 0-9610838-0-8
Library of Congress Catalogue # 83-080208

Text and illustrations are fully protected by Copyright and may not be reprinted, either wholly or in part, without permission.

Preface to the Fourth Edition

FOR MORE THAN THIRTY YEARS this book's well known predecessor served to guide succeeding generations of engineers to an understanding of district heating and how best to use it. However, district heating and cooling has developed considerably since 1951 when the Third Edition was published. Equipment and methods have changed and there are new factors that give the industry an important role in the national concerns as to the utilization of our energy resources.

The Volume was first published in 1921 as *Handbook of the National District Heating Association*, followed by the second edition in 1932 and again in 1951. Beginning in the 1960's there was a real effort to revise the text and publish the 4th edition, but with limited resources, a volunteer staff of authors, and overwhelming assignments to already overworked members, the effort floundered year after year.

The National District Heating Association in the meantime became the International District Heating Association (IDHA) and in 1980 was thoroughly reorganized with a new staff taking a strong advocacy position for district heating and developing affiliations with similar groups. The Edison Electric Institute early recognized the value of a revision to the handbook and supported an in-depth review by an editorial consultant. The appraisal was positive and EEI backed IDHA in developing the fourth edition. The U.S. Department of Energy further assisted the effort with a development contract through the Argonne National Laboratories. The firm of Enviro-Management and Research, Inc. was selected by IDHA to develop the manuscript and coordinate the production.

The membership of IDHA contributed time, effort and resources in furnishing material and checking data, but their patience and understanding in what has seemed to be an insurmountable series of delays, cancellations, and deviations has been exceptional.

In spite of our best efforts there may be some mistakes in the book, and they are our responsibility. We must enter the same plea as that used 200 years ago by Dr. Johnson. A lady had taken him to task for a flagrantly wrong term in his dictionary. When she asked him how he could make such a mistake he replied, "Ignorance, Madam, pure ignorance."

NORMAN R. TAYLOR
KATHARINE L. STIERHOFF
Washington, D.C. 1982

Acknowledgements

This book could not have been written without the help of a great number of people and organizations. The publishers and editors acknowledge gratefully their assistance. In so far as possible we have listed major contributions in the chronological order of their participation as it is an indicator of the long and complex task.

Adequate credit to all that assisted would be an impossible task, but we sincerely appreciate every effort.

The Educational Committee, J. Earl Seiter, Chairman, 1951, who edited and published the Third Edition.

The Educational Committee, Nelson R. Tonet, Chairman, 1972–73, under President Joseph J. Bosl, assembled and edited a draft for the fourth edition.

The Educational Committee, Joseph J. Bosl, Chairman, 1976–77, under President Mack A. Riley, developed participation of federal agencies in the *Handbook*.

Edison Electric Institute funded an editorial appraisal of the Third Edition and draft material for the new version. As a result, EEI made available financial support to IDHA for the Fourth Edition.

U.S. Department of Energy, made available a study grant to develop a contemporary handbook text.
John P. Millhone
Maxine Savitz
Gerald S. Leighton
John Rodousakis

Argonne National Laboratory administered the study grant and provided invaluable technical assistance and services.
Allen Kennedy
Danilo J. Santini
Jess Pasqual

Enviro-Management and Research Inc., Naresh K. Khosla, contractors to IDHA for research and text preparation.

Geothermal Energy Division of the Department of Energy, Eric Peterson, contribution of the chapter on geothermal sources for district heating.

Dr. Gordon M. Reistad, Oregon State University, text development for geothermal resources.

American Society of Heating, Refrigeration and Air Conditioning Engineers, Clinton Phillips, President, Samuel Rosenberg, Handbook Editor, for permission to reprint material.

Babcock and Wilcox, for permission to reprint material and illustrations from "Steam", a reference book, 39th Edition, third printing, copyright 1978.

We also most sincerely appreciate the unaccountable hours contributed by IDHA members and their company staffs who have furnished both helpful suggestions, authoritative material, and who read, reviewed and corrected seemingly endless pages of texts.

Contents

Preface .... *iii*
Acknowledgments .... *iv*

Chapter 1
THE DISTRICT HEATING AND COOLING INDUSTRY 1
An Overview of District Heating and Cooling 1
The History of District Heating 1
District Heating in the U.S. 2
Experience of Other Countries with District Heating 4
District Heating Technology, Markets and Costs 8
Benefits and Barriers 10
The Future of District Heating 11

Chapter 2
OVERALL SYSTEM CONSIDERATIONS 13
District Heating and Cooling Concepts 13
Principle Issues and Barriers 16
Conclusions 49

Chapter 3
SOURCES OF ENERGY FOR DISTRICT HEATING SYSTEMS . 51
Coal 51
Oil 69
Natural Gas 81
Cogeneration 90
Refuse-Derived Energy 98
Geothermal 108
Nonconventional Fuels for District Heating 129

Chapter 4
STEAM AND HOT WATER PRODUCTION PLANT 139
Principles of Combustion 139
Boilers 141
Steam Separators and Superheaters 150
Operation and Maintenance of Equipment 156
Production of Demand and Output 176
Construction Planning, Drawings and Specifications 178
Instrumentation and Controls 179
Draft, Stack and Fans 191

Compressed Air Systems 197
Auxiliary Steam Plant Equipment 198
Water Treatment 205

Chapter 5
AIR CONDITIONING 215
Statistics 215
System Design Considerations 215
Absorption System 219
Mechanical Compression System 223

Chapter 6
DISTRIBUTION SYSTEMS 231
Steam Systems 231
Hot Water Systems 279
Chilled Water Distribution Systems 283
General Considerations for Distribution Loop Installation 289
Standards and Currents Installation Practices 289
Construction Procedures 290
Leak Location 293

Chapter 7
METERING 295
Physical Properties 295
Methods of Metering 299
Hot and Chilled Water Metering 312

Chapter 8
DISTRICT HEATING SERVICE TO THE USER 319
Estimating Steam Requirements 319
Building Space Conditioning 336
Waste Heat Reclamation Systems 356
Steam Refrigeration and Air Conditioning 371
Service Water Heating 387
Humidication by Steam 400

Chapter 9
THE ECONOMIC AND FINANCIAL ANALYSIS OF
COMMUNITY ENERGY SYSTEMS 405
Economics and Financial Management 405
Background for Economic Analysis of Community Energy Systems 412
Examples of Community Energy Systems 413
Economic Feasibility of Community Energy Systems 415
Overview of Economic Analysis of Community Energy Systems ... 417
Estimates of Costs and Revenues 421
Systems Comparison and Selection 441
Sensitivity Analysis of Miscellaneous Considerations 449
Sample Application of the Economic Analysis 451
Rate Making Principles 458
Examples of Rate Designs 461

Appendix *473*
Index *510*

CHAPTER 1

The District Heating and Cooling Industry

AN OVERVIEW OF DISTRICT HEATING AND COOLING

DISTRICT HEATING AND COOLING can be described as a method by which thermal energy from a central source is distributed to residential, commercial and industrial consumers for use in space heating, cooling, water heating and process heating. The central source may be one of any number of types of boiler units, a refuse incinerator, a geothermal source, solar energy or one which utilizes heat developed as a by-product of electrical generation. This latter approach, generally known as "cogeneration," has a high level of energy utilization efficiency.

District heating systems are adaptable to a wide variety of fuel types. This flexibility can benefit the nation and the consumer by providing thermal energy at stable and competitive prices while, at the same time, lessening our dependence on scarce or imported fuels. The district heating concept is not new. First commercial applications in the United States date back as far as 1876. However, modern applications of the district heating concept have not been adopted readily, despite it being particularly well suited to the energy needs of many areas.

In the district heating process, energy is distributed to individual buildings from a central plant by means of steam or hot or chilled water lines. Buildings connected with the system extract energy from the transfer medium rather than generating the useable energy on site at a facility in each building.

District heating is best suited to those areas with a high building and population density in relatively cold climatic zones. In such areas, district heating can maintain stable and competitive pricing. District cooling is applicable in most areas where there are appreciable concentrations of population. Since we have entered an era where formerly low-cost and abundant fossil fuels have become scarce and expensive, district heating and cooling is getting a well-deserved second-look, especially in the high density central cities of our nation.

THE HISTORY OF DISTRICT HEATING

Piped heating systems are a very old concept. Nearly 2,000 years ago piped systems were used by ancient Romans for heating dwellings as well as baths. In more modern times, Sir William Cook in Manchester, England, in 1745, demonstrated the potential of steam heat for buildings through a system of pipe coils in his home. In 1748, Benjamin Franklin built an iron stove-type furnace in an underground chamber and used it to heat a series of row houses

1

by running the flue in a brick and tiled fireproof enclosure beneath the floors. A water heating system was installed in a U.S. building in 1830 and, in 1844, the Eastern Hotel in Boston, Massachusetts, used steam for the first time as the medium for heating a large commercial building. With these advances, including the introduction in 1860 of the first cast iron radiator, a major industry sprang up manufacturing and installing steam and hot water heating systems.

In 1877, Birdsill Holly, a noted hydraulic engineer and inventor, pioneered the first commercially successful district heating system. Using a boiler in his cellar as the central heat source, Holly developed a loop of steam distribution, radiation, condensation, and return for his own home. This was followed by increasingly distant extensions of the system to heat neighbors homes up to 1,000 feet away. The distribution line was iron pipe, wrapped with asbestos, felt, and paper, buried about three feet deep in a wooden box filled with sawdust. His initial efforts were so successful that he was able to raise the necessary capital to found the Holly Steam Combination Company in Lockport, N.Y., which began service with 14 customers. By 1879 Holly's corporation had nearly three miles of line in service, and by 1880 the steam service was extended to include several factories. By the following year the industry had grown so fast that the first district steam equipment manufacturing corporation was formed.

Within a decade, district heat using a steam transfer medium had expanded to ten cities in Pennsylvania and others as far away as DuBuque, Iowa, Denver, Colorado, and New York City.

In 1879, the same year Thomas Edison was installing electric lines in New York City, the Steam Heating and Power Company of New York was founded. Soon thereafter a competing firm, the New York Steam Company was established. As many small electric utility companies evolved to meet the new and growing demand for electricity utilization, it became apparent that use of the exhaust steam from their power generation was an obvious opportunity to add to profits.

As efficiencies of scale began to be added to electrical generation, the district heating industry suffered. The advent of closed-cycle turbine generators lacking exhaust steam, and of larger, more efficient but less centrally located generating facilities limited the growth potential of the steam industry. Steam being a by-product of the generating process which could be sold very inexpensively, had been a second profit center for electric utilities. However, generation of steam separately from electricity greatly increased costs and utilities were forced to raise rates. In 1909, the year the National District Heating Association was founded, about 150 district heating systems existed in the United States. Many operated marginally or at low profit. The cost of converting from exhaust steam to live steam had been a shock to the industry. From that low point, however, the management and profitability of district heating systems improved dramatically through most of the first half of this century.

Since World War II, district heating in the U.S. has remained virtually static, as low-cost and abundant fossil fuels and electricity have overshadowed many of the advantages of district heating. However, European nations during the same period had significant success with hot water-based district heating.

DISTRICT HEATING IN THE UNITED STATES

District heating in the United States is based, primarily, on the use of steam. District heating and cooling systems account for less than one-percent of the total energy demand for space and hot water heating in this country. District heating systems are used in a limited number of cities, in various institutions, and on college campuses. No significant growth in demand for district heating has been noted in recent years (Fig. 1.1). However, there has been renewed interest in renovating and rejuvenating district heating, because of the changes in oil supplies and increases in all fuel prices.

About one-fifth of U.S. energy is used for heating and cooling. Current estimates are that district heating systems could supply about half that energy efficiently. Electrical generating efficiencies increase from about 33% for electricity alone to over 60% efficiency when hot water or steam from generation is used in a district heating system. In most cases, this leads directly to a reduction in the use of oil or natural gas.

Currently, oil is the primary fuel for district heating boilers, developing 48% of the steam (Fig. 1.2). Use of coal and refuse as primary fuels is under serious consideration. There is growing motivation to expand existing district heating systems wherever circumstances make such augmentation possible. While many roadblocks exist, there are both government and private efforts underway to increase the contribution of district heating in the years ahead.

Fewer significant U.S. district heating systems presently employ hot water as the medium for transporting the energy than steam network facilities. Feasibility studies are underway to assess the various aspects of district heating development in the United States. Among the areas being studied are comparisons of hot water and steam transportation mediums, space cooling, cogeneration efficiencies, fuel savings, and costs.

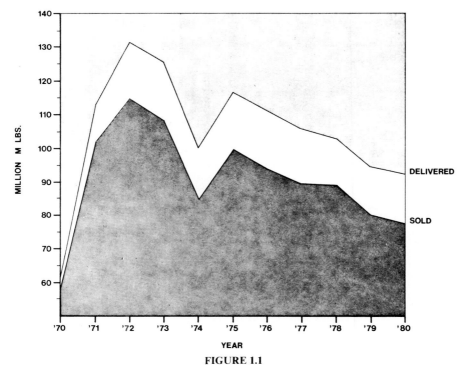

FIGURE 1.1

Ten year summary of steam sendout and sales

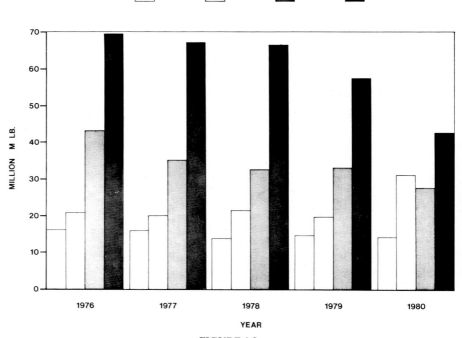

FIGURE 1.2
Pounds of steam produced by fuel type

EXPERIENCE OF OTHER COUNTRIES WITH DISTRICT HEATING

District heating and cooling capacity in several countries are compared in Figure 1.3.

Significant installations of district heating in Europe did not occur until after World War II. Since that time, however, it has developed rapidly and with excellent public acceptance. As the growth of district heating is relatively recent, the European public views it as a "modern" development and approach it with the enthusiasm that greets innovation.

The contemporary success of district heating in Europe has aroused new interest in this country and has led to a movement toward adoption of Europe methods in this nation's cities. While direct application of European methods may not be transferrable to the United States directly because of major differences in power plants, in heating and cooling loads and in patterns of city development, the potential remains great.

The European method uses hot water from back-pressure turbines distributed to customer loads created incrementally as new communities are developed. In this country, new building construction as a percentage of the total existing building volume is low. European systems have sustained winter demand and carry no appreciable air-conditioning loads in summer. In the U.S. where steam is available, it is generally used for heating while electricity powers most cooling machinery resulting in poor load factors for both systems. As a result, electric utilities in the past have heavily promoted electric heating. Existing buildings equipped for steam or electric heat cannot be adapted readily to hot water

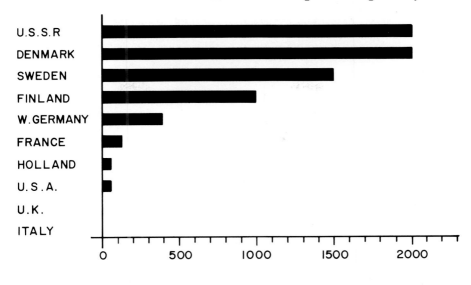

MEGAWATTS THERMAL PER MILLION PEOPLE

FIGURE 1.3

Installed district heating and cooling capacity

systems and hot water cooling devices are not efficient in comparison with electrically-driven units.

Electrical generating practice in the U.S. differs greatly from the European customs. In Europe, turbines generally utilize back-pressure design in sizes ranging from 50 to 300 MW with throttle pressures below 2,400 psi, whereas in this country, units generally use a condensing design with capacities ranging from 600 to 1300 MW at pressures from 2,400 to 3,500 psi.

In addition to these engineering and load differences today, electric utility plants take eight to ten years to site, design, and build. Developers cannot project the utility needs for their buildings on such a long-range basis. In Europe, the considerably smaller plants are built more nearly in the same time frame as housing and commercial developments.

Over the past 25 years, most northern European countries have centralized heat production and combined the generation of heat and electricity. More than 30% of all homes in Denmark are supplied by district heating and 90% of all towns with populations exceeding 2,000 people have some sort of centralized heat supply. The Danish national energy plan includes a heating program that would allow 40% of the country's total heat consumption in 1990 to be met by residual heat from electric power station generation. In Sweden 35 cities and towns have district heating systems using hot water as the heat distribution medium supplied from plants having only hot water boilers.

When heat loads exceed 100 MW, combined heat and power plants are the usual source. The U.S.S.R. has 970 combined heat and power stations with a capacity of 45,000 MW out of a total capacity of 207,000 MW for all electric power stations. West Germany has 472 district heating networks. The government is studying the feasibility of a national grid of district heating systems supplied by large power stations. It has been estimated that 40% of the heat for space and water heating could be supplied in this way.

The district heating programs of several countries are detailed in the following sections.

Finland

In Finland 14% of all homes are served by district heating systems. The majority of these, because of the efficiencies of high density, are in Helsinki. In that city, 65% of the homes are kept warm through district heating, with a goal for 1990 of 85%. Feed and return pipelines for the Helsinki system total 250 miles.

The energy for much of Finnish district heating is supplied by waste heat from nuclear plants. The waste heat is not only utilized in the system, but also reduces by half the effluent heat discharged into the ocean in nuclear cooling processes. In Helsinki, district heating not only has aided in the elimination of environmental pollution, but also has turned a profit for the city.

In 1976, Helsinki had four cogeneration heat and power stations—four heating plants for peak loads and 36 transportable heating plants. Two additional heating stations are planned by 1984 and another pair by 1993.

Sweden

Sweden relies on approximately 50 district heating systems, owned by the communities they serve to provide space heating and domestic hot water. In Stockholm, about 50% of the inhabitants are served by district heating with the goal for the year 2000 set at 90%. District heating is strongly emphasized as part of the nation's national fuels policy.

Sweden is heavily dependent upon imported fossil fuels. It is estimated that, in Stockholm alone, district heating saves an estimated $11 million or more annually in reduced fuel oil consumption. District heating systems are required to connect any eligible applicant to the system. Loans and grants are made available so the new subscriber can afford to make the connection. In small or new communities, mobile boilers may provide the heat but, as the community grows, a more permanent installation is made.

Denmark

One of the earliest European nations to use district heating, Denmark has used cogeneration technology for nearly 60 years. Fifty percent of all energy consumption in Denmark is for space heating, with district systems supplying 40% of all Danish households.

A deliberate emphasis has been put on use of energy sources such as coal, uranium, and residual fuel oil as well as domestic and industrial wastes in district heating applications.

Denmark is a pioneer in the use of refuse, where about 60% of all waste is used for district heating. This supplies 5% of the total heat consumed in the nation. The national goal is to increase this percentage to 75% of all waste.

Hook-up to district heating is not mandatory; however, costs of district heating are kept low enough to generate demand strictly on the basis of competition. A subscriber agrees to purchase heat for a minimum of 20 years— usually the repayment period of the loan covering connection charges.

England

England is beginning to explore expansion of a district heating concept. A policy of regenerating electricity at the absolute lowest cost has led away from experiments in cogeneration. A new philosophy has recently been propounded which would have the government look at cogeneration in terms of electricity as a by-product of heat rather than the alternative.

West Germany

West Germany is heavily dependent upon imported fuels. As a result, the government is studying a variety of alternative space heating technologies. Many cities and towns currently have district heating systems. Although dual-purpose power plants are not widely favored, industrial cogeneration does have public support.

A government study is assessing the possibilities of a nationwide district heating "super-grid" to interconnect all cities with populations of 40,000 or more. Such a grid would utilize heat from all available sources.

Switzerland

With a relatively high standard of living, it is not the economics of fossil fuels which have prompted Switzerland to begin expansion of its district heating systems, but a concern for the environment. With a relatively low urban density and abundant water power, district heating is still in its infancy in this nation, however, its implementation has begun on a small scale.

Italy

The climate of this sourthern European nation is milder than most other nations on that continent. Brescia, on Lake Garda in North Central Italy, has a municipally-owned urban district heating system employing a back-pressure turbine with 30 MW electrical generating capacity. A second unit is just coming on line. Supplemental boilers provide superheated water during peak periods and during warm weather when heat is needed only for domestic hot water.

Union of Soviet Socialist Republics

Russia is the largest user of district heating in the world, with a cogeneration capacity far more than the rest of the world combined. Over 1,000 stations provide heat and electricity to 800 Soviet cities. The centrally planned economy, which can dictate the size, location and composition of new communities, makes installation of district heating systems easy and efficient. As a result, over half of domestic heat in the U.S.S.R. is provided by district heating through cogeneration.

In planning new communities, loads are forecast on a five-to-ten year basis. Before a new thermal power station is built, an 8 to 12 billion Btu/hr heat load and a 200 MW electrical load are required. Until that point is reached, local heat-only boiler plants supply the hot water, while electric needs are provided through a link with the national grid.

Czechoslovakia, Rumania, Poland, Hungary, and Bulgaria

Czechoslovakia leads Eastern European nations in developed district heating capacity. Altogether, 157 cities have district heating systems in that nation. Poland and Rumania have concentrated on large district heating systems. In

Poland and Czechoslovakia, where coal is abundant, district heating is still in its early stages, with small sized systems predominant.

In Rumania, 50% of all space heating is provided through district heating systems; however, only one-third of that comes from cogeneration, the bulk being from single-purpose equipment. Bulgaria has abundant coal and, therefore, has led in the highest use of cogeneration facilities of any of the Eastern European block nations.

DISTRICT HEATING TECHNOLOGY, MARKETS AND COSTS

District heating systems can be classified according to the type of area they serve, with different system technology and design necessary for optimum performance in each area type. Typical classifications by service area or market are:

1. Densely populated urban areas.
2. High density building clusters.
3. Industrial complexes.
4. Low density residential areas.

Studies of existing systems have shown that district heating can be economically productive in the first three markets listed above. The experience of European communities show that, when correctly applied, single family residential areas could be served economically also.

Three main factors determine whether or not district heating will be economically productive in a given environment.

- Heat-load density.
- Annual load factor.
- Rate of consumer connections.

A majority of the capital investment required for a district heating system goes into the costly facilities needed for transmission and distribution. This will run from 50% to 75% of the total. To be cost effective, District Heating and Cooling (DHC) requires a high heat-load density. Economics alone may rule out single-family residential areas under current conditions. Changes in economics or technology such as development of low-cost, non-metallic piping, improved installation techniques, and low-cost metering could change the outlook, however.

For economical operation, a district heating system must connect the maximum number of users in a service area to the system as soon as practical. This rate of consumer connections sets the pace for revenue which, in turn, determines the economic success or failure of the system. Once the system is in operation and the initial consumer connection rate satisfactory, the cost of connecting new buildings into the system is often less than the cost of furnace or boiler installations. Cost of conversion for existing buildings depends on multiple factors, such as age, type and condition of existing equipment, since conversion to district heating becomes most attractive when existing systems are in need of replacement.

Densely Populated Urban Areas

In the central core of densely populated metropolitan areas, district heating systems should be multi-purpose in order to serve as large a number of consumers as possible. A twenty- to thirty-year phased construction period would not be unlikely for such a system. Massive amounts of financing would be required for the miles of distribution pipes and the several thousand megawatts of capacity needed. Often, only a small portion of the total system cost is needed initially, with the bulk of the costs being provided through sales revenues.

In contrast, a system for a smaller city core area would require only a few hundred megawatt capacity and but a few miles of distribution piping. Construction could range from only a few years up to about ten years, with capital requirements running in the tens of millions of dollars. Some characteristics would be common to systems in both areas:

1. A variety of building types and energy uses will be included. Several simultaneous services will be required.
2. Thermal energy sources probably will be surplus heat from electric and industrial plants, urban waste disposal facilities, geothermal wells, or solar collectors.
3. Distribution network costs will comprise a majority of the system costs.
4. Institutional arrangements for achieving a successful system will be extensive and complex, involving both public and private sectors.

High Density Clusters

High density developments include such potential system users as suburban shopping centers, a university campus, a high density highrise residential complex, or a high density mixed suburban development. Characteristics of the system include:

1. Both plants and distribution network will probably be new and designed specifically for the application.
2. The distribution network may be relatively small, comprising a small part of total system cost.
3. Coal fired systems may be used for larger systems, with oil and gas used in smaller applications.
4. Central source may be a new cogeneration plant or a facility making use of surplus heat from an existing industrial or electric plant.
5. Institutional arrangements are usually simple, involving only a few decision-makers.
6. Financing would be from a few million to a few tens of million dollars. Construction would run from a few years to ten years in one or two phases.

Industrial Complexes

Special demands of systems for industrial complexes rule the type of system and its economics. Steam, hot water, or both may be necessary, and industrial process loads will dominate system use. Central plant technology and fuels will be similar to those for high density clusters.

Institutional arrangements should be simple, but varied thermal requirements may make distribution systems complex. A high utilization factor makes for favorable economics.

Low Density Residential Areas

A district heating system for low-density residential developments typically would serve an area dominated by single or duplex residential units. Such systems would probably have the following in common:

1. Cost of the distribution system, most likely low temperature hot water, would dominate construction costs.

2. Water-source heat pumps could augment system capacity.
3. Fuel source could be gas, oil cogeneration, geothermal wells or solar central plants.
4. Central source is likely to be new, with capacities of less than one megawatt to a few megawatts.
5. Institutional arrangements may be moderately complex.
6. High capital costs and low utilization make this type of system marginally economical in most areas.

BENEFITS AND BARRIERS

Revitalizing district heating is analogous to opening a new frontier. Despite the fact that district heating has been in commercial application for over 100 years, new development in this industry has all the aspects of entering a new venture. Benefits beckon temptingly while barriers appear to loom insurmountable. To break down the barriers and to reap the benefits is a challenging and, perhaps, a lengthy task, but the rewards are great.

The benefits include:

1. Conservation of scarce natural resources through using energy more efficiently, increasing conservation efforts, and maximizing the use of each Btu expended. If implemented in the U.S. today, district heating could save up to 2.5 million barrels of oil or natural gas equivalents each day by the year 2000. District heating does this by utilizing waste heat which otherwise goes unused to displace consumption of oil and natural gas. Much greater fuel efficiency is achieved through cogeneration.
2. Stabilization of energy costs and supplies. District heating system central plants can use coal, nuclear fuel, urban solid refuse, geothermal resources, or solar energy instead of the sensitive supplies of imported oil or natural gas reserves. These fuels all are to a greater or lesser degree, more stable in both supply and price than oil or natural gas.
3. Stabilization of thermal services and their costs. For industry to invest capital in expansion, a reasonable return on investment must be likely. If interruption in needed services is likely or if costs lack stability, business cannot afford to make the investment. District heating systems provide the necessary cost and service stability.
4. Creation of short- and long-term employment opportunities. Construction of a small system provides employment for skilled and unskilled workers for several years at the very least. Construction of a major urban system can provide many jobs for nearly a working lifetime. Operation and maintenance of the system provides employment for others, while the availability of reasonably priced, stable thermal services means growth and business expansion which provides still more employment opportunities.
5. Reduction of environmental pollution and improvement in air quality. District heating systems replace small, uncontrolled sources of air pollution with a fully controlled central source. Though air quality in the immediate vicinity of a central source may experience an increase in emissions, the net effect often will be a dramatic reduction in pollution concentration.
6. Establishment of a base for future cooperative efforts in the field of energy planning and management. Cooperation among city governments, utilities, industry, building owners and citizens is essential to almost any

district heating system installation. This cooperative structure can be utilized on a much broader scale.

On the other side of the scale are barriers which must be overcome if district heating is to expand as an effective enterprise in the United States. These barriers are:

1. Electric utilities, which are essential partners in large cogeneration facilities, see problems as well as benefits. Most utility executives are faced with a myriad of problems in the marketing and generation of electricity alone and, hence, hestitate to take on the burdens of what is essentially a new industry. Many executives who are associated with or familiar with existing district heating systems believe them to be marginal operations, to be abandoned rather than expanded. Some utilities, however, are exploring district heating with a positive attitude.

2. Federal policy currently does not support district heating. Neither tax-exempt revenue bond financing on a major scale nor investment tax credits are available for district heating systems under current law. The policies of the Economic Regulatory Administration at present do not encourage cogeneration, and those of the Federal Energy Regulatory Commission do not allow necessary fuel adjustment pass-through to encourage utility company participation and support.

3. Feasibility studies are very expensive, time consuming, and tangled in a web of red tape. In a time of where every dollar is precious and every minute important, necessary studies are long and costly. A simple preliminary study for a district heating system for a large city might cost $50,000. A detailed study could run $500,000 or more. Lack of clear support and direction add to delays and increase costs.

THE FUTURE OF DISTRICT HEATING

Despite the barriers and some years of neglect, the future for district heating in the United States is bright. Barriers can and will be overcome. The technology is not a problem as the barriers are in the social, political and financial arenas. These barriers are difficult, but they can be removed. Bearing more weight than any other factor in the equation is need—which is there and pressing.

The capacity is there as well. If implemented fully in appropriate markets, an analysis for Argonne National Laboratories shows that thermal capacity for district heating in the United States would be approximately 300,000 megawatts—a fifteen-fold increase over present district heating output. Some suggestions which have been made to help lower the barriers include:

1. Education of government and industry officials and potential customers concerning district heating.

2. Development of a practical arrangement so public and private capital can be joined for district heating development. One such arrangement might be public investment of capital with local utilities handling operation of the system.

3. Relaxation of such environmental regulations as might be necessary to allow coal-fired cogeneration to serve U.S. cities.

4. Improved communication and coordination between government and industry to achieve district heating goals.

The agenda is set; the course clear. The United States is ready for a renaissance in district heating.

CHAPTER 2

Overall System Considerations

DISTRICT HEATING AND COOLING CONCEPTS

A DISTRICT HEATING SYSTEM is made up of three major components, as shown in Figure 2.1. The first component is the production plant which provides the steam, hot water or chilled water. Steam and hot water can be produced specifically for the district heating system by boilers burning fossil fuels; however, less expensive heat sources often can be found. Electric generating plants for example, normally discard 70% of the heat content of input fuel and municipal incinerators usually reject all the heat they generate. Recovering this heat and using it in a district heating system can reduce a community's consumption of primary fuels such as heating oil or natural gas.

Chilled water can be produced either by use of an absorption refrigeration machine, electric-driven centrifugal chiller, gas or steam turbine-driven centrifugal chiller, or a combination of turbine-driven mechanical systems and heat-driven absorption systems.

The second component is the transmission/distribution network which conveys energy in the form of steam, hot water or chilled water through pipes from the thermal production plants to consumers. The schematic layout of a simpli-

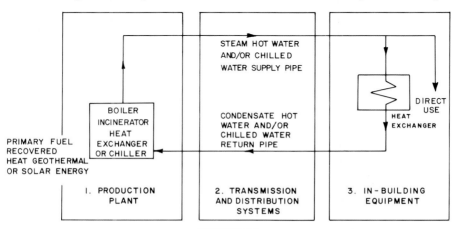

FIGURE 2.1

Three major components of a district heating system

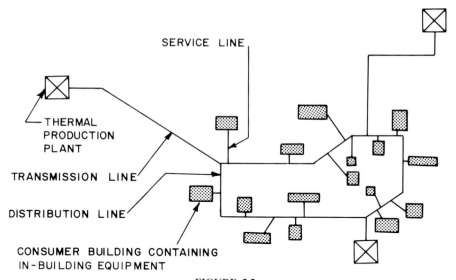

FIGURE 2.2
Schematic layout of a simplified district heating system

fied district heating system is shown in Figure 2.2. This figure also defines the nomenclature of lines utilized in the system.

The third component of the district heating system includes the in-building equipment. When steam is supplied by the district heating system it may be used directly for heating; may be directed through a pressure reducing station for use in a low-pressure (0–15 psig) steam space heating, service water heating and absorption cooling system; or may be passed through a steam-to-water heat exchanger, which transfers heat from one fluid to another in buildings employing hot water heating systems. In the case of hot water systems water-to-water heat exchangers are used most frequently, and many building space heating and domestic water heating systems are of hot water design. When chilled water is also distributed by the district heating system, water-to-water heat exchangers are employed within the building to maintain the district heating system integrity.

Types of District Heating and Cooling (DHC) Systems

District heating and cooling systems are classified according to the thermal energy transfer media used. These include the following systems:

Steam System Types
1. Heat only systems were boiler capacity is committed to supply steam at the design pressure to the distribution network.
2. Cogeneration, dual energy use, or combined heat and power systems, steam used in the system is a byproduct of the electric generation process.
3. Supply/purchase systems, where steam above a base capacity is purchased from other boiler plants, including refuse incineration systems, depending on demand and availability.

Hot Water System Types
1. Hot water is supplied from designated boilers at central locations in the system.

2. Hybrid systems where there is a basic steam system which develops on-site hot water for a localized hot water network.
3. Cogeneration, dual energy use, or combined heat and power systems where hot water is developed as part of the electric generation process.
4. Hot water obtained from geothermal sources.
5. Hot water developed from refuse burning operations or extracted from industrial waste heat.

Chilled Water System Types
1. Chilled water is produced at a central plant by steam-driven equipment.
2. Electrically-driven equipment produces chilled water at a central plant.

STEAM SYSTEMS

The first district heating plant in the United States consisted of a low-pressure boiler supplying low pressure steam to the piping network. The principal change from the original concept and installation in more recent times has been the increase in pressure to meet the needs of customers and to handle the ever-widening distances from the boiler plant. The trend toward locating electric generation facilities away from the urban core of cities has brought about a return to heat-only operations, rather than those using cogeneration in many areas. Fuel for firing heat-only boilers can be varied. Oil and gas currently are the principle fuels, with a 1980 average of 48% of the steam generated from oil, 34% from gas, 16% from coal, and 2% from solid waste. Pressures in system supplied from heat-only boilers range from a low of 8 psig to 650 psig with an average of about 140 psig.

Of the 45 utilities reporting to IDHA, steam sales reported by all companies for 1981 totalled at 77,121 MM lbs, and chilled water sales reported by eight companies totalled at 3,388 M daily tons. Further, 24 companies did not return any of the steam condensate to the boiler plants, the most frequent means of condensate disposal being the sewer system. In the remaining companies, an average of 32% of the condensate was returned. Only one utility reported return of as much as 96% of the condensate. The practice of not returning condensate began when systems used steam generated from abundant low-cost fuel and readily available, good quality, boiler feedwater. The cost of retrofitting condensate returns into existing systems as well as the highly corrosive nature of most condensate steam discourages such construction. There are cases of networks originally designed for condensate return being coverted to single supply systems because of repeated corrosion failures in returns.

Cogeneration, dual energy use (DEUS), or combined heat and power (CHP) systems are based on the sequential generation of electrical or mechanical power and useful heat from the same primary energy source or fuel. The concept is not new in the United States, with the first such system installed about 1905. Steam as a byproduct from the generation of electric power was the source for district heating in most cities until the power production stations were moved to such distant locations that steam could no longer be effectively transported. The topping of turbines delivered 29.5% of steam supplied by utilities in 1980. (The term "topping" means electricity is produced first as opposed to "bottoming" systems where a high temperature is first produced to meet thermal needs and the heat is extracted from the hot exhaust gases, usually through a waste heat boiler which then go to a turbine to produce electric power.)

Privately owned boiler plants were generally efficient and well managed in the early years of steam district heating systems, and were built to meet their owner's specific steam requirements. Utility/customer combinations have often proved profitable for district heating system operations. These combination operations, with their give and take exchange are known as "wheeling" systems. Schemes where operators generate steam for their own use during their work period, but who can divert some supply to the district heating system is a concept gaining in popularity; however, it requires well designed load management techniques to be fully effective.

HOT WATER SYSTEMS

The wide use of hot water systems by utilities in the United States has been limited for a variety of reasons. However, hot water distribution is frequently used in non-utility installations such as in systems on university campuses, in large institutions, at airports, in merchandise centers and at military bases.

In most hot water systems the heated fluid is pumped through transmission piping to a distribution piping network. From there, it flows to the customer's use point through service piping. After heat extraction the cooled fluid is returned through companion lines. Such systems require two pipes of similar size, unlike the single pipe steam system. Since the water is returned to the boiler plant, the amount of fresh water and associated treatment which must be newly introduced to the system is greatly reduced.

Generally, hot water is not utilized in the same manner as steam. At the customer's point of use a heat exchanger, water-to-water or water-to-air, isolates the heat supply from the in-house system. Service hot water is produced in a similar manner, usually through use of a separate heat exchanger.

Where steam is provided and is already an essential part of an industrial/commercial zone, it may be impractical to convert to hot water distribution. However, when new areas are developed i.e., (through urban renewal, rehabilitation or expansion) these may be appropriate for a hot water system. One way to develop hot water district heating is through the hybrid concept, where steam is transmitted for the distance necessary to meet customer commitments, then is fed into a heat exchanger and pumping system for a hot water loop. As customers' requirements change and areas are renewed, the hot water service area can be developed back toward the heat source in a step-by-step fashion. Long range planning must include consideration of phased elimination of heat exchanger stations and full conversion to hot water. Hybrid systems also can be incorporated into energy systems where steam or hot water is purchased from a separate facility.

Hot water may be produced from conventional steam electric generating plants by placing a heat exchanger in the path of the turbine exhaust to heat the system's water supply. This keeps boiler water separate from the water distributed for district heating, as well as materially reducing the cost for water treatment from the level experienced by steam systems where the condensate is not returned.

District heating hot water systems may be developed from geothermal sources. A major concern is the temperature and chemical content of geothermal hot water, which varies greatly with location. In some areas, the water is non-corrosive while in others, it may be unuseable because of the high level of corrosive materials. In some instances, hot water drawn from geothermal wells is utilized for heating and then re-inserted into the ground. In other cases, it is dispersed to lakes, rivers, and streams. In small scale geothermal heating, an "in-well" system may be employed. A heat exchanger coil is inserted into the well, submerged in the ground water and useable heat drawn via supply and return pipes.

District heating supplies may be produced by the incineration of wastes. The systems usually produce steam, which then is distributed or used to heat water for distribution. The cost of steam or hot water produced from wastes is often higher than when using other fuels; however, the advantages from avoiding large landfills and other undesireable disposal systems may make this an acceptable alternative.

Advances in technology have made the capture and use of waste heat from industrial processes attractive. Industries such as metals manufacturing, pulp and paper and chemical processing are good potential heat sources.

CHILLED WATER SYSTEM TYPES

Water is chilled (reduced in temperature of 35F to 40F) and distributed to customers who utilize heat exchangers for space conditioning. Chilled water distribution is limited because large pipe systems are required and effective distances are less than in hot water distribution.

When steam is produced year-round from a process such as trash burning, or where there is little demand for the steam in warm weather, it may be practical to use steam turbines to drive conventional compression chilling devices. If this can be achieved, a better plant load factor results.

Absorption chillers are another method of developing chilled water at the production plant. Such machines are capable of operation at much lower pressures than turbines and the efficiency of steam-driven chilling equipment and controls are rapidly improving.

In plants where cogeneration is practical, the absence of a heat load in warm months may produce a surplus of electric power. This power can be utilized to drive conventional refrigeration machines for the production of chilled water.

System Planning

Development of district heating systems depends on several site-related factors such as the availability and price of alternative energy sources, market potential, peak hourly loads, annual energy use patterns, and the potential for cogeneration. Evaluation of these factors is necessary to determine the feasibility of a new district heating system or the retrofit or expansion of an existing system. No particular type of energy system is applicable in all settings.

The following general guidelines apply to district heating from cogeneration and incineration, and describe conditions which usually must be met before district heating can offer a reasonable, cost-effective energy supply alternative.

When used primarily to meet space heating loads, district heating is economically feasible in locations with a reasonably cold winter season. U.S. Department of Energy studies indicate that district heating systems are usually cost-effective in areas with more than 4,000 degree days[1] (Figure 2.3). However, this rule of thumb does not apply to district heating system applications when used primarily for meeting year-round industrial process loads or for space cooling.

The area to be served by a district heating system should have a high hourly and annual thermal energy demand for each unit of land area. If the thermal

---

[1] W. Pferdehist and N. Kron, Jr., *District Heating from Electric Generating Plants and Municipal Incinerators: Local Planner's Assessment Guide*, Argonne National Laboratory, Argonne, Ill. P. 8.

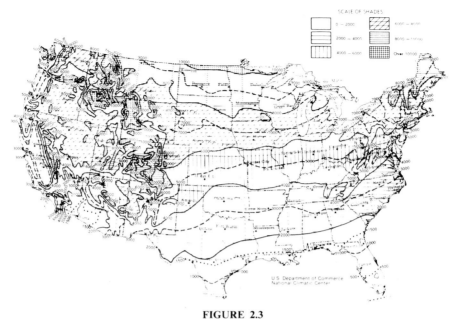

FIGURE 2.3
Normal total heating degree days (base 65°F)

demand density at a site is low, installation costs for a thermal distribution system can be prohibitively high.

For district heating systems to be economically feasible, production plants should be located near the potential district heating and cooling service area. This reduces system energy losses and the cost of the thermal transmission system.

A phased, or staged planning process is essential in evaluating new, retrofitted or expanded district heating systems. An example of this step-by-step planning and analysis is included here for a district heating system with thermal heat sources supplied by cogeneration and incineration. For other new system applications or for retrofit or expansion, steps may be added, modified or eliminated as each case requires (For example, since the retrofit of existing power plants or incinerators are not required, the first two steps would be eliminated.)

The district heating system planning function is a continuing process, even after the system becomes operative. This planning is essential to assure that the system is maintained at peak operating potential and is able to respond appropriately to changing conditions. Because of the long lead time necessary in system development or modification future requirements and changes should be anticipated and planning initiated as far in advance as possible.

The steps detailed below illustrate an orderly planning process for a proposed new district heating system utilizing existing power plants and incinerators as thermal heat sources. Each step is broken down into appropriate tasks.

Step 1: Analysis of Potential District Heat Supplies

Step 1 involves the identification of power plants and incinerators which might be used for district heating. In addition, the thermal power available from each of these sources should be estimated. Electric power plants are analyzed in Task 1 of this step; incinerators are considered in Task 2.

The study area for analysis is the jurisdictional limits of the city or town conducting the study. A regional planning agency might conduct a separate analysis for each town or city to be considered for district heating. In locations where only one is developed to a sufficient density to support district heating, the study area can be limited to the approximate boundaries of that development.

TASK 1: ESTIMATING POTENTIAL HEAT PRODUCTION FROM EXISTING AND FUTURE ELECTRIC GENERATING PLANTS

Existing generating plants should be studied from the point of view of their potential retrofit to cogeneration. New plant designs should be examined for passing modification to heat and power combined used. In this task, an estimate is made of the heat obtainable from these sources.

Heat transport costs, from source to consumer, is critical to the success of a district heating system. Steam or hot water may be considered as the heat-transport medium. Although steam has a much higher heat content per pound than does hot water, steam also requires substantially larger, and therefore more expensive, transmission and distribution pipes. Additionally, the use of water, rather than steam, produces smaller drops in electrical production at the cogeneration plant, lowers plant equipment costs, reduces distribution heat losses, and provides a potential for heat storage.

The choice of heat medium determines the maximum distance over which heat can be transported economically and, thus, determines which electric generating stations may be potential heat suppliers to the system. For steam distribution, the heat source must be within 3–5 miles of the service area. If hot water is used, the maximum distance is increased. Although not applicable in all situations, 15 miles is a reasonable maximum distance for economical hot water transmission.

Each existing power plant used in a hot water system should be within 15 miles of the perimeter of the study area on a large-scale, current, land-use or zoning map. Where a power plant is scheduled to be retired, the retirement date also should be noted. If there are any planned generating stations they also should be indicated on the map along with their expected operational dates. Private utility plans for additional capacity usually are available from the State Public Utility Commission for a period of at least the next 10–15 years.

When considering the use of heat recovered from generating plants, the utility's type of operation must be considered for each plant. In other words, each plant can be described as baseload, cycling, or peaking. Baseload plants meet the utility's minimum electric loads; cycling units provide supplemental power when needed; peaking plants are utilized only when absolutely necessary to meet demands. At least one of the plants selected for district heat supply should be a baseload plant to insure a constant supply of heat. If more than one plant is to be included in the system, cycling and peaking plants can be applied. Determination of the optimal power plant mix requires a detailed analysis.

Worksheet 1 is used to summarize the heat available from large electric generating plants in the area. All required data should be obtained from the electric utility. As shown in the completed version of Worksheet 1 (Figure 2.4), the name of each plant should be entered in column A. Separate lines are used

WORKSHEET 1 : POWER PLANT DATA SUMMARY

A PLANT NAME	B PRIME MOVER TYPE	C FUEL	D OPERATING MODE (BASELOAD CYCLING PEAKING)	E PRESENT OR PLANNED GENERATING CAPACITY (MW_e)	F THERMAL CAPACITY (MW)	G THERMAL CAPACITY $(10^6 Btu/hr)$ COLUMN G = COLUMN F x 3.413	H RETROFITTED GENERATING CAPACITY (MW_e)	I SCHEDULED DATE OF RETIREMENT OR START-UP (INDICATE WHICH WITH R OR S)
POWER PLANT 1	STEAM TURBINE	COAL	BASELOAD	300 (PRESENT)	510	1740	225	R 2000
POWER PLANT 2	STEAM TURBINE	COAL	BASE LOAD	300 (PRESENT)	510	1740	225	R 1995
	STEAM TURBINE	COAL	CYCLING	200 (PRESENT)	340	1160	150	R 1995

FIGURE 2.4

Completed worksheet 1: power plant data summary

to indicate the addition or retirement of units at specific plants. Prime-movers such as steam turbines, gas turbines, or diesel engines plus the fuel requirements are to be entered in columns B and C, respectively. These can be used to identify gas- and oil-burning plants that may require modification to utilize another fuel, and may therefore be prime candidates for district heating retrofit. Each plant's operating mode should be entered in column D, and this information used later to insure the heat availability during peak demand periods. The total electric generating capacity, including both send-out and in-plant usage in megawatts, should be listed in column E for each existing and future plant.

An examination of recent district heating studies indicates that thermal power available for recovery during generation of electricity usually is about 1.7 times the pre-retrofit electric generating capacity. This factor is an average, and does not reflect differences among equipment types and specific plant designs. Present or future electric generating capacity can be multiplied by 1.7 to produce an estimate of the available thermal power from each plant; this number can then be entered in column F of Worksheet 1. The thermal capacity in 10^6 Btu/hr to be entered in column G is determined by multiplying the value in column F by 3.413.

Electric generating capacity of a power plant usually decreases by about 25% following conversion to cogeneration. As a result, values in column E should be multiplied by 0.75 to estimate the post-retrofit electric generating capacity of each plant. Resulting values of retrofitted generating capacity (MWe) then are entered in column I. These dates are useful in planning for incremental construction of a district heating system. The thermal power available from each plant should be noted on the map, as illustrated in Figure 2.7.

TASK 2: ESTIMATING HEATING POTENTIAL FROM SOLID WASTE INCINERATION

Solid wastes can produce heat for a district heating system either directly from waste combustion or from a refuse-derived fuel (RDF). Two options are available for heat recovery from incineration.
1. waterwall incineration, in which heat is recovered from the furnace itself, and
2. heat recovery from incinerator exhaust gases.

Most solid-waste incineration facilities require new construction or extensive retrofit to allow them to produce useful heat. Locations and capacities of these sites vary markedly. Although the total thermal potential of an area's waste can be estimated, plant size and location can be determined only by analysis of local practice and future trends.

Because of the relatively low thermal capacity of incinerators, cost factors indicate that district heating incinerators would need to be located closer to consumption areas than the 15 mile limit set for power plants using hot water. For this analysis, Department of Energy studies suggest that the perimeter of consumption areas should be no further than 3 miles away from the incinerator sites[2]. Probable sites, gleaned from local sources, should be indicated on the same land-use map as power plants.

The amount of heat available from solid wastes can be estimated through

---

[2] Ibid, P. 14.

WORKSHEET 2 :   INCINERATOR DATA SUMMARY

A	B	C	D	E
INCINERATOR LOCATION AND NAME	EXISTING OR PLANNED ?	START UP OR RETIREMENT DATE	CAPACITY IN TONS PER DAY	POTENTIAL HEAT PRODUCTION $(10^6$ Btu/hr)
WESTSIDE INCINERATOR	PLANNED	S 1984	325	92

FIGURE 2.5

Completed worksheet 2: incinerator data summary

simple calculations. Wastes would come primarily from the residential and commercial sectors. Recent studies indicate that wastes collected from these two sectors average 4.29 pounds per capita per day (pcd) in the U.S. Using this figure and the community's population, an estimate of the daily available tonnage of wastes can be obtained from a simple equation. Actual waste collection data should be used in lieu of the estimate where possible.

$$\text{TICAP} = \frac{(4.29 \text{ pcd}) (\text{POP})}{2000 \text{ lb/ton}}$$

where:
TICAP = total waste-processing capacity of incinerator(s), in tons per day
(tpd), needed to process all the solid wastes of a community; and
POP = population of community.
This simplifies to the following equation:

$$TICAP = (2.145 \times 10^{-3}) (POP)$$

The heat content from a community's solid wastes would typically be about 5,000 Btu/lb, and the efficiency of heat recovery incinerators is usually about 68%. Based on these assumptions, another equation can be used to estimate the thermal power available from waterwall incineration of a community's wastes. That is:

$$TITP = \frac{(5000 \text{ Btu/lb (TICAP) (2000 lb/ton) (0.68)}}{(24 \text{ hr/day } (1 \times 10^6)}$$

where:
TITP = total incinerator thermal power in 10^6 Btu/hr.
This, in turn simplifies to: TITP = (0.2822) (TICAP). A waste-processing capacity of at least 300 tpd generally is required to support economically the construction and operation of a municipal incinerator. Therefore, the computed value for TICAP should at least be 300 tpd for a community to seriously consider district heating from incineration. If the waste volume available from a community is less than this amount, it might be possible to build an incinerator which would process wastes from other communities in the region as well. A value for TICAP greater than 600 tpd indicates that more than one incinerator could be considered.

Tentative locations should be selected for new incinerator construction. This information, along with the incinerator waste-processing capacity and thermal production capacity, should be summarized in Worksheet 2, a completed version being shown in Figure No 2.5. The thermal power available from each incinerator should be indicated on the same land-use map used to identify electric generating plants.

Step 2: Identification of District Heating Market Areas

This step identifies geographic areas which can utilize economically the thermal resources identified in Step 1. Selection of market areas is not an exact science, but some basic principles can be used as guidelines in assessing area potential:

1. *Areas should have high thermal load densities.* Thermal load density is crucial because it is the major determinant of local thermal distribution capital and operating costs. Local distribution system costs, encompassing the piping running from the transmission lines to individual service lines, are the largest single component (about 35–40%) of capital costs for a district heating system using retrofitted existing power plants. An area's thermal load density is determined by the thermal load per unit of building floor space in the area, the number of stories of the buildings, and the number of such buildings within the area. Some land uses such as residential which do not have a very high thermal demand per unit of floor space can have high thermal load densities if the buildings at least have several floors and are relatively close together. Other areas such as industrial districts, have high thermal load densities even though the

buildings may be single-story and not close to each other because the thermal loads per unit of floor space are high. In an urban area, the central business district is often the location with the highest thermal load density. A Swedish study indicates the thermal load density common to various land uses in Sweden and its suitability for district heating. These results are shown in Table 2.1. Although the thermal load densities are not universally applicable to U.S. cities, the subjective ratings for district heating suitability generally apply. Task 1 of Step 2 provides a method for estimating thermal densities:

2. *Connected loads should have a high load factor.* The load factor is the ratio between the actual amount of energy consumed annually to the amount of energy that would be consumed if the peak thermal load were to be imposed continuously for a full year. A high load factor maximizes utilization of thermal energy production and transport equipment.

   An area that has both a high thermal load density and a high load factor naturally will have a high density of annual thermal use. Such areas are attractive opportunities for district heating, since distribution costs are comparatively low, and these costs can be quickly recovered from high energy sales per dollar of invested capital.

3. *Market areas should be as close as possible to thermal sources.* Close proximity of thermal loads and sources reduces capital costs, operation and maintenance expenses and heat losses. Transmission line costs usually comprise about 20–30% of all capital costs.

4. *New development or redevelopment areas often are useful in forming the core of the initial service area.*

5. *Major physical obstacles between heat sources and load areas should be avoided whenever possible.* Such obstacles may include rivers, lakes, canyons, mountains, major highways, and environmentally sensitive areas, such as wild-life sanctuaries, or state, local, or national parks. Although heat transmission piping often can be located to overcome these obstacles, costs may be prohibitive.

6. *Groups of buildings under single ownership should be included whenever possible.* Examples include university campuses, medical complexes, military bases, and mixed-use developments. Such customers can be important in building up the initial "threshold" load, below which system implementation is not practical.

7. *Other relevant planning objectives of the community should be considered in selecting district heating service areas.* For example, thermal services from

TABLE 2.1
THERMAL LOAD DENSITY OF VARIOUS AREAS FOR DISTRICT HEATING

Type of Area	Thermal Load Density[a]	
	MW/km^2	10^6 Btu/hr acre
Downtown; high rises	>70	>0.97
Downtown; multi-storied	50–70	0.70–0.97
City core; commercial buildings and multi-family apartment buildings	20–50	0.28–0.70
Residential; two-family houses	12–20	0.17–0.28
Single-family residential	<12	<0.17

[a] Based on diversified peak hourly load.

district heating could improve the economic climate of industrial areas and the central business district or could lead to denser development to further local transportation objectives.

The most attractive service areas in many cases for a district heating system became obvious after consideration of the principles mentioned. This is particularly true in smaller cities where only a few areas may have the minimum required energy density. In larger cities, however, several alternatives might be available. In such instances, a more quantitative selection procedure is required. In either case, quantitative estimates of heat load must be made to insure that loads and supplies are adequately matched.

Step 2 aids in estimating thermal loads and provides assistance in selecting service area boundaries. Two major tasks are included: preparation of a thermal load map and accompanying energy use data, and the application of this information to identify potential service areas. If no candidate service areas can be identified by carrying out these tasks, then district heating is not a viable alternative in the community being considered. However, if one or several alternative service areas are identified, the resulting economic alternatives will be studied in the next step.

The primary value of the following analytical process is in its structure, rather than in the specific numbers of equations provided. As with any planning methodology, recommended procedures must be interpreted and revised in light of actual local circumstances.

TASK 1: PREPARATION OF A THERMAL MAP OF THE STUDY AREA

Quantitative estimates of thermal loads are necessary in order to determine the optimal market areas. The energy load information is used to match thermal supplies and demands. The following three subtasks are an aid in identifying a community's energy-intensive areas, as potentially attractive district heating service areas:

(1) selection of zone size:
(2) elimination of obviously uneconomic zones; and
(3) computation of peak hourly loads and annual energy use.

Selection of Zone Size: A map identifying peak thermal loads in zones within the study area may be useful in identifying collections of contiguous zones that have satisfactory load density, an adequate total thermal load, and enough geographic proximity to be served economically by district heating. To prepare the map, the study area is broken down into zones such as those shown in Figure 2.6. The best zone size depends on the availability of data and manpower to conduct the analysis. The smaller the zones, the more data and effort are required. For most studies, the city block is the preferred zone size. In some cases, the census tract could be used as the zone size. The use of a land area greater than the census tract often does not provide enough detail to separate attractive, energy-intensive loads from nearby low-density loads.

Obviously Uneconomic Zones: Using a zoning map, assessor's data or other local information sources, all zones in which 50% or more of the land area is used for single-family detached housing, single-family attached housing, townhouses, open space, or other obviously non-energy-intensive uses should be noted for later consideration. Other obvious factors can be used to eliminate some zones from consideration. For example, a single, high-density building separated by several miles from the nearest contiguous group of other energy-intensive zones need not receive further consideration. Also, if only a small

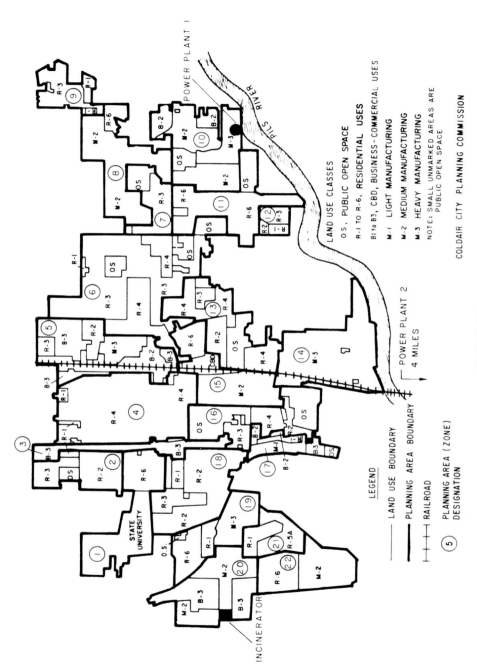

FIGURE 2.6

Sample zones in hypothetical study area

supply of thermal energy is available, initial analysis should be limited only to those zones that have the maximum energy demands (usually high-rise office buildings and industries) or to those that are located extremely close to the thermal sources.

Compute Peak Hourly Loads and Annual Energy Use: Peak hourly thermal loads and annual energy use in remaining zones must be computed. These load estimates are used to find groups of zones for which the total demand equals the available supply. Although it is not necessary to compute annual energy use to match thermal demands with supplies, this data is used in Step 3 to compute system costs. To estimate peak hourly thermal loads and annual energy use, begin by developing separate estimates for each of several major land uses within each zone. Factors expressing peak hourly loads and annual energy use per square foot of floor space for each major land use should be calculated. These factors can then be multiplied by the amounts of floor space devoted to each type land use to estimate the peak hourly thermal load and annual energy use within each zone. Land use categories suggested for use here include medium-density residential, of four stories or less, high-density residential of more than four stories, commercial, institutional, and industrial.

Thermal load analysis should begin by filling out a copy of Worksheet 3 for each zone to be studied. Figure 2.7 provides a completed sample Worksheet 3.

After entering the floor space of each building type in column A of Worksheet 3, the annual energy consumption factor (AECF) should be estimated for each building type and entered in column B. The AECF shows the amount of end-use energy annually required for space heating and water heating in each of the specified building types. The AECF corresponds to *end-use* energy consumption rather than to *fuel* consumption because various types of energy systems consume different amounts of fuel to produce the same end-use heating effect. This result is caused by differences in efficiency among the various types of systems. Sources for values of AECF include the local gas or electric utility, other agencies involved in energy planning, the nearby universities or other research institutions.

If values for AECF are not available, estimates can be made by using the equation:

$$AECF = (ASHF) \times (HDD) + AWHF$$

where:
ASHF = annual space heating factor, in $Btu/(ft^2 \cdot HDD \cdot yr)$;
HDD = average heating degree days; and
AWHF = annual water heating factor in $BTU/(ft^2 \cdot yr)$.
Values for ASHF and AWHF are listed in Table 2.2. Because the average age of structures, building materials, and building operating characteristics vary considerably among communities, values from Table 2.2 should be used only when community-specific data are not available. Industrial energy use data are especially susceptible to wide variation, even within specific industries. A value of HDD can be obtained from Table 2.3 or the nearest office of the U.S. Weather Service.

The corresponding value of AECF for each building type should be multiplied by the floor space to determine the annual energy use (AEU), which can be entered in column C of Worksheet 3. Peak hourly thermal loads of each zone should be calculated after estimating annual energy uses. Heating energy load factors (HELFs), defined as the peak hourly demand for space and water

WORKSHEET 3 : ZONAL ENERGY LOAD AND CONSUMPTION DATA

ZONE NUMBER ___05___

LAND AREA (mi²) ___2.5___

BUILDING TYPE	A FLOOR SPACE (ft²)	B ANNUAL ENERGY CONSUMPTION FACTOR (AECF) (Btu/ft²·yr)	C ANNUAL ENERGY USE (AEU) (Btu) (COLUMN A x COLUMN B)	D HOURLY ENERGY LOAD FACTOR (HELF) (Btu/ft²·hr)	E PEAK HOURLY ENERGY LOAD (PHEL) (Btu/hr) (COLUMN A x COLUMN D)
MEDIUM-DENSITY RESIDENTIAL	2.0×10^6	1.04×10^5	2.08×10^{11}	39.7	7.94×10^7
HIGH-DENSITY RESIDENTIAL	—	—	—	—	—
COMMERCIAL	2.7×10^7	5.86×10^4	1.58×10^{12}	22.4	6.05×10^8
INDUSTRIAL	1.1×10^7	6.93×10^4	7.62×10^{11}	26.3	2.89×10^8
INSTITUTIONAL	0.2×10^7	5.86×10^4	1.17×10^{11}	22.4	4.48×10^7

SUBTOTAL ANNUAL ENERGY USE (SAEU) = 2.67×10^{12}

TRANSMISSION AND DISTRIBUTION LOSSES (11% OF SAEU) = 0.29×10^{12}

TOTAL ANNUAL ENERGY USE (TAEU) = 2.96×10^{12}

SUBTOTAL PEAK HOURLY ENERGY LOAD (SPHEL) = 1.02×10^9

TRANSMISSION AND DISTRIBUTION LOSSES (11% OF SPHEL) = 0.11×10^9

TOTAL PEAK HOURLY ENERGY LOAD (TPHEL) = 1.13×10^9

$$\text{THERMAL DENSITY} = \frac{\text{SAEU}}{\text{LAND AREA}} = 1.07 \times 10^{12} \; \frac{\text{Btu}}{\text{mi}^2 \cdot \text{yr}}$$

FIGURE 2.7

Completed Worksheet 3: Zonal energy load and consumption data

TABLE 2.2

SPACE AND WATER HEATING FACTORS

Building Type	Annual Space Heating Factor: ASHF $(\text{Btu/ft}^2 \cdot \text{HDD} \cdot \text{yr})$	Annual Water Heating Factor: AWHF $(\text{Btu/ft}^2 \cdot \text{yr})$	Hourly Water Heating Factor: HWHF $(\text{Btu/ft}^2 \cdot \text{hr})$
Medium-density residential	11.9	15,000	5.0
High-density residential	10.5	15,000	5.0
Commercial/institutional	7.37	3,300	0.9
Industrial	8.70	4,000	0.9

TABLE 2.3

CLIMATIC DATA FOR SELECTED U.S. CITIES

Location	Heating Degree-Days (HDD)	Winter Design Temperature[a] (WDT) (°F Dry-Bulb)
Boston, Mass.	5,634	9
Chicago, Ill.	6,155	0
Cincinnati, Oh.	4,410	6
Denver, Colo.	5,524	1
Des Moines, Ia.	6,588	−5
Detroit, Mich.	6,232	6
Duluth, Minn.	10,000	−16
Indianapolis, Ind.	5,699	2
Kansas City, Mo.	4,711	6
Milwaukee, Wis.	7,635	−4
New York, N.Y.	4,871	15
Omaha, Nebr.	6,612	−3
Philadelphia, Pa.	4,486	14
Portland, Ore.	4,109	24
Salt Lake City, Utah	6,052	8
Seattle, Wash.	4,424	27
Washington, D.C.	4,224	17

[a] Temperature equalled or exceeded during 97½% of the total hours from December through February.

heating energy in $\text{Btu/(ft}^2 \cdot \text{hr)}$ must be estimated first. If HELF values cannot be estimated from local data, this equation may be used:

$$\text{HELF} = \frac{(65° - \text{WDT})}{24}(\text{ASHF}) + \text{HWHF}$$

where:
  HELF   = heating energy load factor, in $\text{Btu/(ft}^2 \cdot \text{hr)}$;
  WDT   = winter design temperature, in °F;
  ASHF   = annual space heating factor, in $\text{Btu/(ft}^2 \cdot \text{HDD} \cdot \text{yr)}$;
  HWHF   = hourly water heating factor, in $\text{Btu/(ft}^2 \cdot \text{hr)}$;
  65°   = the base temperature used to calculate HDD; and
  24   corresponds to the number of hours in a day.

This equation assumes that space heating energy consumption over a given period of time is proportional to the heating degree days accumulated during that period. Values for HWHF are provided in Table 2.2. Values contained in Table 2.2 are *not* accurate for all applications, and should be replaced by location-specific data where available.

The diversity of user demands must be considered in designing a utility system to serve a large group of users. It is unlikely that all system users experience peak loads at precisely the same time, therefore the peak load for the system as a whole will be less than the sum of all peak hourly loads for individual buildings. To calculate the total peak load for the system, the sum of individual peak loads often is reduced by a *diversity factor*.

Another possible approach is to reduce the heat loads for individual dual buildings by providing for less than extreme conditions, and then adding up individual loads to compute the system load. The temperatures in Table 2.3 correspond to the 97.5% winter design temperature for each location listed. This is the temperature that will be equalled or exceeded 97.5% of the total hours from December through February. A colder winter design temperature produce higher estimates of peak thermal loads for individual buildings. If values for HELF are obtained from local sources, care should be taken that only diversified values are used. Diversity factors for district heating usually range from about 0.60 to 0.80.

Once determined, HELF values should be multiplied by corresponding floor space values to determine peak thermal load for each building type. The result should be entered in column E of Worksheet 3. Columns C and E should then be added vertically to produce subtotals of total annual thermal energy use and

TABLE 2.4

ISSUES WHICH MAY AFFECT DEVELOPMENT, OWNERSHIP, AND OPERATION OF DISTRICT HEATING AND COOLING SYSTEMS

- Regulation
    Regulation of the district heating and cooling company
    Operating income regulation (revenue requirements) Start-up loss recovery
    Fuel or heat source cost pass-through
    Allowance for funds used during construction
    Plant siting
    Service area
    Reliability and availability of service
- Financing
    Capital structure
    Types of debt financing
- Taxation
    Property tax
    Sales tax
    Selective and excise tax
- Pricing policy
    Tariff classification
    Pricing basis
    Rate structure
- Capital investment recovery for building owners
- Allocation of costs and benefits between electrical generation and district heating and cooling for cogeneration power plants
- Displacement efforts on existing energy suppliers
- Hookup policy
- Permits and authorization
    Franchising by cites
    Plant siting
    Start-up and construction

hourly peak load for each zone. These subtotals must be adjusted to account for heat losses during transmission and distribution. Usually, such losses are calculated to be about 10% of total sendout. To compute losses, the subtotals of columns C and E should be multiplied by 1/9 (the subtotals represent 90% of the total amounts). Addition of the subtotals and the losses provides estimates of the total hourly energy load and annual energy use.

Thermal density also must be computed for each zone. This is calculated by dividing the zone's subtotal annual energy use by the land area of the zone. A space is provided on Worksheet 3 for recording the computed value.

Finally, the total annual energy use, the total peak hourly use, and the thermal density of each zone should be recorded on the thermal load map as shown in Figure 2.8. This information is used to select candidate district heating areas.

TASK 2: APPLICATION OF ENERGY-USE DATA IN IDENTIFYING HIGH POTENTIAL DISTRICT HEATING SERVICE AREAS

Subjective considerations and quantitative load data usually lead to one or several obvious candidate areas.

Because the central business district (CBD) is usually the largest number of contiguous energy-intensive zones, it is the obvious area to be considered for district heating service. However, a sufficiently large, intensive load, other than the CBD, could be located near a thermal source. This allows two general approaches to identifying potential market areas. The first approach attempts to identify a separate, sufficiently large and intensive load near each thermal source. The second approach starts with the CBD and incrementally adds adjoining zones. Final selection of market areas should be made through consideration of both approaches. Worksheet 4 (Figure 2.9) is used in both approaches to summarize the information generated.

Step 3: Analyzing Economic Aspects of District Heating

Step 3 develops cost data for comparison of district heating with competing alternatives in a community. The major test of any energy system is how economically it can compete with its alternatives. The economic advantages offered by a district heating system determine the degree to which it can attract and retain customers, and, thus, generate revenues.

A district heating system has the potential of capturing two major markets within its service area. The first are newly constructed buildings or buildings requiring replacement of their present heating systems. These building owners are faced with capital costs for heating equipment, regardless of whether they choose to subscribe to the district heating system. The second market includes existing buildings not requiring replacement of their present heating systems. Owners of such buildings must pay the capital costs for retrofitting their old heating equipment if they select service from the district heating system; however, equipment capital costs probably would not be incurred for several years if the present system is retained.

Although new construction or redevelopment areas usually form the nucleus of a new district heating service area, both the new and existing building markets must use the heating system if a sufficiently large thermal load is to be serviced. If district heating is economically attractive to potential retrofit customers, it should also be attractive to customers in the new development retrofit market because of capital cost considerations. The district heating costs

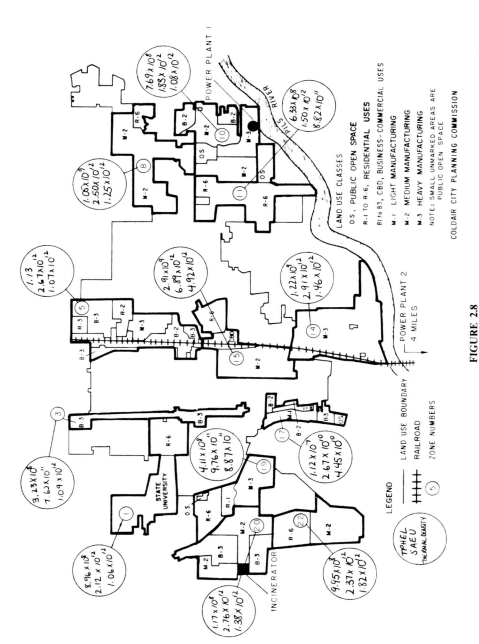

FIGURE 2.8

Thermal load data shown on study area map

WORKSHEET 4: MARKET AREA IDENTIFICATION

A MARKET AREA NAME	B COMPOSED OF FORMER ZONE NUMBERS	C SUM OF SUBTOTAL ANNUAL ENERGY USES (SAEU VALUES FROM WORKSHEET 3) (10^{12} Btu/yr)	D MARKET AREA'S SQUARE MILEAGE (SUM OF ZONAL LAND AREAS) (mi^2)	E ANNUAL THERMAL DENSITY COLUMN C / COLUMN D = COLUMN E (10^{12} Btu/yr·mi^2)	F SUM OF TOTAL PEAK HOURLY ENERGY LOADS (TPHEL VALUES FROM WORKSHEET 3) (10^6 Btu/hr)	G THERMAL POWER OF SELECTED POWER PLANTS (FROM MAP AND WORKSHEET 1) (10^6 Btu/hr)	H THERMAL POWER OF SELECTED INCINERATORS (FROM MAP AND WORKSHEET 2) (10^6 Btu/hr)	I TOTAL AVAILABLE THERMAL POWER (COLUMN G + COLUMN H) (10^6 Btu/hr)	J SURPLUS (+) OR DEFICIT (-) OF HEAT SUPPLY (COLUMN I – COLUMN F)
EASTSIDE	8, 10	4.33	3.7	1.17	1819	1740 – – –	– – –	1740	–79

FIGURE 2.9

Completed worksheet 4: market area identification for source-centered analysis

computed in the next section include the retrofit costs of in-building heating equipment, and thus represent the costs in the retrofit market. Use of these costs will provide a conservative estimate of the overall economic potential of district heating.

To evaluate the economics of district heating, compare the cost per 10^6 of district-heating-produced thermal energy with the cost per 10^6 Btu of heating produced using other fuels. These unit costs are computed by completing Tasks 1–4, summarized as follows:

TASK 1: ESTIMATE THE CAPITAL EXPENDITURES REQUIRED TO ESTABLISH A DISTRICT HEATING SYSTEM

These expenditures include the following cost components: retrofit of electric generating plants; replacement of electric generating plant capacity; in-building equipment retrofit; and construction of incinerators, the local distribution system, and the transmission system.

TASK 2: ESTIMATE THE ANNUAL EXPENSES INCURRED IN THE OPERATION OF A DISTRICT HEATING SYSTEM

These annual expenses are for operation and maintenance (O&M) of the following components:
1. the electric generating plants,
2. district heating incinerators, and
3. thermal transmission and distribution systems.

At electric generating plants, only additional O&M costs caused by cogeneration, rather than total O&M costs, are attributed to the district heating system. Customer end-use equipment O&M is not included because O&M costs for conventional equipment would minimally equal those incurred under district heating.

TASK 3: COMPUTE THE UNIT COST OF DISTRICT HEATING

After a minimum attractive rate of return on investment for the organization operating the district heating system has been set, the annual equivalent of the capital costs computed in Task 1 can be determined. The annual equivalent capital costs can be added to the annual expenses computed in Task 2 to determine total annual costs. Dividing these costs by the total annual delivered thermal energy produces the cost per 10^6 Btu of district heating energy.

TASK 4: ESTIMATE THE UNIT COSTS OF CONVENTIONAL HEATING SYSTEMS

To provide a basis for evaluating the costs of district heating, the cost per 10^6 Btu of heat from conventional systems must be known. This cost can be computed after fuel prices, fuel heat content values, and equipment efficiencies are known.

The results of these calculations are used in the next step to arrive at a preliminary conclusion about the economic feasibility of district heating in the study area.

Step 4: Evaluation of the Feasibility of District Heating

Step 4 provides a means to evaluate and compare the relative costs of district heating and conventional heating to determine the economic feasibility of a district heating system. Also to be considered are some non-economic considerations. A comparison of unit costs shows the relative economic attractions of district heating.

TASK 1: COMPARING CONVENTIONAL AND DISTRICT HEATING UNIT COSTS

If district heating unit costs are less than conventional system costs, consideration should be given to engaging in a more detailed feasibility study. Such a study would be directed at more detailed technical considerations such as the engineering feasibility of retrofitting power plants to be included in the system. Cost estimates would also be refined. If the comparative heating costs for several potential district heating market areas indicate that each has favorable economic implications, each alternative should receive further analysis. Alternatives with the lowest costs should receive the most attention.

TASK 2: CONSIDERATION OF DISTRICT HEATING SYSTEMS WITH COSTS ONLY SLIGHTLY HIGHER THAN CONVENTIONAL SYSTEMS

If projected district heating costs would be higher than those of a conventional system, a life-cycle cost analysis still might indicate a potential positive economic feasibility for district heating. Unit costs of conventional heating systems are based almost entirely on fuel cost and escalate at the same rate as fuel cost escalation. In contrast, district heating unit costs are based largely on capitalization charges. After the system is built, these do not escalate. Fuel costs have comprised only about 10–20% of the total district heating unit costs in the cities that have been studied to date. If all thermal energy for the district heating system were to be supplied by retrofitted power plants, and should the same fuel price escalation rate apply to electric power plants and conventional heating systems, then district heating unit costs would escalate only at a maximum of 20% of the rate at which conventional heating costs will rise. As a result, if district heating unit costs are within 30% of conventional heating unit costs, a further consideration of district heating might be warranted. To implement a system in which first-year costs may be higher, but life-cycle costs are projected as being lower than conventional alternatives, government subsidies of financing from later-year user fees probably would be necessary to make early-year customer fees attractive and competitive.

The assumptions used in the cost analysis should be examined in addition to comparing the unit costs of district heating with its alternatives. Answers to several questions will be helpful in evaluating whether certain cost components should be adjusted. These questions are:

1. What are the present and future options for solid waste disposal? As potential sanitary landfill sites become scarce, remote, and more expensive, the economic feasibility of a heat-recovering incinerator increases.
2. Is renovation or replacement scheduled for any generating units at nearby utility plants? If so, the costs of installing heat recovery equipment could be reduced.
3. Is there excess electric generating capacity in the region? If so, there might be no need to replace electric generating capacity lost because of cogeneration conversions. In addition, if the use of electric space and water heating is prevalent in the community, district heating might replace some electric heating and eliminate the need to maintain current generating capacity.

TASK 3: CONSIDERATION OF NON-COST FACTORS

A district heating system should be evaluated for its ability to help meet other community objectives. Three examples of community objectives which could be served by the establishment of a district heating system are air quality improvement, economic development and energy conservation.

Environmental Impacts

The major areas of environmental impact from a district heating system implementation are related to building and operating power plants in or around urban areas. There the trade-off in air pollutants (specifically sulfur and nitrogen oxides) by replacing oil-burning home furnaces and development of presently undeveloped lands in the vicinity of the district heating distribution system becomes important. Siting the power plants in an environmentally acceptable manner, with consideration for air quality, water quality, noise and land use may be a problem both for the utilities and area residents. This impact problem also is associated with potential overdevelopment of areas near district heating distribution lines.

The most significant factor which would influence district heating development is air quality, specifically building in EPA's "nonattainment areas." A non-attainment area is defined as an Air Quality Control Region (AQCR) in which one or more criteria pollutants (particulates, SO_2, NO_x, CO, oxidants and hydrocarbons) exceed national ambient air quality standards. For non-attainment areas an air pollution source may be built only if an emission tradeoff is carried out. In such a tradeoff, total emissions of the pollutant in the AQCR must be reduced. The tradeoff might involve reduction in emissions from existing plants by retrofitting air pollution control equipment and the elimination of pollutants from individual furnaces. The experience with district heating in Sweden indicates this tradeoff could significantly reduce SO_2 levels in urban areas. In fact, it is probable that urban power plants only will be built or modified if district heating improves air quality.

A concern of those utilities planning cogeneration-based district heating systems in urban areas is that the combination of problems associated with increased boiler capacity and pollutant emissions to handle peak demands for steam and electricity, the inability to adequately retrofit air pollution control equipment on 20–40-year-old urban power plants, and conversion of urban power plants from oil-fired to coal-fired, all counteract emission trade-offs. Some utility spokesmen have expressed the opinion that district heating is technologically and economically workable but that air pollution particulate regulations may prohibit its development because the increased *particulate* emissions from power plants are not offset by reduced *particulate* emissions from oil furnaces.

A similar problem exists for EPA "attainment areas," which are those areas that do meet ambient air quality standards. In these cases, the air quality is regulated by Prevention of Significant Deterioration increments. The siting of a power plant in an attainment area requires that air quality standards be maintained. Air quality is allowed to deteriorate only by a predetermined amount. The same concerns expressed for non-attainment areas are applicable, though to a lesser degree than for attainment areas. The air pollution control requirements add significant costs to building or retrofit of steam sources wherever they are to be located.

Another air pollution factor which has received little attention from environmental regulators is that urban power plant emissions may interact with high rise building occupants directly or be entrained in building ventilation systems before the plumes are diffused and dispersed by meteorological forces. This impact can become significant if power plants are built in urban areas for district heating systems and high-rise buildings proliferate to take advantage of cheap district heating and cooling.

Another potential major environmental impact area for district heating systems is land use and land development. Power plants require over 150 acres to accommodate coal storage, fly ash storage, cooling systems, switchyards, scrubber sludge treatment and the main power plant. Expansion of existing facilities or new rights-of-way for transmission lines to service new urban facilities will have an impact on area land use since many such users are excluded in the transmission corridor. The land use problem is especially critical since land development generally is densest along shorelines, and power plants themselves must be near bodies of water to obtain and discharge cooling water.

Areas available for power plants in urban areas usually are very limited, and often are landfills, existing dumps or deteriorated areas along shorelines. While these areas are more beneficially used if converted to power plant sites, the lack of ground stability in landfills adds to the cost of power plant construction. Long-range urban planning with cooperation between local authorities and the utilities is needed to minimize the environmental problems associated with siting power plants in urban areas.

Yet another environmental impact from district heating sources is noise. Noises such as low tones from transformers, loud waterfall sounds from cooling towers and scrubbers, and high-pitched whines from draft fans add up to a cacophony of sounds audible within 2 to 3 miles of the power plant. In urban areas the noise impact is less severe, since street sounds will interfere with and diminish power plant noises. However, if power plants are to be sited in suburban areas, these noises would be quite noticeable, especially at night. The costs for dampening these noises and making them acceptable could be substantial.

Water pollution may be a major factor if once-through cooling is not allowed and cooling towers must be used. Cooling towers consume large amounts of water, producing water vapor plumes which increase the incidence of fog and potentially modify local climates by increasing rainfall and humidity. Cooling towers can be a hazard to aircraft and may discharge large amounts of waste heat and chemicals. The addition of district heating systems could significantly reduce the size of needed cooling systems, since heat dissipation requirements would be reduced.

Cooling towers are designed to perform adequately even during the most severe summer meteorological conditions. If a power plant is rejecting half as much heat to the environment under summer conditions because it provides heat and chilled water for urban buildings then the towers can be reduced significantly in size. This size reduction can occur despite the probability that full heat rejection may be required for the intermediate seasons of spring and autumn. The reduction in needed cooling system size stemming from waste heat utilization reduces the impact of the heated water discharged during the severe seasons of winter (large thermal temperature differential) and summer (high ambient temperature), reduces evaporation during low river flow conditions, discharges fewer total pounds of pollutants, and reduces potential hazards to aircraft. If air conditioning is *not* provided by the district heating system, however, then cooling system size will not be reduced significantly.

Other water pollution factors which could affect the construction and operation of power plant cooling systems include:

1. dredging requirements for intake and discharge structures may cause a licensing problem,
2. navigation hazards could be caused by intake and discharge structures,
3. upstream and downstream controls on river-located plants could affect operation,
4. there could be adverse effects from power plant discharges mixing with existing water pollutants, and
5. high probability of poor water quality in developed areas might require expensive water treatment facilities.

Solid waste storage and transport probably has the lowest potential environmental impact of the major environmental issues. A beneficial aspect of solid waste problems is that urban refuse can be incinerated and used as a supplementary fuel for steam generation. A district heating system could reduce solid waste volumes in urban areas by two-thirds. Such a system is in use in Milwaukee, WI and has been studied for use in many cities. Most solid wastes from power plants, including fly ash, scrubber sludge, water treatment wastes, and nuclear wastes, can be stored, handled and transported in an environmentally acceptable manner. The major impact is the increased amount of land required for storage of these wastes.

Construction and operation of the district heating system create problems in the areas of land use and noise. The district heating distribution system may have a significant impact on area housing and commercial development along the distribution system route. If district heating is, as it ought to be, economical and advantageous to users, there should be pressure for maximum utilization of the district heating distribution system corridor. Because uncontrolled land development may cause irreversible damage to the ecology of an area, including affecting the food chain, habitat, drainage patterns, and soil conditions, detailed planning and control of the corridor must be carried out. The corridor also can affect land values and housing patterns. Adequate control can bring about beneficial results, since other services requiring trenches such as sewers, cable TV, or telephones, also may be able to use the corridor, thus reducing overall costs to the public.

Noise from district heating system construction, operation and maintenance may have an adverse but temporary impact on suburban areas. General construction activities, such as blasting or use of jackhammers and bulldozers can cause unacceptable sound levels in nearby residences. Other than scheduling activities during daytime, little can be done to reduce this noise.

The overall impact of a district heating end-use system is beneficial. It involves the elimination of air pollutants from buildings burning oil for space heat. If the district heating system provides heat for air conditioning, then elimination of environmental impacts from electric power plant peaking units used to handle summer loads may be credited to the district heating system. On the other hand, the back-up boilers used to supplement heat during peak periods must be tallied as an adverse environmental impact. Based on the Swedish example, beneficial effects from elimination of power plant peaking units generally is greater than the adverse effects from new steam-generating boilers. As metropolitan population increases, the pollution from additional oil burners and increased electric capacity for air conditioning demand is reduced by having a district heating system.

Heat exchangers and tanks needed in homes and buildings served by district heating are quieter, cleaner, safer, and smaller than existing furnaces. The elimination of individual oil and natural gas furnaces have the beneficial secondary effects of reducing:

1. oil tank farm size,
2. oil truck traffic on streets,
3. oil tanker activity in ports, and therefore oil spills,
4. demand for natural gas so it can be used more efficiently,
5. refinery loads and emissions.

Social Impacts

Social impacts of district heating systems include effects on the general population, housing, jobs and businesses, aesthetics and general quality of life. The major district heating concepts which can affect social values include the clustering caused by the distribution system, urban renewal and building rejuvenation associated with district heating system construction, the long-term increase in employment, and the aesthetic impact of power plant siting in urban areas.

Since district heating must be both economical and easy to use if it is to be fully utilized, then the general population should have the desire to connect to the system. Apartments and houses may be built along the district heating distribution system to minimize heating costs and the advantages of lower equipment investment costs. This would increase population in the served urban/suburban area. In addition to residential buildings, commercial and industrial facilities may cluster around district heating systems if zoning laws incorporate this type of growth pattern.

Since district heating supplants oil use, oil distributors will lose some economy of scale and oil used in rural areas and in homes not connecting to district heating may become more expensive. Power plant construction and distribution systems can be included as parts of urban renewal projects.

This type of renewal can encourage migration back to urban areas, save urban space through good planning and minimize sprawl.

Changes in population patterns which increase urban population make district heating attractive. Since district heating costs per capita decrease as population density increases, a beneficial cycle is set in motion. This relationship is shown in Figure 2.10. If district heating initially can attract people because it is less costly and more easily used, it will become more attractive and economical over time. Increased population density has the adverse affect of increased congestion and loss of privacy.

Since district heating will be implemented in the most densely populated areas and areas of potential renewal, it is logical that minority groups will be the first to be affected by district heating. Such groups may perceive district heating as big business experimenting with new ideas and using the poor for testing purposes. To avoid this misconception and gain positive acceptance of district heating, planning and cooperative coordination with civic groups is essential.

In less affluent areas, apartments and homes usually are rented. As a result, actual marketing of district heating will have to be through the area's residential

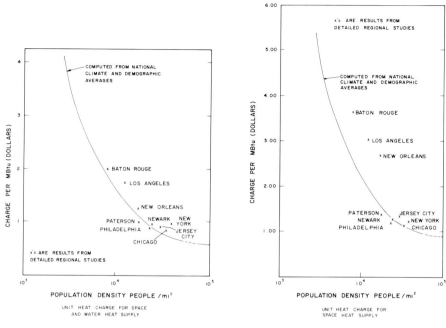

FIGURE 2.10
Population density vs. cost for DH

and office building owners. These owners are in a good financial position to purchase heat exchanger equipment. On the other hand, it may take substantial incentives to motivate those owners to install new heating equipment, since they receive no additional revenues or other benefits from district heating alone.

To avoid future problems in population concentration from oversized district heating systems, the housing in the service area probably will be required to have maximum insulation and other heat conserving facilities. This should make such residential units more attractive to home buyers since heat should be less costly and capital outlays for conservation activities will be minimal. A concern associated with clustering is the need for effective zoning laws. Pressure to maximize land use along the system corridor from industry, commercial establishments and residential developers will be intense. Planners should maximize effective and efficient land use by encouraging apartment or condominium construction. Utilities, builders and homeowners will benefit from multiple units since this reduces district heating capital cost per unit.

Apartments require less heat per unit than do single family houses—often by as much as 50 percent. However, population density more than compensates for the reduction. Monitoring heat use for each unit can be difficult and expensive. Urban renewal and the demand for apartment buildings along with district heating systems should encourage rejuvenation of old or deteriorated apartments. Houses along the district heating network will be able to have modern heating and cooling systems regardless of the age of the previous separate systems.

All these factors will put heavy pressure on land values around district heating corridors which could cause values to increase. Heavy land speculation could occur during planning stages and initial construction. Careful long-range planning must be implemented to avoid congestion, land speculation, and over development, and to maximize efficient land utilization. Utilities, local officials, and urban planners must work together to successfully implement district heating.

Most social impacts can be mitigated by effective initial planning and information dispersal to the public.

Energy Conservation Aspects

In most cities in the United States, natural gas and oil fuel the bulk of space heating and domestic hot water demand. Reserves of both natural gas and oil are limited both nationally and worldwide in the long term. Therefore, energy conservation and conversion to more abundant fuels are matters of national and global concern.

These conservation goals to a great degree can be realized by district heating systems where heat is distributed from a limited number of large production plants to a vast number of heat consumers by a system of hot water pipes or steam pipes in older systems. Large production plants for such systems can run on fuels not practical for use in small domestic plants—for example, coal and uranium, (the fuels for which potentially the biggest reserves exist)—or they can be fueled by the burning of refuse. Heat otherwise expelled to the atmosphere or into rivers from industrial processes or power plants can be utilized. At some future date technology also will allow use of the heat from the sun. Thus, more efficient use of more abundant energy sources is possible in district heating.

Considering these broad community-related factors is important in determining the actual possibility for district heating development in a community. Although economic feasibility must still be proved, these other factors can provide additional impetus, political support and funds for the analysis, design and construction of a district heating system.

Step 5: Implementation Strategies

Step 5 describes actions that could be taken to follow-up the information provided by previous analysis.

DISCONTINUE STUDY

At one extreme, the first four steps may indicate that district heating is not economically or socially justified for the area studied. Because no technology can be expected to work in all situations, this is one valid conclusion. If study results show district heating clearly to be a poor choice, the results should be documented, and filed for future reference.

REQUEST FUNDING FOR ADDITIONAL STUDY

If the study shows district heating to be feasible, funding should be sought for additional work. Funding sources for energy research exist at many government levels and within some private groups.

ENCOURAGE PARTICIPATION BY ELECTRIC UTILITY AND SOLID-WASTE DISPOSAL AGENCY

During this activity, the local electric utility and solid-waste disposal agency should be contacted for information. When results are available, both entities can be helpful in providing support or additional analysis. The utility may be able to use its own engineering staff to look more closely at cogeneration plant costs. In meetings with the utility, possible economic benefits to the utility could form the focus of discussions. In speaking with waste-disposal agencies, important issues include savings from reduced landfill operation, potential revenues from tipping fees and sales of thermal energy.

The roles and responsibilities of local government, the electric utility, the waste-disposal agency, and other private or public parties involved in the ownership and operation of the district heating system could be particularly difficult issues to resolve. Various ownership/operation options should be formulated and discussed early in the feasibility assessment process.

PERFORM AN ENGINEERING FEASIBILITY STUDY

If the study team has funding and has discovered a system that is not more than marginally (30%) more expensive than a conventional system, the next step could be to examine system feasibility in greater detail. Assembly of a conceptual design of the system is necessary, including items such as transmission pipe sizing and routing, specific equipment needed for central plants, and in-building systems. Cost estimates could then be improved based on this more detailed description of system components.

Other issues to be examined in an engineering feasibility study include the following.

Detailed Analysis of Thermal Loads: Values estimated for peak thermal loads and annual energy consumption during Step 2 of the planning process should be verified or revised through a detailed analysis of the buildings in the market area. Prospective customers should be sampled selectively to establish improved estimates of peak load and annual consumption. When completed, the analysis should contain information and data consisting of:

1. Estimates of maximum demand burdens to be imposed upon the system at times of annual and monthly system peaks. In some cases it may be desirable to tabulate this information on an area and/or route basis.
2. Estimates of annual and monthly consumptions, again based on each area.
3. Load factor data on an annual basis. Additional data on a monthly or seasonal basis may be useful in some cases.
4. Annual load duration curves (Figure 2.11) and, where pertinent, similar curves for shorter intervals.
5. Diurnal curves showing the relationship between demand load and outdoor temperature (Figure 2.12). This curve is mandatory for extreme winter conditions. Where cooling load is a significant factor similar curves for extreme summer conditions are also required.
6. The relationship between minimum outdoor temperatures (or maximum temperatures when cooling is a factor) and both short interval and hourly average demands. Where information from existing operations is available, system records offer a convenient method of pro-rating. This data is of particular interest during periods of extended load duration which straddle system peaks.
7. The future growth potential, beyond extensions for current business, should be evaluated and estimated values tabulated.

Coordination Between System Load Growth and Capacity Construction: District heating system growth of serviceable load, from new construction or

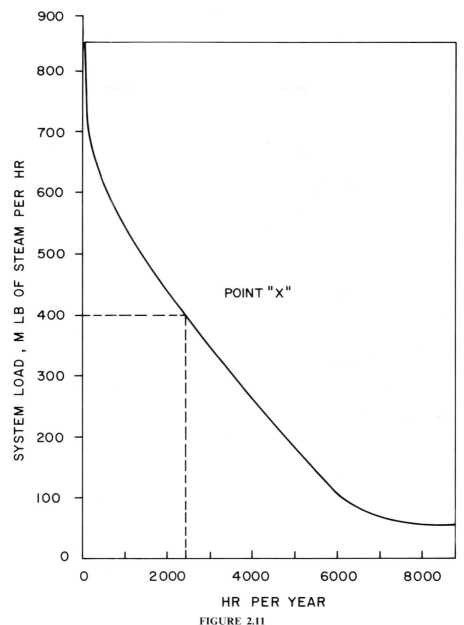

FIGURE 2.11

Load-duration curve for a district heating system

EXAMPLE: Point "X" indicates that during 2500 hours of the year the load is 400,000 lb per hr or higher.

redevelopment, must be projected so that the construction for retrofitting of power plants and incinerators can be planned. Under-utilized thermal production plants can place financial burdens on the system; however sufficient capacity should be available to permit expansion into economically viable areas.

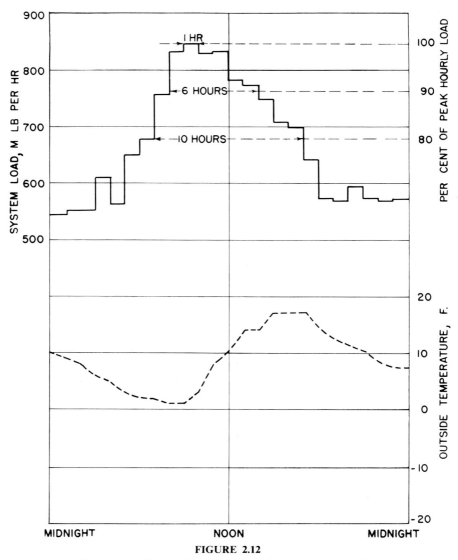

FIGURE 2.12
Diurnal demand load and outside temperature during peak-load day

Coordination Between Operation of Thermal Production Plants and Thermal Loads: In Step 2, at least one selected electric generating plant was assumed to be baseload plant. In some cases, however, one such plant will not be enough to meet the system's thermal demands. Usually it would not be economical to generate thermal energy at cycling or peaking plants not required for simultaneous electric generation. A time study must be conducted to see if the electric generating plants selected for district heating can be operated economically in a cogeneration mode.

Types of Heating Systems in Existing Buildings: A survey of heating systems in existing buildings should be carried out to establish the average age of such systems and to estimate district heating customers' retrofit costs. During the same study, building owners could be asked about their willingness to subscribe to the district heating system if thermal energy were offered at each of a variety of prices.

Establishment of Thermal Supply Temperature: The temperature of hot water supplied by the district heating system should be set as low as possible still able to meet customers' needs. Decreasing supply temperature reduces losses in electric generating capacity and reduces heat losses during transmission and distribution. Customers needing steam for process or heating probably will need high supply temperatures. Temperature requirements can be established through the survey of heating system types, discussed previously.

Possibility of Serving Air-Conditioning Loads: Space cooling can be provided by using absorption chillers powered by district heat. The use of absorption chillers can be economical if the supply heat otherwise would have been discarded, as is usually true for incinerators. Absorption cooling from cogeneration may be questionable because cogeneration causes a decrease in electric generating capacity. Whether it is more economical to operate a generating plant in a cogeneration mode for district cooling or to operate the plant for electric generation only during the cooling season, requires a detailed investigation of cooling loads, electric loads, and generating plant characteristics.

Legal and Institutional Barriers to System Implementation: State and local laws should be investigated for any barriers they may present to system development. At the state level, the utility regulatory commission usually has jurisdiction over district heating activities. Locally, building codes, subdivision regulations and zoning law may effect district heating systems. Also, federal, state, and local environmental protection measures could effect district heating plans.

BUILDING AN ELEMENT INTO THE COMPREHENSIVE PLAN

The local comprehensive area development plan, energy plan, or other document can influence future civic action. They can help clarify a program, publicize it and encourage public involvement. If district heating appears beneficial, it may be wise to begin building a "district heating advisory committee" to verify the system's public acceptability.

ENLIST PRIVATE OR GOVERNMENT SUPPORT

Potential users should be approached to see if they would support further study of a local district heating system. Because of the large investment required, implementation of a district heating system requires the development of a broad base of support within the community. *Factors That Influence the Acceptance of Integrated Community Energy Systems,* by Argonne National Laboratory, is one document that provides insight on the interests of various groups in large-scale energy systems.

ENGINEERING AND DEVELOPMENT OF DESIGNS

If the proposed system has good economics, utility support, reasonable political support, and if the study team is well funded, a mechanical engineering firm may be utilized to transform the basic work from the study into engineering drawings, equipment lists and detailed cost estimates. Final drafting of the construction drawings, an expensive and potentially time-consuming task, should not be done until most institutional and financing arrangements have been finalized.

In following any of the preceding steps toward assessment and possible development of district heating, planners should be careful to involve increasingly detailed feasibility studies with correspondingly increasing commitments from major decision-makers. These decision-makers should develop a sense of "proprietorship" over system plants if implementation is to become a reality. Technical staffs of appropriate governmental agencies, the local utilities, and potential large industrial customers should be involved significantly in the technical analyses. Executives of these agencies and corporations must be kept informed of study results and asked to express their approval through public endorsements, allocation of funds or personnel for further study, and eventually the financial commitments necessary to build and operate the district heating system.

PRINCIPLE ISSUES AND BARRIERS

In any major new proposed system installation, various types of issues and barriers are raised and must be dealt with and overcome. The principal barriers to widespread district heating and cooling (DHC) adoption have proved to be institutional, statutory and regulatory rather than technical and physical. Before a private or public entity can undertake the implementation of a DHC system, arrangements must be established in the areas of ownership, financing, operation, regulation, taxation, and permits. Involved in this procedure are federal, state and local governments; financing institutions; utility companies, major customers; major commercial and industrial interests; local interest groups, and other concerned parties. Anyone whose consent is necessary for the resolution of these issues can delay or impede the progress of the DHC project. The greater the degree of cooperation among the many entities involved in the project, the greater the project feasibility becomes and the lower its capital and operational costs. One example is the assistance offered by tax-exempt financing in lowering the cost of capital investments.

The resolution of such issues involves a complex balancing of competing priorities, and can be achieved only through coordinated action among the involved parties. While most issues can be resolved at local levels, some questions will require resolution at the federal or state levels.

Major Barriers to District Heating and Cooling System Implementation

Various economic, regulatory, legal, environmental, and institutional issues can impact development of district heating systems. Many of these have been identified in recent studies of ownership, operation, and growth of large metropolitan DHC systems. Table 2.4 on page 30 lists some of these issues. Although this list is not complete, it provides a general introduction to the types of issues which must be considered.

One of the main constraints on development or expansion of a DHC system is raising funds for the large capital investment required. Several years of negative cash flow may be anticipated when new systems are installed. This stems from the long lead time before the DHC system actually is placed in operation and begins to produce revenues, and from the gradual buildup of load over several years before substantial revenues can be generated. The perceived risk to investors is high. Electric utilities generally have indicated their unwillingness to invest in new district heating and cooling systems unless some of the major uncertainties are resolved. For example, some states do not have a cost allocation method for determining rates for thermal energy from cogeneration power plants. Market potential and other regulatory issues are also important. Studies conducted in the recent past have recommended that the government provide incentives to overcome some of these uncertainties. Without such action, it apparently is unlikely that the utility industry will risk large outlays for DHC.

Environmental impact is another important element of DHC system development. Because DHC installations can alter pollutant emissions, for better or worse, at a large number of points, the air environmental effects of systems are complex. Groups considering district heating and cooling may see this complexity as an additional barrier to obtaining the required environmental permits necessary to construction of the system. Overall, however, district heating and cooling systems usually will upgrade and improve air quality in the vicinity of the system. Future policies may be expected to encourage the development of such systems. If installation of a DHC system reduces the total amount of pollution emitted in an area, EPA's "bubble policy" allows the system operator to increase pollution emissions from another source outside the DHC system so long as the total emissions provide a net improvement or no degradation in air quality. States are encouraged to follow this policy. The capability of retrofitting an urban area for DHC without adverse local impacts during the time the system is under construction is an important issue. European experience has shown that, with proper planning, large urban areas can be retrofitted without major disruptions. The same should hold true in the United States.

Providing Assurance to Investors

Potential new system owner-investors need assurance and confidence in the long-term economic feasibility of a planned district heating system. Both private and public owner-investors must be assured of a fair economic return in keeping with the risks involved in the very costly development of new utilities and services. Legislative action may be required to define policy and remove probable barriers to owner-investor assurance and confidence in the long-term economic feasibility of district heating system development.

COST ALLOCATION POLICY

The price of hot water obtained from cogenerating power plants owned by regulated public utilities may be critical to the overall feasibility of a project and is a primary concern. A situation is required which will encourage the development of cogenerated hot water without increasing the cost of cogenerated electricity. A cost allocation policy encouraging cogeneration and district heating would assure the long-term reliability and price of cogenerated thermal energy.

CROSS SUBSIDIZATION POLICY

A policy is needed which will allow regulated energy utilities to charge current customers for some limited costs associated with research and development in new energy ventures. The absence of such a policy inhibits research and development of cogenerated district heating systems.

LONG RANGE PERMIT POLICY

The absence of a long-range permit policy and procedure represents a potential barrier to the efficient development of cogenerated district heating systems. A long-range permit policy which recognizes the cost and conservation advantages of cogenerated district heating system development is required. The policy and procedure should allow for reasonable and early assurances that long-range system development plans can proceed without future interruption.

REGULATORY POLICY

The potential for district heating utilities to be regulated by a Public Service Commission during initial development is seen as a potential barrier to private utility development of such systems. The additional expense and loss of operating flexibility imposed by the regulatory process is a cause for concern. A policy is needed that recognizes the need for and advantages of cogenerated district heating, and which would permit initial development to occur within the constraints of normal contractual obligations with non-residential customers. This form of system development should continue until the utility amortizes front-end costs and evolves to the point where it can reasonably serve residential customers.

TAX POLICY

Currently, individual heating systems pay a tax on the fuel used but not on the heat produced. District heating systems also pay a tax on the fuel they use, and must collect an additional tax on the energy they deliver. These taxes combine with property taxes on equipment and pipes to cumulatively penalize users and owners of costly systems designed to conserve energy. A tax policy is required which recognizes the conservation advantages of cogenerated district heating by replacing the numerous taxes with one tax based either upon delivered energy or upon the gross earnings equivalent of delivered energy.

CUSTOMER COMMITMENTS

In order to be assured a customer base which will provide adequate operating and growth revenue, new district heating system owner/operators may desire long-term (ten to twenty year) contracts with their customers. These contracts should be based upon the mutual understanding that no significant barriers exist which would prevent the long-term efficient production and delivery of cost competitive thermal energy.

GOVERNMENT COMMITMENTS

Past state and local government policy has not recognized or supported the cost and conservation advantages of cogeneration and district heating. Neither has it actively promoted or encouraged DHC development, use, and expansion. In the near future this may change, however, as results from a variety of studies are made available and reviewed, and as legislative policy evolves in support of this technology.

CUSTOMER ASSURANCE AND CONFIDENCE

Potential new customers for a DHC system need assurance and confidence of the long-term availability and reliability of competitively priced thermal energy. Several such requirements for customer assurance and confidence in energy supplied through cogenerated district heating have been identified.

COMPETITIVE ENERGY COSTS

Cogenerated district heating must provide not only the assurance and confidence of competitive rates, it must also assure a convenience and supply reliability exceeding that of traditional individually owned and operated systems.

SUPPLY RELIABILITY

A new or expanding utility must have the technical and financial ability to develop stable fuel sources, reliable operating systems, and an organizational structure dedicated to providing long-term reliable cogenerated thermal energy. When a building is tied into a DHC system, this generally precludes the ready availability of alternate heat sources in the event of technical or financial failure.

HOOK-UP POLICY

The question of whether customer hook-up to a district heating system be voluntary or mandatory is very important. Cogenerated hot water district heating system development is quite costly, and voluntary hook-up might not generate the number of customers and operating revenue required by a new system. Mandatory hook-up might attract such customers and required revenues. However, such a policy eliminates the availability of customer alternatives. Taking a course leading to such action violates one of the most valued concepts of a competitive free enterprise economy. Voluntary hook-up is recommended. Various forms of incentives can be used to accelerate customer hook-up to new district heating systems.

BUILDING CONVERSION COST RECOVERY

To receive cogenerated hot water thermal energy, customers must convert or replace part or all of their existing heating systems. Writing off the cost of existing equipment and purchase of needed new equipment and its installation must be absorbed by the building owner, renter, or a third party. Currently, most leases require a benefit pass-through for fuel economy, but prevents pass-through of costs associated with capital improvements to achieve that fuel economy.

UTILITY COMMITMENTS

In order to assure long term, economically attractive and reliable service, long term contracts are most desirable. It is also important to base such contracts upon the mutual understanding that no significant barriers exist which might prevent the utility from providing long term economically attractive reliable future service.

GOVERNMENT COMMITMENTS

Potential customers appear hesitant to commit to long term contracts for cogenerated thermal energy without knowing details of delivered cost and operating reliability. These potential barriers cannot be resolved totally without state and local government commitment to the cost and conservation efficiencies of cogenerated district heating and policies which resolve potential institutional barriers.

CONCLUSIONS

District heating systems can provide significant public benefit at the local, state, and national level in the United States. The technology of cogenerated hot water district heating has proved itself throughout Europe to be capable of providing electrical and thermal energy in a manner which is safe, reliable, fuel efficient, cost effective, and environmentally compatible. We also have the added advantage in this country of being able to cogenerate much of our heat and power requirements using domestic coal supplies—an abundant fossil fuel.

Coal fired cogenerated district heat can supplant natural gas and oil-fired space heating in high and medium density commercial, institutional, and industrial load areas. This replacement can assist in making natural gas and fuel oil supplies available for a much longer period for use in lower density commercial, apartment, and residential areas of our nation's towns and cities. Several factors which could affect the form of ownership and operation, the characteristics of development have been identified and could create unacceptable risks for potential system developers and for customers of cogenerated hot water district heating systems. To effectuate responsible DHC system development, the public and private sectors representing energy consumers, suppliers, regulators, and government agencies at the local, state, and national level must continue to work toward mutually acceptable ends in the development of specific DHC projects, and in the elimination of institutional barriers to their ownership and operation.

CHAPTER 3

Sources of Energy for District Heating Systems

COAL

COAL is the most abundant fossil fuel in the United States, accounting for more than 75% of the nation's known recoverable energy reserves.

Commercial U.S. coal mining began in 1790, near Richmond, Virginia. By 1855, coal had become the country's principal fuel, a position it retained until World War II.

After World War II, oil's popularity rapidly outstripped coal's, with overall demand for the latter increasing slowly, by less than 3 percent per year. This trend reversed in early 1979. Coal production in 1980 exceeded 1979's output by more than 10%.

U.S. coal reserves have been approximated from drilling outcroppings, operating mines, and explorations of minerals and oil. It is estimated that 32 states have 350,000 square miles underlaid with coal, (Figure 3.1). Distribution of these reserves is shown in Table 3.1, by states and tonnages, and at various sulfur levels. Because the Clean Air Act of 1970 made sulfur content an important criterion for purchasing coal, the states with the largest reserves are not necessarily the largest producers. Table 3.2 indicates the ten states with the largest reserves, their total production for 1974, and their relative production rank among all states.

The location of U.S. coal fields are shown in Figure 3.1. The two largest producing regions are the Appalachian area (Pennsylvania, West Virginia, Ohio, western Maryland, eastern Kentucky, Virginia, Tennessee and Alabama) and the Central area (Illinois, Indiana, western Kentucky, Iowa, Missouri, Kansas, Oklahoma and Arkansas).

Two-thirds of the nation's coal reserves are in the Great Plains, Rocky Mountains and West regions, with most of their coal being lignites and subbituminous, with a small amount of bituminous and anthracite. The fields there were not developed in the past because of their distance from major industrial areas. This situation has changed, because most of the coal included has low sulfur content and utilities are purchasing it in far greater quantities. Rapid development of these Western region coal fields is anticipated as a result of their use in production of both synthetic liquid fuels and synthetic gas.

Types of Coal

Commonly accepted classification of coals are discussed below. As coal is seldom 100% "pure," such classifications tend to be arbitrary:

51

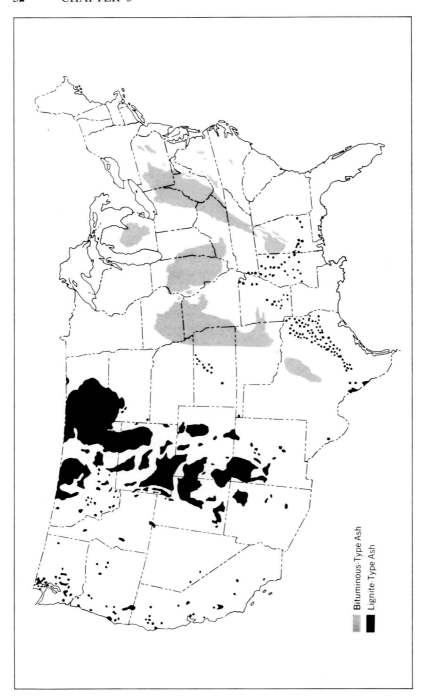

FIGURE 3.1

Coal fields of the United States, (Source, U.S. Geological Survey.)

Bituminous-Type Ash

Lignite-Type Ash

TABLE 3.1

DEMONSTRATED TOTAL UNDERGROUND AND SURFACE COAL RESERVE BASE
OF THE UNITED STATES (MILLION TONS)

State	Sulfur Range, Percent				
	≤1.0	1.1–3.0	>3.0	Unknown	Total[a]
Alabama	624.7	1,099.9	16.4	1,239.4	2,981.8
Alaska	11,458.4	184.2	.0	.0	11,645.4
Arizona	173.3	176.7	.0	.0	350.0
Arkansas	81.2	463.1	46.3	74.3	665.7
Colorado	7,475.5	786.2	47.3	6,547.3	14,869.2
Georgia	0.3	.0	.0	0.2	0.5
Illinois	1,095.1	7,341.4	42,968.9	14,256.2	65,664.8
Indiana	548.8	3,305.8	5,262.4	1,504.1	10,622.6
Iowa	1.5	226.7	2,105.9	549.2	2,884.9
Kansas	.0	309.2	695.6	383.2	1,388.1
Kentucky-East	6,558.4	3,321.8	299.5	2,729.3	12,916.7
Kentucky-West	0.2	564.4	9,243.9	2,815.9	12,623.9
Maryland	135.1	690.5	187.4	34.6	1,048.2
Michigan	4.6	85.4	20.9	7.0	118.2
Missouri	.0	182.0	5,226.0	4,080.5	9,487.3
Montana	101,646.6	4,115.0	502.6	2,116.7	108,396.2
New Mexico	3,575.3	793.4	0.9	27.5	4,394.8
North Carolina	.0	.0	.0	31.7	31.7
North Dakota	5.389.0	10,325.4	268.7	15.0	16,003.0
Ohio	134.4	6,440.9	12,534.3	1,872.0	21,077.2
Oklahoma	275.0	326.6	241.4	450.5	1,294.2
Oregon	1.5	0.3	.0	.0	1.8
Pennsylvania	7,318.3	16,913.6	3,799.6	2,954.2	31,000.6
South Dakota	103.1	287.9	35.9	1.0	428.0
Tennessee	204.8	533.2	156.6	88.0	986.7
Texas	659.8	1,884.6	284.1	444.0	3,271.9
Utah	1,968.5	1,546.7	49.4	487.3	4,042.5
Virginia	2,140.1	1,163.5	14.1	330.0	3,649.9
Washington	603.5	1,265.5	39.0	45.1	1,954.0
West Virginia	14,092.1	14,006.2	6,823.3	4,652.5	39,589.8
Wyoming	33,912.3	14,657.4	1,701.1	3,060.3	53,336.1
Total[a]	200,181.1	92,997.6	92,671.1	50,837.7	436,725.4

[a] Data may not add to totals shown due to independent rounding.
Source, Bureau of Mines bulletin, *Coal—Bituminous and Lignite.*

Anthracite is a clean, dense, hard coal that generates little dust in handling. Although it is somewhat hard to ignite, once started it burns freely, uniformly, with a low smoke level, and with a short flame.

Semianthracite is similar to anthracite, except it has a higher volatile content and ignites more easily.

Bituminous coal encompasses a wide range of coals, including types with distinctly different characteristics. Their caking properties vary from coals that become fully plastic to those from which volatiles and tars are distilled without change of form (classified as "noncaking" or "freeburning"). In general, however, most bituminous coals are nonfriable enough to permit screened sizes to be delivered free of fines. Also, most ignite easily and burn freely with relatively long flame length.

Semibituminous coal is soft and friable; handling creates "fines" and dust. It

TABLE 3.2

PROVEN COAL RESERVES AND PRODUCTION OF TOP TEN STATES WITH
GREATEST RESERVES

State	Demonstrated Proven Reserves (Million Tons)	Production (Thousand Tons)	Production Rank
Montana	108,396.2	14,106	7
Illinois	65,664.8	58,215	4
Wyoming	53,336.1	20,703	6
West Virginia	39,589.8	102,462	2
Pennsylvania	31,000.6	80,462	3
Kentucky	25,540.6	137,197	1
Ohio	21,077.7	45,409	5
North Dakota	16,003.0	7,463	8
Colorado	14,869.2	6,896	9
Alaska	11,645.4	700	10

Source, Bureau of Mines bulletin, *Coal—Bituminous and Lignite.*

ignites slowly and burns with a medium flame length. Its caking properties increase as volatile matter increases. It has only half the volatile-matter of bituminous coals, and so burns with less smoke. (It is sometimes called "smokeless" coal.)

Subbituminous coals, found mostly in the West, have a high moisture content when mined and tend to break up as they dry or when exposed to the weather. They ignite easily and quickly, sometimes on a spontaneous basis when stored. They have a medium length flame and are noncaking and free-burning. They produce low levels of smoke or soot.

Lignite has a "woody" structure. It has a high moisture content and is clean to handle. However, it has a low heating value and tends to disintegrate during drying, making it susceptible to spontaneous ignition. Freshly-mined lignite ignites slowly due to its moisture content. Nonetheless, the char left after moisture and volatile matter are driven off burns easily, similar to charcoal. Low levels of smoke or soot are produced.

Characteristics of Coals

Several coal characteristics determine classification and suitability for given applications. These are volatile matter, fixed carbon, moisture, sulfur and ash. A given type of coal's content of each is reported in a proximate analysis.

Such analyses may be reported as-received, moisture-free (dry), or dry and mineral-matter-free (or ash free). The "as-received" basis is used for combustion calculations and the "dry and mineral-matter-free" basis for classification purposes.

Volatile matter is that portion of coal which is driven off as gas or vapor during a standardized temperature test. The gases and vapors differ materially by relative weight (in comparison to oils and tars). No heavy oils or tars are given off by anthracite and only small quantities are given off by semianthracite. Subbituminous coals and lignite give off relatively low quantities of oils and tars due to their higher volatile content.

Fixed carbon is the combustible residue left after volatile matter is driven off. It represents that portion of fuel that must be burned in the solid state. The form and hardness indicate fuel coking properties and therefore guide the choice of combustion equipment. (Note that fixed carbon is not 100% carbon.)

Moisture of coal is difficult to determine because a sample may lose some of its moisture content when exposed to the atmosphere. This is particularly the case when sample size is reduced for purposes of analysis. As a result, a sample's total moisture content customarily is determined by adding the moisture loss obtained when the sample is air-dried to measure moisture content of the dried sample. Moisture represents only a portion of the water present in coal because the water of decomposition (combined water) and of hydration are not given off under standardized test conditions.

Ash is the noncombustible residue remaining after complete coal combustion. Its weight usually is less than that of mineral matter present before burning.

Sulfur is an undesirable constituent in coal. The sulfur oxides that are formed when coal is burned cause corrosion of combustion systems and contribute to air pollution. Table 3.3 lists sulfur content of typical coals, based on ultimate analysis (see below).

Heating values are reported on as-received, dry, dry and mineral-matter-free, or moist and mineral-matter-free base. Higher heating values of quality coals (frequently reported along with their proximate analyses) can be calculated (in Btu/lb) through application of the Dulong Formula:

Higher Heating Value, Btu/lb $= 14,544 \, C + 62.028 \, (H - (O/8)) + 4,050 \, S$

where C, H, O and S are the weight fractions of carbon, hydrogen, oxygen, and sulfur in the coal.

Other factors used to evaluate coal include ultimate analysis, ash-fusion temperature, grindability, and free-swelling index.

Ultimate analysis is another method of reporting coal composition, in terms of percentages of C, H, O, N, S, and ash in the sample. Ultimate analysis is used mostly for detailed fuel studies and for computing the heat balance (sometimes required in testing of heating devices).

Ash-fusion temperature indicates the fluidity of ash at high temperatures. It is a helpful parameter in selecting coal for use in a particular furnace and in estimating the potential for ash handling or slagging problems.

Grindability index indicates the ease with which a coal can be pulverized. The measure is applied in estimating ball mill capacity.

Free swelling index indicates the extent to which a given type of coal will swell upon combustion on a fuel bed. As such, it is a useful indication of coking characteristics.

TABLE 3.3
TYPICAL ULTIMATE ANALYSES FOR COALS

Rank	Btu/lb As Received	Constituents, Percent by Weight					
		Oxygen	Hydrogen	Carbon	Nitrogen	Sulfur	Ash
Anthracite	12,700	5.0	2.9	80.0	0.9	0.7	10.5
Semianthracite	13,600	5.0	3.9	80.4	1.1	1.1	8.5
Low-Voltage Bituminous	14,350	5.0	4.7	81.7	1.4	1.2	6.0
Medium-Volatile Bituminous	14,000	5.0	5.0	1.4	1.4	1.5	6.0
High-Volatile Bituminous *A*	13,800	9.3	5.3	75.9	1.5	1.5	6.5
High-Volatile Bituminous *B*	12,500	13.8	5.5	67.8	1.4	3.0	8.5
High-Volatile Bituminous *C*	11,000	20.6	5.8	59.6	1.1	3.5	9.4
Subbituminous *B*	9,000	29.5	6.2	52.5	1.0	1.0	9.8
Subbituminous *C*	8,500	35.7	6.5	46.4	0.8	1.0	9.6
Lignite	6,900	44.0	6.9	40.1	0.7	1.0	7.3

Commercial Sizes of Coal

BITUMINOUS

Coal size designations are applied mostly to bituminous coal and anthracite. Sizes of bituminous coal are not standardized. The following sizings are commonly applied:

1. *Run of mine* coal is shipped as it comes from the mine, without screening. It is used for domestic heating and steam production.
2. *Run of mine (8 in.)* is run of mine coal whose oversize lumps have been broken up.
3. *Lump (5 in.)* coal will not go through a five-inch diameter hole. It is used mostly for hand firing and for domestic purposes.
4. *Egg (5 in. x 2 in.)* coal fits through a five-inch diameter hole but is retained on a 2 in. round hole screen. It is used for hand firing, gas production, and domestic firing.
5. *Nut (2 in. × 1¼ in.)* coal is used for small industrial stokers, gas producers, and hand firing.
6. *Stoker coal (1¼ in. x ¾ in.)* is used primarily in small industrial stokers and for domestic firing.
7. *Slack (¾ in. and under)* is used in pulverizers, Cyclone Furnaces, and industrial stokers.

ANTHRACITE

Standardized sizes of anthracite are shown in Table 3.4. Broken, egg, stove, nut and pea sizes are used mostly for hand-fired domestic units and gas producers. Buckwheat and rice are used in mechanical types of firing equipment.

Coal Use and the Environment

Pollutants from burning coal include sulfur dioxide, nitrogen oxides, carbon dioxide and particulates such as dust, soot, fly ash and other tiny particles of solid and liquid matter. Although pollution control devices have greatly reduced pollutant emission, total control has not yet been achieved. The technology used to limit emissions of pollutants includes:

1. *coal washing*, which includes cleaning the coal before it is burned to remove impurities;

TABLE 3.4
COMMERCIAL SIZES OF ANTHRACITE (ASTM) D 310) (GRADED ON ROUND HOLE SCREENS)

Trade Name	Diameter of Holes, Inches	
	Through	Retained On
Broken	4⅜	3¼ to 3
Egg	3¼ to 3	2⁷⁄₁₆
Stove	2⁷⁄₁₆	1⅝
Nut	1⅝	1³⁄₁₆
Pea	1³⁄₁₆	9⁄₁₆
Buckwheat	9⁄₁₆	5⁄₁₆
Rice	5⁄₁₆	3⁄₁₆

2. *electrostatic precipitators*, some of which can remove 90% of the larger particles contained in particulate emissions.
3. *stack gas scrubbers*, used to control up to 95% of sulfur emissions.

Other Environmental Concerns

Some of the other environmental concerns associated with greater reliance on coal include acid rain (or acid precipitation), the greenhouse effects, and solid waste disposal.

ACID RAIN

Some scientists contend that rainfall in parts of the world, including areas of the United States, has become more acidic in recent years. They say that, when acidic rainwater falls to earth, it destroys fresh water ecosystems, damages soil, erodes stone building and monuments, causes poor visibility, and may also damage crops, reduce forest growth and contaminate drinking water. Other scientists question these findings, contending that available data are not adequate to conclude that acid rain is a serious problem. Disagreement also exists over the causes and effects of acid precipitation.

The Electric Power Research Institute (EPRI) states that the relationship between acid rain and coal-burning utilities has not been proven, and that the relative degree of acidity arising from natural and from man-made sources is largely unknown. Natural sources of carbon dioxide, sulfates, and nitrates that contribute to rain acidity, include lightning, volcanos, sea spray and the organic decay of vegetation. The percentage of total atmospheric sulfur compounds from natural sources is believed to be more than 70%. The percentage of total atmospheric nitrogen compounds from natural sources is believed to be in excess of 90%. Further, an examination of the amount of coal burned in the United States during the same time that acid rainfall allegedly has increased reveals that little if any more total sulfur dioxide is today being emitted into the atmosphere as a result of coal burning. Clearly, more research is needed into the causes of acid rain.

GREENHOUSE EFFECT

When any fossil fuel is burned, carbon dioxide is emitted. Although carbon dioxide is harmless, some scientists believe that large concentrations of the substance can cause higher temperatures worldwide (the "greenhouse effect"). By contrast, other scientists feel that the earth is getting cooler because it is reflecting more sunlight due to the forest clearing, overgrazing, and increased land aridity that has occurred over the centuries. Thus, this cooling effect counteracts the greenhouse effect. It is apparent that more research is needed.

WASTE DISPOSAL PROBLEMS

Most scrubbers installed by large coal-burning facilities produce a solid waste called "sludge." It is proving difficult to dispose of sludge in an environmentally acceptable manner due to lack of sufficient disposal sites. This problem is being solved as new designs of scrubbers produce usable sulfur solutions and pure sulfur, instead of sludge.

New Approaches to Environmentally Acceptable Coal Use

Different new processes and techniques have been demonstrated in pilot plants or are undergoing testing in research facilities. These processes and techniques can be grouped into four categories, as follows.

COAL-CLEANING PROCESSES

Washing coal before it is shipped is already in use. The process consists of removing impurities (ash-producing minerals and sulfur) and drying surface moisture. As a result, washed coal emits fewer pollutants and has a higher heat content. Cleaning technologies will permit use of large coal reserves that otherwise could not be used under sulfur oxide emission requirements.

MORE SOPHISTICATED EMISSIONS-CONTROL DEVICES

Experiments are underway to make existing pollution-control devices more efficient. EPRI and EPA are studying ways to improve the performance of electrostatic precipitators to control emissions of very fine particles emitted during coal burning. Experiments also are being conducted to test the efficacy of the "baghouse" device for utilities. A baghouse, used to control emissions from other types of facilities, consists of many bags (about one foot in diameter and 30 feet long) generally made of glass fiber. The bags trap particles and so prevent them from being emitted into the atmosphere. Their use on a small scale has produced efficiency figures of 99.8% removal of total particulate mass and better than 99% for the smaller particles.

Further improvements in current technology can be expected as coal use increases.

NEW COAL TECHNOLOGIES

A number of experimental processes are being tested to burn coal directly in a more environmentally sound way.

One process termed solvent refined coal (SRC), results in an environmentally acceptable fuel being derived from coal originally high in sulfur and fly ash. In the SRC process, coal is mixed with a solvent and treated with hydrogen at high temperature and pressure. Several oil companies are involved in SRC research and development.

A second process, called fluidized bed combustion, removes sulfur from coal as it is being burned. The fluidized bed system uses a stream of air to partially suspend a bed of limestone particles. Coal that has been pulverized is then injected into the bed.

Coal Burning Equipment

There are three general types of conventional coal-burning equipment in common use. These include stokers, pulverized coal-burning equipment and cyclone furnaces. The selection of the most suitable equipment for a particular application consists of balancing the investment, operating characteristics, efficiency, and type of coal that will result in the most economical installation.

The type of coal used influences the choice of firing method as follows:
1. Pulverized-coal Firing: Grindability, rank, moisture, volatile matter, and ash.
2. Stoker Firing: Rank of coal, volatile matter, ash, and ash-softening temperature.
3. Cyclone Furnace Firing: Volatile matter, ash, and ash viscosity.

Approximations for selection of bituminous coals for firing boilers are given in Table 3.5.

STOKERS

Stokers were developed as an improvement over hand-firing early in the history of the steam boiler. Many small- and medium-size boilers are fired with stokers with several types being available. All stokers are designed to feed fuel onto a grate within the furnace. Removal of the ash residue is generally a part of the stoker system design.

Stokers are classified according to the method of feeding fuel to the furnace. Thus, the four types of stokers include: *spreader, underfeed, chain-grate* (or *traveling grate*) and *vibrating grate*. Table 3.6 summarizes the major features of stokers. The type of stoker used in a given installation depends on general system design, capacity requirements, and the type of fuel burned.

Spreader Stokers

Spreader stokers (Figure 3.2) use a combination of suspension burning and grate burning. Coal is continually projected into the furnace above an ignited fuel bed. Fines are partially burned in suspension while large particles fall to the grate where they are burned in a fast-burning fuel bed. This firing method provides good response to load fluctuations because ignition is almost instantaneous on increased firing rate. As such, the spreader stoker is predominate in industrial applications.

Because the spreader stoker burns about half the fuel in suspension, it

TABLE 3.5
COAL CHARACTERISTICS AND THE METHOD OF FIRING

		Pulverized Cyclone	
	Stoker	Coal	Furnace
Max. total moisture[a] (as fired), %	15–20	15	20
Min. volatile matter (dry basis), %	15	15	15
Max. total ash (dry basis), %	20	20	25
Max. sulfur (as fired), %	5	—	—

* These limits are exceeded for lower rank, higher inherent-moisture-content coals, i.e., subbituminous and lignite.

TABLE 3.6
CHARACTERISTICS OF VARIOUS TYPES OF STOKERS (CLASS 5)

Stoker Type and Subclass	Typicl Capacity Range, tons/h	Characteristics
Spreader		
Stationary and dumping grate	100 to 400	Capable of burning a wide range of coals,
Traveling grate	500 to 2000	best ability to follow fluctuating loads,
Vibrating grate	100 to 500	high flyash carryover, low load smoke
Underfeed		
Single or double retort	100 to 150	Capable of burning caking coals and a wide
Multiple retort	150 to 2500	range of coals (including anthracite), high maintenance, low flyash carryover, suitable for continuous-load operation
Chain grate and traveling grate	100 to 500	Characteristics similar to vibrating-grate stokers except these stokers experience difficulty in burning strongly caking coals
Vibrating grate	7 to 750	Low maintenance, low flyash carryover, capable of burning wide variety of weakly caking coals, smokeless operation over entire range

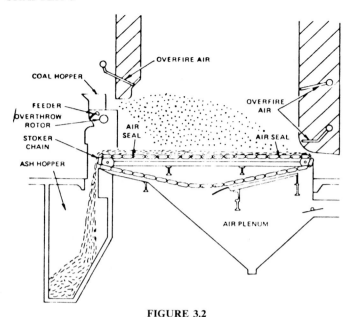

FIGURE 3.2
Spreader stoker, traveling-grate type

generates more particulate matter than other types. Accordingly, it requires dust collectors to trap particulate material in the flue gas before it is discharged to the stack. Fly-carbon reinjection systems are sometimes used to return trapped carbon to the furnace for complete burnout. This process increases furnaces dust emissions and can be used only with very highly efficient dust collectors. Grates are designed with high air flow resistance, to avoid formation of blowholes through the thin fuel bed.

All spreader stokers and particularly those with traveling grates, can use fuels with a wide range of burning characteristics. High moisture, free-burning bituminous coals and lignite are used. Coke breeze can be burned in a mixture with a high-volatile coal. Anthracite is not a suitable fuel because of its low volatile content.

Underfeed Stokers

Underfeed stokers which introduce raw coal into a retort beneath the burning fuel bed are classified as horizontal feed or gravity feed. In horizontal feed types, coal travels inside the furnace in a retort that is parallel with the floor. In gravity feed systems, the retort is inclined by 25 degrees. Most horizontal feed stokers are designed with single or double retorts (some with triple retorts). Gravity feed stokers are designed with multiple retorts.

Coal in a horizontal stoker is fed to the retort by a screw (for smaller stokers) or ram (for larger units). Air is supplied through tuyeres at each side of the retort and through air ports in the side grates. When the retort is filled, coal is forced upward until it spills over the retort to form and subsequently feed the fuel bed. As coal moves upward inside the retort, heat from the active bed above is conducted downward and the volatile gases are distilled off and burned. The rising fuel bed then ignites from contact with the burning bed.

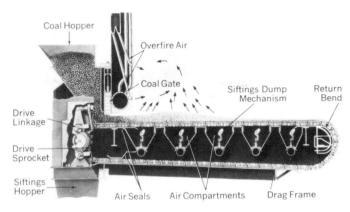

FIGURE 3.3

Chain-grate stoker

Incoming raw coal gradually displaces the fuel bed over the side and tuyeres grates. As a result, the coal is completely burned when it reaches the dump grates.

All types of underfeed stokers can burn a wide range of coal, including caking coal that does not contain an excess amount of fines. Ash-softening temperature is a major criterion in selecting coals because excessive clinkering increases at lower ash-softening temperatures. Generally speaking, horizontal feed stokers are best suited for free-burning bituminous coal.

Chain-Grate and Traveling-Grate Stokers

Chain-grate or traveling-grate stokers vary only in grate construction (Figure 3.3). The links of chain-grate stokers are moved with a scissor-like action at the return bend of the stoker. There is no relative movement between adjacent grate sections of the traveling grates. This makes the chain grate more suitable for handling coals with clinkering ash characteristics.

In either type, coal is fed from a hopper onto the moving grate. The coal then passes under an adjustable gate to regulate the thickness of the fuel bed, and from there into the furnace. As it enters the furnace, the coal is heated by radiation from the furnace gases or from a hot refractory arch. This rapid radiative heating drives off volatile matter and ignition occurs. The fuel continues to burn as it moves along the fuel bed, with combustion being completed at the far end of the grate and the ash is discharged into the pit when the grates pass downward over a return bend.

Chain-grate and traveling-grate stokers can burn peat, lignite, subbituminous coal, free-burning bituminous coal, anthracite coal, and coke, provided it is properly sized. Strongly caking bituminous coals may not be responsive to rapidly changing loads and tend to mat, thus preventing proper air distribution to the fuel bed.

Vibrating-Grate Stokers

Vibrating-grate stokers, (Figure 3.4) are overfeed, mass-burning, continuous ash-discharge units. The sloping grate of a vibrating stoker is water-cooled and is supported on equally-spaced vertical plates that vibrate back and forth in a rectilinear direction. This causes the fuel to move from the hopper through an

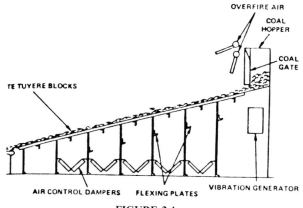

FIGURE 3.4
Vibrating-grate stoker

adjustable gate and then into the active combustion zone. The stoker's air supply moves through laterally exposed areas below the stoker formed by the individual flexing of grate support plates. Ash is discharged into a shallow or basement ash pit.

Frequency and duration of vibrating cycles control coal feed rates and fuel-bed movement. Regulation is performed by automatic combustion controls that apportion air supply to optimize heat release rates.

The vibrating-grate stoker has become increasingly popular due to its simplicity, low maintenance, adaptability to multiple-fuel firing, inherently low flyash carryover, and wide turndown ratio.

The vibrating-grate stoker can burn a range of bituminous coals and lignite. Because of the gentle agitation and compaction caused by the vibratory actions, coal having a high free-swelling index can be burned, and a uniform fuel bed without slow holes and thin spots can be maintained.

PULVERIZED COAL BURNING EQUIPMENT

Pulverized coal is coal that has been ground into a fine powder. Its use has three distinct advantages over solid coal. These are:

1. permits use of low cost, low grade coals that burn satisfactorily when pulverized;
2. provides better fuel-air mixing that reduces air requirements, resulting in heat being carried from the furnace by this excess air, and
3. gives better combustion control with faster response to load changes.

In early pulverized coal installations, coal was dried, pulverized and conveyed to a central bin from which it was fed to the furnace as required. This system required extra equipment to convey the coal to and from the storage bin; storage created a fire hazard.

Most modern power plants use a unit or direct-fired system. Typically, the coal is crushed to sizes from ¾" to 1" and then passed over a magnetic separator to remove tramp iron. The crushed coal is stored in a bunker and fed to the pulverizers (or mills) located adjacent to the boiler which discharge directly to the furnace burners. Several burners often are fed from one pulverizer.

Types of Pulverizers

Four types of pulverizers are used:

Impact Puliverizer

The impact pulverizer is used for smaller boilers. It has one or more sets of hammers mounted on revolving discs that break the coal into powder-like particles. The powdered coal is carried through the pulverizer by an air stream produced by a fan.

Ball Mill Pulverizer

The ball mill pulverizer (or tube mill) pulverizer consists of a slowly-revolving horizontal cylinder that is half filled with steel balls one to two inches in diameter. Worm-like screws feed coal into both ends of the cylinder. These screws have hollow tubes through which heated air also enters the cylinder. The coal and steel balls tend to be carried up the side of the revolving cylinder then tumble down, the heavy balls crushing and pulverizing the coal. An air stream picks up the coal dust and leaves the cylinder through the same spaces that contain the entering coal. The exhauster fan induces an air flow through the mill and discharges the coal-air mixture to the burners.

Ball Race Mill Pulverizer

The ball race mill pulverizer (Figure 3.5) is one of two types most commonly used to generate steam. It consists of an upper stationary race and a lower revolving race that contains steel balls that are six to twelve inches in diameter. A table-type feeder supplies coal to the mill where it falls upon the inner side

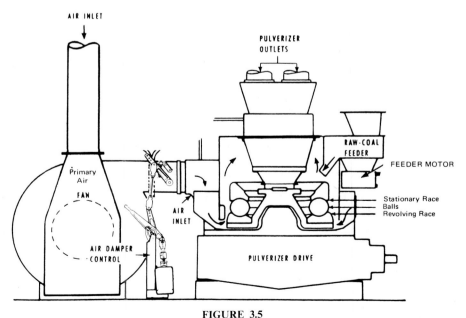

FIGURE 3.5
Ball race mill pulverizer

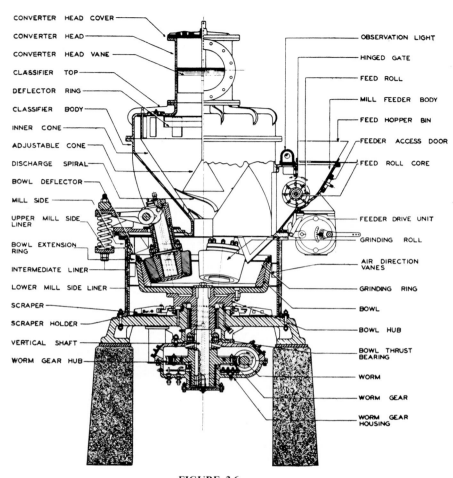

FIGURE 3.6
Bowl mill pulverizer parts

of the races, and is pulverized by the moving balls. The upper stationary race is held down by springs that can be adjusted to vary the crushing force. A primary air fan forces hot air into the space surrounding the races and between the balls and the races. The coal-air mixture then passes through a separator or classifier where oversized particles are returned for further grinding. The properly ground coal and air passes through the classifier to the furnace burners.

Bowl Mill Pulverizer

The bowl mill pulverizer (Figures 3.6) is another type commonly used in steam generation. Inside a rotating bowl there is a small clearance between a grinding ring and spring-loaded rollers. A coal feeder discharges coal into the revolving bowl, where centrifugal force moves it onto the grinding ring at the sides. There the coal is pulverized by the rollers. Hot air enters at the side of the mill bowl and flows upward and across the top of the bowl picking up the powdered coal. The coal-air mixture is then drawn by an exhaust fan through a separator (or classifier) where the oversize particles are removed and returned to the grinding bowl. The remaining fine coal is carried by the air stream to the burners in the furnace.

Mill Feeders

A mill feeder is used in the direct firing or unit system to vary the rate of coal feed in accordance with boiler load. Both drum feeders and table feeders are used.

A drum feeder consists of a slowly revolving drum with pockets on its edge. Coal from a bunker drops into the pockets and then empties into the pulverizer as the drum revolves. Drum speed is varied to control the flow of coal to the pulverizer.

In a table or disc feeder, coal from the storage bunker falls onto a slowly rotating table or disc. An adjustable shear plate scrapes away the outer edge of the coal on the table causing a measured amount to feed to the pulverizer below. The rate of coal feed is controlled by adjusting table speed and shear plate position.

Pulverized Coal Burners

After the coal is pulverized, the coal-air mixture passes through piping to the burners. The air which carries the coal is known as primary air and constitutes about 20% of the total air required for combustion. The other 80% is known as secondary air, and combines with the primary air and coal at the burner. The burner must be designed to give steady ignition and turbulent mixing of the fuel and air.

Figure 3.7 illustrates a turbulent burner. This type uses a large central tube or nozzle with internal ribs to provide uniform distribution of the primary air and coal passing through it. Secondary air travels through a housing that surrounds the coal nozzle with adjustable vanes give a rotating motion to the stream. The coal nozzle has a central tube for inserting an ignition system.

Figure 3.8 illustrates a vertical multitip burner that is located in the furnace roof.

Figure 3.9 shows a *tangential burner* that is located in the corner of the furnace.

Firing Arrangements

There are three types of firing arrangements: horizontal, vertical, and tangential.

Horizontal Firing

A turbulent-type burner is customarily used for horizontal firing (Figure 3.10). Burners are placed in either the front or the rear furnace wall so the flame travels horizontally across the furnace. In some cases the burners are located in opposite furnace walls to produce intense turbulence when the opposing flames meet.

Vertical Firing

A multitip burner is used for vertical firing (Figure 3.11). Burners are located in the furnace arch and fire vertically downward. The flame then makes a U-turn upward to obtain longer travel and more time for combustion.

FIGURE 3.7
Turbulent burner

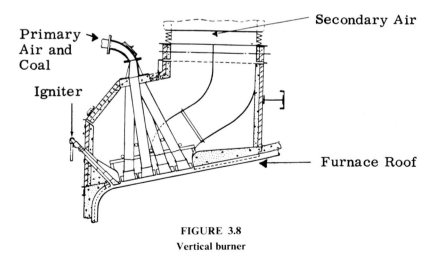

FIGURE 3.8
Vertical burner

Tangential Firing

Tangential firing (Figure 3.12) uses tangential burners located at the four furnace corners. The burners are aimed so that the streams of coal and air from each burner impinge on each other inside the furnace, causing intensive mixing or turbulence.

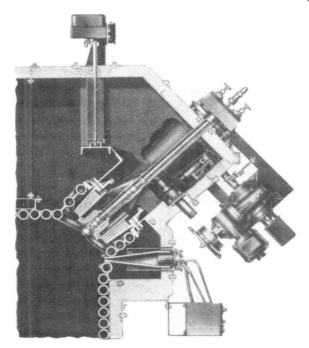

FIGURE 3.9
Tangential burner

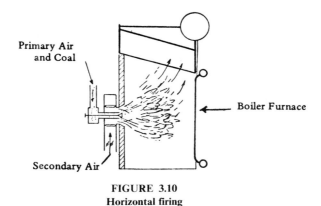

FIGURE 3.10
Horizontal firing

CYCLONE FURNACE

The cyclone furnace is commonly used by the steam-power industry because of its good combustion and furnace performance, ability to use lower grades and ranks of coal in an economic manner, and reduced coal ash problems.

The cyclone furnace is a water-cooled horizontal cylinder whose water-cooled surfaces are studded and covered with refractory over most of their area. The fuel is fired, heat is released at extremely high rates, and combustion is completed inside the cylinder. This method of combustion results in the fuel

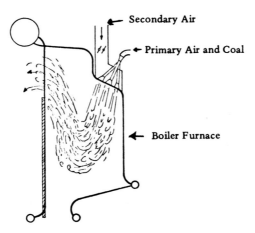

FIGURE 3.11
Vertical firing

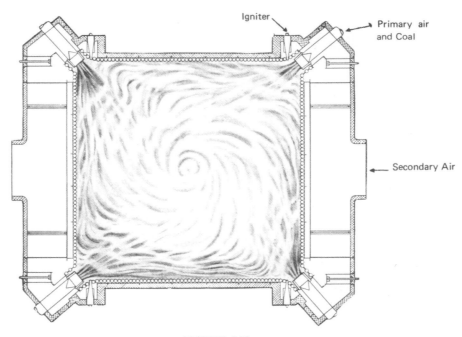

FIGURE 3.12
Tangential firing

being burned quickly and completely within the smaller cyclone chamber, with the boiler furnace being used for cooling the flue gases.

The coal used in a cyclone furnace is crushed so that approximately 95% passes through a 4-mesh screen. The coal enters at the burner end of the furnace, along with primary air. Because the primary air enters the burner tangentially, it imparts a whirling motion to the incoming coal.

Fuel burning results in heat release rates of 450,000 to 800,000 Btu/cu.ft./hr; gas temperatures exceed 3000F. The temperatures are high enough to melt ash into a liquid slag. This slag builds up on the cyclone's walls where it holds incoming coal particles thrown there by centrifugal force. The high-velocity tangential secondary air scrubs the coal, also providing the air needed for combustion and to remove the products of combustion that are discharged through the cyclone's water-cooled re-entrant throat and into the gas-cooling boiler furnace. Excess molten slag drains away from the burner end, discharging through a slag tap opening into the boiler furnace and then into a slag tank. There it is solidified and disintegrated for disposal.

OIL

The American oil industry began in 1859. Domestic production peaked in 1970 and then began to decline. Nonetheless, demand for the fuel continued to grow, resulting in importation of continually greater quantities of "black gold," and this increased dependence on foreign sources and growing vulnerability.

The OPEC oil embargo of 1973–74 marked the end of cheap oil. By 1974 the price was eight times higher than it was five years earlier.

Oil today still is the single most important energy source in the United States. Almost half the energy consumed each year is derived from petroleum, and approximately 50% of that is imported from foreign sources. Proved domestic reserves are estimated at some 27 billion barrels, with potential recoverable resources of about 150 billion barrels. This represents more than 40 times the current annual production of oil in the U.S.

The amount of petroleum resources actually recovered depends on the rate of withdrawal from existing wells, the economics of continued exploration and development of techniques for economic recovery of more oil from reservoirs. As it becomes necessary to drill deeper in less favorable areas, costs increase.

Types and Properties of Fuel Oil

Refining petroleum results in a variety of fuel oils complying with various specifications developed by or in conjunction with the American Society for Testing and Materials (ASTM). Specifications are based on the characteristics of fuel oils required for use in different types of burners. They subdivide oils into different grades as shown in Table 3.7.

Grade No. 1 is a light distillate used in vaporizing-type burners. High volatility assures evaporation of the fuel oil with a minimum of residue.

Grade No. 2 is heavier (API gravity) than Grade No. 1. It is used with pressure-atomizing-type burners (gun burners) that spray oil into a combustion chamber where the vapor mixes with air and burns. Grade No. 2 is used in most domestic burners and in many medium-capacity commercial/industrial burners.

Grade No. 4 usually is a light residual, but sometimes is a heavy distillate. It is used mostly in burners that atomize oils whose viscosity exceeds the limits of domestic burners. Still, its viscosity range is low enough to permit it to be pumped and atomized at relatively low storage temperatures.

Grade No. 5 (Light) is a residual fuel of intermediate viscosity. It is frequently used in burners that can handle fuels more viscous than Grade No. 4 without preheating. Preheating may be necessary in some types of equipment, and is almost always required in colder climates for handling purposes.

Grade No. 5 (Heavy) is more viscous than Grade No. 5 (Light), but is used

TABLE 3.7
ASTM SPECIFICATION D 396 – 69 FOR FUEL OILS

Grade of Fuel Oil[b]	Flash Point, F (C)	Pour Point, F (C)	Water and Sediment % by Vol.	Carbon Residue on 10% Bottoms, %	Ash, % by Wt.	Distillation Temperatures, F (C)			Saybolt Viscosity, Seconds				Kinematic Viscosity, Centistokes				Gravity, deg API	Copper Strip Corrosion	Sulfur, Percent
						10% Point	90%	Point	Universal at 100 F (38 C)		Furol at 122 F (50 C)		at 100 F (38 C)		at 122 F (50 C)				
	Min	Max	Max	Max	Max	Max	Min	Max	Min	Max	Min	Max	Min	Max	Min	Max	Min	Max	Max
No. 1. A distillate oil intended for vaporizing pot-type burners and other burners requiring this grade of fuel	100 or Legal (38)	0[d]	Trace	0.15		420 (215)		550 (288)					1.4	2.2			35	No. 3	0.5 or Legal
No. 2. A distillate oil for general purpose domestic heating for use in burners not requiring No. 1 fuel oil	100 or Legal (38)	20[d] (−7)	0.05	0.35		c	540[b] (282)	640 (338)	32.6[f]	37.93			2.0[d]	3.6			30		0.5[b] or Legal
No. 4. Preheating is not usually required for handling or burning	130 or Legal (55)	20 (−7)	0.50		0.10				45	125			(5.8)	(26.4)					c
No. 5 (Light). Preheating may be required depending on climate and equipment	130 or Legal (55)		1.00		0.10				150	300			(32)	(65)					c

TABLE 3.7—*continued*

Grade of Fuel Oil[b]	Flash Point, F (C) Min	Pour Point, F (C) Max	Water and Sediment % by Vol. Max	Carbon Residue on 10% Bottoms, % Max	Ash, % by Wt. Max	Distillation Temperatures, F (C) 10% Point Max	90% Point Min	Point Max	Saybolt Viscosity, Seconds — Universal at 100 F (38 C) Min	Max	Furol at 122 F (50 C) Min	Max	Kinematic Viscosity, Centistokes — at 100 F (38 C) Min	Max	at 122 F (50 C) Min	Max	Gravity, deg API Min	Copper Strip Corrosion Max	Sulfur, Percent Max
No. 5 (Heavy). Preheating required for burning and, in cold climates, may be required for handling	130 or Legal (55)		1.00		0.10				350	750	(23)	(40)	(75)	(162)	(42)	(81)			[c]
No. 6. Preheating required for burning and handling	150 (65)		2.00[g]						(900)	(900)	45	300			(92)	(638)			[c]

[a] It is the intent of these classifications that failure to meet any requirement of a given grade does not automatically place an oil in the next lower grade unless in fact it meets all requirements of the lower grade.

[b] Outside the U.S.A., the sulfur limit for No. 2 shall be 1.0 percent.

[c] Legal requirements to be met.

[d] Lower or higher pour points may be specified whenever required by conditions of storage or use. When pour point less than 0 F is specified, the minimum viscosity shall be 1.8 ca (32.0 sec. Saybolt Universal) and the minimum 90 percent point shall be waived.

[e] The 10 percent distillation temperature point may be specified at 440 F (226 C) maximum for use in other than atomizing burners.

[f] Viscosity values in parentheses are for information only and not necessarily limiting.

[g] The amount of water by distillation, plus the sediment by extraction, shall not exceed 2.00 percent. The amount of sediment by extraction shall not exceed 0.50 percent. A deduction in quantity shall be made for all water and sediment in excess of 1.0 percent.

in a similar way. Preheating usually is necessary for burning and, in colder climates, for handling.

Grade No. 6, also called Bunker C, is a high-viscosity oil used mostly for commercial and industrial heating. It must be preheated in the storage tank so it can be pumped, and requires additional preheating at the burner to enable atomizing. No. 6 fuel oil is relatively low in cost when compared with other lighter oils. As such, it is the most widely used oil for steam and hot water production.

In referring to Table 3.7, realize that ASTM D 396 is more a classification than a specification. It distinguishes between six generally nonoverlapping grades, one of which characterizes virtually any commercial fuel oil. Quality is not defined as a refiner might control it in his own operations. Thus, Table 3.7 indicates that the distillation temperature 90% point for Grade No. 2 has a maximum of 640 F. Commercial practice rarely exceeds 600 F. (The most recent version of this Table can be found in the latest edition of *ASTM Standards on Petroleum Products and Lubricants.*)

A specific grade of fuel generally is selected on the basis of its cost, preheating and handling costs, equipment cost, availability, and air pollution requirements.

Residual fuel oils are not used in installations with low firing rates and low annual fuel consumption because the cost of preheating cannot be justified. As such, by contrast, large installations with high annual fuel consumption cannot justify the expense of distillate fuel oils.

Table 3.8 provides a guideline for selecting the grade of fuel oil for a specific firing rate. Numerous other selection factors also must be considered, however. These factors comprise the characteristics of fuel oils which determine grade, classifications and suitability for a given application. They are:

1. viscosity,
2. flash point,
3. fire point,
4. pour point,
5. water and sediment content,
6. carbon residue,
7. ash,
8. distillation characteristics,

TABLE 3.8
GUIDE FOR FUEL OIL GRADE
VS. FIRING RATE

Firing Rate, gph	Fuel Oil Grades to Be Considered
Up to 25	No. 2
25 to 35	No. 2, No. 4
35 to 50	No. 2, No. 4, No. 5 (Light), No. 5 (Heavy)
50 to 100	No. 5 (Heavy), No. 6
Over 100	No. 6

9. specific gravity,
10. sulfur,
11. heating value, and
12. carbon-hydrogen content.

VISCOSITY

Viscosity, a measure of a substance's resistance to flow, indicates ease of oil flow (or pumping), as well as ease of atomization. Standard laboratory procedures for determining viscosity are published by ASTM. Viscosity measurements are expressed as Saybolt Seconds Universal (SSU), Saybolt Seconds Furol (SSF) or Kinematic Centistokes.

The relationship between Saybolt Universal, Saybolt Furol, and Kinematic viscosities is shown in Table 3.9.

Heavy oils require preheating because an increase in temperature lowers oil viscosity, thus facilitating effective handling in pumps and burners.

The relationship between oil viscosity and temperature is shown in Figure 3.13.

Proper burner operation requires that the viscosity of the entering oil must be within certain limits. The general range of atomizing viscosities recommended for various types of oil burners is:

Type of Burner	Range of Atomizing Viscosities
Pressure- or mechanical atomizing	35 to 150 SSU
Steam- or air-atomizing	35 to 250 SSU
Rotary-cup-atomizing	150 to 300 SSU

FLASH POINT

A fuel oil's flash point is the temperature at which the gases given off will flash when ignited. As such, flash point indicates the maximum temperature at which oil can be stored and handled. The minimum permissible flash point usually is prescribed by state and/or local laws.

Because light oils contain more hydrogen than heavy oils, they ignite more easily and so have lower flash points. Oil with a low flash point burns more readily than one with a high flash point.

FIRE POINT

Fire point is the temperature at which the gases given off may be ignited and will continue to burn.

POUR POINT

An oil's pour point indicates the lowest temperature at which it can be stored and still flow. Higher pour point fuels generally are used when storage and piping facilities are heated.

WATER AND SEDIMENT

Water and sediment content of fuel oils must be low enough to prevent fouling. Sediment can accumulate on filter screens and burner parts. Water can cause tank corrosion and emulsions in residual oil.

CARBON RESIDUE

Carbon residue is obtained by a test in which a sample of the oil is

TABLE 3.9
VISCOSITY APPROXIMATE EQUIVALENTS AT SAME TEMPERATURE

Kinematic (Centistokes)	Saybolt Universal (Seconds)	Redwood No. 1 (Seconds)	Engler (Degrees)	Saybolt Furol (Seconds)	Redwood No. 2 (Seconds)	Kinematic (Centistokes)	Saybolt Universal (Seconds)	Redwood No. 1 (Seconds)	Engler (Degrees)	Saybolt Furol (Seconds)	Redwood No. 2 (Seconds)
1.8	32	30.8	1.14	—	—	102.2	475	419	13.5	49	—
2.7	35	32.2	1.18	—	—	107.6	500	441	14.2	51	—
4.2	40	36.2	1.32	—	—	118.4	550	485	15.6	54	—
5.8	45	40.6	1.46	—	—	129.2	600	529	17.0	61	—
7.4	60	44.9	1.60	—	—	140.3	650	573	18.5	66	—
8.9	55	49.1	1.75	—	—	151	700	617	19.9	71	—
10.3	60	53.5	1.88	—	—	162	750	661	21.3	76	—
11.7	65	57.9	2.02	—	—	173	800	706	22.7	81	—
13.0	70	62.3	2.15	—	—	183	850	749	24.2	85	—
14.3	75	67.6	2.31	—	—	194	900	795	25.6	91	—
15.6	80	71.0	2.42	—	—	205	950	837	27.0	98	—
16.8	85	75.1	2.55	—	—	215	1,000	882	28.4	100	—
18.1	90	79.6	2.68	—	—	259	1,200	1,058	34.1	121	104
19.2	95	84.2	2.81	—	—	302	1,400	1,234	39.8	141	122
20.4	100	88.4	2.95	—	—	345	1,600	1,411	45.5	160	138
23.5	110	97.1	3.21	—	—	388	1,800	1,587	61	180	153
26.0	120	105.9	3.49	—	—	432	2,000	1,763	57	200	170
27.4	130	114.8	3.77	—	—	541	2,500	2,204	71	250	215
29.6	140	123.6	4.04	—	—	650	3,000	2,646	85	300	250
31.3	150	132.4	4.32	—	—	758	3,500	3,087	99	350	300
34.0	100	141.1	4.59	—	—	866	4,000	3,526	114	400	345
33.0	170	150.0	4.88	—	—	974	4,500	3,967	128	450	390
33.4	180	158.8	5.15	—	—	1,082	5,000	4,408	142	500	435
40.6	190	167.5	5.44	—	—	1,190	5,500	4,849	156	550	475
49.8	200	176.4	5.72	23.0	—	1,300	6,000	5,290	170	600	515
47.2	280	194.0	6.28	25.3	—	1,405	6,500	5,730	185	650	500
51.6	240	212	6.85	27.0	—						

TABLE 3.9—*continued*

Kinematic (Centistokes)	Saybolt Universal (Seconds)	Redwood No. 1 (Seconds)	Engler (Degrees)	Saybolt Furol (Seconds)	Redwood No. 2 (Seconds)
52.9	180	229	7.38	28.7	—
60.2	180	247	7.95	30.5	—
61.5	300	265	8.51	32.0	—
62.9	325	287	9.24	35.0	—
76.3	350	309	9.95	37.2	—
80.9	375	331	10.7	39.5	—
83.1	400	353	11.4	42.0	—
84.5	425	378	12.1	44.2	—
87.8	450	397	12.8	47.0	—

Kinematic (Centistokes)	Saybolt Universal (Seconds)	Redwood No. 1 (Seconds)	Engler (Degrees)	Saybolt Furol (Seconds)	Redwood No. 2 (Seconds)
1.515	7.000	6.171	199	700	600
1.625	7.500	6.612	213	750	645
1.730	8.000	7.053	227	800	600
1.840	8.500	7.494	242	850	730
1.950	9.000	7.934	256	900	770
2.056	9.500	8.375	270	950	810
2.165	10.000	8.816	284	1.000	855

APPROXIMATE VISCOSITY OF FUEL OIL

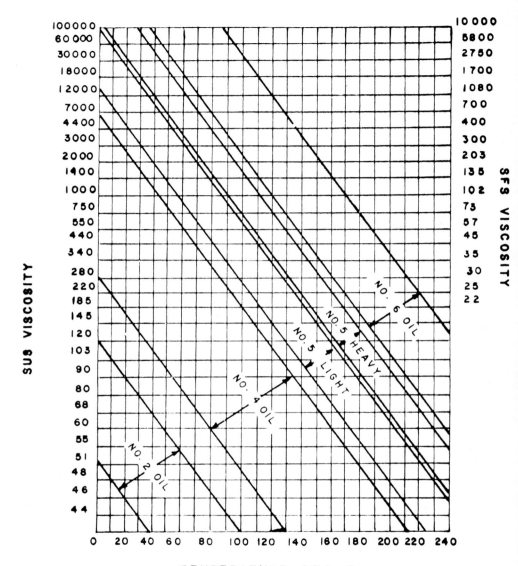

TEMPERATURE DEG. F.

FIGURE 3.13

Approximate viscosity of fuel oil

destructively distilled in the absence of air. For commercial fuels used in proper burners, this residue has almost no relationship to soot deposits.

ASH

Ash is a noncombustible material in oil. An excessive amount may indicate presence of materials that cause high wear on burner pumps.

DISTILLATION

The distillation test identifies the volatility of a fuel and the ease with which it can be vaporized.

SPECIFIC GRAVITY

The specific gravity of fuel oil is used as a general index of its classification and quality. To determine specific gravity, the weight of a given volume of oil is divided by the weight of an equal volume of water at the same temperature.

Special laboratory determinations of fuel oil are made in terms of specific gravity. In practical fieldwork, the gravity is measured by a hydrometer and is read in degrees Baume or API. The API scale, adopted by the American Petroleum Institute, is now generally accepted. Through its use specific gravity may be converted into degrees API by the use of the following formula:

$$°API = \frac{141.5}{sp\ gr\ at\ 60°/60°F} - 131.5$$

Since water has a specific gravity of 1, the formula shows that water has an API gravity of 10. API gravities of commercial fuel oil vary from 10 to 40.

SULFUR

Concern about air pollution has become an important factor in determining the allowable sulfur content of fuel oils. Refiners, to meet legal requirements, are now developing and marketing low-sulfur residual fuel oils. Sulfur content is reduced by refining operations (hydrodesulfurization) and/or by blending various grades and crudes.

Sulfur also is undesirable because its oxides are corrosive. Minimizing low-temperature corrosion by maintaining stack temperatures above the dewpoint temperature of the flue gas, reduces overall thermal efficiency of combustion equipment.

Sulfur content of fuel also must be limited in certain industrial applications because of its adverse effect on product quality. This includes direct-fired metallurgical applications where the work is located in the combustion zone.

Table 3.10 shows sulfur levels of fuel oils recently marketed.

HEATING VALUE

The heating value of fuel oils correlates generally with API gravity. Table

TABLE 3.10
SULFUR CONTENT OF MARKETED FUEL OILS

Grade of Oil	No. 1	No. 2	No. 4	No. 5 (Light)	No. 5 (Heavy)	No. 6
Total fuel samples	93	107	14	12	23	76
Sulfur content						
% wt. min	0.0001	0.02	0.30	0.47	0.50	0.26
max	0.45	1.50	2.095	3.60	3.03	4.63
Average	0.081	0.25	0.87	1.35	1.52	1.60
No. samples with S						
over 0.3%	2	30	12	12	23	75
over 0.5%	0	3	9	11	22	74
over 1.0%	0	1	2	6	16	50
over 3.0%	0	0	0	1	1	4

TABLE 3.11

**TYPICAL GRAVITY AND HEATING VALUE OF
STANDARD GRADES OF FUEL OIL**

Grade No.	Gravity, API	Weight, lb Per Gallon	Heating Value, Btu Per Gallon
1	38–45	6.95–6.675	137,000–132,900
2	30–38	7.296–6.960	141,800–137,000
4	20–28	7.787–7.396	148,100–143,100
5L	17–22	7.94–7.686	150,000–146,800
5H	14–18	8.08–7.89	152,000–149,400
6	8–15	8.448–8.053	155,900–151,300

3.11 shows the relationship between heating value, API gravity, and density for various grades of fuel oil.

When more specific data are lacking, the heating value of fuel oil may be calculated. For uncracked distillate or residue, the formula is:

$$\text{Higher heating value, Btu/lb} = 17,660 + (69 \times \text{API gravity})$$

For cracked distillate:

$$\text{Higher heating value, Btu/lb} = 17,780 + (54 \times \text{API gravity})$$

CARBON-HYDROGEN CONTENT

Grades No. 1 and No. 2 distillate fuel oils contain 84 to 86% carbon. The rest is mostly hydrogen. Heavier grades of fuel oil (Grades No. 4, No. 5, and No. 6) may contain as much as 88% carbon, and as little as 11% hydrogen. An approximate relationship for determining hydrogen content of fuel oils is:

$$\text{Hydrogen, percent} = 26 - (15 \times \text{specific gravity})$$

Oil Burning Equipment

An oil burner delivers fuel oil and air into a furnace in a manner that sustains combustion and controls heat output. Combustion is efficient when the oil is burned completely with a minimum of excess air.

Oil burns only after it is atomized in the presence of air and heat. (Some older types of small burners vaporize the oil, but these are not discussed here.)

Atomizing-type burners inject the fuel oil into the furnace as a very fine spray that forms a cone with the apex at the burner atomizer. The burner also forces combustion air into the oil spray, causing an intimate and turbulent mixing of air and oil. An electric spark, or spark-ignited gas or oil ignitor ignites the mixture, resulting in sustained combustion.

All of these burners can burn the fuel oil completely without visible smoke, when operated with excess air as low as 20% (approximately 12% CO_2 in the flue gases). They all require relatively constant furnace draft, and are available as gas-oil (dual-fuel) burners.

The dual-fuel option permits the operator to switch from one fuel to another for economy, if the fuel in use fails, or if there is a shortage of a fuel. In some cases the changeover from one fuel to another can be made in less than a minute.

While there are many ways of atomizing fuel oil, the most popular involve use of air, steam or mechanical atomizers.

AIR-ATOMIZING OIL BURNERS

Air-atomizing oil burners range in size from 0.5 to 530 gal/hr using Grades No. 2 and heavier. The air-atomizing burner is similar to a pressure atomizing burner, except for the nozzle.

Atomizing air from a pressure blower or compressor is injected into the oil to aid atomization and to help carry the atomizer oil through the nozzle orifice to form a hollow cone of oil spray inside the furnace.

The primary air from a forced draft fan is forced through the burner throat and then mixes intimately with the oil spray inside the furnace. The igniter used is similar to the one used for pressure-atomizing burners.

The burner typically has a wide load range, or turn-down, without changing nozzles: 3-to-1 for smaller sizes and up to 6- or 8-to-1 for larger sizes. Load range is achieved by simultaneously varying the oil pressure, the atomizing air pressure and the combustion air entering the burner. Some designs use relatively low atomizing air pressure of 5 psig and lower; others use air pressure up to 75 psig. The burner uses from 2 to 7 cubic feet of compressed air per gallon of fuel oil (volume on a free air basis).

The wide load range of the air atomizing burner makes it well suited for modulating control. Combustion controls are electrically operated on smaller sizes; larger sizes may use either electric or pneumatic combustion controls.

When properly adjusted, air atomizing burners operate well with 15 to 25% excess air (approximately 12 to 14% CO_2) at full load with no visible smoke and with no more than a trace of carbon monoxide in the flue gas.

STEAM-ATOMIZING OIL BURNERS

Steam-atomizing burners are used mostly on water tube boilers which generate steam at 100 psig or higher, at capacities above 12,000,000 Btu/hr input. Several manufacturers supply this type of burner with coordinated auxiliaries including igniter, motor-driven forced draft fan, oil pump, oil heater, safety interlocks, combustion controls, control panel, etc. Combustion controls are either electric or compressed air operated. A free-standing control cabinet is often used with larger sizes to mount the control equipment and monitors such as meters and gages.

Steam-atomizing burners range in size from 80 gal/hr, using Grades No. 2 and heaver oils, mostly for boilers. Atomization occurs due to the impact and expansion of steam. Oil and steam flow in separate channels through the burner gun to the burner nozzle where they mix before discharging through an orifice into the combustion space. The spray of atomized oil and steam forms a hollow cone.

A forced draft fan supplies combustion air which passes through the directing vanes of the burner register, which give it a spinning motion. From there, air moves to the burner throat which directs it into a cone-shaped oil spray that creates an intimate air oil mixture.

Full-load oil pressure at the burner inlet is generally some 100 to 150 psig. Steam pressure usually is kept higher than the oil pressure by about 25 psig. Load range is accomplished by varying these pressures. Some designs operate with oil pressure ranging from 150 psig at full load to 10 psig at minimum load. This results in a range of turn-down of some 8-to-1, making the steam atomizing burner well suited to modulating control.

Depending on burner design, the amount of steam used for atomizing the oil ranges from 0.5 percent to 3.0 percent of the steam generated by the boiler. When no steam is available for start-up, compressed air is used. Some designs permit the use of a pressure atomizing nozzle tip for start-up when neither steam nor compressed air is available.

When properly adjusted, steam-atomizing burners operate well with 15% excess air (14% CO_2) at full load without visible smoke and with not more than a trace of carbon monoxide in the flue gas. They use from 1 to 5 pounds of steam to atomize a gallon of oil.

MECHANICAL ATOMIZING OIL BURNERS

Mechanical atomizing oil burners use the pressure of the fuel for atomization. In a properly designed system, a high pressure return-flow mechanical atomizer will provide combustion efficiency comparable to that obtainable with a good steam atomizer.

Mechanical atomizers are available in sizes up to 180 million Btu/hr input (about 10,000/lb oil per hr). The acceptable operating range may be as low as 3 to 1 or as high as 10 to 1 depending on the maximum oil pressure used for the system, the furnance configuration, air temperature and burner throat velocity.

Return-flow atomizers (Figure 3.14) are ideally suited for standard grades of fuel oil. They are used in marine installations and some stationary units where the use of atomizing steam is impractical. The oil pressure required at the atomizer for maximum capacity ranges from 600 to 1000 psi, depending on capacity, load range, and fuel.

Good performance over an operating range of 10 to 1 is obtained when the combustion chamber has a relatively small cross section at the burner zone; oil pressure at the burners for full load is 1000 psi; air combustion temperature is significantly above ambient throughout the load range, and air resistance across the burner is 8 to 12 in. of water at full load. Departures downward from any of these values markedly affect the satisfactory load range obtainable from the burners.

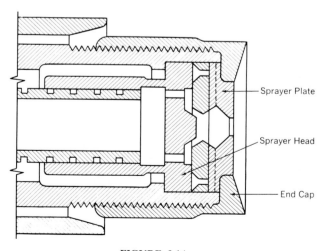

Sprayer Plate

Sprayer Head

End Cap

FIGURE 3.14

Mechanical return-flow oil atomizer detail at furnace end of atomizer assembly showing sprayer head, sprayer plate and end cap.

NATURAL GAS

Natural gas frequently occurs in the same region as petroleum. Due to its low gravity, the gas usually is found above the petroleum, trapped by a layer of nonporous rock. This creates the pressure which causes the gas to be discharged from a well.

Manufactured substitutes for natural gas are discussed in the section on Non-Conventional Fuels.

Gas Reserves

Figure 3.15 shows historical data concerning proved reserves, additions to reserves and annual production in the U.S. Proved reserves are supplies that have already been found by drilling, and which can be recoverable in future years under economic and operating conditions as they now exist.

Proved reserves peaked in 1967 at 292.9 Tcf. Since then, annual production has exceeded annual reserve additions, except in 1970 when Alaskan field reserves were added. At year-end 1979, proved reserves had declined to 194.9 Tcf. This decline may not continue throughout the decade, however, due to

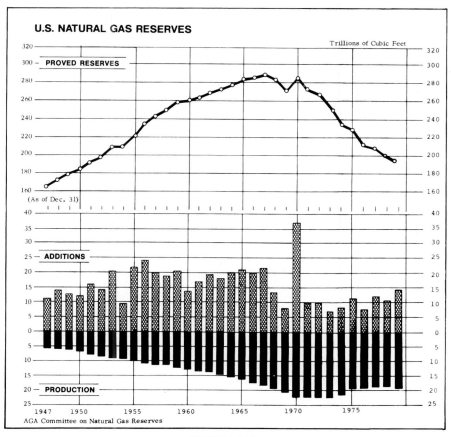

FIGURE 3.15

U.S. natural gas reserves

pricing decontrol that is encouraging greater exploration and improved, more expensive, recovery techniques. Thus, latest estimates published by the American Petroleum Institute and the American Gas Association indicate that 1979 may have marked a turning point. Although proved gas reserves declined, the rate of decline slowed; additions to reserves were approximately 75% of domestic production.

It should be noted that proved reserve data do not represent the nation's total potential ability to continue finding and producing natural gas. According to the American Gas Association, total remaining resources (in addition to proved reserves) are estimated to be between 700 and, 1,200 trillion cubic feet. This is the equivalent of more than 35 to 60 times current annual production. How much of this gas will be found and produced depends on many factors, including pricing, incentives for investment, technological progress, access to new areas, environmental restrictions, and the overall political and economic climate.

Types and Properties of Natural Gas

Natural gas is a mixture of methane (55 to 98%), higher hydrocarbons (mostly ethane), and noncombustible gases.

The properties of commercial natural gases varies depending largely on its geographical sources. Constituents such as water vapor, hydrogen sulfide, helium, liquefied petroleum gases, and gasoline are removed prior to distribution as fuel. As such, the natural gas distributed for use as fuel typically includes: methane, CH_4 (70 to 96%); ethane, C_2H_6 (1 to 14%); propane, C_3H_8 (0 to 4%); hexane, C_6H_{14} (0 to 2%); carbon dioxide, CO_2 (0 to 2%); oxygen, O_2 (0 to 1.2%); butane, C_4H_{10} (0 to 2%); pentane, C_5H_{12} (0 to 0.5%); and nitrogen, N_2 (0.4 to 17%). Odorants (such as mercaptans) are added for safety purposes.

Natural gases can be divided into three types: high inert, high methane, and high Btu, as defined in Table 3.12.

Heating values of natural gases vary from 900 to 1,200 Btu/ft^3, with the usual range being 1,000 to 1,050 Btu/ft^3.

Gas-Burning Equipment

Although gas utilization equipment is as diversified as industry itself, it may be classified according to a small number of categories. Combustion systems differ mainly as to the method of combining oxygen (usually from air) and gas at ratios best suited to produce the heat, temperature, and other conditions wanted.

Industrial combustion systems consist of several major parts which may be either in an integral unit or in an assembly. They are: mixing equipment; ratio control equipment or devices; volume control equipment; and burner or combustion equipment.

TABLE 3.12
GROUP CLASSIFICATIONS OF NATURAL GASES

Group	Nitrogen %	Specific Gravity	Methane %	Btu/ft^3 Dry
High inert type	6.3 to 16.20	0.660 to 0.708	71.9 to 83.2	958 to 1051
High methane type	0.1 to 2.39	0.590 to 0.614	87.6 to 95.7	1008 to 1071
High Btu type	1.2 to 7.5	0.620 to 0.719	85.0 to 90.1	1071 to 1124

Assuming that adequate air and gas are available at a constant pressure and temperature, the energy required for their mixing in various systems is obtained by one of the following four distinct methods:

1. Entraining necessary air by means of the kinetic energy of a gas stream issuing from an orifice in a venturi mixer.
2. Entraining necessary gas by means of the kinetic energy of an air stream issuing from an orifice in a mixing device.
3. Supplying all energy by a pump, compressor, or blower, disregarding entirely the kinetic energy of both gas and air.
4. Using the energy from both gas and air streams.

GAS/AIR MIXING

Ideally, gas jet mixers should be individually designed for each installation to secure the maximum mixture pressure. Practically, the discharge end must conform with standard pipe sizes and the throat diameter can only be varied slightly in each size mixer.

For low-pressure (atmospheric) mixers, which usually entrain only a portion of the total air required, the throat area varies from 35 to 50 per cent of the discharge pipe area; throats may be used "as cast" without machining. For high pressure (above 0.5 psig), where industrial mixers are designed to entrain all air required for complete combustion, the throat area varies from 20 to 30 per cent of the discharge area. For best results these throats should be accurately machined and centered.

The burner discharge area served by a gas jet mixer should be less than that of the outlet pipe, but large enough to handle the volume of gas-air mixture at the pressure developed according to Eq. (1). The coefficient of discharge of the burner discharge area also must be considered.

The amount of fluid (air) that can be entrained by a given fluid (gas) jet depends on the gas pressure at the orifice, the efficiency of entrainment in the mixers, and the resistance to entrainment at the mixer outlet. As these factors

TABLE 3.13

TYPICAL RATIO OF BURNER AREA TO ORIFICE AREA FOR VARIOUS GASES UNDER CONDITIONS STATED

Kind of gas	Heat value, Btu gross	Approx. air-gas ratio	Approx. ratio of burner discharge area to orifice area[a]
Natl. gas:			
Low	976	9.17	214
Med.	1140	10.7	250
High	1245	11.7	286
Propane	2500	25	585
Butane-air mix.	750	6.8	65
Carb. water gas	520	4.37	54
Mixed coke oven and water gas	560	4.8	66
Coke oven gas	595	5.2	100
Mixed natl. & mfd.	800	8.0	159

[a] Burner coefficient of discharge = 1.0.

are independent of size, the mixture pressure that can be developed by a given fluid may be estimated by the empirical Eq. (1).

Table 3.14 gives maximum mixture pressures for various gases calculated from this equation.

$$P_m = \frac{CE^2 GP_g}{(1 + R)(G + R)}$$ Eq. (1)

where:

P_m = static mixture pressure, in w.c. (see Table 3.14)

C = coefficient of conversion of velocity pressure to static pressure in mixer for well-designed mixers:

	C range	C avg
Air entrained by gas	0.85–0.95	0.9
Gas entrained by air	0.60–0.95	0.8

E = coefficient of entrainment, dependent on design (see Table 3.15)

G = specific gravity of *entraining* fluid (air = 1)

P_g = gage pressure of entraining fluid at orifice, in. w.c.

R = ratio of *entrained* fluid to *entraining* fluid

TABLE 3.14

MAXIMUM MIXTURE PRESSURES WITH VARIOUS GASES

(based on entrainment coefficient $E = 1.0$ and velocity conversion coefficient $C = 0.9$)

	Natural gas			Propane	Coke oven
Btu per cu ft, approx.	950	1050	1250	2500	525
Specific gravity, G	0.6	0.62	0.65	1.52	0.45
Pressure,[a] Pg, psig	30	30	30	30	10
Air-gas ratio, approx.	9/1	10/1	12/1	25/1	5/1
Mixture sp gr	0.96	0.975	0.975	1.02	0.91
Air entrained by gas					
Max possible mixture press. ($E = 1.0$, $C = 0.9$), Pm, in. w.c.	4.65	4.0	2.94	2.75	4.1
Mixture press., Pm ($C = 0.9$, E from Table 12-92b), in. w.c.	2.5	2.2	1.6	1.4	3.4
Gas entrained by air					
Max possible mixture press.[b] ($C = 0.8$, E from Table 12-92b), in. w.c.		14.8 avg		16.6	9.4

[a] For pressures Pg other than those given, the following mixture data (air entrained by gas) may be linearly interpolated:

	Natural Gas	Water Gas	Mfd Gas
Specific gravity, G	0.65	0.55	0.50
Heating value, Btu/cu ft	1000	310	530
Pressure, Pg, psig	30	18	30
Mixture press., Pm, in w.c.	3.5	17.8	14.2

Example. The mixture pressure for a 1000 Btu gas at 10 psig = $(10/30) \times 3.5 \times 1.2$ in. w.c.

[b] For well-designed mixers under *ideal* conditions, based on air at 1.0 psig and gas at 0.0 psig; actual mixture pressures may be only 40 per cent of these values; for water gas, 9.8; for mixed gas, 12.0.

TABLE 3.15
AVERAGE COEFFICIENTS OF ENTRAINMENT, E

Kind of gas	Air entrained by gas			Gas entrained by air		
	Air-gas ratio	E	E^2	Gas-air ratio	E	E^2
Natural	10	0.74	0.55	0.10	0.90	0.81
Propane	25	.71	.50	.04	.90	.81
Coke oven	4	.90	.81	.25	.75	.56
Water gas	5	.85	.72	.20	.80	.64
Mixed (natl. & mfd.)	8	0.82	0.67	0.125	0.85	0.72

Gas-air mixtures must be within flammability limits in order to burn. Some combustion systems depend on using the combustion space as a mixing chamber for the gas and air, which are admitted separately. However, most industrial gas utilization requires a method of mixing prior to combustion which can be regulated and will produce consistently uniform results.

Air and gas mixtures at or near stoichiometric ratios ignite readily; therefore, burner equipment should be properly designed to minimize flashback. Proper design provides velocities thru the burner orifice(s) safely in excess of the flame propagation rate of the gas. Standard practice is to place a fire check just upstream from each burner or group of burners for flame entrapment in the event of flashback. On long distribution lines provision should be made to relieve excess pressures due to flashback by installing rupture disks or backfire preventers. Many components for carburetor-type combustion systems are approved and listed by Underwriters' Laboratories and by Factory Mutual Engineering Division.

Air Jet Mixers

The simplest type requires separate valves for air and gas control. By linking valves with identical flow characteristics, the gas and air flows can be kept proportional. If not so linked, the valves may be manually operated separately, but any variation in either gas or air pressure will change the air-gas ratio at the mixer outlet.

A proportioning air jet mixer maintains desired air-gas ratios if the jet and venturi throat are accurately machined and aligned. Gas enters the mixing chamber thru an adjustable orifice and is maintained at zero gage pressure by a sensitive regulator (zero governor) which reduces the normal supply pressure to zero regardless of the flow rate.

In operation, air flow thru the restricted throat aspirates gas maintained at constant pressure at the spud by the governor. The air-gas ratio desired is set by sizing the spud. Once set, an accurate air-gas ratio prevails at all generally used air flows, provided the gas specific gravity and all mechanical conditions remain constant. The air flow can be controlled by a manual or automatic valve in the supply line. This valve is the only volume control that must be operated, gas flowing automatically in proportion at all times.

As the gas flow is determined by the pressure drop between the "zero" chamber supplying the spud and the tee suction or mixing chamber, the governor must maintain "zero" pressure.

Burner Selection

The ratio of the "holding requirement" of the heating application to its maximum requirement has much to do with determining the type and arrangement of the burners. Because of the physical limitations of handling gas and air, each type of combustion system has a definite, limited range of operation. With a given air pressure and a nozzle mixing type of combustion, a useful operating range with the maximum as much as eight times the minimum is possible. In a proportional mixing type of system with 1.0 psig air, the useful range is normally limited to four to one.

For example, if calculations indicate a range of fifteen to one between maximum and holding requirements, a double burner arrangement may be specified. One set operates as holding burners; the second set is turned on under full load conditions. The turndown requirements greatly influence the size of burners selected. Also, the heat pattern of the application must be considered. With only a single burner, the range might be adequate but the heat pattern would be so nonuniform that performance could only be poor.

IGNITION PILOTS IN LARGE BOILERS

The pilot, which is the source of ignition for a main burner, must provide sufficient energy to ignite the main fuel stream quickly and positively.

The time required to establish conditions for ignition at the ignition source point is subject to many variables, such as burner design, furnace configuration, primary aeration, gas concentration gradients between the pilot and main gas flow, and convection currents. In view of the many possible combinations of these variables, data from isolated experiments are useful for reference only.

Increasing the pilot flow rate in effect increases the number of possible ignition sources. The probability that one of these sources is located at a point where conditions for ignition would be quickly established is accordingly increased. On this basis, more effective ignition might be obtained by increasing pilot flame dimension either vertically or horizontally, depending on the relative point location where conditions for ignition are established in the shortest time.

An air purge of four or more furnace volumes to clear the furnace prior to pilot ignition is almost universally accepted as a precaution against accidents. Often means are also provided to monitor pilot piping, since an idle furnace can fill with gas from a leaking pilot valve.

Pilot Sizing

Selecting a pilot size that will reduce the inevitable ignition delay to a reasonable amount is a difficult task. One of the few published experiments shows that a 50-per cent increase in pilot flame height gives a 50-per cent reduction in contact time required to ignite a methane-and-air mixture. The trend of many installations has been to larger pilots, which reduce the ignition puff by reducing the ignition delay on the main burner.

As a guide, pilots may be sized to have a minimum capacity in Btu per hour of 5 per cent of the firing rate of the main burner at the time of light-off. For example, if a 10 MMBtu per hr capacity main burner is lighted off at a low fire rate of 2 MMBtu per hr, the minimum pilot size should be 100 MBtu per hr.

In no case should a pilot burner exceed 400 MBtu per hr capacity at light-off if it is spark ignited. This is the generally accepted level above which the oil or gas burner requires a proven pilot of its own. Moreover, no pilot trial-for-ignition period should exceed 10 sec. The belief that longer times are needed when values are not located immediately adjacent to the pilot burner is not valid, provided that the piping is not vastly oversized.

MAINTENANCE

Planned maintenance, involving periodic inspection of gas burning equipment, helps to ensure economy and safety of operation. The details of scheduled maintenance procedures vary according to (1) the type or part of the equipment and (2) the nature of the service in terms of plant cleanliness and temperature of the air supply.

Table 3.16 presents an overall maintenance program for industrial combustion systems.

The device that mixes the air and gas in exact ratios requires regular attention to ensure proper functioning. The proportioning valves must operate smoothly in order to respond to the small changes in fuel requirements that are caused by turning a burner on or off.

Care should be directed to maintaining the necessary film of lubricant between the working surfaces of the valve. Avoid overgreasing, which may cause a build-up of grease on the accurately machined valve parts and thereby alter the mix ratio. Oil all moving parts as recommended by the manufacturer. Lubricate the motor that drives the compressor according to the manufacturer's instructions.

Many of these controls have operating diaphragms. Most recently made diaphragms consist of synthetic materials that are impervious to the type of gas to be handled. Usually, they are also resistant to the effects of heat up to 150°F.

INDUSTRIAL GAS NOMENCLATURE

Gas-Air Proportioning Systems

Low-Pressure Gas or "Atmospheric" System (gas pressure less than 0.5 psig or 14 in. w.c.): uses the momentum of a jet of low-pressure gas to entrain from the atmosphere a portion of the air required for combustion.

High-Pressure Gas System (gas pressure 0.5 psig or higher): uses the momentum of a jet of high-pressure gas to entrain from the atmosphere all, or nearly all, of the air required for combustion.

Low-Pressure Air System (air pressure up to 5 psig): uses the momentum of a jet of low-pressure air to entrain gas to produce a combustible mixture.

High-Pressure Air System (air pressure 5 psig or higher): uses the momentum of a jet of high-pressure air to entrain gas, or air and gas, to produce a combustible mixture.

Two-Valve System: uses separate controls of air and gas, both of which are under pressure.

Mechanical System: proportions air and gas and mechanically compresses the mixture for combustion purposes.

Mixers and Mixing Devices

Mixer, General: mixes gas and air in any desired proportion.

Manual Mixer: requires manual adjustments to maintain the desired air-gas ratio as rates of flow are changed.

Automatic Mixer: automatically maintains within its rated capacity a substantially constant air-gas ratio at varying rates of flow.

Gas Jet Mixer: uses the kinetic energy of a jet of gas issuing from an orifice to entrain all or part of the air required for combustion.

TABLE 3.16

SUGGESTED MAINTENANCE AND NUMBER OF INSPECTIONS PER YEAR FOR GAS BURNING EQUIPMENT

Type of equipment	Parts of equipment that require maintenance	Maintenance required	Service condition[a]		
			I	II	III
Atmospheric, high- or low-pressure gas	Mixers and venturi injectors	Brush or scrape clean inside; readjust air-mixer shutter; check orifice alignment.	1	4	12
	Burner heads or nozzles	Clean; line up with firing opening; replace or repair if burned or damaged.	1	4	12
	Pilot burners	Clean and readjust to produce satisfactory flame properly located to light main burners; tighten mounting brackets.	3	6	12
	Pressure regulators	Gage outlet pressure at various loads. If not reasonably constant, repair or replace. If regulator does not hold low loads, clean seat. Be sure breather hole is open.	2	4	6
Blast	Blowers	Oil or grease bearings; check for impeller slippage on shaft; clean inlet guard, filter, and inside of case.	2	4	12
	Air-gas mixers	Clean all air passages. Check air-gas ratio.	1	3	6
	Burners, open	Check for proper location in opening; replace nozzle if burned or damaged.	12	12	12
	Burners, closed	Check for tight joint with refractory; check combustion tunnel for smoothness and correct shape; replace nozzle or refractory if damaged or burned.	12	12	12
	Pressure regulators	See pressure regulators above.	2	4	6
	Zero governors	Same as for pressure regulator. It is much more sensitive. Should not be used as shutoff valve unless specially adapted for that purpose. A true zero governor will always leak gas at no load.	2	4	6
Control & protective	Motor and solenoid valves	Check for sticking; oil as required; if leaking, repair or replace.	4	4	6
	Ignition devices	Check for clean spark points, correct spark gap, high-tension leakage, grounds, proper placement for lighting pilots; confirm that pilot flames immediately, and lights main flame.	12	12	12
	Auto pilots	Shut off pilot and make sure automatic feature functions within specified time limit.	12	12	12
	Wiring connections	Check for grounds, open or loose contacts, overloaded wire, sticking relays, defective insulation.	4	4	6
	Electronic equipment	Follow manufacturers' instructions.	12	12	12
	Gas cocks	Assure easy turning, be sure cocks can be turned easily; lubricate if required; check for leakage in open and closed positions; assure access for shutoff in emergency.	12	12	12

TABLE 3.16—*continued*

Type of equipment	Parts of equipment that require maintenance	Maintenance required	Service condition[a]		
			I	II	III
Auxiliaries	Heat surfaces	Remove deposits; if burnouts occur, change firing method or combustion adjustment.	2	4	12
	Secondary air openings	Keep unobstructed; adjust to minimize overventilation; be sure secondary air is getting to all parts of the gas flame.	12	12	12
	Dampers	Same as above; be sure damper is not sticking.	12	12	12
	Flue pipes & building flues	Remove any flue pipe blockage; be sure joints are tight and no holes have developed; be sure there is no sagging in pipe and that roof extensions have not blown down.	6	6	6

[a]I: cleaned air and controlled temperature.
II: average air and temperature conditions.
III: lint, fibers, oil, or soot in air; variable temperatures.

Air Jet Mixer: uses the kinetic energy of a stream of air issuing from an orifice to entrain the gas required for combustion. In some cases, this type of mixer may be designed to entrain some of the air for combustion as well as the gas.

Mechanical Mixer: uses mechanical means to mix gas and air, neglecting entirely any kinetic energy in the gas and air, and compresses the resultant mixture to a pressure suitable for delivery to its point of use. Mixers in this group utilize either a centrifugal fan or some other type of mechanical compressor, with a proportioning device on its intake thru which gas and air are drawn by the fan or compressor suction. The proportioning device may be automatic or may require manual adjustment to maintain the desired air-gas ratio as rates of flow are changed.

Burners

Burner, General: releases air-gas mixtures, oxygen-gas mixtures, or air and gas separately into the combustion zone. Industrial gas burners may be classed as atmospheric burners and blast or pressure burners.

Atmospheric Burner: used in a low-pressure gas or "atmospheric" system which requires secondary air for complete combustion.

Blast Burner: delivers a combustible mixture under pressure, normally above 0.3 in. w.c., to the combustion zone.

Pressure Burner: same as blast burner.

Single Port Burner: has only one discharge opening or port.

Multiport Burner: has two or more separate discharge openings or ports which may be either flush or raised.

Ribbon Burner: has many small, closely spaced ports, usually made up by pressing corrugated metal ribbons into a slot or an opening of some other shape.

Open Port Burner: fires across a gap into an opening in the combustion chamber wall and is not sealed into the wall.

Tunnel Burner: sealed in a furnace wall; combustion takes place mostly in a refractory tunnel or tuyere which is really part of the burner.

Flame Retaining Nozzle: nozzle with built-in features to hold the flame at high mixture pressures.

Proportional Mixing Burner: incorporates an automatic mixer and a burner as an integral unit.

Ring Burner (two types):

a. Atmospheric burner made with one or more concentric rings.

b. Burner used in firing boilers; it consists of a perforated vertical gas ring with air admitted generally thru the center of the ring. Combustion air may be supplied by natural, induced, or forced draft.

Multijet Burner: generally consists of gas manifolds with a large number of jets arranged to fire horizontally thru openings in a vertical refractory plate. These openings are of various shapes: round, square, clover-leafed, etc. Combustion air may be supplied by natural, induced, or forced draft.

Gas-Oil Burner: burns gas and oil simultaneously.

Dual Fuel Burner: burns either gas or oil, but not both together.

Combination Gas and Oil Burner: burns either gas or oil or both together.

COGENERATION

"Cogeneration" is the term used to connote systems which produce electrical (or mechanical) and thermal energy (usually in the form of hot liquid or gases) from a single source at the same time. It is used by electric utilities to provide district heating both for space heating and industrial process heating applications and also is employed by industries who sell their excess electricity and/or thermal energy to neighboring facilities. It is used to some extent by large buildings or complexes of buildings to meet all or a portion of their electrical and/or thermal requirements.

From an electrical utility's perspective, the advantage of cogeneration is its greatly improved fuel utilization efficiency. The overall conversion efficiency of a conventional electric-only plant is about 33% (Figure 3.16); the remaining

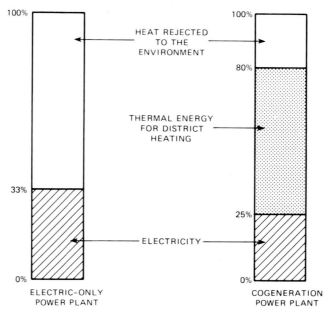

FIGURE 3.16

Comparison of efficiency of electric-only and cogeneration power plants two-thirds of the energy is rejected to the environment through stack-gas losses and the cooling system. By contrast, a cogeneration power plant (Figure 3.16b) can operate at an overall efficiency as high as 80%, but at some sacrifice in electrical output. For each unit of electricity sacrificed, five to ten units of thermal energy are available for district heating. This conservation advantage, coupled with the use of coal or uranium as an energy source, allows the dual-purpose plant to supply relatively inexpensive thermal energy to a district-heating system.

Cogeneration district heating (and cooling) plants came into use early in the twentieth century. They used the exhaust steam from small dual-purpose power plants to heat buildings in the nearby business district. Their use increased until the late 1940s, when inexpensive oil and natural gas was introduced for space heating. At the same time, electric utilities were building large condensing steam-electric power plants in rural areas. Because it was not economical to transport steam over long distances, the older, smaller cogeneration units were retired; inexpensive energy sources for the steam district heating and cooling systems were eliminated, and the cost of supplying steam escalated, thus making district heating and cooling less attractive.

The United States is now beginning to recognize both cogeneration and district heating as important techniques for conserving domestic energy resources.

System Descriptions

Several concepts are now being used to provide cogenerated district heating (CDH).

UTILITY-OWNED TOPPING SYSTEMS

In general, cogeneration systems can be described either as "topping" or "bottoming" configurations.

A system designed primarily to produce mechanical energy (typically for production of electricity) is called a topping system. The thermal energy is derived through capture of the "waste heat" that otherwise would be rejected once the mechanical process was complete.

A "bottoming" system is one designed primarily to produce thermal energy. The thermal energy remaining after the process is complete is used to produce mechanical energy, as to drive small turbines for production of electricity, or pumps or similar apparatus. Electrical utilities rely exclusively on topping systems. A schematic diagram of a utility owned CDH topping system is shown in Figure 3.17.

Topping systems generally are spoken of in terms of the type of prime mover involved.

Steam turbines are the most common prime movers because of their fuel flexibility. The steam boiler can be "fired" by fossil fuels (oil, natural gas, coal, coal-derived liquids and gases, or wood), nuclear fuels or synthetic liquids and gases. Mechanical energy is produced as the high pressure steam drives the turbine; a generator converts the mechanical energy into electricity.

Two types of steam turbines are used.

Extraction steam turbines are very popular for industrial purposes. They permit extraction of steam at those temperatures and pressures most suited for the thermal applications involved (Figure 3.18).

Back-pressure steam turbines are the most commonly used by utilities. They

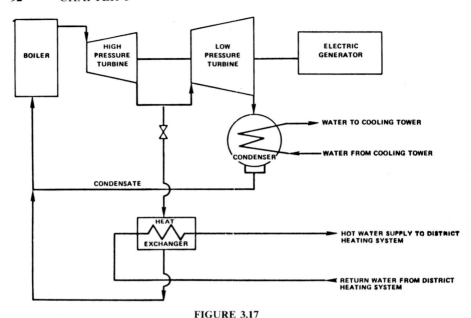

FIGURE 3.17

CDH Topping system combined heat and power

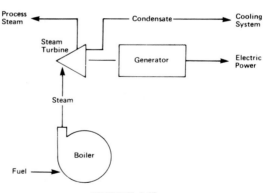

FIGURE 3.18

Extraction cycle

do not permit selectivity, making the thermal energy more suited for district heating than industrial processes (Figure 3.19).

The ratio of power and heat which can be produced in back-pressure turbines depends on turbine efficiency, live steam parameters, the steam cycle (reheat or nonreheat), the feed water heating and the back-pressure. Typical power yield values for combined heat and power plants operating in optimum conditions are shown in Figure 3.20, where power yield = electric output/heat output. Actual average power yields are lower than those shown, however, because heat load variations prevent a plant from operating at the most efficient load levels. In systems where the heat supply temperature varies with the heat load, the

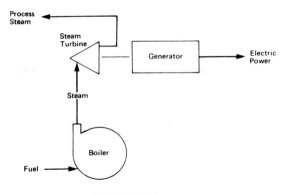

FIGURE 3.19
Backpressure Cycle

power yield of the plan is especially dependent on the shape of the heat load duration curve (Figure 3.21).

The most dominant factor in power generation is the enthalpy drop in the turbine. Assuming that other parameters are constant, electric output increases as back pressure decreases because lower back-pressure causes greater enthalpy drop in the turbine. To maximize power production in a CDH system, therefore, as low temperature as possible is needed for the heat transfer medium.

Consumer requirements set the limits and high supply temperature may not be reduced because of the design of consumer heating systems. This problem may be offset somewhat by allowing the temperature to be reduced when maximum heat demand is not required. (This is being done in many Scandinavian systems where supply water temperature varies between 250–170°F depending on outdoor air temperature.)

Optimum supply temperature also is determined by local factors, such as the number of buildings with steam heating systems. If the water temperature is too low, their heating systems would have to be rebuilt. This investment, however can often be recovered through lower space-heating energy costs.

If electricity and CDH system energy demands were constant or inversely related, the utilities could more easily design or adjust operation to accommodate consumers. This is not normally the case for residential CDH systems, however. During the coldest or hottest periods, electricity and heat/cooling demand tend to peak simultaneously. Europeans solve this problem by installing direct-fired boilers to reduce steam load demand on power plants during peak conditions. System fuel efficiency drops markedly during peak demand conditions. For intermediate seasons (spring and autumn) the power plants run at reduced loads producing mostly electricity with minimal steam generation for heating or air conditioning.

Heating and cooling demand studies have found commercial heat demand to average about 9.1 Btu/ft^2 (floor area)/degree-day, while residential sector demand values are 15 and 10 Btu/ft^2/degree-day for non-apartment and apartment structures respectively. Stated another way, commercial sector demand is 1000 Btu/person/degree-day and 5625 and 3750 Btu/person/degree-day for non-apartment and apartment residential demand. Computed space heat, cooling, and hot water demand for various cities is shown in Table 3.17.

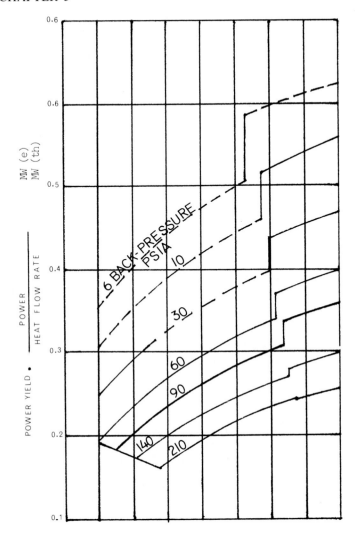

LIVE STEAM	P_s	580	870	1160	1450	1760	2030/580psi	2600/870
PARAMETERS	t_s	840	900	930	970	985	995/995°F	995/995
FEEDERWATER TEMP.	t_f	285	355	390	410	435	445/480°F	520
ELECTRIC OUTPUT	P	10	20	30	35	40	40/50MW	100

FIGURE 3.20

Back-pressure power yield

Other prime movers include gas or combustion turbines and diesel engines. Both burn fuel directly and use the combustion gases to produce mechanical energy to generate electricity. Cogeneration is derived by using exhaust gases from the prime mover for purposes such as process heat and production of low-pressure steam. This steam is produced when hot exhaust gases are passed

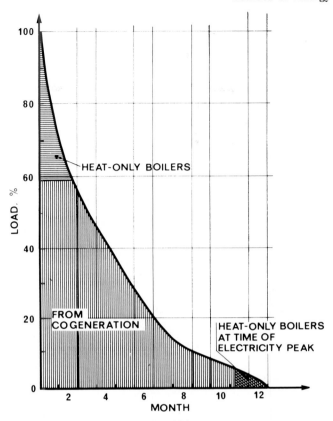

FIGURE 3.21

Heat load duration curve and load split

TABLE 3.17

SPACE HEATING, COOLING, AND HOT WATER DEMAND FOR VARIOUS U.S. CITIES

	New York	Chicago	Phila-delphia	Los Ange-les	New Or-leans	Baton Rouge	Jersey City SMSA	Newark SMSA (part)	Pater-son SMSA (part)
Space heating power (mw)	16,200	2,900	3,800	774	148	74	1,160	1,100	120
Space heat Water rate M gallons/hour	89.3	15.9	20.8	4.2	.81	.41	6.4	6.1	2.3
Water heating power (mw)	2,850	417	586	355	70	28	191	183	65.7
Space and water heating Water rate M gallons/hour	105	18.2	24	6.3	1.2	.56	7.5	7.1	2.7
Full cooling power (mw)	10,227	1,063	2,371	626	357	148	722	685	251
Full cooling water rate M gallons/hour	420	43.6	97.2	25.7	14.6	6	29.6	28	10.7
Serviceable cooling power (mw)	385	0	63	0	21	8.4	25	23	9
Serviceable cooling Water rate M gallons/hour	15.8	0	2.6	0	.86	.34	1	.94	.33

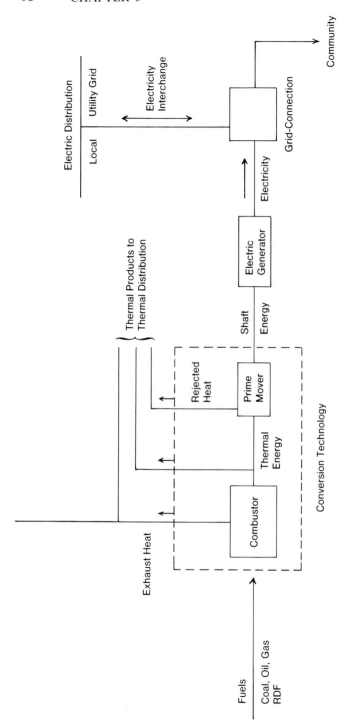

FIGURE 3.22
Grid-connected ICES system

- Boilers and Steam Turbines
- Gas Turbines and Recovery Boilers and Steam Turbines
- Diesel Engines
- Advanced Technologies, e.g., Stirling Engines, Fuel Cells

$$\text{Efficiency} = \frac{\text{Electrical + Thermal Product}}{\text{Fuel}}$$

through a waste-heat recovery boiler which transfers their thermal energy to the water.

The waste heat of a combustion turbine is used to produce more electricity, the hot gases are passed through a waste heat recovery boiler. Thermal energy from the gases is transferred to water in the boiler to create steam which then is fed to a steam turbine to generate electricity. This process is known as combined cycle cogeneration.

Although gas turbines and diesel engines are much more efficient than steam turbines, neither is in extensive use because their operation depends upon relatively scarce, expensive fuels: natural gas or oil (mostly light distillates).

Stirling engines, fuel cells, and thermionic devices are being considered for use with topping cycle cogeneration systems of the future.

INTEGRATED COMMUNITY ENERGY SYSTEMS (ICES)

Integrated community energy systems (ICES) produce electricity, heat, hot water, and chilled water for any types of buildings within a given "community." Not all buildings have to be served, nor do those served have to use the same ICES end products.

An ICES system (Figure 3.22) is operated in parallel with the electrical utility and permits unrestricted interchanges with the electrical utility grid. It is controlled by the thermal demands of the community, and establishes an identifiable system of cost allocation and charges for electrical and thermal products.

There are an estimated 20,000 ICES currently operating. The prime movers for such systems—also called "total energy systems"—are diesels, gas turbines, or direct-fired boilers.

Characteristics of ICES, CDH, and conventional electric power plant systems are compared in Table 3.18.

COMBINATION INDUSTRIAL PROCESS-DISTRICT HEATING SYSTEM

Industrial processes also can be combined with a district heating system, an

TABLE 3.18
COMPARISON OF ICES, CDH AND CONVENTIONAL SYSTEMS

	ICES	CDH	Conventional
Fuel efficiency	50–80%	50–80%	35%
Cost ¢/kwh	2–4		1.5–2.0
External factors favoring:	High power prices	High heating costs	Low power costs
	Low fuel (Oil/NG) prices	High oil/ng/coal prices	Coal/uranium: available/low cost
	Steady heat demand	Commercial/industrial to take up excess heat	Uneven power demand
	Low standby required	Dense population	
	Higher frequency and d.c. current	New towns urban renewal	Electrification Status quo
	Provides heat, chilled water, power	Oil embargo	Can buy power from other utilities
	Independent of grid		
Disadvantages:	Need skilled labor	High capital cost	Low fuel efficiency
	Noisy	Long lead time	Costs rising rapidly
	Fuel storage problem	Long payback	Environmental problem
	Costs uncertain	Needs 100% backup	Air pollution
	Not suitable for continuous operation annually		Waste heat
			Siting

approach being pursued in Sweden. An investigation there showed that 300 companies accounted for 73% of the nation's industrial energy consumption. These included pulp and paper mills, iron and steel works and the chemical industry. The amount of waste heat available from them for district heating purposes amounted to the equivalent of at least one million barrels of fuel oil per year.

Retrofitting Existing Power Plants

Changing to cogeneration by retrofitting existing plants now generating electricity will avoid the long delays associated with construction of new plants, will save scarce fuel, and will reduce capital requirements. (Existing plants can be modified to supply thermal energy at the relatively low capital cost of 20–30 \$/kW/(t). As such, they can produce large quantities of inexpensive hot water.)

The economic criteria for establishing central station cogeneration through retrofit of existing power plants include:
1. thermal and electrical efficiencies of various electric generating units before and after retrofit for cogeneration,
2. variation of climate, fuel use and demand density by location, and
3. building performance and space conditioning technology.

Studies have shown that central station cogeneration by retrofit is most economical in locations dominated by heating loads. Heating loads are more favorable in the northern U.S. both from the point of view of total load and load factor.

REFUSE-DERIVED ENERGY

The recovery of energy from wastes originated in the early 1900's when combustion plants began mass burning waste to generate steam. Further development involved incineration, without heat recovery, solely to reduce waste volume. The use of waterwall furnaces in place of refractory lined furnaces began in the 1950's in Europe, for purposes of heat recovery. Still, most development to date has been directed toward incineration for volume reduction rather than heat recovery.

Worldwide experience indicates that commercialization is feasible although there are a number of technical, economic and institutional barriers that currently limit the use of wastes.

The energy potentially recoverable from all solid waste represents about one-tenth of the current 75 quads of energy consumed annually in the U.S. Many additional benefits can be realized through using wastes as fuel, however. For example, less refuse will have to be disposed of, thereby extending the life of present landfills. Also, virgin materials and fossil fuels can be conserved.

Conversion of wastes into energy has progressed furthest in the field of municipal solid waste (MSW). Only limited efforts have been directed toward energy extraction from industrial solid wastes. Use of forestry waste is also small, being centered mainly in the forest products industry. Limited work is being done on recovery of methane from animal wastes. Use of agricultural crop residues as a feedstock for methane production by anaerobic digestion, at this time, appears to be economically unfeasible.

Municipal solid waste can be defined as the wastes generated by the residential, commercial and institutional sectors of the population. Usually this definition excludes mining wastes, demolition and construction debris, junked automobiles and street sweepings. The large quantities of MSW generated and the methods used in its disposal constitute a major environmental concern. In some standard metropolitan statistical areas (SMSA), MSW may be suitable for large-scale central processing. In rural areas, it is still prohibitively expensive to collect and aggregate these wastes.

According to federal estimates, 200 million tons of urban solid wastes and 14 million tons of sewage solids (dry basis) will be discarded annually in the U.S. by 1985. The combustible portion of these wastes represent a total available Btu content of 2.0 quads. About 65% of this potential is considered available for use in emerging waste-to-energy technologies today. Currently, less than 1% of the nation's total waste stream is processed into production of energy.

Municipal solid waste flows vary widely in composition and generation rate, and consequently no one estimate can be considered the most accurate. In 1975, the EPA, using government and industry trade association statistics, estimated that 136 million tons of solid waste were generated by the residential and commercial sectors of the U.S. (3.4 lbs/capita/day). The 1975 EPA estimates form the basis for the most recent studies on municipal solid waste flows.

The paper, glass and metals fractions of MSW still dominate the waste materials category. The present recovery of these constituents is small and opportunities for energy recovery are not being fully realized.

About 80% of all municipal post-consumer waste is a potential source of energy. This organic portion of the waste stream has a heating value of about 4500 Btu/lb, a value likely to increase when more of the paper and plastics fractions of MSW are utilized. Typical heating values of components of MSW are shown in Table 3.19. A typical proximate and ultimate analysis of raw refuse is shown in Table 3.20.

Future Prospects

District heating and cooling systems represent perhaps the most promising customer for steam recovered from solid waste processing facilities. Currently, fuel costs represent from 50 to 70% of a typical district heating system's overall

TABLE 3.19
TYPICAL HEATING VALUES OF MSW COMPONENTS

Component	Btu/lb.
Food Waste	
Garbage	8,484
Fats	16,700
Rubbish	7,572
Paper	7,096
Leaves	7,693
Grass	6,000
Wood	8,613
Brush	7,900
Greens	7,077
Dirt	3,790
Oils, paints	13,400
Plastics	14,368
Rubber	11,330
Rags	7,652
Leather	8,850

TABLE 3.20
TYPICAL PROXIMATE AND ULTIMATE ANALYSES
OF MSW (RAW REFUSE)

Proximate Analysis	
Moisture	27.0%
Volatiles	44.0%
Fixed Carbon	7.0%
Noncombustibles	22.0%
Ultimate Analysis	
H_2O	27.0%
Carbon	25.5%
Hydrogen	3.4%
Oxygen	21.5%
Nitrogen	0.6%
Noncombustibles	22.0%
Heating value	4,500 Btu/lb

costs; controlling fuel costs, therefore, is a priority. Waste-derived energy may well represent a lower-cost energy source than traditional fossil fuels.

Although MSW plants could feasibly produce other products, steam is the predominant recovered energy product at this time. For example, operational plants at Saugus, Massachusetts, Harrisburg, Pennsylvania, and several smaller incinerator sites are based on steam-producing components designed specifically for district heating and cooling systems. These and other initial projects indicate a natural technological compatibility of resource recovery with district heating systems.

Several approaches are possible to link resource recovery and district heating systems.

Refuse-derived fuel (RDF), either fluff of densified, can be used as a supplemental fuel in conventional utility boilers. These boilers produce a fairly high temperature and pressure steam which can be applied in a cogenerating capacity both for electrical generation and steam heating. The combustion of unprocessed solid waste or RDF in dedicated boilers generally produces a fairly low-temperature and pressure steam, more appropriate for heating purposes than electrical generation or industrial process applications.

Despite the potential compatibility of resource recovery with district heating systems, linkage has not been extensive to date. Major changes are likely, however, because the cost of MSW, relative to conventional fossil fuels, is expected to become progressively lower. Solid waste-derived steam also offers insulation from future fossil fuel shortages, embargos, and other interruptions.

Despite the incentives for utilizing waste to energy processes with district heating systems, actual implementation has been limited.

One of the reasons for this is the high cost of installing new steam distribution pipelines. Thus, the growth of such systems is limited to places where steam lines already exist or where urban renewal or new construction facilitates their placement. This limitation is significant because existing steam lines are found primarily in densely-populated, downtown areas which are incompatible with the concept of heavy refuse truck traffic or disposal facility siting. Furthermore, downtown areas usually face stringent air pollution standards which may place further constraints on the siting of new or additional point sources of pollution.

It is unclear whether combustion of solid waste/RDF is more deteriorating to the atmosphere than conventional fuels. However, federal guidelines allow the exemption of resource recovery facilities from meeting the offset requirements in critical nonattainment areas. Final approval of this exemption rests with each state, but the potential clearly exists for encouraging urban resource recovery sites.

Where existing steam lines are operated by investor-owned utilities, state law may require that fuel savings from use of refuse-derived steam be passed through to consumers. This destroys much of the utility's incentive for incorporating waste to energy processes.

Public utility commissions have also hampered utilities' innovative financing approaches, such as leveraging capital through wholly-owned subsidiaries. Another problem arises in states where a utility's electricity distribution is regulated but its sales are not, as this situation creates the special question of whether thermal customers should bear the extra costs caused by artificially low (regulated) electricity rates. While this issue is not unique to resource recovery involvement it does add to the confusion surrounding the already unclear district heating system economics.

Several states have passed legislation in an effort to promote energy conservation. Additional steps that could be taken include:

1. Encourage inclusion of steam heating/cooling systems in new developments through tax incentives (investment tax audits, depreciation, etc.).
2. Allow exemptions for RDF fuel savings from automatic fuel adjustment clauses.
3. Allow exemptions from point source standards or eliminate offset requirements for waste fuel systems.
4. Explicitly allow inclusion of resource recovery capital costs in rate base.
5. Allow in the rate base for construction work in progress for resource recovery facilities.
6. Provide loan guarantees.
7. Prohibit new point source pollutants for heat or energy generation unless waste to energy systems are included.
8. Grant zoning requests for downtown waste processing facilities.
9. Issue specific guidelines defining public regulatory jurisdiction over waste-to-energy district heat systems.
10. Where feasible, encourage government energy/heat consumers to enter into long-term contracts with district heating systems.

Combustion Systems

Three types of combustion systems are used for generating steam from waste. These are: mass burning steam generation, mass burning, controlled air, modular combustor with heat recovery, and suspension firing of prepared refuse, described as follows:

MASS BURNING STEAM GENERATION

For many years, steam was recovered from MSW by adding waste-heat boilers to conventional, refractory wall, mechanical grate incinerators. The poor operating characteristics and high maintenance costs associated with this approach, gave rise to waterwall combustors. They recover from 15 to 20% more energy, require less excess air and refractory maintenance (due to operation at a lower wall temperature), provide better burnout of the refuse, and need smaller pollution control equipment.

In operation, (Figure 3.23), as-received refuse is transferred from a receiving pit into the waterwall combustor's furnace feed hopper by means of an overhead, traveling crane with a grapple bucket. From the hopper, wastes are continuously fed to the furnace and burned on an inclined moving grate system. Noncombustible and unburned material falls off the end of the grate and is water-quenched.

Water flows through closely-spaced steel tubes that are welded together to form the waterwalls. Integrally constructed waste-heat boilers generate steam while reducing exhaust gas temperature. Superheaters and economizers are used when necessary.

Several different grate systems are used to move the refuse through the furnace. All produce a tumbling action to cause rapid ignition and better burnout.

Combustion air is introduced into the furnace beneath the grates (underfire air) to aid combustion and keep the grates cool. Air is also introduced above the fuel bed (overfire air) to promote mixing of the gases (turbulence) and to complete combustion of the refuse gases.

The combustion gases leaving the boiler sections are passed through air pollution control equipment (generally electrostatic precipitators) and exhausted to the atmosphere through a stack. Boiler efficiency is typically 63 to 68%.

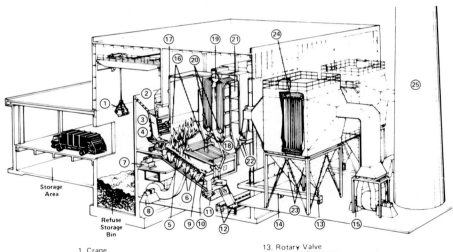

1. Crane
2. Feed Hopper
3. Feed Chute
4. Feeder Rams
5. Reverse Reciprocating Stoker
6. Undergrate Air Plenum Chambers
7. Hydraulic Pump
8. Forced Draft Fan
9. Automatic Siftings Removal Systems
10. Residue Roller
11. Residue Discharger
12. Residue Conveyors
13. Rotary Valve
14. Fly Ash Conveyor
15. Induced Draft Fan
16. Overfire Air Nozzles
17. Waterwalls (Welded Panel Const.)
18. Boiler Fly Ash Hoppers
19. Steam Drum
20. Bottom Boiler Drum
21. Economizer
22. Economizer Fly Ash Hopper
23. Fly Ash Hoppers
24. Electrostatic Precipitators
25. Stack

FIGURE 3.23

Typical mass burning steam generator

Development of waterwall combustors began in Europe in the 1950's. The Europeans rapidly commercialized the technology in the 1960's and 1970's; there are now more than 100 waterwall incinerator installations operating in Europe. The first large-scale waterwall combustor in the U.S. was installed by the U.S. Navy in Norfolk, Virginia, in 1967.

Implementation of the technology has moved somewhat slowly in the U.S. due to greater availability of landfill space and lower cost of fossil fuel.

While the U.S. has more mass burning steam generating facilities in operation than any other type of large-scale resource recovery facility, many of these systems are still experiencing significant operational problems, particularly boiler tube failures and high particulate emissions. Other common problems are grate wear, crane failures, pit fires and less than optimum combustion control.

Boiler tube failures have been caused by corrosion and erosion. To correct this problem, silicon carbide coating are being applied on boiler wall tubes near the grate. This has eliminated wall tube corrosion on these areas with only minor reduction in heat transfer efficiency.

Correction of the high particulate emission problem has been more difficult, despite use of electrostatic precipitators. Improved control over the combustion process may mitigate the problem, but additional or alternative methods of air pollution control are also necessary. The presence of large particles in the off-gas suggests the use of multi-cyclones preceding the precipitators. Bag houses may also be an attractive alternative if an acceptable bag material can be found to withstand gas temperature up to 600°F.

MASS BURNING, CONTROLLED AIR, MODULAR COMBUSTOR WITH HEAT RECOVERY

Controlled air, modular combustors are characteristically prefabricated package units, operated at substoichiometric oxygen requirements. It is claimed that they can meet federal air pollution regulations without pollution control devices. The largest single module in operation processes up to 50 tpd of solid waste, but several vendors are now claiming single module capacities of up to 250 tpd. Processing capacities of several hundred tons per day can be achieved by operating these units in parallel. Multiple-unit installations provide system redundancy and backup capability. The larger units would be equipped with ash removal equipment for continuous operation. Modular units are also sized to handle as little as 5 tpd. When capacity is less than 20 tpd, however, waste is typically processed on a batch rather than continuous basis.

Typical modular combustors (Figure 3.24) employ a two-chamber design. As solid waste is received, it is charged into a primary refractory-lined combustion chamber, using a ram or auger-type feeder. Under-fire and in some cases over-fire air is blown into the primary chamber at sub-stoichiometric oxygen requirements. The heat released from partial combustion of the organics is used for the endothermic volatilization of the remaining organic compounds. Temperature in the primary chamber is maintained at 1500°F to 1800°F by controlling refuse feed rate and combustion air flow.

Because of the relatively low air-flow rate, gas velocity in the primary chamber is kept low to reduce fly ash entrainment. Hot gases from the primary chamber contain organic vapors and some fly ash (both carbonaceous and inert). The gas has a heat value of approximately 100 to 500 Btu/dscf. These gases flow into a secondary combustion chamber where they are mixed with air and fossil fuel (natural gas or oil).

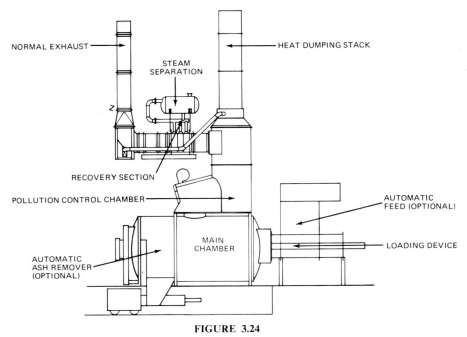

FIGURE 3.24

Typical controlled air, modular combustor

A dump or exhaust stack is provided on the secondary chamber. If there is no immediate steam demand, hot gases exiting from the secondary chamber can be exhausted to the atmosphere rather than being passed through the boiler. When demand for steam is low, gas flow can be split between the boiler and the exhaust stack.

Oil- or gas-fired burners are provided in both combination chambers. The primary chamber burner is typically used only at system start-up to help bring the contents of the chamber up to operating temperature. The secondary burner is used to maintain proper temperature to ensure near complete combustion of the off-gases from the primary chamber. Auxiliary fuel requirements in the secondary chamber range from 0.3 to 1.0×10^6 Btu/ton. Total system excess air is from 100 to 200%.

Operating facilities often experience similar problems. One of these is that production of low-pressure steam (275 psig or less) limits its marketability. Another is that potential steam supply often exceeds demand because of fluctuating customer requirements and, in this situation, energy must be wasted to the atmosphere.

Boiler tube fouling due to fly ash carryover from the secondary combustion chamber is a problem at some facilities necessitating boiler tubes requiring cleaning as frequently as at two week intervals.

Modular combustor facilities also experience problems with glass which slags in the primary chamber if the operating temperature is too high. The molten glass tends to plug underfire air ports and to adhere to refractory walls.

SUSPENSION FIRING OF PREPARED REFUSE

Suspension firing of prepared refuse is based on the principal of reducing the refuse size so that it burns uniformly in suspension. A size reduction of the refuse fuel to a maximum 2 in. × 2 in. must be accomplished before the refuse is pneumatically conveyed to the boiler. This sizing is required to avoid plugging transport lines and to allow suspension burning. A typical preparation system for suspension firing is shown in Figure 3.25.

Tangential Firing

In tangential firing of refuse in suspension, the refuse and heated air are directed tangent to an imaginary circle in the center of the furnace. Fuel and air are mixed in a single fire ball aiding in the even distribution within the furnace. The lighter fraction of the refuse quickly burns in suspension. The larger and more dense refuse material falls to a grate in the bottom of the furnace to complete the combustion. Several rows of tangentially directed air nozzles between the fuel compartments and the stoker maximize suspension burning of the heavier refuse material as it falls to the grate.

Suspension firing of prepared refuse has many advantages over the other systems. They include:

1. faster boiler response rate,
2. smaller grate,
3. normally can be retrofitted to a solid fuel-fired boiler for heat inputs to 20% with pulverized coal firing,
4. higher thermal efficiency due to the ability to use lower excess air,
5. reduced potential for furnace wall corrosion,
6. resource recovery potential, and
7. high sludge disposal potential.

Disadvantages include:

1. need for additional fuel preparation and transport equipment,

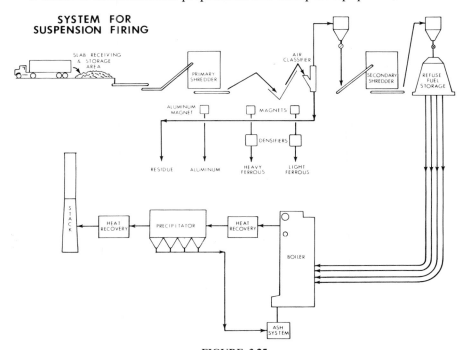

FIGURE 3.25

System for suspension firing

2. higher auxiliary power requirements (due to the preparation system), and
3. higher fly ash quantities leaving the furnace.

The boilers used with this system can generate steam to 825°F. Maximum temperature is limited to avoid excessive superheater corrosion. As tube metal temperatures approach 900°F, the superheater tube corrosion rate increases significantly.

Chlorides in the refuse are believed to be a cause of corrosion in the superheater. The reaction of gas phase sulfuric acid with deposited chloride releases HCl near the heated tube surface. A subsequent reaction may involve the stepwise formation of volatile ferric chloride and/or unstable chloride or oxy-chlorides of other alloy components.

The design of a suspension-fired refuse boiler requires that the furnace be sized for a maximum outlet temperature of 1600°F to reduce ash build-up and plugging of the convective heating surface. The convective surface must be designed with wide tube spacing to allow for possible ash build-up without bridging from tube to tube.

A maximum flue gas velocity of 25 ft/sec is employed in all convective areas to minimize turbulence and subsequent tube erosion or fouling. In-line tube arrangements are required to assure the cleanability of all tube surfaces. Retractable soot blowers are employed to maximize the cleaning of the tube surfaces.

Combustion gases should be cooled to 600°F before entering the electrostatic precipitator. This is normally accomplished with an economizer section. A skimmer type hopper is used at the precipitator entrance to catch any large material carried from the furnace. The precipitator is located in the medium gas temperature range to avoid high or low temperature effects on the fly ash that may alter the particulate removal efficiency.

Proper operating procedures probably have as much effect as any other consideration in minimizing wastage. Many plants, especially in Europe, have found that less frequent use of sootblowers will reduce the exposure of cleaned tube surfaces and makes the metal less vulnerable to attack. The deposits are protective unless the tube surfaces are at such a temperature that an accelerated molten phase or chloride attack can occur.

Even with highly prepared refuse, the possibility of fuel chemistry and heat value fluctuations must be recognized and the boiler circulation system designed accordingly. The boiler steam drum should be oversized to account for water level fluctuations that can occur with rapid heat input changes to the furnace. The riser, downcomer and furnace proportions must likewise be designed to allow for rapid response to changing fuel conditions.

SPREADER STOKER FIRING OF PREPARED REFUSE

Spreader stokers also can be used to fire prepared refuse. The raw refuse is prepared so it has a 6″ top size and 95% is less than 4″. A typical preparation system is shown in Figure 3.26. The prepared refuse is delivered on demand to small storage/metering bins at the boiler front where the refuse is delivered at a controlled rate to the pneumatic refuse distributors located in the furnace front wall. A screw feeder in the bottom of each bin is controlled by the combustion control system to respond to the steam demand rate. High pressure air is delivered to the pneumatic refuse distributors to assure even feed of the grate surface. The air quantity required for the refuse distributors is approximately 5% of the total air required for combustion.

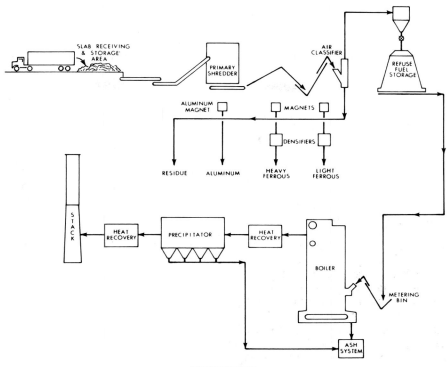

FIGURE 3.26

System for spreader stoker

The refuse delivered to the boiler has a greater percentage of large material that will burn on the grate surface than does a full suspension system, but there is a sufficient quantity of the light fraction to allow for suspension burning above the grate. The suspension burning, combined with the metering bins located near the boilers, will produce fast boiler response to maintain stable operation when the fuel or steam demand quickly changes. The grate employed with this firing system is a continuous ash discharge type which travels from the rear toward the front of the furnace. The stoker is almost identical to the continuous ash discharge spreader stokers currently used for stoker firing coal or other waste cellulose fuels.

With the spreader stoker refuse firing system, a single boiler can handle the fuel derived from waste inputs in excess of 1500 tons/day. Total steam temperatures are limited to 825°F to avoid excessive corrosion when firing 100% refuse.

The advantages of this system include:
1. fast boiler response rate,
2. dual-fuel (solid waste fuels or coal) capabilities,
3. reduced potential for furnace wall corrosion,
4. high thermal efficiency due to lower excess air,
5. resource recovery potential, and
6. high sludge disposal potential.

The disadvantages of this system include:
1. requirement for additional fuel preparation,

2. higher auxiliary power requirements (due to the preparation system), and
3. higher fly ash quantities leaving the furnace.

All other design considerations are the same as those for previous sections covering prepared refuse for suspension burning and need not be repeated.

GEOTHERMAL

The internal heat of the Earth comprises an essentially inexhaustible energy source, limited only by man's ability to extract it. With today's technology, we are able to reach only the thermal energy contained in the upper portions of the Earth's crust. Most of this energy is highly diffuse. However, in some areas it is concentrated into deposits that can be exploited either for direct uses (nonelectric) or for generation of electricity.

Presently, geothermal energy is being used at a significant level in the U.S. and other countries. The Geysers resource area in Northern California, where electricity is being produced at a rate of over 900 megawatts (MW_e), is the largest single geothermal development in the world. The total electricity generation in the world is rapidly expanding with an anticipated "more than doubling" of capacity by 1982, from the 1300 MW_e level in 1976. In the near future, it is expected to increase at an accelerating rate. The direct application of geothermal energy for space heating and cooling, water heating, agricultural growth-related heating and industrial processing represents more than 1800 megawatts of thermal energy (MW_t). Of the present 1800 MW_t worldwide, the U.S. portion comprises some 85 MW_t, with major applications occurring in Iceland, New Zealand, USSR, and Hungary, as shown in Table 3.21. The direct applications in the U.S. are expected to have a doubling time of about 2 to 6 years during the period 1980 to 2000.

The present direct use of geothermal energy in the U.S. is mainly for space and water heating in residences and institutional buildings. Klamath Falls, Oregon, and Boise, Idaho, have a long history of reliance on geothermal energy for these purposes. A dozen or so additional localities have had minor amounts, and many more communities have either recently started using geothermal

TABLE 3.21
WORLDWIDE DIRECT APPLICATION OF GEOTHERMAL ENERGY[a]

Country	Thermal Power (MW_t)
Iceland	632
New Zealand	210
Japan	44
USSR	364
Hungary	366
Italy	49
France	25
China	21
Romania	22
Czechoslovakia	21
USA	85
Others	10
Total	1,849[b]

[a] Only resources above 104°F and uses other than bathing are considered.
[b] The total use above 60°F is about 2650 MW_t.

energy or are planning for its use. Boise has had a geothermal district heating system in operation since the 1980's. The system has recently received renewed attention with the retrofitting of government buildings to use the geothermal energy, and the planning of a greatly expanded use for other institutional and residential buildings. In Klamath Falls, the Oregon Institute of Technology is completely heated from three wells about 2000 ft deep located on the edge of the campus. The campus system is relatively new, being installed in the early 1960's, but Klamath Falls has been using geothermal energy for space heating since the early part of this century. However, the traditional use of geothermal energy in Klamath Falls has not been district heating but rather individual building heating from single shallow wells using downhole heat exchangers. To make systems more economic, plans are now well underway for district heating from one or two wells in the downtown area of Klamath Falls. The system is to initially serve 14 government buildings, with subsequent expansion to 115 private commercial buildings.

The two main uses of geothermal energy in the agricultural growth applications are for heating of greenhouses and aquaculture facilities. Some of these have existed for a number of years, but there have been many new ones developed over the past several years.

The primary industrial uses of geothermal energy in the U.S. are for food processing, mostly milk pasteurizing and vegetable dehydration. Worldwide, primary applications are for space and water heating, space cooling, agricultural growth applications and food processing. The main exceptions are diatomaceous earth processing in Iceland, and pulp and paper processing in New Zealand.

Types of Geothermal Energy Sources

Classified as resource types, geothermal deposits include: convective hydrothermal (dry steam or hot water reservoirs), geopressured reservoirs (hot water, methane, and hydraulic pressure), hot dry rock, normal-gradient heat, radiogenic heat resources, and magma (molten rock).

HYDROTHERMAL

In convecting hydrothermal deposits, heat is transferred by convective circulation of water or steam. Heated fluids tend to rise in permeable rocks while the denser, cooler fluids tend to descend. Thus, geothermal heat is transferred toward the surface.

Most hydrothermal convection systems deliver a mixture of hot water and 10 to 30% steam at the well head. The fluids flash to steam as pressures decrease toward the surface. In some systems, however, wells produce saturated or superheated steam, usually with no associated liquids. Pressures in these relatively rare systems appear to be controlled by vapor rather than by liquid. Accordingly, the systems are called "dry-steam" or "vapor-dominated" systems. Their steam can be piped directly through a turbine to produce electricity. Although this type of steam has been used successfully, few dry steam reservoirs exist. In the future, an additional fluid may be introduced to a vapor-dominated geothermal system, then circulated through it to recover the energy. This procedure is now in the research stages.

Hot water hydrothermal systems are dominated by circulating liquid which transfers most of the heat and largely controls subsurface pressures. Most of the known hot-water systems are characterized by hot springs that discharge at the surface.

The temperatures of hot-water systems can be divided into three ranges: above 300°F (for possible generation of electricity); from 190°F to 300°F (for space and process heating or possible generation of electricity); and below 190°F (for possible direct heating only in specific locations).

These resources, referred to as "liquid-dominated" systems are more than 20 times as common as the vapor-dominated systems. They can be produced either as hot water or as a two-phase mixture of steam and hot water, depending on the pressure maintained on the production system. If the pressure in the production casing or in the formation around the casing is reduced below the saturation pressure at that temperature, some of the fluid will flash and two-phase fluid results. If the pressure is maintained above the saturation pressure, the fluid remains single-phase.

The quality of liquid varies substantially from site to site, ranging from water of potable quality to fluids that have more than 300,000 ppm dissolved solids. The U.S. Geological Survey classifies the degree of salinity of mineralized waters as follows:

Dissolved Solids, ppm	Classification
1,000 to 3,000	Slightly saline
3,000 to 10,000	Moderately saline
10,000 to 35,000	Very saline
More than 35,000	Brine

In reference to the classifications given by the U.S.G.S., geothermal fluids range from nonsaline to brine, depending on the particular resource. Table 3.22 indicates the composition of fluids from a number of geothermal wells in the U.S. As can be seen, the quality varies substantially and the harshness of the fluid increases with increasing temperature.

GEOPRESSURED RESOURCES

An unusual geothermal resource is that referred to as "geopressured". The term arises from the very high pressures that are present in such systems. The pressures range from about 1.4 to 1.9 times the hydrostatic pressure corresponding to a particular depth, while in most geothermal systems the pressure at a given depth is closely equal to the hydrostatic pressure. The high pressures result from subsidence and the isolation of large pockets of fluids that support a major percent of the weight of the overburden.

The identified geopressured resources occur in areas where the temperature gradients are in general not much larger than the normal value for the whole of the earth's crust, and to a large degree have relatively high temperatures (up to 550°F) because they occur at great depths (up to 22,000 feet). In addition to the thermal energy in these resources, the high pressure allows hydraulic energy to be recovered and many of the geopressured fields have dissolved natural gas which can be recovered from the geothermal fluid.

In the U.S. the largest geopressured resources occur in wide belts both onshore and offshore under the gulf coast of Texas and Louisiana. They exist in the form of individual geopressured deposits partitioned by geological faults. Geologists believe these individual reservoirs are 200 to 250 feet thick.

TABLE 3.22

COMPOSITION OF FLUIDS FROM SEVERAL HYDROTHERMAL GEOTHERMAL RESOURCES

Location	Resource Area					
	Boise, ID	Klamath Falls, OR	Beowawe, NV	Raft River, ID	Baca, NM	Salton Sea, CA
Temperature, °F	176	201	270	295	340	482
Species in Fluid	Concentration (ppm or (mg/l))[a]					
Total dissolved solids	290		855	1319	6898	(220,000)
SiO_2	160	119	329	91.8	835	(350)
Na	90	231	214	368	2010	(5,100)
K	1.6		9	65	541	(12,500)
Li	0.05		Trace	1.1		(220)
Ca	1.7	36		52	36	(23,000)
Mg	0.05	0.2		1.9		(150)
Cl	10	61	50	611	3770	(133,000)
F	14		6	5.5		
Br				<2.5		
I				0.035		
SO_4	23	484	89	63	58	
S				<0.2	2.2	
NO_3				0.19		
P				<0.003		
NH_4				4.53		
NH_3			3			
H_2S	Trace		6.1			
HCO_3	70	51	41	86.6	118	
CO_3	4		168		0	
CO_2	0.2					
Al	Minor		0.2			(0.04)
As	0.05					(1)
B	0.14		1	0.3		(350)
Ba	0.2			0.4		(270)
Cr	Minor					(0.6)
Cu	0.08		Trace			(8)
Fe	0.13			3.2		(1,300)
Mn	0.01		Trace	0.08		
Ni	Trace			3.5		(2.4)
Sr	0.01			1.3		(500)
Ti	Trace		Trace			
V			Trace			
Zn	Trace, minor					
Hg	0.02					
Si				44		
H_2	0.0054					
He	0.0016					
CH_4	0.065					
N_2	18.51					
O_2	0.0029	3.1				
Ar	0.62					
Comments:	Well name unknown. Near old penitentiary	Wendling well	Vulcan well 2	Well RRGE I	Well Baca II. Flashed fluid sampled.	

[a] Most analysis are for liquid samples only and do not reflect the non-condensible gases.

HOT DRY ROCK RESOURCES

Substantial energy exists in "rock" of very low permeability throughout the U.S. The major high temperature resources of this nature that are the closest to the earth's surface are closely associated to cooling magma chambers, but resources with temperatures adequate for direct applications can be considered to exist over wide regions. Although this "hot dry rock" type resource is extensive, its actual value is unknown because economic extraction technology has not been illustrated at this point in time. There is a large-scale research effort, both in this country and worldwide, directed at developing technology to achieve economic extraction of the thermal energy from this very large resource.

NORMAL-GRADIENT HEAT RESOURCES

Geographical areas where the prevailing temperature gradient may be very close to the normal gradient can have valuable geothermal resources, particularly from the viewpoint of direct application such as district heating. Whether or not a normal-gradient area has a valuable resource depends primarily on the existence of a sufficiently permeable aquifer at a depth where the temperature is interesting. In the U.S. such resources have been identified in the northern Great Plains, and are considered good possibilities in other large basins throughout the U.S.

RADIOGENIC HEAT RESOURCES

Along the Atlantic Coastal Plain, geothermal resources have been identified that are apparently due to radiogenic heat sources concealed beneath thick sedimentary layers of low thermal conductivity. Evidently, the basement granitic rocks contain moderate concentrations of uranium and thorium from which, through radioactive disintegration of the isotopes, energy is given off. The low conductivity sedimentary material has tended to insulate these resources, resulting in geothermal gradients as high as 24°F per 1000 feet. Efforts have only recently started to identify and quantify these resources, and more effort is needed to develop a true assessment of this resource.

MAGMA RESOURCES

The temperatures of buried magma range from 1,112°F to 2,732°F. Although estimated annual energy potential of U.S. magma resources is several hundred times the nation's total annual energy consumption, technical and materials problems attendant with its recovery are formidable.

Many years of study and development will be required before direct tapping and use of magma heat becomes possible.

Feasibility and Design Factors

A geothermal district heating and cooling system is economically feasible when the anticipated return on investment is sufficient to justify the cost of construction.

Construction costs can be divided into three main components, as follows:
1. heat production
   a. exploration and assessment
   b. drilling
   c. collecting mains
2. transportation
   a. main pumping station
   b. supply mains
3. distribution system
   a. distribution pumping station

b. street mains
c. service branches
d. consumer connections

The cost of each component is site specific. Costs from two geothermal district heating projects in Iceland (Reykjavik and Akureyri), illustrate the relative proportion of the costs in those settings:

Production	15 to 25%
Transportation	18 to 20%
Distribution	58 to 66%

Costs of some projects now underway in the U.S. are estimated as:

Production	8 to 30%
Transportation	15 to 30%
Distribution	50 to 64%

At present day costs, geothermal energy can be expected to cost much less than the least cost conventional fossil fuel in situations where the site specific factors of the application and resource lie toward the most favorable end for geothermal energy. On the other hand, when the factors lie toward the least favorable end, then geothermal energy probably will not be competitive. Due to the continued expected escalation of fossil fuel prices, geothermal energy is expected to be competitive for a much broader range of the factors (regarding application and resource) in the future than it has even in the most recent past.

Factors which affect the feasibility and cost of geothermal heating and cooling systems include:

1. cost of capital
2. depth of the resource
3. distance between resource location and application site
4. well flow rate
5. temperature of resource
6. allowable temperature drop
7. load size
8. load factor
9. heating density
10. composition of fluid
11. environmental concerns
12. ease of disposal, and
13. resource life.

COST OF CAPITAL

In a system where costs are related primarily to capital costs, an increase in the interest rate paid for borrowed capital has almost the same influence as an equal percentage increase in the capital costs themselves. Thus, as the interest rate increases, the economic viability of a particular geothermal system decreases.

DEPTH OF THE RESOURCE

Well costs are quite often one of the biggest items in the overall cost of a geothermal system. As the depth of the resource increases, so does the cost of the overall system. Consequently, the relative economic advantage of using geothermal energy decreases significantly as the resource depth increases.

The cost of well drilling varies from area to area. Figure 3.27 presents drilling and completion well costs experienced in U.S. wells ranging in depth from 1500 ft to 10,400 ft during the period 1974 to 1979. Notice that the plot is semi-log and that the drilling cost per unit depth increases dramatically with depth.

DISTANCE BETWEEN RESOURCE LOCATION AND APPLICATION SITE

For direct use of geothermal energy, the application must be close to the resource. Although geothermal or secondary fluids can be transmitted over distances as large as about 60 miles without too large of a temperature loss, such transmission usually is not economically feasible. Under favorable conditions, economic viability can usually be achieved for separation distances up to about 15–20 miles.

WELL FLOW RATE

The energy output of a production well varies directly with the flow rate of fluid. As such, the energy cost at the wellhead varies inversely with the well flow rate. Typical good resources have production rates of 400 to 800 GPM per production well.

TEMPERATURE OF THE RESOURCE

The available temperature of a geothermal system is the temperature associated with the prevailing resource. Because of the natural convection that occurs in fluid-dominated systems (the only ones being used at this time) temperature is relatively uniform throughout the depth of the resource, and the common belief that "a higher temperature can be obtained by somewhat deeper drilling" does not hold true. Although drilling could be continued through the fluid-dominated region into a region that is not permeable enough to permit natural convection and a higher temperature would be achieved, the available flow rate would probably be too low to yield an economic resource. Generally

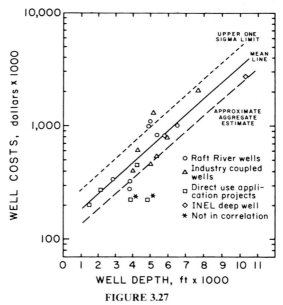

FIGURE 3.27

Well costs versus depth; corrected to 1978 prices

speaking, the temperature limitations of the resource affects the potential applications, and the ways in which specific applications can be met. Restricting attention to space heating, including water heating, maximum flexibility occurs when the resource temperature is about 180°F or higher. At 180 to 200°F temperatures, the application is by direct heat exchange with the heating fluid within the building, or in situations where the geothermal fluid is particularly benign by direct use within the space. Direct use of the geothermal fluid as the building heating medium permits better efficiency, an increase in the permissible temperature differential at a given temperature, and a smaller amount of circulating hot water with smaller pipes and lower heat loss. Such use is only recommended, however, if the fluid has been shown to be benign.

The economic advantage of resources at temperatures above approximately 200°F for district heating lie in increased energy output per well rather than reduced distribution system costs, because it appears to be the sentiment in most worldwide geothermal district heating applications that it is better to operate the district heating system as hot water below the atmospheric boiling point rather than at temperatures above the boiling point.

As the temperature of the resource decreases from about 180°F the user system becomes more complicated. Although direct application for space heating is possible for temperatures down to 120°F and slightly below, in normal circumstances they would not be economic for large scale application because the flow rates of geothermal fluid per unit of heating would be much too large. At such temperatures it appears that the use of heat pumps are required for the most economic operation. The specific temperature range at which a heat pump, rather than direct exchange, is desired is site specific. A system in the Paris basin in France uses a 140 to 160°F resource and heat pumps for heating 10,000 apartments in a reportedly economical installation.

It is usual to not rely on the geothermal resource temperature to be adequate to provide the capacity to meet the peak demand of the district heating system. Normally an auxiliary boiler will be incorporated into the design to allow an increase in temperature, or flow, or both, to the district system during times of peak demand. When the geothermal resource temperature is particularly low, perhaps it may only be used as a source of energy for preheating, but the application for this is very limited in district heating systems.

ALLOWABLE TEMPERATURE DROP

Power output from a geothermal well is directly proportional to the temperature drop of the geothermal fluid that is effected by the user system because the well flow rate is limited. Consequently, a larger temperature drop means decreased energy costs at the wellhead. If there is a loop fluid, such as shown in Figure 3.28, and if the maximum loop fluid temperature approaches the geothermal supply fluid temperature, the loop fluid must also have a reasonably large temperature drop across the user system. This is in contrast to many conventional and solar systems that circulate a heating fluid with a very small temperature drop. As a result, different design philosophies and different equipment are required.

LOAD SIZE

Large-scale applications are advantageous due to economy of scale. The most usual near-term applications are not likely to be very large, however, making it important to properly match the size of the application with the production rate from the geothermal resource. Figure 3.29 shows a schematic diagram of initial investment at the wellhead as a function of production rate. This illustrates the step costs for one well, one well being pumped, and two wells. As can be seen, the lowest priced energy occurs for an application sized to use a production rate just less than that which would require the second well. For larger applications identical minimum energy costs would occur at production rates just less than that which would require the third, fourth, etc. wells.

HEATING DENSITY

Heating density is the possible connected heat demand for district heating divided by the ground area. High heat density is desirable because the distribution network which transports hot water to the buildings is so expensive. The most favorable situations are where multistoried buildings are located quite close together, but not so densely situated that the cost of laying and maintaining the network becomes excessive as it might in a downtown area (where the underground area may already be largely dedicated to electricity, subways and

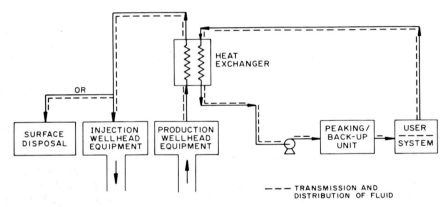

FIGURE 3.28

Geothermal direct utilization system with wellhead heat exchanger

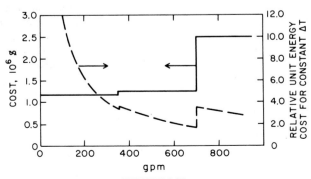

FIGURE 3.29

Cost of the geothermal water investment at the wellhead in terms of yield—Dogger aquifer, Parisian region

other plumbing, and the carrying out of any construction becomes difficult and expensive). On the other hand, in many instances single family residences in suburban settings represent heating densities that are marginal in terms of their ability to support district heating. In these cases every effort must be made to design and construct the system so as to minimize the impact of the capital costs of the distribution system. Furthermore, it is possible that some of the more dense areas of the system may have to share some of the extra cost of the less dense areas as has been the case in electricity and natural gas distribution systems. (It should be noted, however, that in Denmark heating densities corresponding to three to four single family houses per acre are routinely served with district heating systems.)

The energy density can be increased by adding water heating, cooling, and industrial loads to the basic space heating requirements as well as increasing the building density. All of these increase the heating density and, therefore, permit more energy to share the expense of the distribution system.

LOAD FACTOR

Load factor is defined as the ratio of the average load to the designed capacity of the installed system. It reflects the fraction of time that the initial investment in the system is working. Because geothermal system costs are primarily initial investment rather than operating costs, load factor has a significant impact on the viability of using a geothermal system. As load factor increases, the economic viability of using geothermal energy improves.

There are two main ways of increasing load factor. One is to select applications where it is naturally high. The other is to use peaking approaches, so that the load which the geothermal system is designed for is not the application peak load, but rather a reduced load that occurs over a longer period.

When geothermal space heating is involved, the system typically is designed to meet about 60% of peak load. As such, the geothermal system is able to provide about 80 to 90% of the annual heating energy requirement. Figure 3.30 illustrates a load-duration curve with the geothermal system designed for 60% of the recommended design load. The cross-hatched area under the curve

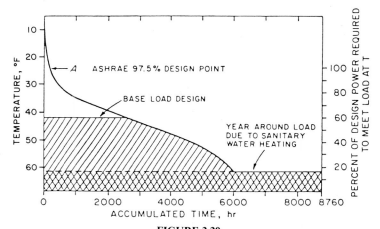

FIGURE 3.30

The temperature and power for space heating and sanitary water heating versus accumulated time at or below the given temperature for a particular location

represents the energy delivered by the geothermal system. Designed in such a manner, the distribution system will operate with a load factor dictated by the climate and system served. Representative load factors are 0.25 to 0.35 for locations such as New York City, Portland, Oregon, and Boise, Idaho. The geothermal production system operates with a load factor of (1/0.6) times that of the distribution system. Peaking approaches are commonly used to accommodate load variations that occur due to annual cycles of temperature, daily cycles of temperature, and personal habits such as the lowering of thermostats at night, different working hours, shower times, etc. The two main ways of supplying this peak are by the use of a fossil-fuel peaking station or variable pumping of the geothermal resource with consequent large drawdown of the geothermal reservoir.

Storage is an alternative to peaking that thus far has been used mostly to meet short-term load increases that occur on a daily basis, primarily due to personal habits. The storage is typically in large tanks designed to hold about 20% of the peak flow over a 24-hour interval.

The inclusion of sanitary water heating and industrial applications in a district space heating system are beneficial not only because they increase the overall size of the energy load and the energy demand density, but primarily because they increase the load factor (see Figure 3.30 for the influence of the sanitary water heating). For those resources where sanitary water heating to the required temperature is not feasible, preheating is usually desirable. The inclusion of space cooling may or may not increase the load factor, depending on the temperature of the geothermal resource and the prevailing ratio of the cooling load to the heating load (see section on geothermal district cooling).

COMPOSITION OF FLUID

As already indicated, the quality of the produced fluid varies from potable to heavily brined. Fluid quality greatly influences fluid treatment/material selection (to avoid corrosion and scaling effects) and the disposal or ultimate end use of the fluid. Special attention must be given to the quality of the fluid when selecting equipment and fluid disposal systems. In some cases, fluid quality necessitates use of extra equipment or special disposal systems which increase the cost of the geothermal system. In other cases, it may allow additional end uses of the fluid, thereby decreasing the cost of geothermal energy.

ENVIRONMENTAL CONCERNS

The successful use of geothermal energy, like other forms of energy, requires consideration of different environmental concerns, and the compliance with application regulations. The most significant environmental concerns are presented in Table 3.23.

EASE OF DISPOSAL

Depending on the particular resource involved and applicable environmental regulations, special cooling, treatment and/or injection disposal systems may be required. Ease of disposal affects system costs. For example, when fluid injection is required, being able to get by with shallow wells and/or small pumping requirements is far less expensive than having to employ deep wells and/or large pumping requirements.

TABLE 3.23

PRIMARY ENVIRONMENTAL ISSUES THAT MAY ARISE IN SPECIFIC APPLICATIONS OF GEOTHERMAL RESOURCES

Issue	Potential Environmental Impact	Comments
Ecological	Damage to plants and animals.	Many geothermal resources are located in sensitive areas where there is a potential impact of this nature. With proper planning and design, this problem can be minimal.
Air quality	Emission of various gases into the atmosphere.	Certain resources have some H_2S, radon or other non-condensible gases, which must be properly designed for.
Noise	Noise pollution.	Primarily a problem during drilling or testing. Can be minimized by proper noise abatement procedures.
Surface water quality	Degradation of water quality from thermal, chemical or natural radioactive properties of disposed fluids.	Proper disposal system design and planning for accidental releases are required to minimize the impact on water quality.
Land use	Conflict of geothermal use of land with other uses such as agriculture, recreation, etc.	Since surface area required for geothermal development is relatively small, this issue can usually be readily resolved.
Geological alteration	Subsidence and/or induced seismic activity.	Subsidence can be a problem in sedimentary resource areas when fluid injection is not used. Induced seismicity is not a major concern except for cases of deep high pressure fluid injection.
Water supply and hot springs alteration	Alteration of existing and potential water supplies or hot springs activities due to withdrawal of geothermal fluid and/or energy or injection of geothermal fluids.	Geothermal development near water supplies and hot springs may be restricted or prohibited because hydrologic information is usually inadequate to predict the impact of the development.
Archaeological/cultural resources	Destruction of archaeological areas and/or infringement on cultural resources (historical, paleontological).	May restrict areas to which development is possible. Conduct archaeological survey of prospective development area and do not develop problem areas.
Socio-economic	Change in existing economic structure, population and social patterns.	Primarily a concern for large-labor intensive developments in sparsely populated areas. Can be controlled with adequate planning.

RESOURCE LIFE

Resource life has a direct bearing on economic viability for obvious reasons. Experience suggests that resources can be developed to permit lives of 30, 40 and 50 years or more with proper system design.

Geothermal District Heating System Equipment

Most of the equipment used in geothermal district heating systems—pumps, heat exchangers, storage vessels and piping—are of routine design. However, the great variability of geothermal fluids and their general tendency to cause corrosion and scaling requires particular attention insofar as equipment selection is concerned.

Generally speaking, corrosion and scaling can be limited by proper system and equipment design and treatment of the geothermal fluid. Treatment consists of the addition of corrosion and/or scaling inhibitors to the geothermal fluid, usually as it comes from the production system. The major drawback to this approach is the large quantity of additives required, and resulting high cost. In addition, it may be necessry to remove the added chemicals from the system effluent stream prior to disposal.

Insofar as proper system and equipment design are concerned, three primary concepts are applied:

1. restrict the number of equipment components that come into contact with the geothermal fluid, particularly for the harsher geothermal fluids;
2. select component designs that can either be easily cleaned or that provide continuous cleaning during operation for those equipment items that are particularly sensitive to corrosion deposits and scale buildup; and
3. select proper materials for those components that come into contact with the geothermal fluid.

The third factor—proper selection of materials—is important in all systems. It requires knowledge of the chemical composition of the geothermal fluid under consideration. Unfortunately, the composition of the fluid varies from resource to resource, and to some extent, even from well to well within the same resource. This, along with the fact that the presence of just minor amounts of certain substances can greatly influence the amount of corrosion or scaling that can occur, substantially limits the applicability of generalized rules of thumb for material selection. The technology for selection of materials for use with geothermal fluids is still in the development stage with much work having recently been done and follow-on work continuing.

The chemical species that are the major offenders regarding corrosion and scaling from geothermal fluids are listed in Table 3.24.

Hydrogen ion (pH). The general corrosion rate of carbon steels increases rapidly with decreasing pH, especially below pH 7. Passivity of many alloys is pH dependent. Breakdown of passivity at local areas can lead to serious forms of attack, e.g., pitting, crevice corrosion and stress corrosion cracking.

Chloride. Chloride causes local breakdown of passive films which protect many metals from uniform attack. Local penetration of this film can cause pitting, crevice corrosion, or stress corrosion cracking. Uniform corrosion rates can also increase with increasing chloride concentration, but this action is generally less serious than local forms of attack.

Hydrogen Sulfide. Probably the most severe effect of H_2S is its attack on certain copper and nickel alloys. These metals have performed well in seawater but are practically unusable in geothermal fluids containing H_2S. The effect of H_2S on iron-based materials is less predictable. Accelerated attack occurs in some cases and inhibition in others. High-strength steels are often subject to sulfide stress cracking. H_2S may also cause hydrogen blistering of steels. Oxidation of H_2S in aerated geothermal process streams increases the acidity of the stream.

TABLE 3.24
MAJOR CORROSION AND SCALING SUBSTANCES CONTAINED
IN GEOTHERMAL FLUIDS

Substance	Major Impact (Corrosion or Scaling)	Form
Hydrogen	Corrosion	Ion
Chlorides	Corrosion	Solid
Hydrogen sulfide	Corrosion	Gas
Carbon Dioxide	Corrosion	Gas
Ammonia	Corrosion	Gas
Sulphates	Corrosion	Solid
Oxygen	Corrosion	Gas
Transition metals	Corrosion	Solid
Silicates	Scaling	Solid
Carbonates	Scaling	Solid
Sulfides	Scaling	Solid
Oxides	Scaling	Solid

Carbon Dioxide. In the acidic region, CO_2 can accelerate the uniform corrosion of carbon steels. The pH of geothermal fluids and process streams is largely controlled by CO_2. Carbonates and bicarbonates can display mild inhibitive effects.

Ammonia. Ammonia can cause stress corrosion cracking of copper alloys. It may also accelerate the uniform corrosion of mild steels.

Sulfate. Sulfate plays a minor role in most geothermal fluids. In some low chloride streams, sulfate will be the main aggressive anion. Even in this case, it rarely causes the same severe localized attack as chloride.

Oxygen. The addition of small quantities of oxygen to a high-temperature geothermal system can greatly increase the chance of severe localized corrosion of normally resistant metals. The corrosion of carbon steels is sensitive to trace amounts of oxygen.

Transition Metal Ions. "Heavy" or transition metal ions might also be included as key species. Their action at low concentrations on most construction materials is ill-defined. However, the poor performance of aluminum alloys in geothermal fluids may be due in part to low levels of copper or mercury in these fluids. Salton Sea, California geothermal fluids contain many transition metal ions at greater than "trace" concentrations. Some oxidized forms of transition metal ions (Fe^{+3}, Cu^{+2}, etc.) are corrosive, but these ions are present in the lowest oxidation state (most reduced form) in geothermal fluids. Oxygen can convert Fe^{+2} to Fe^{+3} which is another reason to exclude oxygen from geothermal streams.

PUMPS

Pumps are used for three primary purposes in geothermal applications: production, circulation and disposal.

For circulation and disposal, whether surface disposal or injection, standard state-of-the-art centrifugal hot water circulating pumps are used. These are routine engineering design selections with the only special consideration being the selection of appropriate materials.

Production pumps require more than routine selection for two primary reasons:

1. There is usually only one production pump per production borehole. As a result, pump redundancy is not easily built into the system; a highly reliable unit is best.
2. There is a substantial amount of development work currently being devoted to production pumping systems, particularly at higher temperatures.

Production well pumps fall into two classifications: "wellhead pumps" and "downhole pumps."

Wellhead Pumps

Wellhead pumps usually are referred to as vertical lineshaft pumps or lineshaft pumps. An above-ground driver, typically an electric motor, rotates a vertical shaft extending down the well the length of the pump. The shaft rotates the pump impellers within the pump bowl assembly which is positioned at such a depth in the wellbore that adequate NPSH will be available when the unit is operating.

Lineshaft pump have their long vertical shafts supported in two different ways. One way is to have bearings inside a tube that is concentric to the shaft and of slightly larger diameter (enclosed lineshaft pump). The other way (open lineshaft) is to have the bearings supported from the column pipe.

The reliability of lineshaft pumps decreases as the pump setting depth increases because of the lineshaft bearings.

In the enclosed lineshaft pump, a lubricating fluid is pumped or gravity fed through the tube to lubricate the bearings. Oil has been used successfully in this application for some geothermal systems but there has been little experience with its use in systems that have temperatures greater than 300°F. In some of the higher temperature systems, water has been pumped through the tube to provide the lubrication. However, water can lead to mineral deposits on the bearings, thus making use of water treatment necessary.

The bearings in open lineshaft pumps are lubricated by the production fluid as it moves up through the column pipe. Such pumps are widely used in domestic water supply systems but have been used with little success in geothermal applications.

Downhole Pumps

The electrical submersible pump is the primary type of downhole pump. It is a commercially available product that can be readily used for geothermal resources at temperatures below 250°F. Units to operate at resource temperatures above this value are presently being tested.

The electrical submersible pump system consists of three primary components that are located downhole: the pump, the drive motor and the motor protector.

The pump is a vertical multistage centrifugal type. The motor is usually a three-phase induction type that is oil-filled for cooling and lubrication. (Motor cooling is accomplished by heat transfer to the pumped fluid moving up the well.) The motor protector is located between the pump and the motor. It isolates the motor from the well fluid while at the same time allowing for pressure equalization between the pump intake and the motor cavity.

The electrical submersible pump is considered to be a good candidate for geothermal well pumping because it has several advantages over the lineshaft pumps, particularly for wells requiring greater pump bowl setting depths. As the well gets deeper, the submersible becomes less expensive to purchase and easier to install. Moreover, it is less sensitive to vertical well deviation and the poor assembly conditions that normally exist at the wellhead.

A recent development in submersible pumps that permits easy removal of the pump without removing the wellhead discharge pipe improves the desirability of the submersible units. In this newer unit, the submersible pump assembly is suspended in the wellbore with a cable. Pump servicing is accomplished merely by lifting the unit with the cable and removing it from the well piping through a stripper valve. Such a procedure can allow the pump to be removed without the use of well "kill fluids" to hold back the flow as would be required in the usual pump service operations.

Another type of downhole geothermal pumping system, under development since 1972, has a turbine and pump located downhole with a condenser at the surface and piping serving as a steam generator. It uses thermal energy from the geothermal fluid to drive the turbine, which drives the pump. Since this latter system is in the development stage it will not be considered further here.

Heat Exchangers

The principal types of heat exchangers used or being seriously considered for use in transferring energy from the geothermal fluid are:
1. plate,
2. shell and tube,
3. downhole,
4. direct contact, and
5. plastic tube.

PLATE HEAT EXCHANGERS

Use of plate heat exchangers is becoming widespread in geothermal applications. They are being used for low temperature applications in France, high temperature applications in Iceland and low and medium temperature applications in the U.S.

The plate heat exchanger (Figure 3.31) consists of a series of stamped plates that are placed one behind the other with seals between consecutive plates. A few or many plates can be stacked together. They are held in place by long bolts that extend through header plates and which, when tightened, press the plates against one another and compress the seals.

Plate heat exchangers have been widely used for many years in the food processing industry and in marine applications. They have two main characteristics that make them desirable for many geothermal applications:
1. They are readily cleaned. By loosening the main bolts, the header plate and the individual heat exchanger plates can be removed and cleaned.
2. The stamped plates are very thin and may be made of a wide variety of materials. When expensive materials are required, the thinness of the plates allows this type of heat exchanger to be much less expensive than other types.

These heat exchangers have additional characteristics that influence their selection in specific applications:
1. Approach temperature differences are usually smaller than those for shell and tube heat exchangers.
2. Pressure drops are usually larger than those for shell and tube heat exchangers.

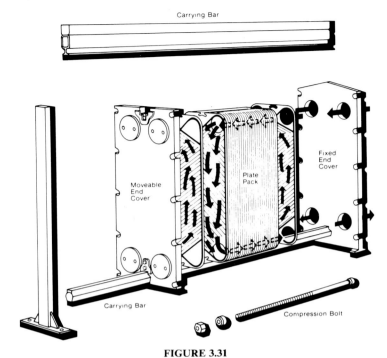

FIGURE 3.31
Plate heat exchanger (courtesy of Alfa-Laval)

The geothermal fluid is routed along one side of each plate with the heated fluid routed along the other side. The plates can be readily manifolded for various combinations of series and parallel flow.

3. Heat transfer per unit volume is usually larger than for shell and tube heat exchangers.
4. Applications are restricted for temperatures less than 500°F because of limitations on elastomeric gaskets.
5. Increased capacity can be accommodated easily; all that is required is the addition of plates.

The closer approach temperatures are particularly important in low temperature geothermal applications.

SHELL AND TUBE HEAT EXCHANGERS

This commonly applied type of heat exchanger is being used only in a limited number of geothermal applications, because the plate heat exchanger appears to have an economic advantage when specialized materials are required to minimize corrosion. However, when mild steel shells and copper or silicon bronze tubes can be utilized, the shell and tube heat exchanger usually is more economical.

Two specialized designs of shell and tube heat exchangers are being developed for geothermal energy use with geothermal fluids that have a high potential for scaling. These are the "fluidized bed" (Figure 3.32) and "APEX" (Advanced Geothermal Energy Primary Heat Exchanger) concepts.

The fluidized bed heat exchanger is used with fluids that have high scaling potential. It consists basically of a shell-and-tube heat exchanger with the

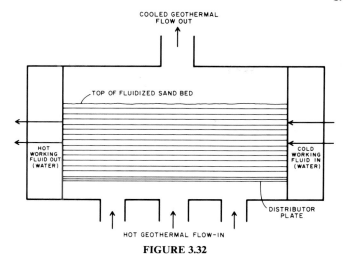

FIGURE 3.32

Schematic of horizontal arrangement of a liquid-fluidized-bed heat exchanger.

geothermal fluid passing through the shell side. The fluid passes up through a bed of particles, such as sand, which surrounds the tube bundle. The bed is fluidized by the fluid flow and provides a constant scrubbing action against the tubes, keeping them from scaling while also increasing the heat transfer rate. The configuration can accommodate either horizontal or vertical tube bundle assemblies. Because of the rapid mixing in the fluidized bed, the shell side temperature distribution approaches isothermal. As a result, such heat exchangers must operate with series staging to get the energy out of the geothermal fluid.

The APEX heat exchanger is similar to the fluidized bed design in that a scouring agent such as sand is used to help keep the heat transfer surface clean. In the APEX design, however, the abrasive material is injected into the geothermal stream just before the geothermal stream enters the tubes of a shell and tube heat exchanger. As the geothermal stream leaves the heat exchanger, it enters a disengaging zone and the abrasive material and any precipitated solid material is removed.

DOWNHOLE HEAT EXCHANGERS

In shallow geothermal resource areas, heat exchangers located within the wellbore can have applicability for relatively small scale direct applications. These downhole heat exchangers are presently used in a number of localities in the U.S.; Figure 3.33 shows a typical installation.

A downhole heat exchanger consists of pipes or tubes suspended in the cased wellbore. A secondary fluid is circulated from the user system through the exchanger. Geothermal fluid passes by the exchanger because of thermosyphoning caused by cooling from the heat exchanger. The systems with higher outputs have perforations in the well casing near the bottom and just below the water level to promote thermosyphoning.

These systems have not been tested in a large number of resource areas, so their general applicability is still somewhat in question. In resource areas like that at Klamath Falls, Oregon, where over 400 downhole heat exchanger

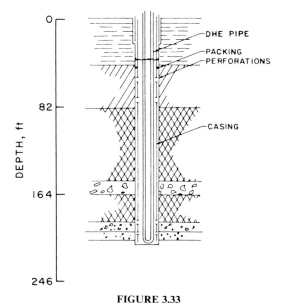

FIGURE 3.33
Typical downhole heat exchanger (DHE) installation

systems are in operation, it appears that economic desirability relative to surface heat exchanger systems exist when a single well output, typically less than 0.8 MW$_t$, is adequate for the application and the wells are relatively shallow, up to about 650 ft.

PLASTIC TUBE HEAT EXCHANGERS

Plastic tube heat exchangers that have been developed for heat recovery from corrosive sources appear to have good potential for application in geothermal systems of a limited temperature range. Because the commonly used fan coils have copper-based tubes, they are unsatisfactory for most geothermal fluids. Plastic tube heat exchangers with an upper temperature limit of 120°F and designed for air heating are presently available. These could be used in low temperature geothermal applications to a limited extent, but—more importantly—it appears that developing products will have a higher allowable temperature and, consequently, much greater applicability. Such units will be substantially larger than the present fan coil units, but the corrosion and scaling resistance appears to outweigh the increase in size.

DIRECT CONTACT HEAT EXCHANGERS

In direct contact heat exchangers, now being developed, the geothermal fluid is brought into direct contact with another fluid that vaporizes at the desired recovery temperature and then separates from the geothermal fluid. Similar direct contact heat exchangers is very common in oil refineries where the exchange is between relatively clean fluids. Figure 3.34 shows schematics of various configurations of direct contact heat exchanger systems.

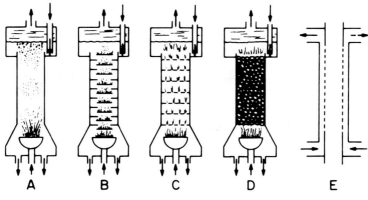

FIGURE 3.34

Schematic of various types of direct contact counter flow devices: (A) spray tower, (B) baffle tower, (C) perforated plate tower, (D) packed tower, and (E) wetted wall tower.

PIPING

Standard low-carbon steel pipe is the most common type of pipe used for geothermal transmission and distribution lines. This type of pipe is the least costly for many installations and, when selected with adequate corrosion allowances, has given acceptable lifetimes. However, because the mild steel is subject to severe corrosion when free oxygen is present, it is necessary to maintain a tightly sealed system.

Other types of piping, particularly those made of nonmetallic materials, appear to have applicability in geothermal systems.

Fiberglass reinforced plastic (FRP) pipe is being increasingly used for geothermal applications at temperatures up to about 212°F. Its primary advantage is a noncorrosive nature, particularly in regard to external corrosion in direct buried lines. FRP pipe also has some advantage over steel pipe in that expansion considerations are not so severe and there is less pressure drop for a given flow rate. Disadvantages of the FRP pipe are temperature limitations and in larger sizes, its pressure limitation, particularly at the higher end of the temperature range.

The use of *PVC plastic pipe* in geothermal applications is much more restricted because of the temperature limitation. Its maximum recommended temperature is about 125°F.

Asbestos cement pipe has been used in a number of geothermal applications, primarily disposal lines, with good success. Recent studies have presented different conclusions regarding the economy of using asbestos cement piping.

A variety of nonmetallic materials, particularly concrete polymer composites, plastics and refractories, are being evaluated for their use in geothermal applications through Brookhaven National Laboratory. The concrete polymer composites have shown exceptional promise, even at temperatures up to 460°F.

METERING EQUIPMENT

District heating metering systems, for the purpose of billing consumers, can be based on quantity of water used (volume-metering), quantity of heat used (energy metering), quantity of water used times the supply temperature, or specified apportionment factors (nonmeter billing).

Water volume meters in use in the district heating sector use mechanical principles to measure water flow through a counter which registers the passing volume of water. This type of meter helps make consumers more economy-conscious in running their systems to achieve the greatest possible cooling of the district heating water. Recall that in geothermal energy systems achieving a large cooling of the district heating fluid (large ΔT) is particularly important because it directly influences the total power that can be achieved from a well. Volume meters cost little to purchase and operate. The objection to volume metering is the variance in supply temperature to the consumer's installation.

There are two components in *energy metering:* quantity of flow and temperature differential across the system. Multiplication of these two values provides a measurement of the system's heat consumption. This method provides a favorable solution to heat measurement because consumers are billed on the basis of actual heat consumed, but such a system would be detrimental to a geothermal based system because it would not encourage the achievement of a large ΔT of the district heating fluid.

In order to retain the encouragement of the consumer achieving a large ΔT of the district heating fluid and to overcome the disadvantage of purely volume metering, some Europeans feel strongly that the billing should be based on the quantity of "volume used times the supply temperature." This appears to make the most sense from both the supplier and consumer viewpoints.

Nonmeter billing—billing in proportion to a consumer's installation (cubic volume or floor area)—reduces costs associated with the purchase, servicing and replacement of meters, as well as meter reading. This method is not suitable where there is variation in insulation standards, a mix of high- and low-density housing, or buildings of varying age.

GEOTHERMAL DISTRICT COOLING

The use of thermal energy to drive cooling systems has occurred for many years. However, there has been little use of geothermal energy for cooling, with space cooling in the Rotorua International Hotel at Rotorua, New Zealand being the only widely reported occurrence. The application there uses a lithium bromide/water absorption unit to produce the cooling. Geothermal fluid at about 300°F and 90 psia is passed through a heat exchanger to heat water in a piping circuit to a temperature of about 250°F. This heated water is used to (i) drive the absorption unit, (ii) provide space heating, and (iii) heat sanitary water.

In recent years, because of the emphasis on solar energy and waste heat, there has been a substantial amount of interest in various types of systems that can use thermal energy to produce cooling. It appears though, at least for the immediate future, that the absorption unit must still be considered the most likely candidate for supplying space cooling from geothermal resources. New designs for these units have good performance from heated fluid supply temperatures as low as about 140°F.

Absorption cooling from geothermal energy requires resource temperatures somewhat higher than the 140°F temperature level indicated as about the minimum temperature at which reasonable performance can be expected from the absorption units themselves. It can be expected that new applications will occur with resource temperatures as low as about 160°F. However, for the same reasons as discussed previously with respect to space heating, the economics of operation improves as the temperature of the resource increases above this value.

Space cooling with absorption units from the same geothermal resource that is used for space heating has the potential to improve the overall economics of the geothermal energy use. The potential for improvement is due primarily to a potentially increased load factor. However, whether or not the providing of space cooling will actually improve the load factor depends on the temperature of the geothermal resource and the ratio of the cooling load to the heating load. The load factor will in general be increased if the peak thermal energy required to operate the cooling system (cooling load divided by the cooling unit coefficient of performance (usually about 0.65 for a single stage absorption unit for the recommended range of operation)) divided by the temperature drop that the cooling unit can extract from the geothermal fluid is less than the heating load divided by the temperature drop that the heating system can extract from the geothermal fluid. Otherwise, the size of the geothermal system will have to be increased because of the space cooling requirement. Since the minimum temperature for absorption cooling is greater than that for space heating, the greatest load factor improvement will occur when the cooling load is less than the heating load and the resource temperature is substantially above the minimum required to operate the absorption unit. It is expected that large scale district systems will require geothermal resources with temperatures of about 200°F or greater and that the systems to be used with geothermal resources will be designed to extract a relatively large temperature drop from the geothermal fluid.

The first large geothermal space cooling application to be built in the U.S. is presently in the design phase. The city of El Centro, California is planning to use 235°F fluid from the Heber resource area for providing about 65 tons of cooling with absorption units.

NONCONVENTIONAL FUELS FOR DISTRICT HEATING

A variety of nonconventional fuels—some available; some under development—can be used for district heating and cooling systems. These include: nuclear, solar, wood, oil shale, refuse derived fuels, and coal derived synthetic fuels.

Nuclear

Nuclear power can be used to meet domestic space heating requirements. One approach involves use of waste heat from large nuclear power plants, but this depends on the location of such plants in relation to urban centers, low temperature distribution techniques, total electricity demands of the area, and other factors. In any case, the use of such heat is confined to areas with large population concentrations.

One way of avoiding use of fossil fuels in smaller urban centers involved reliance on small, low-cost reactors designed exclusively for heating. Nuclear district heating plants are being designed for this purpose.

BACKGROUND

The first project studies concerned with small nuclear plants designed for heating only were carried out in Sweden by ASEA in the mid-1950's. The work eventually resulted in construction of an underground nuclear district heating station at Agesta, which started supplying the Stockholm suburb of Farsta with 200 milj Btu/h of heat in 1963, with capacity for also generating about 10 MW of electric power. The station was operated satisfactorily until 1973, when it was rendered unprofitable by low oil prices.

World-wide oil price increases during 1973/74 caused radical changes and renewed conceptual studies into small, low-temperature nuclear heating plants. An extensive study was launched in 1976 and a basic design has been produced for a mini-reactor designed for production of hot water only close to urban areas. The project study is named SECURE for *S*afe and *E*nvironmentally *C*lean *U*rban *RE*actor.

As planned, the SECURE reactor is best suited for supplying the base thermal load, with fossil-fired hot water stations being applied to meet peak load.

Typical demand-duration curves for built-up areas in Scandinavia show that a 210°F water supply can satisfy the vast proportion of heat demand. A heating reactor with a thermal rating of 500 milj Btu/h could serve communities with 50,000–100,000 inhabitants.

DESIGN PHILOSOPHY

A nuclear reactor designed for district heating would have to be sited in a built-up area to minimize capital requirements for the district heating network and to minimize parasitic thermal losses from district heating piping.

It is essential for the nuclear district heating plant to be so safe that, in spite of the prevailing nuclear power debate, matters concerned with the siting of the stations can be processed without undue delay.

Reactor Design

A typical district heating nuclear plant is shown in Figure 3.35. The reactor core is located in a large pool comprising a cold water and boron mixture. When this mixture enters the reactor core, the reactor shuts down automatically because the boron absorbs neutrons in the core and so inhibits the neutron chain reaction.

The reactor vessel itself has no pressure retaining function. There are permanent open connections without any valves or other obstacles between the reactor water inside the vessel and the pool water boron outside the vessel at the top and the bottom of the reactor vessel.

During normal operation, mixing the cold highly borated pool water and the warm low-boron reactor water is prevented by a gas bubble in the hole at the top of the reactor vessel. The gas bubble is kept in place by the pressure drop across the core existing as a result of the reactor water circulation through the core.

Any reduction in the core coolant flow which could jeopardize the cooling of the core causes a reduction in the pressure drop in the core, as shown in Figure 3.36. The gas bubble then flows out of the reactor vessel and cold, high-boron water flows into the core from the pool. The reactor will thus be shut down and cooled. This process conforms with the laws of thermodynamics, without the assistance of any actuated mechanical or electrical equipment.

No control rods for fast shut down of the reactor are required. Reactor scram is initiated by simply stopping the reactor coolant pumps. This reduces the core coolant flow and the reactor is inherently shut down and cooled. As shown in

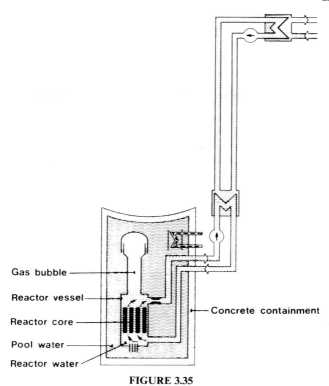

Gas bubble

Reactor vessel

Reactor core

Pool water

Reactor water

Concrete containment

FIGURE 3.35

Normal operation and heat production to district heating grid

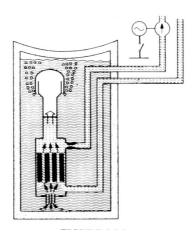

FIGURE 3.36

Inherent reactor shut down by reactor coolant pump trip

Figure 3.37 the cold high-boron water volume in the pool is sufficient for absorbing the decay heat of the reactor following a shutdown for more than 24 hours, without water temperature exceeding 212°F.

The large reactor pool is slightly pressurized and contained in a cylindrical prestressed concrete containment fitted with a concrete lid (Figure 3.38). The height of the containment is 75 ft. and the diameter 30–50 ft., depending on the thermal rating of the reactor.

The reactor core consists of fuel rods of uranium dioxide, similar to those used in conventional boiling water reactors. The difference is that the fuel rods

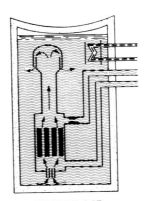

FIGURE 3.37
Inherent core cooling by natural circulation to pool water

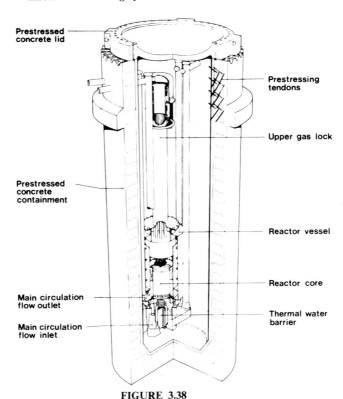

FIGURE 3.38
Reactor containment and reactor vessel

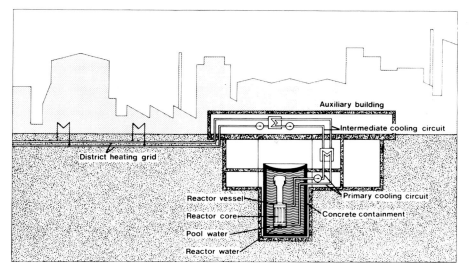

FIGURE 3.39
Station layout

are shorter and the power density at the rods is appreciably lower, resulting in a very low fuel and cladding temperatures. This reduces the frequency of cladding defects as well as the release of fission products from the fuel to the reactor coolant in the event of their occurrence.

Heat produced in the reactor core is transferred to the reactor water which is heated from 200°F to 250°F when flowing through the core. The heat from this water is transferred to an intermediate circuit which, in turn, transfers it to the district heating grid. In the district heating system the water flow is heated from 160°F to 210°F, (other temperatures can be accommodated).

The heat exchangers and pumps of the systems are conventional devices, all located outside the concrete vessel behind biological shields in the reactor service room. They are directly accessible for maintenance and service (Figure 3.39). Such a plant can be adopted to above-ground siting, recessing siting or underground siting, depending on local conditions.

ENVIRONMENTAL IMPACT

A well-designed nuclear-based district heating system can provide municipal heat with negligible pollution. Waste heat is insignificant and there is no smoke and no liquid radwaste. Drainage water from the reactor system is collected, treated and reused as make-up water to the reactor.

Gaseous radioactivity release during normal operation causes less than one one-thousandth of the dose due to natural radiation. Gaseous radioactivity release following a postulated accident is less than the natural radiation dose during one day.

ECONOMY

Although the investment required to develop a nuclear-based district heating system is relatively high, operating costs are low, especially so because the cost of nuclear heat is affected only to a minor extent by the price of uranium.

The single most significant economic variable of such an approach is likely to be the outlays required to contend with opposition which any type of nuclear plant engenders. In some cases, the emotionalism associated with nuclear opposition may make this approach unfeasible.

Solar

Heat from the sun comprises a potentially major source of energy for "fueling" district heating systems. At the present time, only a tiny fragment of the solar energy potential is being realized, with less than 1% of the nation's total energy consumption being derived from sunlight. By contrast, the amount of solar energy which reaches the earth is 22,500 times as great as worldwide energy usage.

The concept of collecting solar heat and putting it to useful work originated some 200 years ago in France. There, scientists and engineers attempted to construct a solar furnace designed for operation of water pumps.

Solar water heaters were introduced in Arizona, California, and Florida early in the 1900's. World War I Army camps in Southern California used thermo-syphon heaters similar to but larger than those now used in Australia, Israel, and Japan. Low-cost water heaters using natural gas, oil, and electricity ended the use of solar heaters in the U.S. except for a few applications. Lack of natural gas and the rapidly rising cost of electricity and petroleum-based fuels have now made major changes in the economics of solar energy utilization.

Although the rising cost of more conventional energy sources has offset some of the barriers to more widespread use of solar energy, other obstacles still remain.

The principle obstacles include:

1. The relatively low heat intensity of sunlight, which rarely exceeds 300 Btu/h/ft^2. Consequently, when large amounts of energy are needed, large collectors must be used. This poses somewhat of a restriction on district heating in particular, because the central plant must be located relatively close to end users. The land is relatively expensive in any event; the large land mass required for collector siting or solar ponds could in many cases be too costly.
2. Sunlight is intermittent, varying from zero at sunrise to a maximum at noon and back to zero at sunset. A means for storing energy usually must be provided at nighttime and during periods of low solar irradiation.
3. Sunlight is subject to unpredictable interruption due to clouds, rain, snow, hail, or dust.
4. The cost of solar collectors is still relatively high. This situation is expected to change as the cost of solar equipment declines due to new technology and mass production, while the cost of conventional energy steadily increases.

The obstacles associated with central station solar facilities are not at all insurmountable. In fact, the Electric Power Research Institute (EPRI) already has plans for large-scale solar electrical generation. One plan includes use of a large receiver filled with helium placed on an 80-story tower surrounded by 0.5 square miles of reflectors. The reflectors will "track" the sun and so be able to radiate energy equivalent to 1,000–2,000 suns to the receiver. Heated to 1,500°F, the helium in the receiver will run through a turbine to produce electricity and then through a dry cooling tower to be reused.

Another type of central receiver concept uses air—not helium—as the working fluid. Once heated to 2,000°F to make electricity, the air is exhausted to the atmosphere. A cooling tower is not required. The EPRI program's second-generation solar thermal power plants are designed to use steam for the heat transfer fluid instead of gas. This offers an alternative to large cooling water requirements, which is significant because most solar-thermal plants will be sited in the arid regions of the southwestern United States.

Wood

Forest lands comprise some 9.6 billion acres, equivalent to about 27% of the world's land area. Productive forest area is estimated at 6.4 billion acres, with some 4 billion acres being considered economically accessible.

Until the latter part of the nineteenth century, when it was replaced by coal, wood was the principal source of heat energy. It is no longer a major source due to forest depletion and the increasing demand for wood as lumber and for production of paper, plywood, rayon, and other products. Today, the burning of wood and bark for steam generation is largely confined to locations where it is available as a by-product or waste from the lumber, furniture, plywood and pulp industries. In producing lumber from logs, half the wood may be discarded as sawdust, bark, shavings, slabs and ends, all of which can be used as fuel. Also, waste-wood liquors from the pulp industry wood wastes are used extensively in other parts of the world, and to a lesser extent in the U.S. to produce alcohol for fuel. New methods of barking logs and producing pulp are continually reducing the quantity of waste available for fuel. More profitable end uses are also reducing the availability of wood for fuel.

Wood, in common with all types of vegetation, is composed primarily of carbohydrates and consequently has a relatively low heating value compared with bituminous coal and oil. Selected analyses and heating values of several types of wood and analyses of wood ash are given in Table 3.25.

Oil Shale

Oil shale deposits are widely distributed throughout the world, with the largest reserves being in the United States and Canada. Table 3.26 indicates the countries with the largest reserves. The production of oil from shale oil has not progressed past the pilot plant stage in the United States. This is primarily because foreign oil is cheaper than oil extracted from shale.

Refuse-Derived Fuel (RDF)

MECHANICAL PROCESSES

Refuse-derived fuel (RDF) can be developed in different ways. In general, the process entails primary shredding to reduce nominal particle size of the waste to about 4 inches. After ferrous metal is removed, the shredded waste stream is injected into a strong, vertically rising air stream. The lighter, mostly combustible fraction, is carried up by the air current. The heavier, mostly noncombustible fraction is pulled by gravity down through the air stream where it drops out the bottom of the "air classifier." The light fraction is processed further to improve its fuel characteristics. This further processing generally consists of a second shredding step. It can also entail screening to remove fine inorganic particles. Modified supplementary fuels can also be produced by treating the organics with a chemical embrittling agent and then grinding them to a powder-like consistency or by densifying the organics in a pellet mill. This

TABLE 3.25
ANALYSES OF WOOD AND WOOD ASH

Wood analyses (dry basis), % by wt	Pine Bark	Oak Bark	Spruce Bark[a]	Redwood Bark[a]
Proximate				
Volatile matter	72.9	76.0	69.6	72.6
Fixed carbon	24.2	18.7	26.6	27.0
Ash	2.9	5.3	3.8	0.4
Ultimate				
Hydrogen	5.6	5.4	5.7	5.1
Carbon	53.4	49.7	51.8	51.9
Sulfur	0.1	0.1	0.1	0.1
Nitrogen	0.1	0.2	0.2	0.1
Oxygen	37.9	39.3	38.4	42.4
Ash	2.9	5.3	3.8	0.4
Heating value, Btu/lb	9030	8370	8740	8350
Ash analyses, % by wt				
SiO_2	39.0	11.1	32.0	14.3
Fe_2O_3	3.0	3.3	6.4	3.5
TiO_2	0.2	0.1	0.8	0.3
Al_2O_3	14.0	0.1	11.0	4.0
Mn_3O_4	Trace	Trace	1.5	0.1
CaO	25.5	64.5	25.3	6.0
MgO	6.5	1.2	4.1	6.6
Na_2O	1.3	8.9	8.0	18.0
K_2O	6.0	0.2	2.4	10.6
SO_3	0.3	2.0	2.1	7.4
Cl	Trace	Trace	Trace	18.4
Ash fusibility, F				
Reducing				
Initial deformation	2180	2690		
Softening	2240	2720		
Fluid	2310	2740		
Oxidizing				
Initial deformation	2210	2680		
Softening	2280	2730		
Fluid	2350	2750		

[a] Salt-water storied.

TABLE 3.26
COUNTRIES HAVING LARGEST RESERVES OF OIL FROM OIL SHALE AND BITUMINOUS SANDS

Country	Type of Resource	Quantity (Million Metric Tons)	Year of Reference
China, P.R. of	Shale	21,000	1973
Canada	Shale	24,860	1965
	Sand	50,250	1963
United States	Shale	145,000	1972
	Sand	2,175	1973
Colombia	Sand	155,400	1971

Source, World Energy Conference, *Survey of Energy Sources*, 1974.

latter variation then produces a small, dense fuel pellet very similar to coal nuggets which are suitable as a fuel in a stoker-fired boiler equipped with a grate.

PYROLYSIS

RDF can also be developed through pyrolysis, the destructive distillation of the organic fraction of solid waste. Pyrolysis occurs when organic material is exposed to heat in the absence or near absence of oxygen. It differs from combustion in that it is endothermic (heat absorbing) rather than exothermic. Processes under development use heat from part of the waste to provide the heat absorbed during pyrolysis and recover the remaining heat in the form of stream or a gaseous or liquid fuel.

All processes reduce the solid waste to three forms: gas (primarily hydrogen, methane, carbon monoxide and carbon dioxide), liquids (water and organic chemicals such as acetic acid, methanol and benzene) and solids (a carbonaceous char). The form and characteristics of the fuel fraction varies for each of the different processes under development and is a function of the reaction time, temperature and pressure in the pyrolysis reactor, the particle size of the feed and the presence of catalysts.

To maximize gas production, reactor temperatures are held in the range of 1400 F to 3000 F with pressures ranging from 1 to 70 atmospheres. Ideally, the reaction is allowed to take place in the absence of diluting gases so that the product is the volatile matter of the solid waste. If air is used in the reactor, the gases produced will be diluted by the nitrogen in the air (air is approximately 79% nitrogen and 21% oxygen). As a result, some processes have been developed which use oxygen, thus resulting in a higher heat content fuel gas. Other systems indirectly transfer the heat to the gasifier to minimize dilution of the product gas.

Heating solid waste releases gases and leaves a carbon residue called char. In some reactors, the residue reaches such high temperatures that the ash and other noncombustibles, such as cans and glass, melt to form a slag which can be removed from the reactor in a molten state and quenched to form a glassy aggregate.

Residues produced from pyrolysis are biologically inactive and may be safely disposed of in sanitary landfills. Solid residues from the noncombustibles portion of the refuse, such as glassy aggregate, may be used for construction and paving. If the char is not consumed in the process, it has a higher heating value of approximately 9000 Btu/lb. Its high ash content (50%), however, severely limits its usefulness. Failure to consume all the char in the process represents a loss in energy recovery.

Coal-Derived Synthetic Fuels

Several companies are developing methods for production of synthetic gas, methanol, and oil from coal and some of the technologies involved are almost ready for full-scale commercial operation. Thus, it is estimated that, by 1990, coal-derived liquids could supply from 0.1 million to 0.3 million barrels a day (mbd) and that coal-derived gas could supply 0.3 mbde to 0.8 mbde.

COAL-DERIVED GAS

The production of coal-derived gas is conducted either by processing in gasification plants or by using underground (in situ) gasification techniques.

Depending upon the degree of processing used, the Btu content of coal-derived gas ranges from 100 to 1,000 Btu per cubic foot. (Pipeline gas derived from conventional sources contains approximately 1,000 Btu.)

The technology used for production of coal-derived high Btu (900 or more Btu/ft^3) gas involves five basic steps: coal preparation and pretreatment, gasification, shift conversion, gas purification, and methanation. Medium Btu gas production omits methanation.

Only the high Btu synthetic gas (SNG) is considered to be a substitute for conventional gas. Low and medium Btu gas are only suitable for combustion on-site or relatively short distances away. Nonetheless, low and medium Btu gas could become important because it permits utilities to provide gas to district heating and industrial customers where use of conventional natural gas may be prohibited by regulatory constraints.

COAL-DERIVED LIQUID

There are several methods for converting coal into liquid fuel. These include pyrolysis, solvent refining, and direct and indirect liquefaction.

Pyrolysis involves heating pulverized coal to breakdown its molecules into liquids and gases.

In solvent refining, coal is pulverized and mixed with an oil-type solvent, thus converting coal into a liquid heavier than crude oil.

Direct liquefaction uses a catalyst to add hydrogen to either the liquid product from solvent refining or raw coal.

Through indirect liquefaction, coal first is gasified with steam and catalyzed to produce a liquid fuel.

CHAPTER 4

Steam/Hot Water Production Plant

DISTRICT HEATING has been defined here as "the distribution of thermal energy from a central source for space heating and cooling." This central source can be either a boiler-only unit or a cogeneration power plant. The cogeneration plant produces both electricity and thermal energy, and has the advantage of greater overall energy-utilization efficiency. While some of the heat conversion equipment was described earlier, this chapter discusses the principles of combustion and additional major equipment. Guidance is also provided on the methods of equipment selection and sizing as well as their operation and maintenance.

PRINCIPLES OF COMBUSTION

Combustion may be defined as the rapid chemical reaction of oxygen with the volatile elements of a fuel. There are just three combustible chemical elements of significance: carbon, hydrogen, and sulfur. Sulfur is usually of minor significance as a source of heat, but it can be of major significance in corrosion and air pollution.

Carbon and hydrogen when burned to completion with oxygen unite as follows:

$$C + O_2 = CO_2 + 14,100 \text{ Btu/lb of C}$$
$$2H_2 + O_2 = 2H_2O + 61,100 \text{ Btu/lb of H}_2$$

Air is the usual source of oxygen for boilers and these combustion reactions are exothermic and the heat released is relative to the pounds of carbon and hydrogen burned. The objective of good combustion is to release all of this heat while minimizing losses from system imperfections and superfluous air. In order for fuel to burn completely, four conditions must be met. These are generally referred to as air and the "three T's" (turbulence, temperature, and time), defined as follows:

Air: The amount of air required for combustion depends on the fuel, equipment, and operating conditions involved. It is determined from manufacturer's recommendations and actual trial. Too much air causes an excessive amount of hot gas to be discharged from the stack, resulting in large heat losses. Too little air permits some of the fuel to pass through the furnace unburned or only partially burned. The best proportion of air-to-fuel must be determined and maintained to secure high efficiency.

Turbulence: Turbulence refers to the mixing of air and fuel. Air and fuel must be mixed thoroughly because each combustible particle must come into close contact with the air's oxygen for combustion to occur. Inadequate air distribution and mixing result in excess air in some portions of the fuel bed or combustion chamber, and too little air in others.

Temperature: Although combustible material comes into intimate contact with the air all the time, it usually does not burn. A chemical reaction, termed oxidation, is taking place, but it is slow, like the rusting of steel. However, when the combustible material reaches its ignition temperature, oxidation accelerates, resulting in combustion. Accordingly, the fuel and air mixture must be maintained at a temperature high enough to promote combustion.

When the flame comes into contact with the relatively cool boiler tubes or shell, carbon particles are deposited as soot. When boilers are operated at a low rating, the low temperature result in incomplete combustion and excessive smoke.

Time: Air supply, mixing, and temperature determine the rate of combustion. In all cases, a certain amount of time is required to complete the process. When equipment is operated at very high ratings, there may not be enough time to permit complete combustion. This results in unburned fuel being discharged from the furnace in the form of solids or combustible gases. The losses may be substantial

In complete combustion of hydrocarbon fuels, all hydrogen and carbon in the fuel is oxidized to H_2O and CO_2. Generally, for complete combustion, it is necessary to supply excess oxygen, or excess air, beyond that theoretically required to oxidize the fuel. Excess oxygen or air is usually expressed as a percentage of the air theoretically required to completely oxidize the fuel.

In stoichiometric combustion of a hydrocarbon fuel, fuel is reacted with the exact amount of oxygen required to oxidize all carbon, hydrogen, and sulfur in the fuel to CO_2, H_2O, and SO_2. Hence, exhaust gas from stoichiometric combustion theoretically, contains no incompletely oxidized fuel constituents or oxygen. The percentage of CO_2 contained in products of stoichiometric combustion is the maximum attainable, referred to as stoichiometric CO_2, ultimate CO_2, or maximum theoretical percentage of carbon dioxide.

Stoichiometric combustion, that is, combustion at zero excess oxygen without formation of incompletely combusted fuel products, is seldom realized in practice due to imperfect mixing and finite reaction rate. Economy and safety dictate that most combustion equipment operate with some excess air. This assures that fuel is not wasted and that equipment is sufficiently flexible to provide complete combustion despite variations in fuel properties and in the supply rates of fuel and air. In practice, combustion equipment is designed and operated to assure complete but not stoichiometric combustion. The exact quantity of excess air supplied to any particular combustion equipment depends on such factors as:

1. expected variations in fuel properties and in fuel and air supply rates;
2. equipment application;
3. degree of operator supervision required or available; and
4. control requirements.

For maximum efficiency, combustion at low excess air is desirable.

Incomplete combustion occurs when any fuel element is not completely oxidized in the combustion process. For example, a hydrocarbon may not completely oxidize to carbon dioxide and water, but may form partially oxidized compounds such as carbon monoxide, aldehydes, and ketones. Conditions which promote incomplete combustion include:

1. insufficient air and fuel mixing (causing local fuel-rich and fuel-lean zones);
2. insufficient air supply to the flame (providing less than the required quantity of oxygen);

3. insufficient reactant residence time in the flame (preventing completion of combustion reactions);
4. flame impingement on a cold surface (quenching combustion reactions); or
5. a too-low flame temperature (slowing combustion reactions).

Incomplete combustion represents inefficient fuel use; may be hazardous, due to production of carbon monoxide; and contributes to air pollution.

BOILERS

A boiler is a pressure vessel designed to transfer heat to a fluid. The fluid usually is water in the form of a liquid or steam.

A boiler is designed to absorb the maximum amount of heat released in the process of combustion. The heat is transmitted to the boiler by radiation, conduction, and convection. The percentage of heat transmitted through each process depends upon boiler design.

Heat radiated from a hot to a cold body is "radiant" heat. It depends on the temperature difference and the color of the body receiving the heat. Radiant heat absorption increases with furnace temperature. Many factors are involved, but the most significant is the area of the tubes exposed to heat rays.

Heat which passes from the gas to the tube by physical contact is transmitted through conduction. The heat passes from molecule of metal to molecule of metal with no displacement of the molecules. The conductivity or heat absorption qualities of the material through which the heat must pass determines the amount of absorption.

Heat transmitted from hot to cold bodies by movement of the conveying substance is "convection" heat. In this case, the hot body is the boiler gas; the cold body, the boiler tube containing water.

In boiler design, each form of heat transmission is treated separately, while in the boiler operation all three forms of heat transmission occur simultaneously and cannot be considered separate from each other.

Significant progress has been made in boiler design from the standpoint of safety, efficiency and flexibility. Recent advances in design include forced circulation of water, pressurized furnaces, large-capacity units producing 5 to 6 million pounds of steam per hour, hot water boilers, automation, and extremely high steam pressures and temperatures.

Boilers are built in a variety of sizes, shapes, and forms to fit conditions peculiar to the individual plant, and to meet varying requirements. Increasing fuel cost mean more attention is given to improving a furnace's combustion efficiency. Many boilers are designed to accommodate a variety of fuels so as to take advantage of those most economical.

Boiler Classifications

Boilers can be classified based on working pressure, temperature, fuel used, size and shape use, and steam or water type. A brief discussion of various basic classifications is as follows.

WORKING TEMPERATURE/PRESSURE CLASSIFICATION

Boilers are built to meet American Society of Mechanical Engineers (ASME) Codes. The specific requirements are the ASME Boiler and Pressure Vessel Code Section IV for Heating Boilers (low pressure boilers), and the ASME Code Section I for Power Boilers (medium and high pressure boilers).

Low pressure boilers are built for maximum working pressures of 15 psi steam and up to 160 psi hot water. Hot water boilers are limited to 250°F operating temperature. Controls and relief valves which limit temperature and pressure are not part of the boiler, but are installed as protection.

Medium and high pressure boilers are those designed to operate at above 15 psi steam, above 160 psi water, or up to 250°F water temperature.

Water boilers may be of the low pressure type designed for relatively low temperature heating systems and are built to, and limited by, the ASME Code to 30 psi working pressure. Cast-iron boilers rated at 50 psi, 80 psi, or 100 psi working pressures are also manufactured. Low pressure steel water boilers are also available for any working pressure up to the ASME Code provision under which it is built and tested, and must be equipped with a relief valve opening at that rated pressure, or lower.

Medium/high pressure water boilers are frequently constructed of steel, and manufactured to meet special installation requirements.

FUEL USE CLASSIFICATION

Boilers may burn coal, wood, various grades of fuel oil, all types of fuel gas, or operate as electric boilers. A boiler designed for one fuel type may or may not be convertible to another type of fuel. Some boilers can be adapted to burn coal, oil or gas and several designs allow firing oil or gas with convenient and quick conversion.

CONSTRUCTION MATERIALS

Cast Iron Boilers

Cast-iron boilers are manufactured of individually cast sections, assembled into blocks of sections. The number of sections assembled together determines boiler size and energy rating. Sections may be vertical or horizontal. The vertical design is the most common. The boiler may be dry base with the firebox beneath the fluid-backed sections, wet leg with the firebox top and sides enclosed by fluid-backed sections, or wet base with the firebox surrounded by fluid-backed sections.

The three boiler types can be designed to be equally efficient and testing and rating standards apply equally. The wet base design is easiest to adapt for combustible floor installations. Codes usually demand a floor temperature under the boiler no higher than 90°F, plus room temperature. A wet base steam boiler at 215°F or water boiler at 240°F cannot meet this requirement without adequate floor insulation.

Steel Boilers

Steel boilers are fabricated into one assembly of a given size and rating, usually by welding. They can be categorized into two general types, fire-tube boilers and water-tube boilers.

Fire-tube boilers are low-pressure, low-capacity units, used for the most part in small plants. A fire-tube boiler consists of a large steel cylinder which contains a nest of small diameter steel tubes. Hot combustion gases pass through the tubes and transfer heat to the water in the shell.

Water-tube boilers differ from a fire-tube boiler in location of water and gas flow. The water circulates through the tubes and the hot combustion gases flow through the furnace. The hot gases contact the tubes and transfer heat to the water. The cross-sectional area of the water tubes is smaller than that of the shell of a fire-tube boiler, thus water-tube boilers may be designed for higher steam pressures and temperatures than fire-tube boilers.

A fire-tube boiler has some possible advantages over a water-tube boiler of comparable steam capacity. It occupies less space and is less costly to purchase and install. Fire-tube boilers also have some drawbacks. The large surface area of the shell limits steam temperatures and pressures' and the large volume of water required often results in poor circulation with sluggish responses to varying steam demands. Changes in temperature cause the tubes and shell to expand and contract unevenly which may cause leaks at the tube ends.

Water-tube boilers tend to be more efficient and flexible than fire-tube boilers. Water-tube boilers respond quickly to changes in steam demand and carry high overloads. Pressure is exerted on small diameter tubes rather than on a large shell and circulating water prevents unequal heating and cooling.

The water-tube construction allows for greater boiler capacity, and the use of higher pressure, with greater versatility in arrangement, permitting the most efficient design of the furnace, superheater, reheater and other heat recovery components. One drawback of a water-tube boiler is that it requires a costly foundation structure.

Water-tube boilers can be classified as straight-tube or bent-tube types. Straight-tube boilers, have generally been supplanted by modern designs of bent-tube boilers, which are more economical and serviceable.

Bent-Tube Boilers

Many important modern designs of boilers, such as the two-drum Stirling, the Integral-Furnace, the Radiant, and the Universal Pressure are included in the "bent-tube" classification. All bent-tube boilers today, with the exception of those with stoker or flat refractory floors, have water-cooled walls and floors.

Integral Furnace Boiler

The integral furnace boiler is a two-drum boiler adaptable to shop assembly and shipment as a package in the smaller capacities. Figure 4.1 shows a low-

FIGURE 4.1

Type FM Integral-Furnace boiler. Shop-assembled unit, complete and ready to operate

(Courtesy of The Babcock & Wilcox Co.)

capacity integral furnace boiler designed for shop assembly. This package boiler is shipped complete with support steel, casing, forced draft fan (unmounted in larger sizes), firing equipment, and controls, ready for operation when steam water, fuel, and electrical connections are made. Only a stub stack is required. It is built for outputs from 10,000 to 180,000 lb of steam per hr. Steam pressures range to 925 psi and temperatures to 825 F. Units can be fired with oil, gas, or a combination. A forced draft fan is required, as the casing is airtight (welded) and the combustion gases are under pressure.

Two-Drum Stirling Boiler

The possible arrangements for the connecting tubes, with one upper steam drum directly over one lower drum, led to the development of a design known as the two-drum Stirling boiler, (Figure 4.2). This design is standardized over a wide range of capacities and pressures with steam flows varying from 200,000 to 1,200,000 lb/hr, design pressures to 1750 psi and steam temperatures to

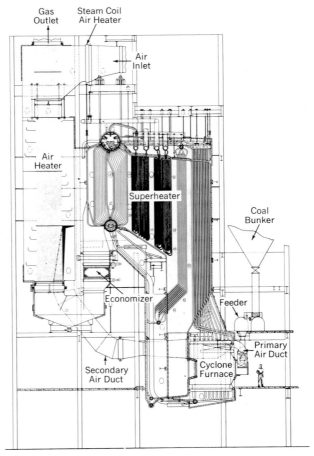

FIGURE 4.2

Two-drum Stirling boiler for Cyclone-Furnace firing. Design pressure 1575 psi; steam temperature 900F; maximum continuous steam output 550,000 lb/hr.

(Courtesy of The Babcock & Wilcox Co.)

1000°F. The firing may be by Cyclone Furnace, pulverized coal, oil or gas. The two-drum Stirling boiler is used in industrial and utility applications.

High Pressure and High Temperature Boilers

A single-boiler, single-turbine combination is most commonly used in central power plant stations and where electric power is the end product of heat transformation. Investment and labor costs decrease as size increases, thus there is an incentive to use very large electrical generators. Important factors in large boiler units for this application are:

1. high steam pressure,
2. high steam temperature,
3. bleed feedwater heating and,
4. reheat.

High steam pressure means high saturation temperature and low temperature difference between steam and exit gas. High steam temperature means high initial temperature and, usually, reheating to high temperature for reuse of the steam. Bleed feedwater heating lowers the temperature difference in an economizer and increases the gas temperature leaving the economizer. An air heater is then used to lower the exit-gas temperature.

Increasing steam pressures and temperatures has necessitated proportionally more superheating surface and less boiler surface. When pressures exceed 1500 psi in a drum-type boiler, the heat absorbed in furnace and boiler screen tubes is almost enough to generate the steam. It usually becomes more economical to use economizer surface for additional evaporation required and to raise the feedwater to saturation. All the steam then is generated in the furnace, water-cooled wall enclosures of superheater and economizer, boiler screen, division walls, and in some cases the outlet end of a steaming economizer.

Radiant Boiler

The radiant boiler drum type (Figures 4.3 and 4.4) is a high pressure, high-temperature, high capacity boiler. It can use coal, natural-gas and oil firing. Boiler convection surface is at a minimum in these units.

The Carolina-type radiant boiler illustrated in Figure 4.3 is a pulverized-coal-fired unit with hopper bottom construction for dry ash removal. Components are integrated to coordinate the fuel fired with the turbine throttle requirements. Sizes are available in reasonable increments of width and height to permit selection of economical units for the required steam conditions and capacity.

Figure 4.4 illustrates the E1 Paso-type radiant boiler for natural-gas and oil firing. This is a compact and economical design suitable for these fuels because of the cleanliness of natural gas and the relatively minor ash problems encountered with oil as compared to coal.

Universal Pressure Boiler

The universal pressure boiler is a high capacity, high temperature boiler. It is functionally applicable in the pressure range from 2000 to 4000 psi. Firing may be by coal, natural gas or oil.

The working fluid is pumped into the unit as liquid, when it passes through all the pressure part heating surfaces it is converted to steam at the desired temperature. No circulation of water occurs within the unit. For this reason a drum is not required. The universal-pressure boiler may be designed to operate at either subcritical or supercritical pressures.

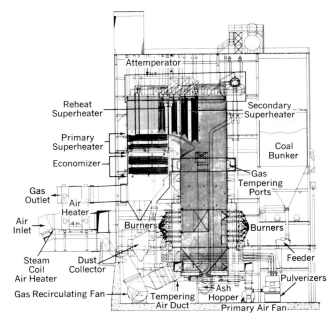

FIGURE 4.3

Carolina-type Radiant boiler for pulverized-coal firing. Design pressure 2875 psi; primary and reheat steam temperatures 1000F; maximum continuous steam output 1,750,000 lb/hr.

(Courtesy of The Babcock & Wilcox Co.)

Figure 4.5 illustrates a pulverized-coal-fired universal-pressure boiler for a 1300 Mw capacity electric generating unit. Figure 4.6 is a natural-gas-fired installation, supplying steam for a 750 Mw generator.

BOILER EFFICIENCY

Boiler efficiency is defined in two ways: overall efficiency and combustion efficiency.

Combustion efficiency is figured as input minus stack (chimney) loss, divided by input.

Overall efficiency is figured as gross output divided by input. Gross output is measured in the steam or water leaving the boiler. Overall efficiency is lower than combustion efficiency by the percentage of heat lost from the boiler outside surface (this loss is usually termed radiation loss). Precise overall efficiency can be determined only by laboratory test under test conditions. Approximate combustion efficiency can be determined under any operating condition by measuring operating flue gas temperature and percentage CO_2, and then consulting a chart or table for the fuel being used.

PERFORMANCE CODES AND STANDARDS

Most heating boilers are rated according to standards developed by The Hydronics Institute, The American Gas Association (AGA), and The American Boiler Manufacturers Association (ABMA).

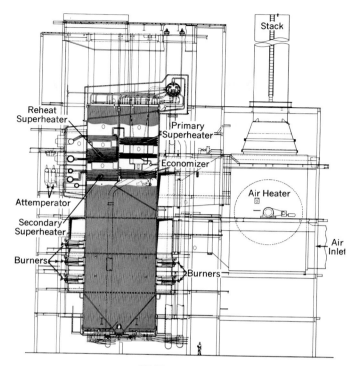

FIGURE 4.4

El Paso-type Radiant boiler for natural-gas and oil firing. Superheater outlet pressure 2625 psi; primary and reheat steam temperatures 1005F; capacity 3,770,000 lb steam per hr.

The Hydronics Institute has developed a standard for rating cast-iron and steel heating boilers based on performance obtained under controlled test conditions. The gross output obtained by test is subject to certain limiting factors such as flue gas temperature, draft CO_2 in flue gas, and minimum overall efficiency. This Standard applies primarily to oil-fired equipment, but also is used for gas fueled ratings in dual-fueled units.

Gas boilers are design-certified by AGA based on tests conducted in accordance with the American National Standard Z21.13.

ABMA has adopted test procedures for commercial/industrial and packaged firetube boilers based on the ASME Performance Test Code, Steam Generating Equipment (PTC 4.1). The units are tested for performance under controlled conditions with minimum levels of efficiency required.

SIZING OF BOILERS

Boiler sizing includes selection of output to meet load. Gross output of the boiler is the rate of heat delivered by the boiler to the system under continuous firing at rated input. Net rating (as rated by the Hydronics Institute) is gross output less a fixed percentage to allow for estimated piping heat loss plus an added load for initially heating up the water in a system (pickup).

Piping heat losses vary considerably. If all piping heat loss is defined as load then the loss is zero. If piping runs through unheated spaces, heat loss from the

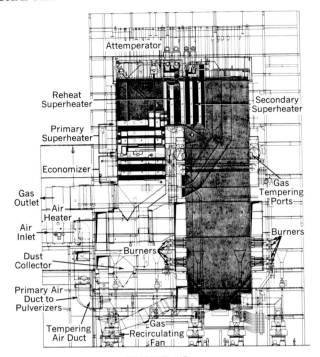

FIGURE 4.5

Single-row arrangement of cyclone steam separators with scrubbers.

(Courtesy of The Babcock & Wilcox Co.)

piping may be much higher than accounted for by the fixed "net rating" factor. Pickup is also variable. No pickup factor is necessary when actual load is less than design load. On the design coldest day extra system output is needed to pick up the load from a shutdown or low night setback. If night setback is not used or if there is not an extended shutdown period pickup load does not exist. Input capacity for pickup in a standby system can be in the form of excess capacity in base load boilers or in a standby boiler.

If piping and pickup losses are low or negligible, boiler sizing can be simplified so that boiler gross output equals the design load. If piping loss and pickup load are large or variable, those loads should be calculated, and appropriate gross boiler capacity added. Unless terminal units can deliver full boiler output under pickup conditions at an inlet water temperature lower than boiler high limit setting, rated boiler capacity cannot be delivered. System input (boiler output) will be greater than system output, water temperature will rise, and the boiler will cycle on the high limit control, delivering an average input to the system much lower than the boiler gross output. Boiler capacity must be matched by terminal unit and system delivery capacity.

BOILER INPUT/OUTPUT CONTROL

Boiler controls are generally designed to control the rate of fuel input in response to control signals representing load change. Thus, an average boiler output equals load within some control tolerance. Boiler controls include safety

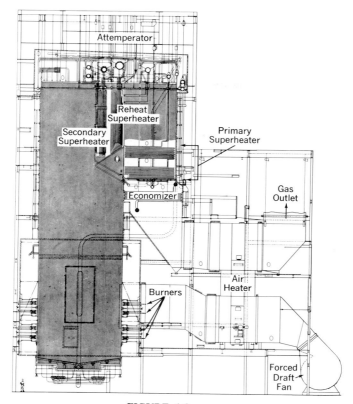

FIGURE 4.6

Universal-Pressure boiler for natural-gas firing. Superheater outlet pressure 3850 psi; primary and reheat steam temperatures 1005F; capacity 5,455,000 lb steam per hr.

controls acting to shut off fuel flow when unsafe conditions develop, and may possibly include control of steam flow or water flow to the system.

The control signal for a change of boiler input is a change in temperature or pressure in response to a load change. As load increases steam pressure drops as more steam is used, or water temperature drops as additional heat is extracted, or air temperature drops. The change may be noted at the boiler, in outdoor air, at the load, or at some other point. In larger hot water systems, a good example is a temperature switch, in the boiler, in a supply main, or in a storage tank, which cycles the boiler burner in response to water temperature change. Control system designs and diagrams are furnished by boiler manufacturers. Control diagrams or specifications to meet special safety requirements are available from insurance agencies (such as FIA, FM, or IRM) governmental bodies, and ASME. Such special requirements usually apply to boilers with inputs of 400 million Btu per hour or greater, but may apply to smaller sizes. The boiler manufacturer's provide installed and prewired boiler control systems, with diagrams, when the requirements are known.

When a code applies to a boiler installation, the details of control system requirements may be specified by the inspector only after boiler installation. Controls as needed must then be supplied, and the control design completed according to the inspector's instructions. It is essential that the heating system designer or specifying engineer determine the applicable codes, establish sources of necessary controls, and provide the skills needed to complete the control system.

STEAM SEPARATORS AND SUPERHEATERS

In the past, impurities in steam, as well as "carry-over," were frequently encountered ("carry-over" is the passing of water and impurities to the steam outlet). "Carry-over" was brought down to a minimum by separating water from the steam through the installation of baffles and the dry pipe.

The dry pipe design has proved to be reasonably effective for small boilers but unsuited for units operating at high rating and for steam drums with limited steam capacity. Adding a baffle ahead of the dry pipe offered some improvement in steam quality but was still not wholly satisfactory.

Pure steam is needed for process, for the superheater, and for the turbine and engine. Increased boiler capacity and high rating is aided by the fact that the modern boiler is protected by clean feedwater. External and internal feedwater treatment is supplemented by the use of steam scrubbers and separators.

Cyclone Separators

Cyclone separators illustrated in Figure 4.7 are commonly used to overcome many of the shortcomings of the baffle and dry pipe. For one drum, a single or double row of cyclone steam separators with scrubbers, runs the entire length

FIGURE 4.7

Double-row arrangement of cyclone-type primary steam separators, with scrubber elements at top of drum for secondary separation.

(Courtesy of The Babcock & Wilcox Co.)

of the drum with baffle plates located above each cyclone. A series of corrugated scrubber elements are placed at the entrance to the steam outlet and water from the scrubber elements drains to a point below the normal water level.

In Figure 4.7 operation occurs as follows:

1. steam and water from the risers enter the drum from behind the baffle plate to mix with the water (washed) before entering the cyclone; the cyclone is open at top and bottom;
2. water is thrown to the side of the cyclone by centrifugal force;
3. additional separation of water and steam occurs in the passage of steam through the baffle plates;
4. on entering the scrubber elements, water is also removed with steam passing to outlet header.

Separators of this type reduce the solids' carry-over to a very low value, depending on the type of feedwater treatment employed, the rate of evaporation, and water solids' concentration. The cyclone and scrubber elements may be removed for cleaning and inspection.

Superheaters

Steam heated above the temperature corresponding to its pressure is said to be "superheated." This steam contains more heat than saturated steam at the same pressure.

In a steam turbine, high superheat is of great importance. Friction losses and erosion of turbine blades are greatly lessened by the absence of moisture in steam. If dry saturated steam is used in a turbine, condensation occurs at an increasing rate as the steam passes through succeeding stages. Friction losses increase rapidly, since the condensate is inert material which acts to slow the speed of the turbine rotors. With superheated steam, condensation can be limited to only a few stages in the turbine discharge end. This reduces windage loss and friction between rotor and enveloping vapor because of lower density and the absence of moisture in the initial stages.

Pipelines carrying steam lose heat by radiation. If steam entering a line is dry saturated any loss in heat immediately will cause a portion of it to condense. The condensate is usually discharged from the line through traps and wasted. In addition to the heat loss due to radiation there also is loss of heat in the condensate. If the condensate is returned to the hotwell, a portion of the heat in the liquid is recovered. By adding a sufficient amount of superheat to the steam, it can be transported in the line without condensation loss.

Use of saturated steam in many processes results in variable moisture in the steam at the point of use. Savings in steam consumption, and, frequently, increased output can be obtained through the use of dry saturated steam. This may be achieved by superheating the steam sufficiently to overcome the condensation which occurs in the process-steam pipelines.

Installation of a superheater in a boiler reduces the amount of work that must be done by the evaporative surfaces to produce the same power. In essence, the installation of a superheater has the effect of increasing plant capacity. In addition, a properly designed superheater increases the thermal efficiency of the steam-generating unit. This increase in efficiency varies with the capacity and may average from 2 to 5 percent.

Superheating apparatus can usually be installed in existing boiler units with little or no change. Thus, it offers a relatively inexpensive means to gain significant advantages. The higher the superheat, the greater the economy. The highest practical degree of superheat should be used, consistent with plant conditions, to take full advantage of the superheater installation.

Design and location of a superheater to meet operating characteristics depend on a number of factors, any one of which may materially affect the installation's results. Design should then be left to those who are specialists in this equipment. Some of the important variables are:

1. temperature difference between the steam and the gas;
2. amount and velocity of steam through superheater;
3. design of furnace;
4. location of superheater in relation to boiler heating surface;
5. type and size of boiler;
6. capacity at which desired superheat is to be obtained;
7. baffle arrangement;
8. many intangibles that may influence specific application. The experience factor;
9. fuel;
10. type of fuel-burning equipment; and
11. amount and velocity of the gas.

TYPES OF SUPERHEATERS

A superheater is a system of tubes located in the path of the furnace gas. It receives saturated steam coming from the generating portion of the boiler. As the steam passes through the superheater, additional heat is added from the furnace gas so the steam temperature is raised and its volume increased.

Superheaters may be of the convection, radiant, or combination convection and radiant type.

Convection superheaters absorb heat chiefly by the flow of hot gas around the tubes. A strictly convection superheater has a rising steam temperature characteristic. Mass flow and the temperature of the gas entering the superheater zone as well as the steam flow from the boiler increase with an increase in the firing rate. These changes in temperature produce a greater mean temperature difference between the gas and steam. This, together with the higher gas mass flow, causes an increased rate of heat absorption, resulting in an increased steam temperature. A convection superheater not shielded from the furnace combines the effects of radiant and convection absorption resulting in a constant degree of superheat.

Radiant superheaters absorb heat by direct radiation from the furnace. They are usually located in one or more furnace walls. Since the furnace temperature, and the amount of available heat from radiation, does not rise as rapidly as the rate of steam flow, a radiant superheater has a falling characteristic. That is, the steam temperature drops as the steam flow rises. High mass flow of steam through the units is necessary to minimize tube failure. This can be done only at the expense of pressure drop. This type of superheater is generally used in combination with a convection superheater.

Combination Convection and Radiant Superheaters

Combination convection and radiant superheaters are sometimes used when uniform steam outlet temperatures are desired. This combines the rising steam temperature characteristics of the convection superheater with the falling steam-temperature characteristic of the radiant superheater. In a combination convection and radiant superheater the convection section lies between the first and second gas passage, and the radiant section is shown above the screen tubes in the furnace. Steam leaving the boiler drum first passes through the convection section and then to the radiant section and to the steam header. Even this arrangement may not produce the desired results in maintaining a constant steam temperature within the limits prescribed. In such cases, a bypass damper at the bottom of the second pass of the boiler is sometimes employed. A damper of this type can be operated to bypass the gas or portion of the gas around the convection section, thus controlling the final steam-outlet temperature for various boiler ratings.

At times the superheat temperature may exceed desired limits even though the bypass dampers are employed, so a desuperheater is used. This device adds water to the steam to reduce its temperature before the steam enters the turbine.

Final exit-steam temperature is influenced by such factors as gas flow, gas velocity, gas temperature, steam flow and velocity, ash accumulation on furnace walls and heat-exchange surfaces, method of firing, burner arrangement, and type of fuel fired.

As noted, in the convection superheater, steam temperature increases with the rating, whereas in the radiant superheater steam temperature decreases with the rating. For maximum economy a constant superheat and uniform steam temperature is desirable to avoid the problem of expansion and contraction in the steam header and turbine.

Overheating of superheater tubes is a matter for the designer, who may produce uniform steam flow and velocity of steam through the tubes. This is done in a number of ways: by spacing the takeoffs from the steam drum to the superheater, by installing baffles in the superheater header, by placing ferrules in the tubes at the steam entrance to the tubes, or by other means. Care must be taken to obtain uniform flow without an excessive pressure drop through the superheater. The superheater must also be designed to permit drainage when the unit is placed in or taken out of service.

Twin furnaces may be used in modern boilers, one containing the superheater and the other the reheater section. The superheater is usually a combination radiant and convection section; constant steam temperature is possible.

ECONOMIZERS AND AIR HEATERS

The greatest loss in the boiler heat balance is that due to heat in the flue gases. To operate a boiler unit at maximum efficiency it is necessary to minimize this loss. This can be done by installing economizers and air preheaters.

It is possible theoretically to reduce the flue-gas temperature to that of the incoming air. Economic limitations, however, prevent carrying the temperature reduction this far, since the fixed charges on the added investment to accomplish this are more than offset any savings obtained. If temperature reduction is carried below the dew point (the temperature at which condensation occurs), corrosion difficulties occur. Savings resulting from the installation of heat-recovery apparatus must be balanced against added investment and maintenance costs.

An economizer is a heat exchanger located in the gas passage between the boiler and the stack, designed to recover waste heat from the products of combustion. It consists of a series of tubes through which water flows on its way to the boiler. Economizers may be "parallel-flow" or "counterflow" types or a combination of the two. In parallel-flow economizers the gas and water flow in the same direction; in counterflow economizers, in opposite directions.

In parallel flow, the hottest gases come into contact with the coldest feedwater; for counterflow, the reverse is true. Counterflow units are considered more efficient, resulting in increased heat absorption. The gas side of the economizer is usually single-pass construction. Gas baffling is sometimes used to increase heat transfer. In operation, water enters at one end of the economizer and is directed through a system of return bends and headers until it enters the steam drum at a higher temperature. Economizers are referred to as "return tubular" because the water is made to pass back and forth through a series of return bends.

Economizers originally were constructed of cast-iron. Today steel is used. Access to the tubes is obtained through removal of forged-steel handhole covers, the tubes being rolled into the headers. Such economizers were used when the intention was to hold the pressure drop to a minimum and when feedwater conditions required internal inspection and cleaning.

Economizers using flanged joints instead of headers, are frequently constructed. Such units have the advantage of employing a minimum number of return-bend fittings, of the absence of handhole fittings and gaskets, and of freedom from expansion difficulties. A number of take-offs to the steam drum provides uniform water distribution to the drum without disturbing the water level.

A modern economizer consists of a continuous coil of tubes rolled into headers at each end. This has the advantage of eliminating gaskets and handholes. It also permits acid cleaning of tubes, not possible with previous designs.

Tubes range from 1 to 2 in. in diameter. Design usually provides a ratio of boiler to economizer heating surface of approximately 2:1. In many cases the economizer surface is made as large as that of the boiler heating surface. The size of the economizer used is influenced by factors such as cost, space availability, type of boiler units, nature of feedwater employed, and whether or not an air preheater is to be installed. When both an economizer and an air preheater are to be installed, exit-gas temperature should be prevented from dropping below the dew point.

In large central power stations, economizers and air preheaters both are installed for maximum efficiency. For the modern plant, typical efficiencies might be as follows: boiler efficiency, 74 percent; boiler and economizer, 82 percent; boiler, economizer, and air preheater, 88 percent.

An air preheater consists of plates or tubes having hot gases on one side and air on the other. The heat in the gas leaving the boiler or economizer is recovered by the incoming air. This reduces the temperature and increases the efficiency. There are two types of air preheaters, "tubulars" and "plate."

The tubular type consists of a series of tubes through which the combustion gases pass, with air passing around the outside of the tube. In the illustration shown in Figure 4.8 baffles are arranged to make the preheater a three-pass unit. Tubes are expanded into tube sheets at top and bottom. The entire assembly is enclosed in a steel casing. The plate-type air preheater rotates slowly, exposing a section of the plates alternately to the exit gases and to the entering air. The plates comprise the heating surface.

In the regenerative air preheater, the heating elements are stationary, with cold air hoods at top and bottom rotating across the heating surfaces. The air preheater is shown mounted vertically but can be arranged horizontally or angularly to accommodate station installation design. The heating elements are assembled in bundles for ease in installation or removal.

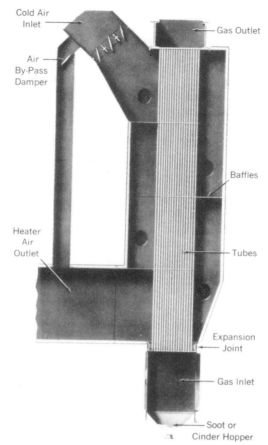

FIGURE 4.8
Tubular air preheater showing baffle arrangement.
(Courtesy of The Babcock & Wilcox Co.)

To increase the service life of the elements, consideration is given to the following problems and solutions:

1. excessive temperature at the hot end—by the use of scale-resistant steel;
2. corrosion at the cold end—by greater sheet thickness, low alloyed steel, enameled sheets, glazed ceramics, honeycomb blocks made of ceramics;
3. danger of clogging—by enlarged passage cross section; enameled sheets.

The unit is equipped with shifting soot blowers using superheated steam or compressed air. Washing and fire-extinguishing devices consist of a series of spray nozzles mounted both in the flue duct at the upper collar seal level and within the top air hood. Washing can be accomplished with the boiler remaining in operation and without reaching the gas side. Thermocouples, mounted at the cold end close to the heating surfaces and in the flue-gas and air ducts, serve to monitor temperatures falling below the acid dew point of the flue gases. They also give early warning of fire danger.

Air heaters are standard equipment in power plant design. They are justified by increased economy of operation. The degree of preheat depends on factors such as furnace and boiler design, type of fuel-burning equipment, and fuel cost. Preheated air accelerates combustion by producing more rapid ignition and facilitates the burning of low-grade fuels. In the process, it permits the use of low excess air, and increases efficiency. When coal is burned in pulverized form, preheated air assists in drying the coal, increasing mill capacity and accelerating combustion.

Care must be taken for stoker firing, depending on the type of stoker and fuel burned, not to operate with too high preheated-air temperatures. High temperature may damage the grates and difficulty may be experienced with matting of the fuel bed. The degree of preheating is determined by the kind of fuel, the type of fuel-burning equipment, and the burning rate or grate heat release. Preheated air at 300°F is usually considered the upper limit for stokers. For pulverized fuel, high-temperature preheated air is tempered when it enters and leaves the pulverizer.

In an air preheater, a low air-inlet, low exit-gas temperature or combination of the two may result in corrosion when fuels containing sulfur are burned, and the metal temperature falls below the dew point. Two dew points need to be considered: the water dew point, which occurs at approximately 120°F, and the gas dew point, which varies with the quantity of sulfur trioxide in the gas.

The acid dew point occurs at a higher temperature than the water dew point. The metal temperature is considered to be approximately the average of the air-gas temperature at any given point. Corrosion can be prevented by preheating the air before it enters the preheater, by bypassing a portion of the air around the preheater, and by using alloys or corrosion-resistant metals.

Added draft loss from use of an air preheater requires the installation of an induced-draft fan. The use of an air preheater increases the overall unit efficiency from 2 to 10 percent; the amount of increase depends on the unit location, the rating, and whether or not an economizer is also installed.

OPERATION AND MAINTENANCE OF EQUIPMENT

Operation and maintenance procedures to be followed in a boiler plant depend to a large extent upon the size of the plant, the type of combustion equipment, operating pressures, operating temperatures and other factors relating to the specific plant. There are, however, standard practices which the operator should follow to assure safe, continuous service and efficient operation.

Because it is so essential to production operations, maintenance of district heating production plants must be planned. The most important preventive maintenance practices include periodic shutdowns through inspection of all equipment and such replacement and repairs as may be necessary. The procedures require use of instrumentation and recordkeeping to identify conditions and repair needs.

It should be noted that the guidelines which follow are of a general nature only. Wherever possible, the manufacturer of the equipment involved should be contacted to obtain pertinent literature describing the maintenance procedures suggested.

Monitoring Normal Operations

A boiler in service producing hot water or steam is involved in a continuous process. Fuel, air, and water are supplied while hot water, steam and the waste products of ash and flue gases are discharged. It is the operating engineer's duty to keep these materials flowing in the correct proportions as required to maintain the steam pressure or the hot water supply temperature.

Reliable measurements of various temperatures and pressures in the process thus become a necessity for the safe and efficient operation of the production plant.

MEASURING TEMPERATURES

In general temperatures that need to be measured and monitored fall into three categories—metal temperatures, gas temperatures, and temperatures of steam and water.

Monitoring steam and water temperatures has been an important standard procedure for years. Quick start-ups and the matching of steam temperatures to allowable turbine temperatures increase the need for quality monitoring.

Measuring superheater and reheater tube temperatures to prevent exceeding safe metal temperatures is essential. Tube temperatures in various circuits of once-through boilers also must be monitored as a guide to operations. Current designs of drum-type boilers have relieved much of the concern over stresses in thick-walled drums, since experience indicates that a firing rate which is regulated to protect superheaters and reheaters also handles safe pressure-rise rates on the drum. In a drum-type unit, however, it is still advisable to check drum differential temperatures during rapid cooling. Air heater tube temperatures need monitoring to make sure that they remain above the dew point to insure against sulfur corrosion.

During pressure-raising periods gas temperatures in several areas should be monitored carefully. Temperatures of gas entering the superheater are checked as a protection for the superheater metal.

During pressure and temperature-raising periods of operation in gas-fired units equipped with regenerative air heaters, it is possible for the colder rotating, air-heater elements to condense moisture generated in the flue gas by the hydrogen in the fuel. As the air heater moves through the air stream the condensed moisture can be swept into the air and carried to the burners. This, in turn, can depress flame temperature below the ignition point, with consequent flame failure. For regenerative-type air heaters, gas temperature entering the heater should be measured to indicate when the air heater may be safely rotated and not cause loss of ignition. On gas-fired units, it has been found that gas temperature entering the air heater should be at least 400°F before rotating the air heater. Operating with an air-rich furnace atmosphere during start-up may make this precaution unnecessary.

Gas temperatures also are monitored leaving the regenerative air heater to prevent air heater corrosion.

MEASURING PRESSURES

Certain pressure and pressure differential measurements are absolutely mandatory for safe operation.

In both pressurized and suction-type units measurement of furnace pressure is required to assure that design pressures of the casing or containment are not exceeded. Some form of differential gas or air pressure measurement, in conjunction with time lapse, is required as an indication that the setting has been adequately purged prior to firing. This becomes a necessary operating guide to assure proper fuel-air relation at the burners.

Water and steam pressure on a drum-type boiler should be measured as an operating guide, once the safe pressure rise or pressure reduction rate has been established. Water pressure on a once-through boiler should be measured to make sure that a safe pressure exists prior to firing. Differential pressure on a once-through unit must be determined to establish adequate, safe minimum flow. Differential pressure when measured across various portions of the unit, serves as an index of internal cleanliness.

MAINTAINING EFFICIENCY

In maintaining efficiency, one of the best procedures is to analyze the major losses of efficiency. A pulverized-coal-fired utility boiler would show this typical heat balance:

Dry gas loss	5.16%
Loss due to hydrogen and moisture in the fuel	4.36%
Loss due to unburned combustible	0.50%
Loss due to radiation	0.30%
Loss due to moisture in air	0.13%
Manufacturers margin and unaccounted loss	1.50%
Overall efficiency	88.05%

Minor losses are usually lumped into one percentage figure and labeled "unaccounted for." There are a large number of these minor losses, but the total heat loss itself is small. The largest of these minor "unaccounted for" losses is the loss due to sensible heat in the ash or slag.

The boiler operator can adjust boiler operations to effect a significant amount of control over the losses listed as dry gas loss due to unburned combustible.

Variables in Efficiency Losses

Two primary variables are responsible for dry gas loss—stack temperature of the gas, and the weight of the gas leaving the unit. Stack temperature varies with the amount of deposit on the heat-absorbing surfaces throughout the unit, and varies with the amount of excess combustion air. The effect of excess air both increases the gas weight and also raises exit-gas temperature. Both effects increase dry gas loss and contribute to a reduced efficiency. An approximate one-percent reduction in efficiency occurs for about a 40°F increase in stack gas temperature in coal-fired installations.

Unburned combustible loss in coal-fired units includes the unburned components in the ash-pit refuse and in the flue dust. The constituents of this residue may include a diversity of compounds. In calculating the unburned loss, however, all constituents are normally treated as pure carbon.

Unburned combustible loss varies with the volatile matter and the ash content of the coal. However, these conditions are normally beyond the operator's control. Excess combustion air is the controllable variable affecting this loss. Increasing air normally results in reducing combustible in the refuse and increasing efficiency. No ready rule exists for figuring this loss, since coal volatility and ash content vary too widely. The curves of Figure 4.9 show the change in efficiency loss due to combustible in flue dust with changes in combustible content of the flue dust, percent ash in the coal, and percent of ash up the stack. This figure illustrates that the higher the combustible ash content of the coal and the greater the percentage of flue dust to the stack, the greater the efficiency loss.

Monitoring Efficiency

Regular and continuous monitoring of flue-gas temperatures and flue-gas

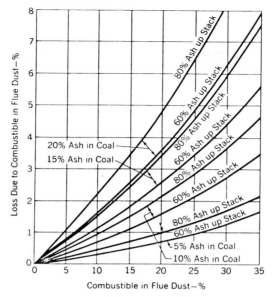

FIGURE 4.9

Variation of flue dust combustible losses for coals of different ash content and percent of ash up the stack

(Courtesy of The Babcock & Wilcox Co.)

oxygen content by periodic checks on combustibles in the refuse and by a regularly calibrated recorder or indicator will indicate if original efficiencies are being maintained. If conditions have varied from the established performance base, necessary corrective adjustments or maintenance steps must be taken:

1. High combustible in the refuse is an indication of a need for adjustments or maintenance of fuel-preparation and burning equipment.
2. High excess air normally increases exit-gas temperatures and draft losses and usually requires an adjustment to the fuel-air ratio. However, the high excess air may be caused by excessive casing leaks, cooling air, sealing air, or air heater leaks.
3. High exit-gas temperatures and high draft losses with normal excess air show dirty heat-absorbing surfaces and indicate the need for sootblowing.

Maintaining Water Level

Maintaining a proper water supply is a most important consideration in boiler-plant operation. The operator must be familiar with every detail of the water supply system. The operator must know where the supply is obtained, and what the possibilities are for possible failure. He must also know what type of pumps are employed, how the pumps are driven, what type of feedwater regulator is used, where the bypass valves are located, and if there is an auxiliary feedwater-piping system.

The operating engineer must supply hot water to the boilers, as required, to replace that which is being evaporated. The boilers usually are equipped with regulators which control the flow to maintain the right level. Automatic devices which relieve the operator of making repetitive adjustments do not, however, relieve him of the responsibility of maintaining the water level. Frequent checks must be made of the water level in the heaters, in the softeners or other sources of supply, of the temperature of the water, of the boiler feed pump performance, of feedwater-pump pressure, and of the level in the boiler-gauge glass.

Water columns improperly set or leaking, foaming, or stopped-up connections will cause water columns to show false levels. The water column should be blown down at least once each 8-hr shift and the high- and low-water alarm checked. The feedwater regulator should be blown down and checked as indicated in the manufacturer's instructions. While recorders and other devices are convenient, they must be checked frequently with the water level in the gauge glass.

Since it is desirable to use hot feedwater, the temperature should be maintained as high as feasible with the equipment available. The water flow rate to the boiler should be as nearly uniform as the steam requirements will permit.

Maintaining the water level can be difficult because the boiler is filled with a mixture of water and steam bubbles during operations. When the water level in the drum drops, the normal reaction is to add water. This happens both with hand and automatic controls. Water added at a temperature lower than the water in the boiler causes the steam in the bubbles to condense. This action, in turn, decreases the volume of the steam and water mixture in the boiler and results in a further drop in level. The normal reaction is to add even more water. When the normal ratio of water to steam bubbles is restored, however, the level in the drum will be too high. The result of these actions is a cycle in which the water level in the drum is alternately high and low. To avoid this condition the water flow to the boiler is regulated in proportion to the steam discharge. A three-element feedwater controller accomplishes this by sensing the drum level, feedwater flow, and steam flow and regulating the feedwater supply accordingly.

OUTAGE MAINTENANCE

Outages for preventive maintenance must be scheduled as required to prevent equipment failures. For the district heating plant, schedule must take into account system load variations. Generally it is preferable not to shut down large boilers during the peak load seasons. The ability of a boiler unit to remain in operation until a scheduled outage time continually must be monitored by instruments and visual observations.

Internal Cleanliness and Inspection

To assure safe, dependable operation one of the best preventive measures that can be taken is maintaining boiler water conditions that insure against any internal tube deposits which could cause overheating and tube failures. The chordal-type thermocouple can be used to measure the extent of internal deposits and to indicate the time when chemical cleaning is needed. Measurement of the waterside pressure drop across a once-through boiler is also a way to establish when internal chemical cleaning may be required. In addition, with some types of water-treatment programs the inability to maintain normal boiler water conditions can indicate a possible tube leak.

Checking the boiler during regularly scheduled out-of-service periods where in-service measurements are not taken, or when they do not indicate a need for cleaning, is recommended to doubly insure continued operating availability. Low pressure, drum-type boilers allow for careful visual inspection to establish the need for internal cleaning. Inspection and determination of the size and type of deposit by turbining and weighing it will establish just exactly what has to be removed and what will remove it.

Today's modern, high pressure generating units, with complex circuitry and all-welded construction makes visual examination difficult and often inconclusive. It is usually better and easier to remove one or more representative tube sections from the high heat input zone of the unit for examination and measurement of internal deposits. The weight of the deposit per unit of internal area (expressed in grams-per-square-foot) is compared with empirically confirmed weight limits. The physical and chemical nature of the deposit is investigated and the need for internal cleaning decided.

Steam-drum internal inspection should be an important part of any out-of-service inspection. This is particularly so if operating checks of steam leaving the drum indicated excessive solids in the steam. All baffling and steam-separating equipment should be in its proper place, and all joints designed to prevent leakage should be tight. If the drum is inspected shortly after the boiler is drained, and before any internal cleaning is begun, it is usually possible to observe evidence of carry-over-producing leaks. In removing baffles, plates or steam separators for inspection, parts should be match-marked to assure proper fit upon reassembly.

There are two commonly used methods for removing scale from the boiler's heating surface. The mechanical method consists of passing a power-driven cutter or a knocker through the tubes. The chemical method employs materials that will partly or totally dissolve the scale, and in this way removes it from the surfaces.

Mechanical

Mechanical cleaners are made of small motors driven by steam, air, or water. A hose must be small enough to pass through the tubes that it is to clean. A hose attached to one end of the motor supplies the steam, air, or water as well as providing a means by which the operator "feeds" the unit through the tube and withdraws it when the cleaning is complete.

Chemical

Chemical cleaning of internal heating surfaces was introduced in cases where it was difficult or impossible to clean by other methods. The process now is widely used, and is considered the quickest, cheapest, and most efficient method for cleaning internal surfaces in boilers of all sizes. It is important, however, to use a procedure of known reliability and to keep it under careful control.

The procedures outlined are offered with the understanding that site conditions vary widely. The user must depend on competent chemical supervision of his own choice, and have access to consultants as to the particular boiler-water and scale problems. There are companies which are specially equipped to provide a complete chemical-cleaning service.

Four steps generally are required in a complete chemical-cleaning process for a boiler:

1. The internal heating surfaces are washed with an acid solvent containing an appropriate inhibitor to dissolve deposits completely or partially and to disintegrate them.
2. Clean water is used to flush out loose deposits, any solvent adhering to the surface, and soluble iron salts. Any corrosive gases that may have formed in the unit are removed.

3. The unit is treated to neutralize and "passivate" the heating surfaces. The passivation treatment produces a passive surface or forms a very thin protective film on ferrous surfaces so that formation of "after rust" on freshly cleaned surfaces is prevented.
4. The unit is flushed with clean water as a final rinse to remove any remaining deposits.

External Cleanliness

External cleanliness is important to efficient operation. Measuring boiler and air heater gas temperatures and gas-side pressure drops during the operating period of the unit will show if external fouling, not removable by normal sootblower operation, is occurring and will give some idea of the location of the accumulation. During down periods, the entire unit should be thoroughly inspected with the following ideas in mind:

1. Discovering any signs of erosion or corrosion. A complete inspection of heat-absorbing surfaces should always be a part of annual outages, and this inspection should be especially rigorous if any unusual operating conditions have preceded the outage.
2. Discovering the condition of fuel-preparation and burning equipment, especially if sampling of ash has indicated the presence of increasing amounts of unburned combustible material. Air-flow regulating or adjusting equipment such as dampers, or burner-register doors, should be free from warpage or overheating, and operate freely over its control range. Fuel distribution equipment, such as burner impellers or burner-line distributors should be examined for signs of erosion or for signs of burning or overheating. Coal conditioners, pulverizers, and feeders should be inspected.
3. Detecting any signs of tube overheating, especially if thermocouples have indicated this possibility. Furnace wall tubes should be checked for swelling, blistering, or warping.
4. Finding tube misalignment occurring from warpage or from detachment of support hangers, brackets or spacers.
5. Determining the condition of any refractory exposed to flue gases, such as burner throats or walls, and areas in convection passes (especially if operating conditions have been usually severe such as when operating intermittently or with a known reducing atmosphere).
6. Locating any deposits of ash or slag, not removed by sootblowing, which could interfere with heat transfer or free gas flow through the unit.

When ash deposits contain a great deal of sulfur they should be removed before any extended outage. These deposits can absorb ambient moisture and form sulfuric acid which will corrode pressure parts. Many ash deposits resulting from the burning of severely fouling solid and liquid fuels are removable by water washing.

Units can be designed for water washing with ample drainage of wash water and sluiced ash. An out-of-service period is required for all pressure parts. Air heaters can be sectionalized so that areas may be isolated and washed without total shutdown of the unit.

Washing facilities should be supplied with a means for providing varying degrees of alkalinity with hot water for water washing the air heater. This avoids acid corrosion from varying quantities of sulfur, as the drain from the air heater should be maintained at a neutral condition. Hot alkaline water in the presence of sulfur deposits precipitates out iron salts, and this is especially necessary with sulfur-bearing fuels.

The normal sootblower system is successfully used in many plants by connecting the supply of wash water to the sootblower steamheader system. Drain facilities should be open and ready for wash water discharge to catch-basins. Wall areas or tubes, in a widely-spaced arrangement, allow cleaning by a protracted soaking with the wash water. Areas where surfaces are closely spaced, such as in regenerative air heaters, can be cleaned by high-pressure water jets. Inspection will indicate which areas require particular attention. The wash water effluent should be checked periodically during washing to assure that an alkaline pH is maintained.

Out-of-service washing should be scheduled so that surfaces can be dried immediately after cleaning. A good approach is to water wash just before returning a unit to service. A unit that must remain out of service after washing should be dried at a low firing rate to prevent corrosion.

During a maintenance outage, corrective steps should be taken to prevent recurrence of problems revealed by inspection or by information obtained from monitoring instruments. Some of these might be:

1. Readjustment of sootblowing to prevent external erosion caused by channeling of gases between convection surfaces and walls.
2. Recalibration of all instruments to assure their functional reliability.
3. Adding gas baffling to prevent external erosion caused by channeling of gases between convection surfaces and walls.
4. Resealing of the boiler setting on suction-fired units to reduce air infiltration evidenced by an increase in unburned combustible in the ash.
5. Rechecking start-up procedures, since overheating of superheater tubes may have occurred from too rapid start-up or from carry-over of solids in steam.

Placing Boilers In Operation

Several factors must be taken into consideration before placing a boiler in service. These depend upon whether it is new, whether it has been out of service a long time for repairs, or whether it has been "down" for only a few days.

Hydrostatic tests must be made on new boilers and on those which have had extensive replacements of pressure parts before they can be placed in service. Such tests consist of completely filling the boiler with water and of developing a pressure 1½ times the working pressure. The water temperature must be at least as warm as the temperature of the air in the boiler room and never less than 70°F. The test pressure of 1½ times the working pressure must not be exceeded by more than 6 percent. A 150-psi-pressure boiler is hydrostatically tested at $150 \times 1.5 = 225$ psi, and the test pressure must not be allowed to exceed $225 \times 1.06 = 238.5$ psi.

Boilers which are new or which have accumulated a deposit of oil or grease must be cleaned by boiling them out with an alkaline detergent solution. Such an alkaline cleaning must include the boiler, waterwalls, economizer, and superheater; however, the cleaning solution must not enter nondrainable-type superheaters. Caustic solutions will injure the gauge glass, so a temporary glass must be provided for use during each cleaning. A typical cleaning solution contains 2 lb each of soda ash, trisodium phosphate, and caustic soda for each 1,000 lb or water contained in the unit to be cleaned.

When the boiler unit is placed back into normal operation, the manhole and handhole covers must have been replaced and the pressure section of the boiler made ready for operation, the interior of the gas passages should be inspected to see that all scaffolding, ladders, and tools have been removed, and fan and damper operations should be checked.

After taking these precautionary measures, the various valves should be checked and arranged for start-up in the following manner: the blowoff, the water-column gauge-glass drain, the gauge cock, and the feedwater valves must be closed; the drum vent and the cock to the steam gauge must be opened. When valves are used on the lines from the boiler drum to the water column, they must be open and locked or sealed. The drains should then be opened, except in cases in which superheaters are filled with water during the starting-up period.

The boiler is then filled with water, using the auxiliary feed connections. The drum should not be filled to the normal operating level since the water will expand when heat is applied and will cause the level to rise.

The fire in the furnace may now be started and the steam allowed to blow from the steam drum for a few minutes before the vent valve is closed. Closing all superheater drains except the outlet allows a small quantity of steam to circulate through the superheater tubes and prevent excessive temperatures.

The rate of combustion should be regulated to allow 45 min. for small and medium-sized 150-psi boilers to reach line pressure. For large high-pressure boilers, allow from 45 min. to 2½ hr., depending upon the size and superheater arrangement. When pulverized coal or oil is burned, it may not be possible to regulate the combustion rate low enough to provide the necessary safe time for bringing the boiler up to pressure. Under these conditions, the burner should be allowed to operate for a few minutes and then taken off to allow the heat to distribute through the unit, thus preventing excessive temperature differentials and the resulting unequal expansion.

In installations with nondraining superheaters, it is necessary to carefully control the warm-up rate, since all water must be evaporated from the super-heater tubes before the boiler is placed on the line. Water remaining in the superheater would restrict the flow of steam and cause the tubes to overheat. With drainable superheaters, the drains should be opened for a short blow before the boiler is "put on the line."

All water must be drained carefully from the boiler steam-line header and it must be filled with steam before the valve is opened and the flow established. This may be done by opening the drain and back-feeding steam from the main through the bypass around the main-header valve. When the pressure in the boiler header gets close to that in the main header, the main-header valve and throttle are opened but the drain is not closed. Before the boiler is put on line, the superheater drains are opened for a short blow to make sure all water has been removed. Check the water level, and if it is not enough below standard (2 to 6 in.) to compensate for expansion when the boiler starts to steam, the blowdown should be opened and the excess water removed. When the boiler-drum pressure is from 10 to 25 lb below the header pressure, the stem of the nonreturn valve should be unscrewed so that it can open when the boiler pressure exceeds the steam-line pressure. If there is no nonreturn valve, pressure in the boiler should be approximately equal to the mainheader pressure before opening the valve at the boiler outlet. If waterhammer or vibration occur while the valve is being opened, the valve must be closed at once to allow the pressure on the boiler to drop, so the entire operation can be repeated. When a boiler is not connected to a common header, it is a good procedure to open all drains and raise the steam pressure on the entire system at the same time.

Before a boiler is put in service for the first time, each of the safety valves must be checked for the correct setting by allowing the boiler outlet valve to remain closed and raising the boiler pressure until each valve opens. The opening and closing pressure of each valve must be recorded and the valve adjusted until specified results have been reached. Some plants open the safety valves by hand each time the boiler is put in service. Cables attached to the valve handle and extending to the operating floor aid in this operation. The safety valve should not be opened until enough steam pressure is available to prevent dirt from sticking under the seat.

The drain may be closed when the boiler is in service and the fuel feed regulated to maintain a low rate of steam flow. The draft gauges should be checked and the fans and dampers adjusted to establish the required flow of air to, and gases from, the boiler unit. The water level and feedwater-supply pressure should be checked, then the feedwater regulator put into operation.

Maintaining Boiler Auxiliaries

Good maintenance of boiler auxiliaries is necessary to keep the boiler itself operating efficiently. Auxiliaries that require regular maintenance include valves, piping, pumps, fans, motors, preheaters, and electric circuits and control devices.

VALVES AND PIPING

Valves control the flow of fluids through a steam generating system. All valves have two basic features regardless of type: a passage for fluid flow, and a movable part that opens and closes the passage.

Valves are checked regularly by opening and closing them through their complete cycle. The most common problem with valves is fluid leakage through the packing around the valve stem. The valve must seat properly, move freely, and not leak. Shutoff valves close only when trouble occurs in the system. These valves isolate equipment and shut off fluid flow to prevent damage to workers and equipment. Shutoff valves may deteriorate if not operated regularly and should be tested whenever equipment is down.

A good practice when testing most valves is to open the valve wide and then turn the handle down a half-turn to prevent binding. This practice should not be followed when testing backseating valves, however. Backseating valves are found in high-pressure piping and must remain wide open.

All moving parts of a valve must receive proper lubrication to help prevent wear from friction (galling), and to keep metal surfaces from binding and sticking together. Packing must be replaced when leakage occurs or when friction develops.

Corrosion is the most serious maintenance problem with piping. Internal corrosion results when makeup water containing dissolved oxygen flows through piping, and when air leaks into the system. Proper deaeration and rapid leak repair keep internal corrosion at a minimum. Leakage around valves, joints, and steam traps must be considered and monitored.

External corrosion occurs when moisture collects on the outer surface of the piping system. It proceeds rapidly if the surrounding air contains sulfur oxides. External corrosion can be prevented by wrapping a waterproof covering around the piping or by using protective coatings such as paint.

Piping must be checked regularly for leaks caused by corrosion. Faulty piping sections should be replaced at once. If equipment cannot be shut down for repairs, the damaged section can be strapped or clamped with a suitable material. Permanent repairs can be made as soon as the piping is out of service.

PUMPS

Maintenance procedures for pumps vary with pump design, but some general maintenance practices apply to all pumps. Pumps require regular lubrication to keep bearings from overheating, rusting, or corroding. The manufacturer's manual gives the recommended type of lubricating oil or grease. Too much or too little lubricant can damage the bearings and cause them to fail, so the proper amount is important. Lubricant should be drained and bearings flushed regularly to keep them free from dirt and other impurities.

FANS

Fans as components of a boiler unit require frequent inspection to detect and correct irregularities that might cause trouble. The period of continuous fan operation usually is long compared with other power plant equipment. This continuity of operation can be assured by proper lubrication and cooling of fan shafts, couplings and bearings.

Fan couplings and bearings must be aligned carefully with the driving equipment, making due allowances for the vertical movement of the fan rotor caused by temperature rise of the bearing supports going from cold to running conditions.

A fan requires proper static and dynamic balance to assure smooth and lasting service. This balance should be checked after each maintenance shutdown by running the fan at full speed, without air flow then with full air flow. Special instruments may be needed especially with larger fans, to set the amount and location of weight to be added for static balance.

Fans handling gases with entrained abrasive dust particles are subject to blade erosion and erosion of the housing near the discharge. Abrasive-resistant materials and liners can reduce such wear.

ELECTRIC MOTORS

Common maintenance problems of electric motors are improper lubrication and dust. Dust acts as an insulator on windings, brushes, and other motor parts. It traps heat and interferes with proper cooling. Heat can build up and lead to unsafe temperatures and cause serious motor damage.

Improper lubrication can cause bearing wear. The manufacturer's manual gives the proper type of lubricant, and the correct amount.

PREHEATERS

The two major maintenance problems of air preheaters are fouling, and metal corrosion of surfaces exposed to flue gases. Fouling results when soot and fly ash form deposits. A flue gas temperature increase or abnormal reading on the draft gage usually indicates that the preheater needs cleaning.

Preheater surfaces can be cleaned with air or steam sootblowing, or by washing the preheater with warm water. When washing a preheater, however, the water may react with ash deposits and form an acid solution which must be neutralized by rinsing the preheater with an alkaline solution.

Corrosion results when the preheater metal temperature falls below the dewpoint of the flue gases. Flue gas moisture condenses, and reacts with sulfur oxides to form acids. Corrosion also occurs when ash deposits absorb moisture. It is a special problem in rotary preheaters since the acid deteriorates the thin metal elements.

Maintenance of Superheaters

Internal deposits and faulty operating methods are the two primary causes of superheater-tube failures. Inadequate steam flow during start-up, shut-down, and banking may subject superheater elements to excessive gas temperatures without the sufficient cooling effect of the steam. Careful control of furnace conditions is essential at these periods to prevent overheating the elements. The superheater tubes are subjected to the heat of the gases during starting, but no steam will pass through them until the boiler water has reached steaming temperature. When the boiler develops a slight pressure, the drum vent valves are closed, and all vented steam is passed through the superheater. The vent valve or drain on the superheater outlet leader must be totally open until the unit is placed on the line. Variations in the opening of this valve should be made according to instructions of the boiler manufacturer. The firing-up period must provide enough time to permit evaporation of condensate trapped in the tubes, especially in the pendant type of superheater.

The superheater safety valve is always set at a lower pressure than the boiler-drum safety valves to protect the superheater during possible sudden load loss. This allows steam flow through the superheater for cooling.

The superheater outlet-header vent valve is opened wide as soon as the boiler stops delivering steam during unit shut-down. The drain valve remains open until the boiler is placed on the line again.

Proper control of furnace conditions during banking periods is important in protecting tubes. At such times, the superheater outlet vent valve must be opened to provide steam flow until the furnace gas temperatures are reduced to a safe level for the protection of the superheater. Most superheater tube warping and failure result from not following the appropriate precautions during starting-up, shut-down, and banking periods.

Internal deposits from water carryover cause the greatest number of tube failures. Solids in the water dry out and tend to build up deposit of concentrated material which insulates tube metal from the cooling effect of the steam. Even a thin deposit can cause overeheating and tube failure.

Feedwater conditioning to prevent foaming and priming is the appropriate corrective measure. Concentration of solids in the boiler must be kept at a level low enough to prevent carryover. Steam separators and baffles in the boiler drums must be checked for leakage and steam tightness. This is especially important after a unit has been overhauled and where parts of these elements have been removed to gain access to boiler tubes. Spray from leaks in the baffles or steam separator contaminates the steam going to the superheater, and the solids separate out in the superheater tubes.

Keeping the outside of superheater tubes and supports clean helps to control maintenance costs. Slag and ash deposit build-up causes lancing of gases and localized overheating, which in turn, imposes extra weight on supporting elements. Slag or ash build-up between superheater supports and boiler tubes insulates the hangers from the cooling effect of the steam and water in the tubes, and may cause burning of hangers.

A checklist should be developed for use during boiler unit outages of short duration and during overhaul. This list should include a check of all the elements relating to alignment, warning, and bulging. The condition of hangers, spacers, link supports, and lugs should be checked, as should superheater tube connections at the inlet and outlet headers where steam leakage might occur. Failure to repair such leaks promptly can result in steam cutting of the tube seats. Pressure drop through the superheater should be monitored as an indication of the internal cleanliness of the unit. Check the alignment, location, and operation of the soot blower nozzles with relation to the superheater elements.

Welding is the best and quickest way to repair a burned-out tube. However, it must be done by a certified welder under the direction of an authorized inspector.

Maintenance of Economizers

An economizer usually is one of the first heat-recovery units added to the steaming unit in boiler installations. By design, it provides lower-cost heating surface than that in the boiler. It absorbs heat from the flue gases before they pass to the stack or air preheater. The economizer heats the feedwater before it is passed to the boiler.

Operating pressures, feedwater conditions, and station design all affect design of the economizer system. Boiler pressures not in excess of 250 psi permit use of cast-iron tubes and headers. Undeaerated water and limitations in chemical treatment indicate use of cast-iron for its resistance to corrosion, and restrict design to straight tubes for mechanical cleaning. Low feedwater temperatures stemming from lack of steam-turbine stage-heating facilities impose an internal as well as an external corrosion problem best solved through use of cast iron.

Higher steam pressure, and the higher temperatures brought with it, indicate the use of steel and economizer designs with more economical tube size and spacing as well as improved tube forms and arrangements. These are made possible through deaeration proper treatment of feedwater, and preheating of the water going to the deaerator up to temperatures above the dew-point temperatures of the flue gases.

Internal corrosion will result from oxygen in aerated water. Oxygen in the water is driven off as the water temperature rises in the economizer and attacks the internal surfaces of the tubes. Deaerating heaters of proper design and capacity will give practically complete elimination of oxygen and reduce carbon dioxide in the feedwater.

Treatment of economizer feedwater is essential in eliminating scale formation and preventing corrosion. Undissolved solids in the feedwater build up in the economizer tubes. This, in turn, reduces heat transfer and restricts flow through the unit. The pH of the feedwater should be maintained at a value of 8 or more to reduce the corrosive effect on steel tubes.

Pressure drop across the economizer is a good indicator of the tubes internal condition. The straight-tube economizer lends itself to mechanical cleaning. However, chemical cleaning can be used in this type of unit, and must be used for adequate cleaning of the continuous-tube type and most modern designs.

External cleanliness of the economizer affects its efficiency appreciably. Modern designs provide tube spacing and arrangements to permit effective use of soot blowers for this reason. Temperatures of the gases before and after the economizer can indicate the condition of the unit. The elements must be adjusted carefully and checked at each boiler outage to maintain the correct position of the nozzles and avoid steam-jet encroachment on the tubes.

Water vapor in the flue gases condensing on the tubes can cause external corrosion. Sulfur in the gases combines with the condensate and sets up active corrosion of the tubes. The percentage of sulfur products in the flue gases, the type of fuel, and method of firing, all influence the extent of such corrosion. The most effective correction for this source of corrosion is by maintaining a feedwater temperature above 212 F in such cases.

Maintenance of Air Heaters

The type of air preheaters commonly used in power plants are tubular, plate, or regenerative types. In a tubular heater the gas travels in a single pass inside the tubes while the air passes outside the tubes in single or multiple passes. The plate type is arranged for counterflow of gas and air through narrow alternating lanes. The heating surface in the regenerative air preheater is made up of many specially formed steel sheets called heating elements. These elements absorb heat from the flue gas flowing through one-half of the preheater structure and release it to the incoming cold air passing through the other half of the structure in counter-flow. The heating elements are arranged in a cellular rotor which revolves slowly within the preheater. The rotor moves alternately through the air and gas streams providing continuous heat transfer.

The most important factors in maintenance of all types of air heaters are cleanliness of surfaces exposed to flue gases and control of corrosion on these surfaces. Fuel characteristics and the type of firing, have significant effects on the ash accumulations on the gas-swept surfaces. Ash from stoker-fired installations seems to cause more problems than ash from pulverized-coal furnaces.

With some coals the ash deposits as a hard, cement-like accumulations. In others the ash is soft and tends to pack. Coals which develop a more abrasive ash tend to keep tubes or plates clean and highly polished without excessive wear of these surfaces. The short and straight-through passages of the regenerative heater help reduce formation of ash deposits. An increase in draft loss and exit-gas temperatures are indications of excessive fouling of these surfaces.

Cleaning mediums and methods vary according to the individual installation. Steam and air most generally are used in coal-fired units. Washing is used most often with oil-burning installations, however, washing with warm water has been used successfully in all cases.

Air heater corrosion is likely to occur where cold entering air reduces the metal temperature below the gas temperature dew point. Water vapor in the gases condenses at these points where acid can be formed in the presence of sulfur dioxide and sulfur trioxide in the gas. This condition results in a cumulative corrosion deterioration of tubes and plate sections. The corrosive effect on crimped sheets and rotor seals in the discharge end of the regenerative heater may be a major maintenance expense in this type of unit. The design of such units provides for their regular replacement when necessary.

Rotor seals which limit the loss of the air to the flue gas are subject to the same corrosive conditions as the cold-end heating surface. They should be inspected and replaced, if necessary, at least once a year to insure minimum leakage.

Maintenance of Forced- and Induced-Draft Equipment

Forced- and induced-draft fans usually are designed for rugged use. The service of each, especially the forced-draft fan, is reasonably simple; however, it is important during the long periods of operation. Forced-draft fans have experience records of many years without major repairs. Induced-draft fans which are protected by dust collectors have similar favorable records. Without such protection, however, induced-draft fans on pulverized-coal installations usually require blade replacement every 6 to 12 months.

Maintenance of Stacks

All stack connections should be airtight and protected against leakage by tight dampers when not in use. Cold air leakage to the stack lowers the stack temperature and available draft, and also increases the quantity of gas the stack must handle. In some cases factory wastes are discharged through a boiler stack for high atmosphere dispersion. This procedure requires careful consideration because of possible air pollution and increased costs for stack maintenance.

A stack is subject to the erosive action of ash in the flue gases, to acid corrosion by sulfur products, and to deterioration from continuous exposure to the weather.

Erosion or wastage of stack material normally occurs at the stack entrance or throats and necked-down sections, where the direction or the velocity of the gas changes. These sections may need replacement after long operations. Reduction in stack maintenance justifies use of abrasive-resistant materials and coatings.

Low exist gas temperature from a boiler unit is desirable for efficiency. Too low a temperature, however, may result in the sulfuric acid condensation. This acid corrodes steel or steel-lined stacks. The limit to which flue gases can be cooled without condensation depends upon the sulfur trioxide and moisture content of the flue gas.

Acid corrosion can destroy steel stacks in as little as a few months. Corrosion resistant metals, refractory coatings, and high temperature acid resistant paints all help prolong stack life. Refractory stacks may deteriorate from exposure to the chemicals and water vapor in the gases. Long exposure in wet weather (during out-of-service periods) and insufficient drying on start-up can contribute to increased maintenance costs.

Maintenance of Cyclone Separators

A cyclone separator is an air pollution control device installed in the flue gas stream to trap ash and dust particles. As dirty air travels through the cyclone in a swirling pattern, dust and ash fall into a hopper. Cyclone separators have no moving parts but are susceptible to clogging and wear. Dirt can clog inlet and outlet openings, and erode the inner surface of the cyclone.

When a cyclone separator is shut down for cleaning, dirt and ash buildups must be removed and the unit checked for wear.

Maintaining Compressed Air Systems

Good maintenance of compressed air systems is necessary to keep compressors operating properly. Intake filters must be checked regularly and cleaned or replaced when necessary. Water jackets and intercoolers must be inspected for plugging, especially if the cooling water is dirty. Regular lubrication is necessary in most air compressors to protect the compressor cylinder from heat and water. If the compressor has a lubricating system, the oil level in the crankcase should be checked daily.

Equipment Repairs

Equipment repairs must meet stringent requirements. This should not be surprising in light of the rigid requirements for design, fabrication and field erection of steam generating equipment. Experienced supervision, skilled man-power and adequate tooling are all necessary for the effective repair work. In some situations the assistance of the manufacturer may be required. This is particularly true when engineering design, metallurgy, welding technology and special tool development are involved. The manufacturer's construction capabilities often can reduce the downtime required to complete maintenance and repairs.

Performance records and inspection reveal the nature and amount of repair and adjustment to equipment necessary to return the unit to dependable operation. The equipment manufacturer can recommend, guide, or carry out the work, but the final decision on what will be an acceptable, dependable repair rests with the operating company and with insurance or state inspectors.

TUBES

If a boiler tube fails it is better to replace it rather than to weld it or attempt other repairs. There are two ways to remove tubes.

One is to burn off the faulty tubes 1 in. or more inside the sheet or drum; the other is to pull the entire tube length through the tube hole. The tube, type of boiler, and tube arrangement indicate the method that should be used. It is usually best to burn out the old tube, if possible. All bent tubes must be burned out, since they will not go through the tube holes. It is sometimes necessary to remove several good tubes in order to reach the faulty ones. In a straight-tube boiler, the tubes in the outside of the pass may be burned off at the end, but those in the inner rows must be pulled through the tube holes, as they cannot be reached without removing the outer tubes.

DRUMS

At times, corrosion, caustic embrittlement, and overheating makes it necessary to repair or replace boiler drums, shells, and water legs. These repairs and replacements should always be made by qualified boiler mechanics. Bags on the shells may be repaired by heating and driving back into place, provided the metal is not too badly damaged by overheating. This is determined by the boiler inspector. If the metal has lost its tensile strength or the bag extends over a large area, a patch must be applied. If a blister develops, defective metal must be cut away to determine the extent of the damage. If the plate has been weakened, it will be necessary to apply a patch. Patches must be applied from the inside of the drum or shell so the pressure will help hold them in place and prevent the formation of a pocket for the accumulation of scale and sludge. There are three methods of attaching patches to boiler drums and shells: bolting (referred to as a "soft patch"), riveting (known as a "hard patch"); and welding.

All caulking of joints, patches, and rivets must be done from inside the boiler whenever feasible as a precaution against caustic embrittlement. If continued difficulty is encountered with leakage at a joint or around the rivets, the boiler should be inspected. A rivet should be removed and the metal tested in a laboratory to determine its tensile strength and other physical properties. If a crack is found in a longitudinal joint of a boiler, the boiler should be removed from service. This location is difficult to patch satisfactorily because of the stress to which it is subjected. In many states a boiler in this condition must be permanently removed from service.

Failure can occur in the plate and stay bolts of water legs in both fire- and water-tube boilers. The plate cannot be repaired by riveting because only one side is accessible. Field welding is permitted if enough stay bolts are included in the patch to hold the pressure without considering the strength of the weld. Burned metal must be removed and the patch fitted in place and welded according to established standards.

BAFFLES

Some boiler types require baffles to direct the gases for maximum heat transfer to the tubes effectively. Boiler baffles are made from refractory, alloy, or standard steel depending upon the temperature of gases to which they are to be exposed. Refractory baffles are used near the furnace when high temperatures are encountered, and are constructed in special refractory shapes which are made to fit the exact location. Some baffles lie on a row of tubes, while others run at an angle across the tubes. To make repairs it is necessary to secure the refractory shapes for the specific application. Skill and patience are required to insert these tile shapes in baffles which are at an angle with the tubes.

FURNACE WALLS

Some boilers and furnaces require refractory walls, which account for an appreciable portion of boiler maintenance. It is, therefore, important to reduce this expenditure as much as possible.

Solid refractory walls are lined with first-quality firebrick. This lining often can be patched or replaced without rebuilding the entire wall if the repairs are made before the outer section has become too badly damaged. The lining must be "keyed" to the outer wall, and expansion joints provided.

Air-cooled refractory walls are built to provide an air space between the outer wall and the refractory lining, which may be a separate wall constructed of first-quality firebrick, moldable refractory material, or tile supported by cast-iron hangers. Air circulation through the space between the two walls carries away some of the heat, and results in a reduction in wall temperature and a possible decrease in maintenance. The lining must be adequately tied to the outer wall to prevent expansion and contraction causing bulge and making it fall into the furnace. Cast-iron hangers provide support for the tile lining. The initial cost of these walls is high, however, and many tile forms must be stocked for replacements. Once the lining has failed, the cast-iron hangers are quickly destroyed by the heat of the furnace.

Consideration must be given to the quality of the refractory material. Operating temperatures, ash characteristics, slagging, and flame impingement all must be considered when selecting refractory lining for furnaces. If the fusion temperature of lining is not high enough for the operating temperatures, the inner surface will become soft and in extreme cases melt and flow. This results in rapid deterioration. Ash fusion on the wall surfaces causes the inner face to spall. The removal of clinkers, whether the unit is operating or out of service for maintenance, will almost always crack off some of the furnace lining. Flame impingement results in a high localized temperature and eventual lining failure.

Repairs and replacements to boiler equipment must be done often enough to prevent small jobs from developing into major projects. The furnace wall must be repaired before steelwork is damaged. It is not appropriate to remove and replace serviceable parts. Some thinning of the furnace wall and burning of stoker castings are expected and allowable.

Maintenance Schedules and Reports

The key to an effective planned maintenance program is to make regular inspections and keep accurate records of equipment conditions. Report forms such as the ones shown in Figure 4.10 and Figure 4.11 indicate what to look for when inspecting a piece of equipment. This information also serves as a guideline for scheduling equipment repairs or adjustments.

OPERATION

Management of a production plant involves the planning requisite to the selection and use of the optimum boiler units to meet the daily requirements of the system on the most economical basis. Such selection may be related to a single plant or to the several plants of a multi-plant system taken collectively.

Procedures in making these selections include the preparation of hourly and daily maximum demand forecasts. These are based upon historical relationships between system steam requirements and pertinent climatic conditions. Figure 4.12 is an example of the relationship of daily maximum demands to minimum outside temperature. Figure 4.13 is that for hourly demands vs. outside temperatures.

Predicated upon these forecasts, boiler operation schedules are established which will provide adequate capacity including that for reserve.

Pump Inspection Report—Recovery Area

Fill in "Yes" or "No" or "NR" (Not Running)

Inspector ____________

Date ____________

	Bearings				Seals					Miscellaneous		
	Pump		Motor		Packing		Mech.			Ground	Couplg Gd. in Place	Press Gage Oper?
	Norm Temp?	Noisy?	Norm Temp?	Noisy?	Norm Leak?	Tight Pack?	Needs Repack?	Leak?	Vibration?			
No. 1 Stor. Tank												
No. 2 Stor. Tank												
No. 3 Stor. Tank												
No. 4 Stor. Tank												

FIGURE 4.10

A typical report form for planned maintenance inspection

CHECKLIST FOR PLANNED MAINTENANCE OF AIR COMPRESSOR

Item or Component	Frequency				
	Daily	Weekly	Monthly	6 Months	Yearly
Air pressure	x		x		
Intake air filter	x		x		
Crankcase oil level	x			x	
Compressor bearings			x		

FIGURE 4.11

Frequency chart for a planned maintenance

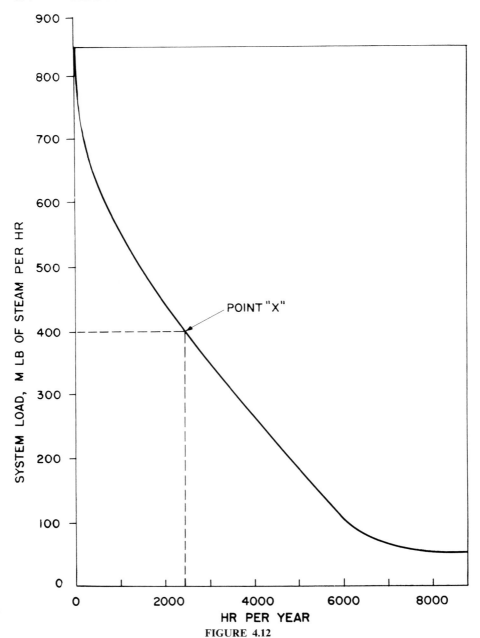

FIGURE 4.12

Load-duration curve for a district heating system

Example: Point "X" indicates that during 2500 hours of the year the load is 400,000 lb per hr or higher

Capacity scheduled as reserve should be adequate to assure delivery of system requirements in the event of the loss of the largest single boiler scheduled for service. Such capacity is more appropriately provided on a systemwide

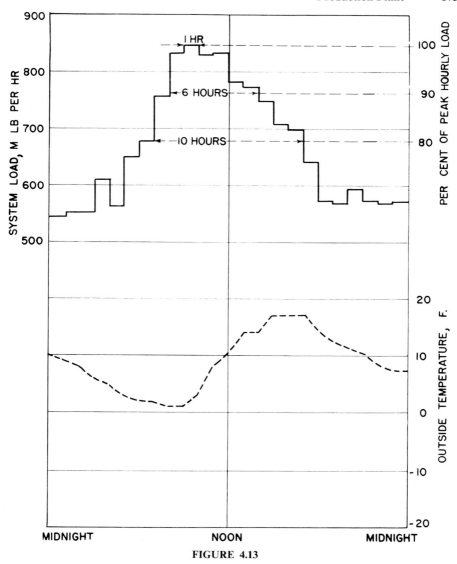

FIGURE 4.13

Total system load and outside temperature during peak-load day

basis, rather than on the basis of each individual plant providing its own reserve, except where distribution system limitations dictate otherwise.

In scheduling boilers for operation, those with the higher operating efficiencies should be loaded up to their optimum operating levels insofar as practicable. Other pertinent factors include the availability and cost of both fuel and labor. In this context the effects of common operating difficulties upon boiler capabilities should not be overlooked.

The goal of the operating staff is to obtain the best possible performance of the plant equipment. Operating characteristics and performance curves should be available for all components of equipments. The latter then provides a basis upon which to develop operating standards which, if followed, will provide operating levels that will result in the most satisfactory and economical operation. Departures from such standards should be investigated and the causes thereof corrected.

Where both steam and motor driven auxiliaries are available, operating norms should be provided which will facilitate selection of the most economical drive for the variety of probable conditions.

Due to availability of reserve capacity the output levels of individual boilers may be so adjusted as to obtain maximum attainable overall operating efficiencies. This is facilitated by plotting the combined full and other load sensitive operating coats against output for individual boilers and then determining the optimum combination for specific system load conditions.

It is desirable to have at least the minimum required reserve capacity available for immediate use. However, in some circumstances, capacity which can be made available within two hours may be acceptable as reserve. With oil, gas or pulverized coal firing such availability may be accomplished by occasional short interval firing which keeps the boiler hot at normal or subnormal pressures. Stoker fired units may be banked and sufficient stoker operation provided to merely keep the fuel bed in condition.

Control of operations as management function requires a continuing review of economy of operation and performance of plant equipment. Sufficient instrumentation is prerequisite for efficient operation as well as for providing accurate records of performance for evaluation purposes.

Competent supervisory and operating personnel are essential. Staffing should be carefully planned and controlled. Operators should be thoroughly briefed on the equipment and instructed in their duties. New operators should be thoroughly trained, carefully supervised, and periodically evaluated during the probationary period prior to their qualifying for their position.

PREDICTION OF DEMAND AND OUTPUT

Accurate prediction of demand requires prediction of the weather, especially temperature, and wind conditions and a knowledge of the system characteristics. In many cases frequent reports are available from the U.S. Weather Bureau either by telephone or by teletype. Weather records are also available for many years past. However, each heating company should take hourly readings from a properly located calibrated thermometer to be used as an operating guide and for indication of trend. A series of curves similar to those in Figure 4.4 should be plotted for past heating seasons to show the relation between temperature and demand, and to show the changes from year to year as customers are added to or removed from the system. In general, three charts will be required for each season, one chart for normal workdays, one for Saturdays, and one for Sundays and holidays. Some systems may require daily charts which vary with the seasons.

At the beginning of each heating season and whenever a new large block of load is added, preliminary charts must be made based on the previous period with changes estimated in accordance with changes in customers. As the season develops new points are added and the curves modified accordingly. Since days of similar temperature characteristics frequently show somewhat different heating-system demands, the curve cannot be a perfect guide. For most systems visual inspection of the average and maximum curves as shown in Figure 4.14 will suffice, the upper curve being approached for higher wind velocities,

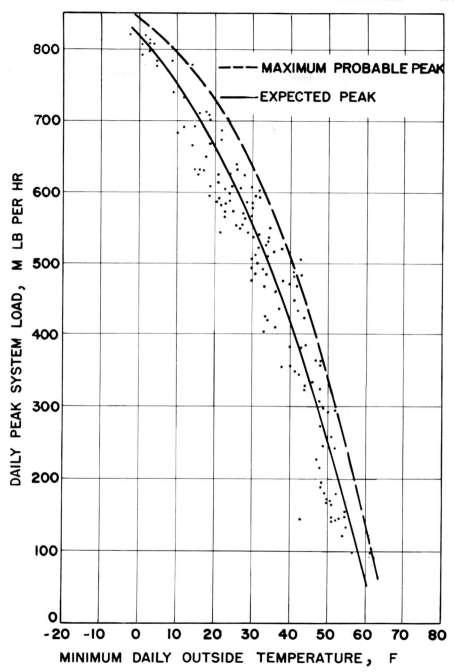

FIGURE 4.14
Relation between daily-peak system load and minimum daily temperature

sustained cold weather, rain, less sunshine and for days following Sundays and holidays.

For very large systems, or for any system where many boiler units are required to meet the demand, a more detailed method will be of value. Briefly, the method consists of using, in addition to the basis factor of outside temperature, five factors, the influence of which have been evaluated by careful study. These factors are the day of the week, the mean temperature of the preceding day, the average wind velocity, the average humidity, and the building volume served. A chart made for each factor indicates the deviation of expected demand from that determined from basic temperature, and the combined application of all the additions and subtractions permits forecasting demand effectively.

Regardless of the system used, the forecaster always has a difficult problem. If the forecast is too low, curtailment may be necessary and customers will be seriously inconvenienced, or if too high, operating costs may be increased due to the operation of excessive capacity. Since service to the public is the essence of the district heating business, it is fundamentally necessary to play safe with borderline cases.

CONSTRUCTION PLANNING, DRAWINGS AND SPECIFICATIONS

Planning is essential for any major undertaking. Through the planning process, a logical course of action evolves and a responsible estimate of time, energy and materials needed to meet overall goals and objectives develops. In construction planning, those general concepts are particularly applicable.

In planning for construction of a power plant, drawings and specifications must be prepared in order to obtain responsive bids and to exercise proper supervision over purchasing and construction. The objective of drawings and specifications is to describe the work to be done, setting out the details of the results meant to be achieved. These drawings and specifications must be clear, concise, coordinated, complete and capable of but one interpretation. The drawings describe the work graphically, while the specifications are verbal descriptions.

The drawings should indicate the location of equipment, including interconnecting piping and wiring. The specification detail the particular type and quality of materials and workmanship. Between the two, the work to be done should be clearly set forth with nothing essential omitted and avoiding inconsistencies or ambiguities. The specifications set forth the particular functions and limits of each item shown on the drawings though they also may include some general provisions which relate to the work as a whole.

For example, the drawings for a piping system for an industrial or institutional power plant will show a piping layout with detailed dimensions and will indicate the pressure characteristics of the system. The specifications should list all design requirements: design pressure and temperature; operating pressure and temperature; the grade designation of piping, fittings and valves; the type and pressure characteristics of joints; and any special requirements. These piping specifications also will have provisions covering the brands and quality of materials and workmanship, including inspection and acceptance requirements.

In specifying power plant equipment a "performance specification can enhance job economics and efficiencies." A performance specification includes only such descriptions or physical limitations as are necessary to provide for the desired quality of materials and workmanship. Within this framework it is desirable that the manufacturer or contractor be given as much freedom as possible to provide equipment which will best fulfill the functional requirements of the installation. By reason of his specialized experience, a manufacturer or contractor often is in a much better position than the individual power plant designer or consultant to determine the detailed design of his particular equipment or installation.

Overly detailed description or the use of proprietary names in the specifications can have the effect of limiting the number of qualified suppliers or those willing to bid. Such drawings and specifications are required for Federal and State Requirements to meet permit requirements.

INSTRUMENTATION AND CONTROLS

Instrumentation and controls are essential parts of all district heating boiler plants. They assure safe, efficient, economical, and reliable operation of the equipment. They range from simple manual devices to complete automatic measurement and control systems.

Measurements may be observed directly on indicating instruments or they can be recorded continuously and displayed in chart forms. Direct indicating instruments usually employ graduated scales, calibrated to indicate the variable being measured. For example, the scale of a differential pressure gage may be presented in inches of water. Various scale configurations are possible, depending on the applications. Many newer measuring instruments utilize readout scales in digital formats.

Instrument characteristics of importance are: accuracy, sensitivity, reproducibility, responsiveness, and fidelity. A brief description of each follows:

Accuracy: There are two aspects to instrument accuracy. One relates to the ability of a measuring device to display or record the actual value of the quantity being measured. The other relates to the ability of a control device to maintain nearness to the specific value desired. Deviation from the actual value in both cases is labeled "static error" and is usually calibrated and provided by manufacturers of measurement and control devices.

Sensitivity: Measuring device sensitivity is the smallest change in the sensed variable the device can display. Control sensitivity is the smallest input that results in an output. The "dead zone" is that operational input range through which the device fails to respond.

Reproducibility: This is the repeatability factor, or ability of measuring instruments or control devices to indicate or produce an identical output in response to repeated identical inputs. Gradual deviations in repeatability and reproducibility is called "drift" which occurs in both measuring and control devices.

Responsiveness: Measuring devices must track changes in the sensed variable as closely as possible. If the instrument does not respond to change it is said to be "measuring lag." The amount of time during which the instrument does not respond is called "dead time." "Lag" and "dead time" also applies to controller responsiveness.

Fidelity: Both measuring devices and controllers are activated by some input stimulus. The accuracy with which they steadfastly respond to input changes with time is fidelity. "Dynamic error" describes the difference between input change and instrument change or control action.

Temperature Measuring Devices

Heat exchange, heat balance, and many other aspects of steam generation, or hot water production involve the need to measure temperature. Operating engineers must have accurate temperature readings to control operation of the boiler plants.

Common temperature measuring instruments are listed and described in Table 4.1. The most common ones are briefly discussed as follows.

GLASS STEM THERMOMETERS

Possibly the most common type, these devices consist of a glass tube with constant inner diameter calibrated to proportionately display expansion of the volume of liquid mercury or alcohol in the reservoir. Readings are taken directly from a scale painted on the tube.

BIMETALLIC THERMOMETERS

This type of device is composed of two metallic alloy elements that expand and contract at two different rates. With a change in temperature the metals are displaced from each other, causing an indicator to move. A common configuration involves forming the element into a spiral or coil, with one alloy free to move with respect to the other. The scale for such instruments can indicate a range from $-300°F$ to $800°F$.

FILLED SYSTEM THERMOMETERS

This device consists of a sensing bulb, a capillary tube, a spiral or helical expandable element, an indicator, and a suitable fluid such as mercury. Rising temperature causes the fluid to expand, applying force to the spiral and causing the pointer to move. The indicating scale is often in the form of a circular chart.

THERMOCOUPLES

These are electrochemical devices that convert a change in temperature to electrical voltage. Two dissimilar metallic wires are joined at one end and attached to a meter circuit at the other end. Heat applied to the joined end causes a voltage to be induced across the other open end. The joined end is the "hot junction" or sensing end while the other end comprises the "cold" or "reference" junction. The voltage produced increases in proportion to the hot junction temperature. A millivoltmeter is coupled to the cold junction, with the meter indicator calibrated in units of temperature.

RESISTANCE THERMOMETER

Since the electrical resistance of certain conductive materials rises with temperature, this feature can be sensed and coupled to an indicator. Although used in applications similar to those of thermocouples, above $950°F$ their indications tend to become unstable.

RADIATION THERMOMETER

Based on the sensing of radiant energy, such as infra-red, these devices concentrate the incoming energy through an optical lens onto a thermopile. They are used to measure extremely hot substances in inaccessible areas or where direct sensing would be impossible.

TABLE 4.1

TEMPERATURE MEASUREMENT

No. Measurement Means	Application	Range, °F	Precision, °F	Limitations
1. Glass-stem thermometers				
Mercury-glass thermometer	Temp of gases and liquids by contact	−38/575	Less than 0.1 to 10	In gases, accuracy affected by radiation
Alcohol-glass thermometer	Do.	−100/100	Do.	Do.
Pentane-glass thermometers	Do.	−200/70	Do.	Do.
Jena or quartz mercury nitrogen thermometers	Do.	−38/1000	Do.	Do.
2. Gas thermometer	Primary standard	−459/1000	Less than 0.01	Requires considerable skill to use
3. Resistance thermometers				
Platinum-resistance thermometer	Precision; remote readings; temp of fluids or solids by contact	−320/1800	Less than 0.02 to 5	High cost; accuracy affected by radiation in gases
Nickel-resistance thermometer	Remote readings; temp by contact	−150/300	0.3	Accuracy affected by radiation in gases
Thermistors	Do.	Up to 600	0.1	
1. Thermocouples				
Pi-Pt-Rh thermocouple	Standard for thermocouples	500/3000	0.1 to 5	High cost; also, requires expensive measuring device
Chromel-alumel thermocouple	General testing of high temp; remote rapid readings by direct contact	Up to 2200	0.1 to 15	Less accurate than above
Iron-constantan thermocouple	Do.	Up to 1500	0.1 to 15	Subject to oxidation
Cooper-constantan thermocouple	Same as above, especially suited for low temp	Up to 700	0.1 to 15	
Chromel-constantan thermocouple				
5. Beckman thermometers (metastatic)	For differential temp in same applications as in glass stem thermometer	5°C diff	0.01°C	Must be set for temp to be measured
6. Bimetallic thermometers	For approx temp	0/1000	1, usually much more	Time lag; unsuitable for remote use; unreliable
7. Pressure-bulb thermometers				
Gas-filled bulb	Remote-testing	−100/1000	2	Caution must be exercised so that installation is correct
Vapor-filled bulb	Do.	20/500	2	Do.
Liquid-filled bulb	Do.	−50/2100	2	Do.
8. Optical pyrometers	For intensity of narrow spectral band of high temp radiation (remote)	1500 upward	15	
9. Radiation pyrometers	For intensity of total high temp fadiation (remote)	Any range		
10. Seger cones (fusion pyrometers)	Approx temp (within temp source)	1000/3600	50	
11. Indicating crayons	Approx temp (on surface)	125/900	±1%	
12. Melting and boiling points of materials	Standards	All except extremely high temp	Extremely precise	For laboratory use only

Pressure Measuring Devices

The accuracy needed, the magnitude of the pressure, and operating conditions all influence the form of pressure measuring instruments selected. Some of the more common devices to measure pressure are described briefly as follows.

MANOMETERS

Although they are the simplest gas or liquid pressure measuring devices, manometers utilize a wide variety of fluids and mechanical configurations, depending on the range to be indicated. Fluids used vary from mercury for high pressure to those lighter than water for low pressures. Figure 4.15 shows an inclined manometer used for reading small differentials at low pressure. Figure 4.16 illustrates a high pressure manometer. Manometers are accurate enough to be acceptable for ASME Performance Test Code applications. If more accurate precision is required, as for measuring flow orifice differentials, hook gages or micro-manometers are available.

PRESSURE GAGES

A commonly used type of pressure gage is the Bourdon tube gage. They are produced for a wide range of static pressures with various precision and accuracy. Scale subdivisions should be chosen carefully for the application. Scale divisions of 0.1% of full scale should be specified for applications requiring such precision, as in hydrostatic testing of pressure parts or boiler efficiency tests. For more general operating measurements, scale divisions of 1% of full scale can be used.

DIFFERENTIAL PRESSURE GAGES

Differential pressures are usually measured by means of diaphragm-type gages. Opposed bellows gages are used for a wide range of differential pressures. Typical applications involve differentials from 2 to 1000 psi at pressures above 6000 psi, as in reading fluid pressure drops through boiler circuits.

New differential pressure gages are based on use of transducers that rely on

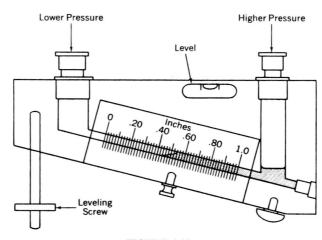

FIGURE 4.15
Inclined differential manometer

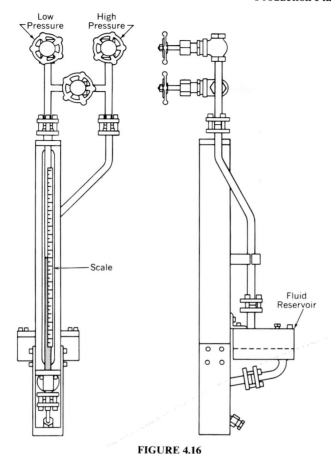

FIGURE 4.16
High-pressure mercury manometer

energy transfer properties of several components such as crystals or strain gages mounted on diaphragms. Although they need frequent calibration their use is expected to find wider applications where this feature is not a hindrance.

Flow Measuring Devices

To ensure safe, efficient, and intelligent operation of a district heating system, it is necessary to measure and indicate the flow of steam, water, gas, and air. The most dependable methods for accurate measurements involve the use of an orifice, flow nozzle, or venturi tube as the primary measuring component. Pressure drop or differential pressure created by such restrictions can be converted into flow rates by suitable calculations.

Generally, orifice plates are used for steam, gas, or oil flow. Water flow usually is measured through use of a venturi tube. A comparison of advantages and disadvantages of these various common methods is shown in Table 4.2.

To ensure accurate flow measurement results, a few important factors must be observed, no matter which method is used.

TABLE 4.2

ADVANTAGES AND DISADVANTAGES OF VARIOUS TYPES OF PRIMARY ELEMENTS

Advantages	Disadvantages
Orifice	
(1) Lowest cost	(1) High nonrecoverable head loss
(2) Easily installed and/or replaced	(2) Suspended matter may build up at the inlet
(3) Well established coefficient of discharge	side of horizontally installed pipe unless
(4) Will not wiredraw or wear in service during	eccentric or segmental types of orifices
test period	are used with the hole flush with the
(5) Sharp edge will not foul up with scale or	bottom of the pipe
other suspended matter	(3) Low capacity
	(4) Requires pipe line flanges, unless of special
	construction
Flow Nozzle	
(1) Can be used where no pipe line flanges	(1) Higher cost than orifice
exist	(2) Same head loss as orifice for same capacity
(2) Cost less than venturi tubes and capable of	(3) Inlet pressure connections and throat taps
handling same capacities	when used must be made very carefully
Venturi Tube	
(1) Lowest head loss	(1) Highest cost
(2) Has integral pressure connections	(2) Greatest weight and largest size for a given
(3) Requires shortest length of straight pipe on	size line
inlet side	
(4) Will not obstruct flow of suspended matter	
(5) Can be used where no pipe line flanges	
exist	
(6) Coefficient of discharge well established	

Source, *ASME Performance Test Code* 19.5-1972.

1. Location with respect to bends or cross section of piping.
2. Need for straightening vanes in the approach to the device.
3. Type and location of pressure taps.
4. Condition and dimension of piping surface adjacent to device.
5. Direction of flow in relation to position of device.
6. Overall configuration of piping between primary element to differential pressure measuring instrument.

A detailed discussion of the variety of metering available for steam and water flow indication is presented in Chapter 7.

Where a high degree of precision is not required, such as measuring flow of combustion air as flue gas, a pitot tube traverse usually is made. For this purpose, test connections or sampling points are located at a zone in the duct, flue, or pipe when reliable flow characteristics are obtainable. The pitot tube measures velocity pressure, i.e., the difference between total and static pressure, when it is inserted facing the air or gas flow stream.

Combustion Measuring Devices

The products resulting from combustion that are present in stack gas are identified and measured as to level of concentration through combustion testing. The residual elements usually of interest are carbon dioxide (CO_2) and carbon monoxide (O_2). The devices usually used for stack gas measurements are described briefly as follows.

ORSAT APPARATUS

This device provides the most definitive results. The procedure involves sampling a specific amount of stack gas and measuring successive volumes after selective intimate contact with certain absorptive solutions. A reduction in volume after each absorptive stage identifies the amount of each component being tested.

FYRITE APPARATUS

This is another simple and portable absorbing instrument that senses and measures the volume of combustion products on a one at a time basis.

SMOKE TESTER

The measurement of smoke is an indication of the completeness of combustion. The smoke tester pumps a measured volume of gas through a paper filter that is clamped into place. After the tester is placed into the flue, a definitive number of pump strokes are made. The paper is removed and the smoke density is compared to a standard oil smoke scale.

DRAFT GAGE

Furnace draft in units of pressure and inches of water are measured by this instrument. The stronger the draft, the faster combustion gases leave the furnace. Permanent draft gages are installed in large systems while portable draft meters are available for smaller units that may not be fully instrumented.

THERMOMETER

Stack temperature measurements up to 1000°F are made as a regular aspect of combustion testing, using a dial-type thermometer.

HYGROMETER

This is really a dew point meter and is the basic device used to measure sulfuric acid dewpoint of combustion gases inside of flue and economizers. It is based on the condensation of moisture on a probe detector that is inserted and progressively cooled.

PH METERS

The degree of acidity or alkalinity in water must be controlled in any water process system. Pure neutral water has a pH value of 7. Solutions that are acidic (below 7) encourage corrosion while solutions that are alkaline (above 7) encourage undesirable calcium carbonate scale deposits.

Instrument Selection and Positioning

Instrumentation of a boiler system is based on considerations of desired safety and operational economy. While many different instruments can be employed it may be helpful to divide the potential measurements into three priority classes ranging from desirable but not necessary, optimally necessary, and absolutely necessary. An analysis must be made of general plant configuration, operating characteristics, experience of the crew, and preference of decision-makers. Once installed, all instruments must be easily maintained if they are to provide data of value to the managers.

Table 4.3 lists frequently employed instruments, their preference according to the weighted priorities and some notes on location of each.

The position of each instrument may be as important as its selection. Only those indicators that actually help the operators should be positioned on the boiler control panels. Their readings should be helpful to the operators in making adjustments. Other readings may be positioned in a distributed fashion off the control board. Suppliers of both equipment and instruments should be consulted to ensure that no installation constraints are overlooked in this analysis and planning.

AUTOMATIC CONTROLS

Instruments alone do not ensure economic system operation. It is the close control of equipment, made possible by knowledge of operating conditions, that result in improved economy. Generally, boiler controls involve coordinating the following factors:

1. fuel economy,
2. combustion air,
3. removal of products of combustion,
4. steam pressure or hot water temperature,
5. feedwater supply.

Boiler controls can be classified according to end use, from the simplest to the most complex. A general description of common controls follows.

Off-On Controls

Small boilers usually employ off-on controls. Such controls feed fuel and air in an established ratio to sustain efficient combustion. Any change in pressure causes a pressurestat or mercury switch to start the coal stoker, oil or gas burner, or forced-draft fan. Off-on controls are not the best ways of producing combustion efficiency in multiple boiler systems. Since control pressures are difficult to maintain within close tolerances, in multiple boiler installation, one boiler frequently appropriates most of the load. Instead of equipping each boiler with an off-on control, it is better to install a single master device to control all the boilers simultaneously. Or, an off-on sequence control can cycle the units as required.

Positioning Type Controls

Applied to all types of boilers, these devices consist of a master pressure controller which responds to change in steam pressure and actuates the forced-draft damper to control airflow and the lever on the stoker to adjust the fuel-feed rate. Such stokers usually have constant-speed forced-draft fans equipped with dampers or inlet vanes positioned to control the air for combustion. Furnace-draft controllers are used to maintain the draft within desired limits and operate independently of the positioning-control system.

The only time the airflow and fuel feed are in agreement is at a fixed point, usually where control calibration was made. This is because the airflow is not proportional to damper movement. Variables affecting this relationship are the type of damper, variations in fuel-bed depth, variations in fuel quality, and lost motion in control linkage. Thus, frequent manual adjustment to synchronize the previous control is needed.

TABLE 4.3

INSTRUMENT LOCATION CRITERIA

Boiler-plant Instruments

Location and Function	*Weighted preference	Instrument on boiler control board	Notes
Furnace			
Draft indicator to show draft at the furnace apex	A	Yes	5
Capped openings to permit checking or testing for CO_2 temperature, draft, etc.	B		
Especially desirable for new designs and unusual operating requirements. Also desirable to include additional openings throughout the rest of the unit, to permit readings to be taken without disturbing the permanently installed operating instruments.			
Boiler			
Gage to show boiler-drum steam pressure	A	Yes	
Indicator and recorder	B–A	Yes	
Draft indicator to show draft at boiler exit	B	Yes	
Indicator to show flue gas temp, at boiler exit	B	Yes	
Indicator and recorder	C–B	Yes	
Steam-flow/air-flow recorder or steam-flow/CO_2 recorder. May be recorded also on separate instruments.	B–A	Yes	1
Drum water-level indicator (not water-level gage)	C	Yes	1
Drum water-level indicator and recorder	C–B	Yes	1
Superheater			
Gage to show superheated steam pressure	A	Yes	
Indicator and recorder	B	Yes	
Indicator to show temperature of superheated steam	A	Yes	
Indicator and recorder	B–A	Yes	
Economizer			
Draft indicator to show draft at economizer inlet	B	Yes	
Draft indicator to show draft at economizer outlet	C–B	Yes	
Indicator to show temperature of water entering economizer	B	Yes	
Indicator and recorder	B	Yes	
Indicator to show temperature of water leaving economizer	B	Yes	
Indicator and recorder	B	Yes	
Indicator to show temperature of flue gas entering economizer	B	Yes	
Indicator and recorder	B	Yes	
Indicator to show temperature of flue gas leaving economizer	B	Yes	
Indicator and recorder	B	Yes	
Air Heater			
Draft indicator to show draft at air heater inlet	B	Yes	
Draft indicator to show draft at air heater outlet	B–A	Yes	
Pressure indicator to show air pressure at air heater inlet	B	Yes	
Pressure indicator to show air pressure at air heater outlet	B–A	Yes	
Indicator to show flue gas temperature at air heater inlet	B	Yes	
Indicator and recorder	C	Yes	
Indicator to show flue gas temperature at air heater outlet	B–A	Yes	
Indicator and recorder	B–A	Yes	
Indicator to show air temperature at air heater inlet	C–B	Yes	
Indicator and recorder	C–B	Yes	
Indicator to show air temperature at air heater outlet	B–A	Yes	
Indicator and recorder	B–A	Yes	
Feedwater			
Gage to show feedwater pressure	A	Yes	
Indicator to show temperature of feedwater. May be the same as economizer inlet.	B	Yes	
Indicator and recorder	B	Yes	
Water-flow indicator and recorder	C–B	No	4
Steam			
Steam-flow indicator and recorder. May be the same as steam-flow air-flow.	B–A	Yes	1
Fuel			
Gage to show pressure of liquid or gaseous fuel	A		
Primary air-pressure indicator for pulverized fuel	A	Yes	
Fuel meter for liquid or gaseous fuel	B–A	No	
Weigh scale totalizer for raw coat to pulverized-coal feeders	B–A	No	

TABLE 4.3—_Continued_

Boiler-plant Instruments

Location and Function	*Weighted preference	Instrument on boiler control board	Notes
All Stokers			
Windbox air-pressure indicator	A	Yes	
Overfire air-pressure indicator	C–B		
Spreader Stokers			
Undergrate air-pressure indicators—one for each section	A	No	2
Traveling-grate Stokers			
Undergrate air-pressure indicators—one for each compartment	A	No	2
Speed-of-grate indicator	C	Yes	3
Indicator and recorder	C	Yes	3
Underfeed Stokers—None for single retort without zoned areas			
Undergrate air-pressure indicators for each zone of zoned single- or multiple-retort-type machines	A	No	2
Speed indicators	C	Yes	3
Indicator and recorder	C	Yes	3
Pulverizers			
Pressure indicator to show primary air pressure leaving exhauster	A	Yes	
Draft indicator to show draft at mill air inlet	A	No	4
Draft indicator to show differential draft across mill or mill classifier	A	No	4
Indicator to show temperature of hot gas or air to mill	C–B	Yes	
Indicator to show temperature of hot gas or air entering mill. This is tempered gas or air.	C–B	No	4
Indicating ammeter in mill motor circuit or pressure gage connected into mill turbine steam chest	A	Yes	
Indicator to show temperature of primary air and coal leaving mill	A	Yes	4
Indicator and recorder	B	Yes	4
Pulverized-coal Feeders			
Speed indicator	C	Yes	
Revolution-counter	C	No	3
Burners			
Indicator to show air pressure in windbox	A	Yes	
Indicator to show air pressure in burner compartment	A	No	2
Draft Fan			
Indicator to show fan speed, if adjustable-speed type	C	Yes	
Dampers			
Damper-position indicators	C	Yes	

* A, Instruments which are absolutely necessary.
* B, Instruments which are optimally necessary.
* C, Instruments which are desirable, but not necessary
* A combination of any letters indicates an intermediate recommendation.
Note 1. Exact locations of connections in accordance with instrument manufacturer's specification.
Note 2. Zone, section or compartment pressure indicators should be mounted where the operator can see the fire, as well as the indicator.
Note 3. Counters located at the machine.
Note 4. Location near the machine.
Note 5. (I^1) is an alternate location.

The variables are partly corrected through the proper alignment of levers and connecting linkage between the power unit and the damper and fuel-feed levers which they operate. This type system can be provided with a convenient means for manual control operation from a central point. A remote manual-control system can be used for changing the distribution of the load between boilers or for making adjustments in the fuel-feed rate to compensate for changes in fuel quality. A positioning-type control has this advantage over the off-on control; the fuel and air can be provided in small increments to maintain continuous operation, thus eliminating off-on cycling.

Metering Controls

These are used when the fuel rate and Btu input vary widely because of variations in fuel supply and heat content and when combination fuels are burned. The fuel and air are metered maintaining the correct air-fuel ratio for best combustion results. The steam (or water) flow can be a measure of fuel feed. That is accomplished by measuring the pressure drop across an orifice, flow nozzle, or venturi. Air for combustion can also be metered by passing the air though an orifice. But, most frequently, airflow is measured by the draft loss across the boiler or air preheater (gas side) or across the air preheater (air side). The air side is frequently chosen as the point of measurement in order to avoid dust and dirt's clogging the lines and fouling the control system.

Metering-type controls are more accurate than positioning systems, since compensation for variables is obtained through metering without regard for levers, linkage, lost motion, damper position, or fuel variables. Also, the fuel-air ratio can be readjusted from the air-stream flow relationship. Metering controls usually incorporate a remote manual station where the control system can be modified and where hand or automatic operation is possible.

Feedwater Controls

Feedwater controls or regulators are of the self-contained, self-operated, thermo-hydraulic, or pneumatic or electrically operated types. Feedwater controls regulate the flow of water to a drum-type boiler to maintain the level in the boiler drum between desired limits. The control system will vary with the type and capacity of the boiler as well as the characteristics of the load.

Most shop-assembled boilers in the low capacity range and the low operating-pressure range come with self-contained feedwater control systems of the thermo-hydraulic or thermostatic types. The thermo-hydraulic type is generally used with boilers having an operating pressure between 60 and 600 psi and capacities not exceeding 75,000 to 100,000 lb/hr under steady load conditions.

Pneumatic or electrically operated feedwater controls are classified as single element, two element, or three element types. These systems are used with high capacity boilers and those operating at high pressures.

In *single-element feedwater control*, the water in the drum is at the desired level when the signal from the level transmitter equals its set point.

If an undesirable water level exists, the controller applies proportional-plus-integral action to the difference between the drum-level and set-point signals to change the position of the regulating valve. A hand-automatic station gives the operator complete control over the valve. A valve positioner can be included in the control-valve assembly to match the valve characteristics to the individual requirements of the system.

Single-element control will maintain a constant drum level for slow changes in load, steam pressure, or feedwater pressure. However, since the control signal satisfies the requirements of drum level only, excessive "swell or shrink" effects will result in wider drum-level variations and a longer time for restoring drum level to set point following a load change with single-element control than with two- or three-element control.

Two-element control comprises a feedforward control loop which uses steam-flow measurement to control feedwater input, with level measurement assuring correct drum level.

The drum level element of the controller applies proportional action to the difference between the drum-level signal and its set point. The sum of the drum-level error signal and the flow signal determines the valve position. The steam-flow measurement maintains feedwater flow proportional to steam flow; the drum-level measurement corrects for any imbalance in water input vs steam output caused by deviations in the valve-position/water-flow relationship, and provides the necessary transient adjustments to cope with the "swell or shrink" characteristics of the boiler.

Three-element control is a cascaded-feedforward control loop which maintains water-flow input equal to feedwater demand. Drum-level measurement keeps the level in the drum from drifting due to flow metal errors, blowdown, or other causes.

The drum-level element of the controller applies proportional action to the error between the drum-level signal and its set point. The sum of the drum-level error signal and the steam-flow signal is the feedwater-demand signal. The feedwater demand signal is compared with the water-flow input and the difference is the combined output of the controller. Proportional-plus-integral action is incorporated to provide a feedwater correction signal for valve regulation or pump speed control.

Combustion Control

Many varieties of combustion-control systems are available. They may operate pneumatically, hydraulically, electrically, electronically, and sometimes in combination.

For the *pneumatic system,* all instruments in the control loop are air-activated measurements, to and from central points. Steam pressure is controlled by parallel control of air and fuel; high-low signal selectors function to maintain an air-fuel mixture.

Airflow to the furnace is controlled by automatic positioning of the forced-draft inlet vanes. Furnace draft is maintained at the desired value by controlling or positioning of the induced-draft fan damper. Feedwater flow to the boiler drum is controlled separately.

Adjustment is provided at the panel board for steam-pressure set point, fuel-air ratio, furnace draft, and drum-level set points. The controls would include pneumatic switches for bumpless transfer from automatic to manual control; and manual control can be accomplished from the control panel.

Automatic combustion control is justified by the benefits it provides: added safety, improved operation, reduction in manpower requirements, lower steam costs, etc. Combustion-control systems are available to meet the needs of both the small and the large power plant. Selection should be made on the basis of justifying installation and maintenance cost by lower overall steam costs. Each system should be as simple as possible to accomplish the purpose for which it was installed. Controls should be so located as to make them accessible for servicing and calibration; they should be kept clean and in working order. Neither the instrumentation nor the combustion control, per se, improves the performance; they must be maintained and records of operation analyzed if best results are to be secured.

Burner Controls

Various devices are employed to prevent operation of boilers when a hazardous furnace condition exists or to assist the operator to start and stop the burners and fuel handling equipment. The control system must also prevent damage to burners and fuel equipment from malfunction while avoiding false trips to fuel equipment when a truly unsafe condition does not exist.

Other important factors in the design of the burner control system are the method and location to be used in the start-up, shutdown, operation, and control of the fuel equipment. These factors must be understood before purchase, design or application of a burner control system.

Burner control systems vary from a simple manual control system used to start or stop the burner equipment to a complex burner and fuel management system. Sophisticated controls can be used that will recognize the level of fuel demand to the boiler, will know the operating range of the fuel equipment in service, will reach a decision concerning the need for starting up or shutting down the next increment of fuel equipment, and will select the next increment based on the firing pattern of burners in service. Such demands for the start-up or shutdown of fuel preparation and burning equipment can be initiated by the control system without the immediate knowledge of the operator.

The degree of operating flexibility allowed by a burner control system is closely related to the degree of operator participation. A higher level of automation reduces the flexibility of the operator in handling situations where a piece of equipment fails to perform as expected.

The cost of the burner control system is also important. It varies significantly with the functional requirements and degree of operating flexibility, as well as the type of equipment (solid state or relay) and packaging desired for the system. So, a true evaluation of cost cannot be reached without a complete understanding between the customer and vendor of the factors involved.

Total Automation

Total automation (TA) control is employed by many combined steam-electric district cogeneration plants. The basic TA concept is to provide the maximum amount of control and monitoring that is consistent with the desired levels of safety, equipment protection, and efficiency.

DRAFT, STACK AND FANS

A flow of air is required to supply the proper amount of oxygen for complete combustion to take place. The air is also required to remove the combustion by-products. The flow, confined to ducts, boiler settings, heat exchangers, flues and stacks, is created and sustained by fans and stacks. Either the stack alone or a combination of fans and stacks must produce the required pressure differential for the flow.

Draft

Draft is a term commonly used to designate static pressure in a furnace, air or gas passage, or stack. It is also usual to speak of draft in any one of the four categories: natural draft, induced draft, forced draft, and balanced draft.

The term "natural draft" is used to indicate a pressure differential caused by gravity. Natural draft occurs when a difference in density between the hot gas in the stack and the colder air of the surrounding atmosphere results in a negative pressure at the stack entrance.

When air or the products of combustion flow inside a unit under the influence of a progressively decreasing pressure below that of the atmosphere, the system is operating under induced draft. This is the case where stacks alone furnish a sufficient natural draft to meet low draft loss requirements or where stacks are supplemented with induced draft fans to meet higher pressure differentials.

The term "forced draft" is used when air or flue gases flowing in a unit are maintained at pressures above atmospheric. This will generally imply the use of a forced draft fan.

Balanced draft refers to a point in the system where the draft is zero (static pressure = atmospheric pressure). It is also used to describe a unit in which the top of the furnace operates at slightly less than atmospheric pressure.

PRESSURES AND FLOWS

While draft refers to static pressure, it is also important to be able to determine the total pressure at any point. This amounts to static pressure plus the velocity pressure, where velocity pressure is the equivalent of the kinetic energy of the flowing air or gas divided by specific volume.

It is customary to designate drafts and associated pressures in inches of water because measurements made with Pitot or static tubes are conveniently indicated in inches of water with a simple U-tube gage. The velocity pressure in inches of water is determined as follows:

$$H_w = \frac{1}{5.2v} \cdot \frac{V^2}{2g_c}$$

where:

H_w = velocity pressure, in. water
V = fluid velocity, ft/sec
g_c = conversion constant, 32.2 ft/sec^2
v = specific volume of the air or gas, cu ft/lb

Knowledge of the average velocity pressure permits determination of the quantity of air or gas flowing in a duct or flue, as follows:

$$Q = 1098A \sqrt{H_w v}$$

where:

Q = flow rate, cu ft/min
A = flue or duct area normal to the flow, sq ft
H_w = velocity pressure, in. water
v = specific volume of air or gas, cu ft/lb

STACK EFFECT

Stack effect is the difference in pressure caused solely by the difference in elevation between two locations in vertical ducts or passages conveying heated gases. Like natural draft, it is the result of the action of gravity. The intensity and distribution of this pressure difference depend on the height and arrangement of ducts and passages, and on the gas temperature in each.

It is necessary that proper stack effect considerations be incorporated in the selection of fans or stack height. This factor must be included in order to provide not only the draft needed to overcome flow losses within the unit, but also to allow for the net stack effect of the system.

Stack

Stacks were used in early boiler design to meet the entire draft requirement through the stack effect alone. This holds true today as well for many smaller modern units.

However, for larger units equipped with economizers, superheaters and air heaters, it is not economical or practical to operate the entire unit from natural stack induced draft. Such units require fans in addition to the stack. Either the entire unit must be under pressure from a forced draft fan or must use both induced and forced draft fans for a balanced draft operation.

Height and diameter of stacks for natural draft units depend upon:
1. necessary gas flow from the stack;
2. average temperature of the gases passing up the stack and temperature of the surrounding air;
3. draft loss through the boiler from the point of balanced draft to the stack entrance, and
4. barometric pressure.

The influence of altitude on barometric pressure is indicated in Table 4.4.

No formula covers the many factors involved in a determination of the stack height and diameter adequately. For practical purposes, the most important points to consider are:
1. temperature of the surrounding atmosphere and temperature of the gases entering the stack;
2. drop in temperature of the gases within the stack because of the heat loss to the atmosphere and air infiltration; and
3. stack draft losses associated with the gas flow rate (due to fluid friction within the stack and the kinetic energy of gases leaving the stack).

FACTORS AFFECTING STACK HEIGHT

A stack functions to disperse combustion gases as well as create a draft. Increasing stack height enlarges the area of dispersion. In narrow valleys or locations where there is a concentration of industry, increased stack height may be necessary for the comfort and health of the community.

Some district heating plants located near airports, are prohibited from using high enough stacks for adequate dispersion. In such cases the stack may be narrowed down at the top to increase the discharge velocity, simulating the effect of the higher stack. However, such "necking" down of a stack adds considerable amounts of flow resistance which can only be balanced by a mechanical-draft system.

STACK DESIGN

Several factors need to be considered in the design of stacks. In addition to the stack height and diameter, economic and structural factors also must be

TABLE 4.4
EFFECT OF ALTITUDES ON BAROMETERIC PRESSURE

Ft Above Sea Level	Pressure In. Hg	Ft Above Sea Level	Pressure In. Hg
0	29.92	6,000	23.98
1,000	28.86	7,000	23.09
2,000	27.82	8,000	22.22
3,000	26.82	9,000	21.39
4,000	25.84	10,000	20.58
5,000	24.90	15,000	16.89

considered. For example, stack material selection is influenced by material and erection costs, stack height, means of support (i.e., whether the stack is supported from a steel structure or a foundation) or erosive and corrosive elements in the flue gas.

Static analysis is made to determine the dead weight load, the horizontal load due to wind and, in some cases, the effect of earthquake forces on the stack. Structural adequacy is checked by making both a static and a dynamic analysis of loads. Dynamic analysis is used to check for deflections.

Fans

Fans move air or gas by adding sufficient energy to the stream to initiate motion and overcome flow resistance. A fan consists of a bladed rotor, (impeller) which does the work, and a housing to collect and direct the air or gas discharged by the impeller. Power requirements depend on the volume of air or gas to be moved in unit time, pressure differences across the fan and the efficiency of the fan and its drives.

Power is usually expressed as shaft horsepower, input horsepower to motor terminals, (if motor driven) or theoretical horsepower computed by thermodynamic methods. The important factors for fans are the power input to the shaft and the power required figured by thermodynamic calculations.

FAN TYPES

Mechanical-draft fans commonly used in district heating plants are of the centrifugal type. These have blades mounted on an impeller rotating within a spiral housing. The fan characteristics are determined by the blade design. Backward curved blades produce low resultant velocities for a given tip or peripheral speed. Forward curved blades impart high velocities. Radial blades and radial tipped blades operate between the extremes.

Selection of fan type is best left to the manufacturer who will guarantee satisfactory operation. Besides the operating conditions of volume, pressure and temperature, many other factors must be considered, such as method of drive, speed of drive, method of control, space limitations, allowable noise and vibration, corrosion and/or erosion due to materials contaminating the gas, point of most continuous operation, range of operation, etc.

PRINCIPLES OF OPERATION

Fans produce pressure and/or flow due to the rotating blades of the impeller, which impart kinetic energy to the air in the form of velocity changes. These velocity changes are resultants of tangential and radial velocity components, in the case of centrifugal fans, and of axial and tangential velocity components in the case of axial flow fans.

Centrifugal fan impellers produce pressure from two related sources:
1. the centrifugal force created by rotating the air column enclosed between the blades, and
2. the kinetic energy imparted to the air from its velocity leaving the impeller.

This velocity, in turn, is a combination of the rotating velocity of the impeller and air speed relative to the impeller. When the blades are inclined forward, these two velocities are cumulative; when backward, oppositional. Backward-curved blade fans are generally somewhat more efficient than forward curved blade fans.

Factors describing operating characteristics of fans include:
1. horsepower (hp) required to drive the fan;
2. fan speed (in rpm);
3. pressure, stated as static pressure, measured in inches of water (abbreviated in W.G. in which W.G. stands for water gage or the height of a column of water), and
4. capacity (in cfm).

Fan laws express how these factors relate to each other. They are as follows:
1. The first fan law states "air quantity is directly proportional to fan speed."
2. The second fan law states "pressure varies in direct proportion to the square of fan speed. Using static pressure (SP) as the pressure developed by the fan."
3. The third fan law states "the required horsepower is directly proportional to the cube of the fan speed."

Accordingly, if air volume is reduced by 10%, power savings will amount to approximately 30%.

FAN DRIVES

Fan drives normally use electric motors, since they are less expensive and more efficient than any other type drive. For fans of more than a few horsepower, squirrel-cage induction motors are most common. This type motor is relatively inexpensive, reliable and highly efficient over a wide load range. Often it is used in large sizes with a magnetic or hydraulic coupling for variable speed installations.

In the smaller sizes for some variable speed installations, wound-rotor (slip-ring) induction motors are used. If a d-c motor is needed, the compound type is usually selected. A steam turbine drive costs more than a squirrel-cage motor, but is less expensive than any of the variable speed electric motor arrangements in sizes over 50 hp. A steam turbine may be more economical than the electric motor drive in plants where exhaust steam is needed for process, or on large utility units using the exhaust steam for feedwater heating.

FAN CONTROL

Fans rarely exist in applications where they operate continuously at the same pressure and volume discharge rate. To meet the needs of the system, some means of adjusting fan output becomes necessary. Common methods for controlling fan output are inlet damper, inlet vane control and variable speed.

Damper control allows variable resistance in the system to alter the fan output as required. However, damper control wastes power because excess pressure energy must be dissipated by throttling.

Advantages are:
1. Continuous rather than a step type of control. This makes it effective throughout the entire range of fan operation.
2. Least expensive type of fan drive as a constant-speed induction-type a-c motor may be used.
3. Ease of operation of adaptation to automatic control.
4. Lowest first cost of all control types.

Centrifugal fans are most economically controlled with inlet vanes. Inlet vanes are designed for use on dirty gas as well as clean air.

Experience with forced draft, primary air and induced draft fans has shown that inlet vane control is reliable and reduces operating cost. It also controls stability, controls accuracy and minimizes hysteresis.

Inlet vane control regulates air flow entering the fan and uses less horsepower at fractional loads than outlet damper control. The inlet vane gives the air a varying degree of spin in the direction of wheel rotation and allows the fan to produce the required head at lower power. Although vane control offers considerable efficiency savings over damper control at any reduced load, it is most effective for moderate changes close to net load operation. Initial cost is greater than for damper control but less than for variable speed control.

Speed control results in some efficiency loss since no variable speed driver works as efficiently throughout the entire fan load range as a direct connected constant speed a-c motor. The loss in efficiency depends on the type of speed variation.

A number of commonly used variable speed arrangements are:

1. variable speed d-c motor;
2. variable speed steam turbine, and
3. hydraulic coupling.

FORCED DRAFT FAN

Forced draft fans are used with boilers operating with both forced and induced drafts to push air through the combustion air supply system into the furnace. The fan discharge pressure must be high enough to equal the total resistance of air ducts, air heater, burners, fuel bed and any other resistance between the fan and the furnace. The furnace is the point of balanced draft or zero pressure. Output volume of the forced draft fan must equal the quantity of air required for combustion plus air heater leakage. In many boiler installations, greater reliability is obtained by two fans operating in parallel. If one fan is out of service, the other usually can carry 60% or more of full boiler load, depending on how the fans are sized.

In establishing necessary characteristics for a forced draft fan, the system resistance from fan to furnace is calculated using the actual weight of air required for combustion plus the expected leakage from the air side of the air heater. Standard boiler design practice bases all calculations on 80 F air temperature entering the fan. The results are then adjusted to test block specifications by safety factors.

The forced draft fan is sized for the entire system for pressurized units without an induced draft fan.

In boiler service, a forced draft fan operates under far more rigorous conditions than the ordinary ventilating fan and selection must consider the following general requirements:

1. Efficiency. High efficiency over a wide range of output is essential since boilers operate under varying load conditions.
2. Reliability. Modern boilers often operate continuously for long periods without shutdown for maintenance or repairs. The fan must have a rugged rotor and housing and conservatively loaded bearings. The fan must also be well balanced, the blades shaped so they will not collect dirt and disturb this balance.
3. Stability. Fan pressure must vary uniformly with volume over the capacity range. This makes boiler control easier and assures minimum disturbance of air flow when adjustments to the fuel-burning equipment change the system resistance. When two or more fans operate in parallel, the pressure-

output curves must have characteristics similar to the radial tip or backward-curved blade fans in order to share the load equally over the shut-off point.

4. Overloading. Motor driven fans should have self-limiting horsepower characteristics so that the driving motor cannot overload. Horsepower should reach a peak and then drop off near the full-load fan output.

INDUCED DRAFT FAN

Boiler units designed to operate with a balanced furnace draft or without a forced draft fan require induced draft to move gaseous products of combustion over heating surfaces and through the passages between the furnace and stack. If it is not practical or economical to design for natural draft, induced draft fans discharging essentially at atmospheric pressure are used to provide the required negative static pressure.

Gas weight used to calculate net induced draft requirements include the weight of combustion product gas at maximum boiler load plus any air leaking into the boiler. Net gas temperatures are calculated on unit performance at maximum load.

An induced draft fan is basically the same as a forced draft fan except that it handles higher temperature gas which may contain erosive ash. Excessive maintenance from erosion can be avoided by protecting casing the blades with replaceable wear strips.

GAS RECIRCULATING FAN

Gas recirculating fans are used for controlling steam temperature, furnace heat absorption and slagging of heating surfaces. They generally are located to extract gas at the economizer outlet and move it into the furnace. Proper fan selection is dictated by the high static pressure required for tempering furnace temperatures at full load on the boiler unit, or by the high volume requirement at partial loads for steam temperature control.

Though gas recirculating fans have similar requirements to induced draft fans, the designer must consider additional factors. Since the gas recirculating fan operates at higher gas temperatures, intermittent service may cause thermal shock or imbalance. When the fan is not in service, suitable protection in the form of tight shut-off dampers and sealing air should be provided to prevent the backflow of hot furnace gas. A turning gear is often used on large fans to rotate the rotor slowly to avoid distortion.

COMPRESSED AIR SYSTEMS

Compressed air systems compress air above atmospheric pressure to provide power for pneumatic tools and controls. Drives for compressed air systems are usually electric motors, but compressors in large district heating plants can operate on steam from turbines.

The most common type of air compressor used in a district heating plant is a reciprocating compressor. Reciprocating compressors are either single-stage or multistage.

A single-stage compressor uses one or more compression cylinders of the same size. Air at normal pressure enters through an intake filter. The air is filtered at intake to prevent compressor damage from dirt or other particles.

The air enters the cylinder. It is compressed by a piston, and is discharged through a valve system into a storage container.

The multi-stage compressor utilizes two or more cylinders of different diameters. The first stage is the "low-pressure" cylinder which has the larger diameter. After first-stage compression, the air is transferred into the second, or "high pressure" cylinder. Here further, higher compression occurs before the air is discharged to its storage container.

During the compression operation the air must be cooled, since the compression process generates heat. A water jacket is usually used to cool a single stage compressor, while the multi-stage compressor uses an inter-cooler between the first and second stages. This inter-cooler is a nest of tubes containing water. The water circulates through the tubes, drawing off the heat, as the air circulates around the tubes. For further cooling, an after-cooler is inserted between the compressor and the storage container. The after-cooler operates on the same principle as the inter-cooler.

AUXILIARY STEAM PLANT EQUIPMENT

General auxiliary equipment found in steam plants is necessary to allow the major equipment to perform its function. Boiler operation requires that feedwater be heated and conditioned. Steam and water must flow from one part of the plant to the other through pipelines of adequate strength and size. Condensate must be automatically removed from steam lines. This prevents the possibility of waterhammer and of steam-heating coils keeping water from blanking the heating surface and decreasing the rate of heat transfer. Filters, pumps, and a variety of feeding devices must be used in lubricating machinery. This auxiliary equipment requires careful handling and maintenance to keep it working.

Closed Feedwater Heaters

A closed feedwater heater is one where heat in the steam is transferred through tubes separating water from the steam. A shell made of either steel or cast iron holds the steam for heating and contains tubes which supply the heat transfer surface (Figure 4.17). The tubes are made of copper or brass to resist the corrosive action of the water. Closed feedwater heaters are classified according to the number of times the water traverses the length of the unit before being discharged as one to four "pass." The heater shown in the Figure is baffled to provide four passes for the water. A good closed feedwater heater heats the water to within a few degrees of the steam temperature. In a closed feedwater heater, steam and water do not mix. Further, one pump may be used to force the water through several heaters to utilize steam from several extraction points in the steam turbine. Closed feedwater heaters are not suitable for heating hard water which forms deposits on tube surfaces that in turn retard heat transfer and restrict flow.

Open Feedwater Heaters

In open feedwater heaters, steam and water come directly into contact and the outflow is a combination of inlet water and steam. Such systems are designed so that the temperature of the outlet water approaches the saturation temperature of the supply steam.

In open feedwater heaters, a combination of makeup water and condensate is sprayed into the heater to provide thorough mixing of the water and steam.

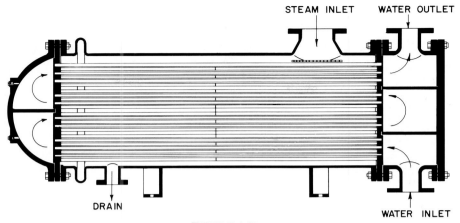

STEAM INLET   WATER OUTLET

DRAIN

WATER INLET

FIGURE 4.17
Closed feedwater heater

This results in rapid heating of the water and removes oxygen and other nondensable gases, which are vented. Heated and deaerated water is collected in a storage compartment of the heater or a separate tank. When the water level in the storage compartment or tank drops, a valve opens to provide makeup water to the heater.

The interior of the deaerating section of the heater is made of corrosion-resistant material. Condensate, which is above the temperature and pressure in the heater may be returned uncontrolled through a separate nozzle. In this way, all the heat content of the high-temperature condensate is reclaimed in the heater. The heater and water storage section is elevated to provide the necessary suction head on the boiler feed pumps. Sodium sulfite or hydrazine often is added to the water in the heater storage tank to remove the last trace of dissolved oxygen.

Feedwater heaters usually are selected to operate in a range of from 5 to 15 psig. The heaters reduce oxygen content of the water to 0.005 ml per liter and the carbon dioxide to zero. However, to maintain these levels, the heater must be vented adequately and pressure must be maintained at design levels.

Relief valves are provided to make sure that the safe pressure limits are not exceeded. The storage section must have an overflow valve or loop seal to limit the level. Because the level in the storage section is critical, it is advisable to have a level indicator on the control panel and an annunciator alarm, to warn the operating engineer when the level is too high or too low.

Steam pressures in the heater and the water level in the storage tank are regulated automatically. Even so, the amount of feedwater in the storage section will last only a few minutes if the supply fails. Usually, if steam pressure is maintained in the heater, the water will be deaerated satisfactorily. However, a dissolved oxygen analysis should be performed occasionally on the effluent water.

Ion-Exchange Water Conditioners

The problem of hard water can be solved through use of a sodium zeolite water softener. This type of softener exchanges hardness in the form of calcium and magnesium ions for sodium ions which do not produce hardness. Ion exchange material is contained in a steel tank designed to withstand the working pressure. Raw water is introduced above the bed. Ion exchange takes place as the water flows downward through the zeolite.

Normally the outlet water from these softeners is metered at zero hardness. When an outlet water sample indicates some hardness, the exchange material exhausted must be restored by regenerating with a brine solution (sodium chloride).

The regeneration process includes three steps:

1. The softener first is taken out of service. Then a current of water is passed up through the zeolite bed. As this water agitates and regrades the zeolite, it also washes away dirt deposited during the softening procedure.
2. After backwashing, the brine is introduced through a water-actuated eductor. The brine is distributed evenly above the zeolite bed, assuring an even flow through the bed and regeneration with a minimum of salt. During the process, zeolite sodium content is replenished, and the calcium and magnesium are removed as soluble chlorides.
3. Calcium and magnesium chloride, together with the excess salts, must be washed from the zeolite bed by a slow flow of rinse water after the salt has been introduced. After completion, softener may be returned to service.

Evaporators

Evaporators are used to remove impurities in water. Heat is applied and the steam or vapor produced leaves the impurities concentrated in the remaining water. When the steam or vapor is condensed, the resulting condensate has a high degree of purity.

A typical evaporator includes a steel shell with the necessary outlets and a bank of tubes making up the heating surface. Steam inside the tubes gives up heat to the surrounding water and is condensed. The condensate flows out through a trap which prevents the tubes from becoming flooded with condensate and also prevents steam from being discharged. The heat from the steam evaporates the water surrounding the tubes, and the resultant vapor leaves the unit through the outlet, while impurities remain within the shell of the evaporator. The vapor is at a lower pressure and temperature than the steam supplied to the evaporator. The rate of evaporation depends upon the temperature difference between the steam in the coils and the water surrounding them.

In the design and operation of an evaporator, consideration must be given to several details to ensure service and performance. Both the tube bundle and the shell must be designed to be strong enough to withstand the pressure involved. The shell must have a safety valve to prevent damage as a result of accidental over-pressure. As in boiler operations, priming and foaming may also occur in evaporators. This fault is overcome by designing the unit for sufficient water surface to prevent excessive agitation by steam bubbles and by installing moisture eliminators in the top of the shell at the steam outlet. The operator must keep liquid concentration low enough to prevent foaming and see that the water is at the specified level in the gage glass. Careless operation can result in solids' being carried over with the vapor, thus diminishing the advantages derived from the use of the evaporator.

Boiler Blowdown

In order to limit concentration of solids in boiler water it is necessary to discharge ("blowdown") some of the concentrated boiler water and replace it with makeup water. This procedure results in energy losses, because the water blown down had been chemically treated and heated to the temperature corresponding to the boiler pressure.

A good way to conserve energy is to recover heat from boiler water drained during continuous blowdown. Several flash tank and heat exchanger arrangements are available for reclaiming the water heat from boiler blowdown.

Steam Traps

A steam trap is a device attached to the lower portion of a steam-filled line or vessel which will pass condensate but will not allow the escape of steam. Traps are used on steam mains, headers, separators, and purifiers, where they remove the water formed as the result of unavoidable condensation or carry-over from the boilers. They are also used on all kinds of steam-heating equipment in which the steam gives up heat and is converted into condensate. Coils used in heating buildings, in water heaters, and in a wide range of industrial processing equipment are included in this classification.

Whether a trap is used to keep condensate from accumulating in a steam line or to discharge water from a steam-heated machine, its operation is important. If it leaks, steam will be wasted; if it fails to operate, water will accumulate. A satisfactory trap installation must pass all the water that flows to it without discharging steam, must not be rendered inoperative by particles of dirt or by an accumulation of air, and must be rugged in construction with few moving parts so that it will remain operative with a minimum of attention.

Many types of steam traps are available. Although these traps vary in design, they all utilize one of three basic operating principles: density, temperature, or velocity. From this group, four have emerged that presently fill the majority of requirements.

The balanced pressure thermostatic trap features bellows operation and is regulated by steam pressure and temperature as condensate flows to the trap. When condensate is close to steam temperature, vapor pressure inside the bellows causes the bellows to expand and tightly close the orifice. As condensate backs up in the cooling leg, the temperature begins to drop and the bellows contracts, opening the orifice and allowing the condensate, air, and noncondensable gases to be discharged.

Thermostatic traps are most efficient when used with very light loads. In this situation, the trap is less affected by condensate and the frequent changes in temperature. Other advantages of thermostatic traps include the ability to handle startup loads and to work efficiently against high back pressure.

Thermostatic traps are seldom used on applications where dirt, flash steam, or hydraulic shock may be encountered. The presence of any one of these can permanently impair operation and possibly cause the trap to fail completely.

The float and thermostatic steam trap is used most often on applications where the system being drained operates on a modulating steam pressure. This means that the pressure in the heat exchange unit can vary anywhere from the maximum steam supply pressure down to vacuum under certain conditions. Thus, under conditions of zero pressure, only the force of gravity is available to push condensate through the trap.

Float and thermostatic steam traps provide immediate drainage of condensate and incorporate a built-in thermostatic vent for eliminating air and noncondensable gases. The actual operation of the trap is quite simple, yet very efficient. A ball float is connected by a lever to the valve, and once condensate reaches a certain level in the trap, the float begins to rise, allowing condensate to be drained. The float is positioned above the orifice, so the condensate forms a water seal and helps prevent the loss of live steam. Since there are no pressure fluctuations due to intermittent operation, condensate is discharged at a constant temperature. At the top of the trap is a thermostatic air vent that discharges air and noncondensable gases as soon as they reach the trap and allows for maximum condensate drainage. This thermostatic air vent is responsive to temperature and will open at a temperature a few degrees below saturation. Therefore, this type of trap handles a large quantity of air due to its separate orifice.

Float and thermostatic traps also provide excellent service during startups and on very light loads. They operate efficiently against the presence of back pressure and respond immediately to slugs of condensate. Again, there are restrictions as to the types of applications these traps are capable of handling, for they have very poor resistance to the effects of dirt, hydraulic shock and flash steam. Despite these limitations, float and thermostatic traps have proved to be highly durable and efficient and continue to be used extensively on low pressure modulated systems.

The disc trap is very small and light and is consequently used on applications where space is limited, such as tracer and drip lines. The disc is the simplest of the four traps, having only one moving part. As condensate and air enter the trap, they pass through an inlet orifice, a control chamber, and, in some designs, a heating chamber. The heating chamber is designed to insulate the trap against severe weather conditions, and it is not a standard feature of all disc traps manufactured. The flow of condensate lifts the disc off the inlet orifice, allowing the condensate to flow through the outlet passages. When steam reaches the disc, increased flow velocity across the face of the disc reduces pressure at this point and increases pressure in the control chamber, closing the orifice. Controlled bleeding of steam from the control chamber reduces pressure, causing the trap to open and discharge any condensate that may be present. The trap then recloses in the presence of steam and continues to cycle at a controlled rate.

Besides the disc trap's simplicity and small size, it also offers advantages such as resistance to hydraulic shock, the complete discharge of all condensate when open, and intermittent operation for a steady purging action.

These advantages, while important, must be weighed against the disadvantage of inability to handle back pressure and startup air loads. In addition, the disc provides very poor resistance to dirt and wear and consequently results in a greatly increased loss of steam. The disc trap's relative dominance in the area of refineries and chemical plants is now being challenged, especially in light of today's heavy emphasis on energy conservation and long-term dependability.

The inverted bucket trap is a mechanical trap and operates on the difference in density between steam and water. Exactly as the name implies, the trap contains a small submerged inverted bucket that floats in the presence of steam and sinks whenever the weight of accumulated condensate exceeds a certain level.

When a bucket is down, a valve at the top of the trap is wide open. As the initial flood of condensate enters the trap and flows under the bottom edge of the bucket, it fills the trap body, and the bucket remains completely submerged. The excess condensate is then discharged through the open valve. As steam begins to flow to the trap, it collects until the bucket becomes buoyant. The bucket will then continue to rise and lift the valve toward its seat. Any air and carbon dioxide present in the system continually pass through a vent in the bucket and collect at the top of the trap. As the flow of condensate begins to increase, it will collect in the bucket, displacing steam until the bucket begins to lose buoyancy and pulls the valve away from the seat. This movement opens the orifice, allowing the accumulations of air and condensate to be completely discharged. This discharge will continue until more steam enters the trap and floats the bucket, at which time the entire cycle begins to repeat itself. This operation provides intermittent discharge of condensate, but continually handles all the condensate as quickly as it forms. The advantages and disadvantages of these four types become increasingly relevant as costs for energy requirements continue to grow.

Steam traps require regular maintenance to keep steam losses to a minimum.

As a very general guideline, steam traps should be checked according to the following timetable:

1. Process equipment at a high capacity operation (daily).
2. Process equipment at a medium capacity operation (medium).
3. Process equipment at a low pressure operation (annually).
4. Drip and tracer lines (every three months).

Some methods of testing steam traps are: A listening device is held against the trap cap. The difference between the intermittent discharge of some traps and the continuous discharge of others should be audible. A trap blowing steam is distinguishable by the sound of higher velocity.

The pyrometer method of testing can be combined with the listening method. A bright spot is filed on the trap inlet and outlet lines. If the temperature of the trap is at or near true steam temperature and the temperature of the trap discharge is at or near temperature corresponding with steam pressure in the return line, the trap is operating correctly. Fluctuations of the pyrometer needle when the thermocouple is contacting the discharge line indicate intermittent discharge. A blow-through condition may be indicated by equal temperature of both the inlet and discharge lines.

Infrared thermal measuring instruments may also be used to check the difference in temperature between the inlet and discharge sides of the trap. These "thermal guns" can check a steam trap as far as 100 ft away, facilitating checking of traps in hard to reach areas.

Steam trap problems can be identified and corrected using the troubleshooting guide provided in Table 4.5. Further, the trap manufacturers can be consulted to obtain guidance in establishing an effective program of steam trap testing and maintenance.

Pipeline Separators and Strainers

The air, steam, and gas flowing in a pipeline often include particles of moisture, oil, and other foreign matter. These impurities must be removed by separators or strainers located in the pipeline. There are many types of separators, and all employ the same principle. The moving stream is directed against a baffle or obstruction which suddenly changes the direction of flow of the steam, air or gas. Since particles of moisture or oil are heavier than the steam, air, or gas they are dropped out of the main stream at the point of direction change and remain in the separator.

A live-steam separator is used in a vertical steam line between the boiler and engine pump or turbine. This is a baffle-type separator in which both the baffle and the walls contain slanting corrugations. The moisture collected by these

TABLE 4.5

STEAM TRAP PERFORMANCE DIAGNOSIS GUIDE

Trap doesn't discharge
1. Steam pressure too high, pressure-regulating out of order, boiler-pressure gage reads low, steam pressure raised without altering or adjusting trap. On the last item consult trap maker; he can supply parts for higher pressure or tell you how to adjust trap.
2. Plugged strainer, valve, or fitting ahead of trap; clean.
3. Internal parts of trap plugged with dirt or scale; take trap apart and clean. Fit strainer ahead of trap.
4. Bypass open or leaking; close or repair.
5. Internal parts damaged or broken; dismantle trap, repair.

Trap won't shut-off
1. Trap too small for load; figure condensate quantity to be handled and put in correct-size trap.
2. Defective mechanism holds trap open; repair.
3. Larger condensate load from (a) boiler foaming or priming, leaky steam coils, kettles or other units, or (b) greater process load; find cause of increased condensate flow and cure, or install larger trap.
Note: Traps made to discharge continuously won't show these symptoms. Instead, the condensate line to trap overloads; water backs up.

Trap blows steam
1. Open or leaky bypass valve; close or repair.
2. Trap has lost prime; check for sudden or frequent drops in steam pressure.
3. Dirt or scale in trap; take apart and clean.
4. Inverted bucket trap too large, blows out seal; use smaller orifice or replace with smaller trap.

Trap capacity suddenly falls
1. Inlet pressure too low; raise to trap rating, fit larger trap, change pressure parts or setting.
2. Back pressure too high; look for plugged return line, traps blowing steam into return, open bypass or plugged vent in return line.
3. Back pressure too low; raise.

Condensate won't drain from system
1. System is air-bound; fit suitable vent or trap with larger air capacity to get rid of the air.
2. Steam pressure low; raise to the right value.
3. Condensate short-circuits; use a trap for each unit.

Not enough steam heat
1. Defective thermostatic elements in radiator traps; remove, test and replace damaged elements.
2. Boiler priming; reduce boiler-water level. If boiler foams; check fires and feed with fresh water while blowing down boiler at ¼-min intervals.
3. Scored or out-of-round valve seat in trap; grind seat or replace old trap body with new one.
4. Vacuum pump runs continuously; look for a cracked radiator, split-return main, cracked pipe fitting, or a loose union connection. Or pump shaft's packing may leak.
5. Too much water hammer in system; check drip-trap size. Undersized drip traps can't handle all condensate formed during warm-up so hammering results. Fit larger trap if drip lines are clean and scale-free. Size for warm-up load, not for load with mains hot.
6. System run down; older heating plants are sometimes troublesome because a large number of trap elements are defective. Easiest cure is replacement of all thermostatic elements in the radiators. This is low-cost, sure.

Back flow in return line
1. Trap below return main doesn't have right fittings; use check valve and a water seal, or both depending on what the trap maker recommends.
2. High-pressure traps discharge into a low-pressure return; flashing may cause high back pressure. Change piping to prevent return pressure from exceeding trap rating.
3. No cooling leg ahead of a thermostatic trap that drips a main; condensate may be too hot to allow trap to open right. Use a 4- to 6-ft. cooling leg ahead of thermostatic traps on this service. Fit strainer in cooling leg to keep solids out of trap.

corrugations is deposited in the well, and drained off by a steam trap. The flow reversal at the lower edge of the baffle separates steam from moisture.

Oil separators are not effective in removing all the oil from steam, air, or gas, so secondary filtering often is necessary. Condensate is passed through a filter to remove the last trace of oil before it is returned to the boilers. Filters are used for cleaning compressed air when small amounts of oil are objectionable.

Strainers can remove foreign matter from liquids flowing in a pipeline. Such a two-element arrangement provides for continuous service, as the shutoff valves place one element in operation while the other is being cleaned.

The most likely difficulty to be encountered by operating engineers with pipeline separators is failure of the trap to discharge the oil or water removed. Some separators have gauge glasses to show the level of water and oil in the bowl. However, it is difficult to keep these clean enough to be of any value.

WATER TREATMENT

Water treatment is a major concern in boiler maintenance. Inadequate water conditioning results in scale formation, corrosion, carryover, and caustic embrittlement.

Scale is a deposit of solids on the heating surfaces. Scale formation is caused by impurities initially dissolved in the boiler feedwater. As the water becomes concentrated and exposed to boiler pressures and temperatures, these impurities become insoluble and precipitate out as a deposit on heating surfaces. Water which contains scale-forming impurities is called "hard-water" and consumes a large quantity of soap before a lather is produced. Such impurities are found in some amount in almost all water supplies. The hardness of a given water sample can be determined by adding a standard soap solution to a measured amount of the water and noting how much is required to produce a lather. Hardness may be classified as temporary, carbonate, sulfate, or noncarbonate. Carbonates produce a soft, chalk-like scale, and this hardness may be removed by heating. Sulfate hardness produces a hard, dense scale and requires chemical treatment.

Scale reduces heat transfer, which can cause overheating of tube metal. Scale formation can be avoided by removing these minerals before water enters the boiler, by adding chemicals to the water to cause these solids to form a soft sludge which can be removed by blowdown, and bleeding off water.

Corrosion affects boilers, economizers, feed heaters, piping, and other system components. It is caused by a high acid concentration in water or by dissolved gases. It can be remedied by neutralizing water acidity with an alkali, taking care to keep the water from becoming too alkaline; by removing gases by deaeration, followed by a chemical "scavenger" to absorb remaining traces, and by feeding a corrosion inhibitor along with organic substances to protect surfaces of boiler and return lines.

Carryover occurs when water passing over steam causes erratic superheating, which, in turn, causes mechanical problems with engines and turbines. When solids pass over they are deposited in superheaters and on turbine blades. Oily water, high alkalinity, and suspended solids, are the main causes of foaming which leads to carryover. Blowdown and antifoam agents help combat carryover.

Caustic embrittlement occurs when sodium hydroxide in water is allowed to concentrate. This condition often results in metal failure along drum seams, under rivets and at tube ends. Embrittlement can be stopped by maintaining low hydroxide alkalinity, avoiding leaks at stressed metal and through use of special inhibiting agents.

Since water never exists in the totally pure form, all raw waters contain varying amounts of dissolved and suspended minerals or gases. Water impurities also exist in feedwater, condensate and boiler water. This makes the need for water treatment even more important for proper boiler operation. It is recommended that assistance be obtained from a water treatment consultant in order to select the most appropriate process and equipment for a specific installation and existing conditions.

WATER SOFTENING

In water, minerals dissolve as tiny particles called IONS which carry an electrical charge. The ions increase water's electrical conductivity and hardness. Both can damage a boiler. Increased conductivity can lead to rapid corrosion, while high level of hardness cause scale and sludge to form. Calcium and magnesium mineral salts are among those most often found dissolved in water. Two devices for removing those mineral salts are chemical and ion exchange softeners.

Chemical softeners convert dissolved mineral salts to solid form with soda ash and lime, and are most effective when the water is heated above its boiling point by steam. The heat removes some of the dissolved gases, reduces the amount of softening chemicals required, and speeds the softening process.

The softener is a large cylinder-shaped tank. Water comes into contact with steam at the top (Figure 4.18). Lime and soda ash enter the upper section of the softener and mix with the water as it is heated. After reacting with the mineral salts, the chemicals form solids or precipitates which settle to the bottom of the tank. The softened water then passes through an outlet and flows through filters which remove the solids.

Ion exchange softening uses a thick bed of grainy materials called resins that look like sand. Untreated water flows through the ion exchange softener (see Figure 4.19), where the resin bed absorbs the mineral ions and replaces them with other ions which do not create hardness. When the resin bed's capacity for

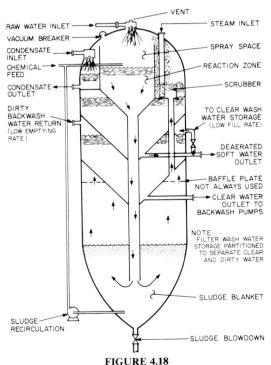

FIGURE 4.18
A chemical softener (hot process)
Illustration from the Betz Handbook of Industrial Water Conditioning, Eighth Edition
(Courtesy of Betz Laboratories, Inc.)

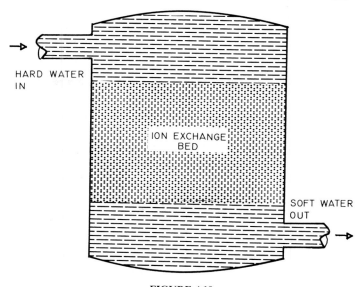

FIGURE 4.19
An ion exchange water softener

absorbing hardness ions is exhausted, it must be regenerated with a strong salt solution to replenish its supply of softening ions. For example, the commonly used sodium zeolite softener replaces scale forming calcium and magnesium ions with sodium ions. A brief description of the various ion exchange softening processes is as follows.

SODIUM ZEOLITE SOFTENING

Sodium zeolite softening is the most common process used for boiler feed-water treatment. In this process, water passes through a bed of zeolite material which exchanges sodium ions for scale forming ions of magnesium and calcium. After passing through the zeolite process, the water still contains as much sulfate, bicarbonate and chloride as before and there is no reduction in the overall amount of dissolved solids and the alkalinity content. When it is necessary to reduce the amount of total dissolved solids, zeolite must be coupled with other methods such as lime zeolite softening.

HOT LIME ZEOLITE SOFTENING

In this process hydrated lime is used to react with the bicarbonate alkalinity of the raw water. The precipitate is calcium carbonate and is filtered from the solution. To reduce silica, the natural magnesium of the raw supply can be precipitated as magnesium hydroxide, which acts as a natural absorbent for silica. These reactions are carried out in a vat or tank located just ahead of the zeolite softener tank. The effluent from this tank is filtered and then introduced into the zeolite softener. Some residual hardness always leaks from the hot-process softener and must be removed in the final process. The hot lime process operates at about 220°F. At this temperature the potential for the exchange of sodium for hardness ions is greater than at a lower temperature, and the result is a lower hardness effluent than can be achieved at ambient temperatures. A schematic illustration of the system is shown in Figure 4.20.

Hot lime zeolite—split stream softening

Many raw water types softened by the first two mentioned processes would contain more sodium bicarbonate than is acceptable for boiler feedback purposes. Sodium bicarbonate will decompose in the boiler water to create caustic soda. Caustic soda in high concentrations is corrosive and promotes foaming. The American Boiler Manufacturers Association has adopted the standard that the alkalinity should not exceed 20% of the total solid content of the boiler water. Split stream softening helps reduce the alkalinity content.

A second zeolite tank is required which has a zeolite resin in the hydrogen form in addition to the usual tank with the resin in the sodium form. The two tanks are operated in parallel. In one tank, calcium and magnesium ions are replaced by hydrogen ions. The effluent from this tank with the resin in hydrogen is on the acid side and has a lower total-solids content. The flow can be proportioned between the two tanks to produce an effluent of any desired alkalinity as well as with excellent hardness removal. When the hydrogen resin is exhausted, it is regenerated with acid. Figure 4.21 is a flow diagram of a typical system.

DEMINERALIZATION

Demineralization is another ion exchange process. In this process, hydrogen cation (positively charged metallic-type ions) exchange converts dissolved salts to their corresponding acids, and basic anion (negatively charged sulfate, carbonate and chloride-type ions) exchange removes these acids.

The two types of resins can be located in separate tanks. In this system, the two tanks are operated in series in a cation-anion sequence. The anion resin is

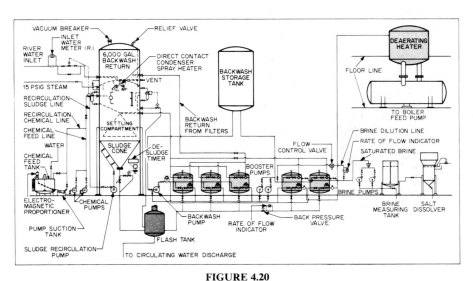

FIGURE 4.20
Hot lime/hot ion exchange softening system
Illustration from the Betz Handbook of Industrial Water Conditioning, Eighth Edition
(Courtesy of Betz Laboratories, Inc.)

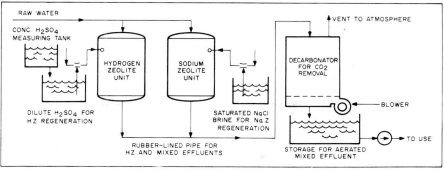

RAW WATER

CONC. H₂SO₄
MEASURING TANK

VENT TO ATMOSPHERE

HYDROGEN
ZEOLITE
UNIT

SODIUM
ZEOLITE
UNIT

DECARBONATOR
FOR CO₂
REMOVAL

BLOWER

DILUTE H₂SO₄ FOR
H Z REGENERATION

SATURATED NaCl
BRINE FOR Na Z
REGENERATION

TO USE

RUBBER-LINED PIPE FOR
HZ AND MIXED EFFLUENTS

STORAGE FOR AERATED
MIXED EFFLUENT

FIGURE 4.21

Hydrogen and sodium zeolite units in parallel

Illustration from the Betz Handbook of Industrial Water Conditioning, Eighth Edition

(Courtesy of Betz Laboratories, Inc.)

regenerated after exhaustion with a solution of sodium hydroxide. The cation resin is regenerated with an acid, either hydrochloric or sulfuric. Some leakage of cations always occurs in a cation exchanger, resulting in leakage of alkalinity from the anion exchanger.

In another arrangement, known as the mixed-bed demineralizer, (Figure 4.22) the two types of resins are mixed together in a single tank. In the mixed-bed demineralizer, cation and anion exhanges take place virtually simultaneously, resulting in a single irreversible reaction that goes to completion. Regeneration is possible in a mixed bed because the two resins can be separated hydraulically into distinct beds. Resins can be regenerated in place or sluiced to external tanks.

Raw water for drum-type boilers operating above 2000 psi drum pressure and water for once-through units should be prepared by passing the liquid through a mixed bed demineralizer as a final step before adding to the cycle.

Demineralization leaves the effluent nearly neutral. With almost all salts removed, the problem of chemical control of the boiler water is minimized.

FEEDWATER DEAERATION

Gases dissolved in water can cause many corrosion problems. For example, oxygen in water produces particularly severe pitting because it is localized. Carbon dioxide corrosion often is encountered in condensate systems and, less commonly, in water distribution systems. Water containing ammonia readily corrodes copper and copper-bearing alloys. Deaeration is widely used to remove these dangerous dissolved gases from water to help control corrosion. It most especially is used to remove oxygen from boiler feedwater systems.

Pressure deaerators, which are the tray type or the spray type are commonly used to prepare boiler feedwater. In general, the boiler feedwater is deaerated by spraying it into a steam atmosphere. This heats the water to within a few degrees of the temperature of the saturated steam. Since the oxygen's solubility in water is very low under these conditions, 97 to 98 percent of the oxygen in the incoming water is released to the steam and purged from the system by venting. Remaining oxygen is insoluble under equilibrium conditions, but not readily released to the steam. As a result, water leaving the heating section of the deaerator must be scrubbed vigorously with steam to remove the last traces of oxygen.

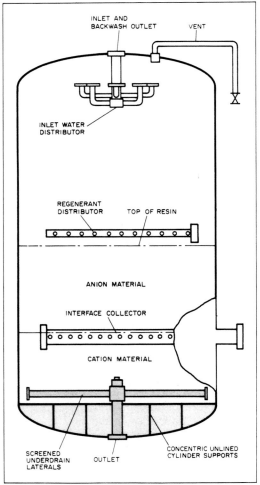

FIGURE 4.22

Mixed bed ion exchange unit, showing internal distributors

Illustration from the Betz Handbook of Industrial Water Conditioning, Eighth Edition

(Courtesy of Betz Laboratories, Inc.)

This equipment must be kept in peak operating order over the complete load range. If the deaerator operates under a vacuum at low loads, the entrance of air must be prevented. Oxygen concentrations at the deaerator outlet should be consistently less than 0.007 ppm.

OXYGEN CONTROL

As a further assurance against the destructive effect of dissolved oxygen, it is a good practice to use chemicals to remove the last traces of oxygen from feedwater.

Sodium sulfite may be added to the deaerated water in sufficient quantities to maintain recommended concentrations. Figure 4.23 shows the recommended sulfite concentration as a function of boiler pressure. The amount of sulfite which can be carried safely decreases as pressure increases. At the high

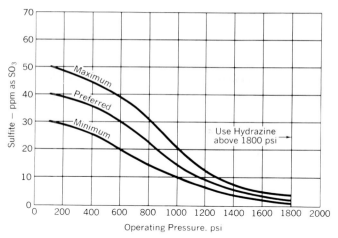

FIGURE 4.23

Recommended sulfite residual in boiler water
(Courtesy of The Babcock & Wilcox Co.)

temperatures associated with the higher pressures, sulfite decomposes into acidic gases that can increase corrosion. Consequently, sulfite should not be used at pressures greater than 900 psi. On boilers with spray attemperation, sodium sulfite should be added after the attemperation take-off point. About 8 ppm is required to remove 1 ppm of oxygen.

Where economizers are used, sulfite residuals from 10 to 15 ppm and pH values above 8.3 may be maintained in the feedwater to protect the economizer section of the system against oxygen attack.

Hydrazine is another chemical used to neutralize the corrosive effects of free oxygen. It comes with oxygen to form water and nitrogen and, therefore, does not increase the concentration of solids in the boiler water. Ammonia is formed from the hydrazine and is carried from the boiler with the steam, where it neutralizes carbon dioxide and reduces corrosion in the condensate return lines.

Hydrazine is a toxic liquid and must be handled with care. Because pure hydrazine is highly flammable and has a low flash point, a 35 percent solution, which has no flash point is usually used.

PH CONTROL

Makeup water supply with a low pH can produce serious acid attack on metal surfaces in the preboiler system. Surface water supplies may be contaminated with acid mine water drainage. Waters contaminated by trade wastes also may have a low pH. Even if the original makeup water source is *not* low in pH, feedwaters can become acidic from sources in the process system.

Water with a low pH atacks a steel, but with a general rather than a localized corrosion. Neutralizing the pH with an alkali such as soda ash or caustic soda is effective. In systems which use deionized makeup, neutralizing amines such as morpholine and cyclohexlamine can be used. Where economizers are used, the feedwater pH should be well above neutral. A pH range of 8.3 to 9.0 normally is sufficient to insure against acid attack.

BOILER CORROSION AND CONTROL

Proper treatment of the preboiler system will effectively protect against corrosion by dissolved oxygen or low pH. Problems often develop with the direct introduction of undeaerated water into the boiler for hydrostatic testing or rapid cooling of the boiler in taking it out of service. Insufficient control of chemical cleaning methods also may be responsible for corrosion through acid attack or corrosion cells initiated by the redepositing of copper on freshly cleaned surfaces.

To remove dissolved oxygen completely, an excess of chemical deaerant is needed in the boiler water. Daily tests will indicate the amount of excess. Records should be kept of the amount of chemical deaerant fed. This record provides a constant check of mechanical deaeration efficiency as well as an indication of any dissolved oxygen infiltrated into the system. A drop in chemical deaerant residual and the accompanying need to increase the feed of the chemical deaerant indicate a problem. The system must be checked to find the source of increased oxygen and measures must be taken to alleviate the condition.

BOILER WATER TREATMENT

Boiler water treatment involves the use of chemicals for direct or internal treatment. Chemicals are added to the boiler water either to precipitate the impurities so that they can be removed in the form of sludge or to convert them to salts which will stay harmlessly in solution. Phosphate salts are used extensively to react with the hardness in the water and prevent scale deposits. However, phosphate reacts with the hardness in the water to form sludge; which in some cases may result in objectionable deposits. Organic compounds then are used to keep the sludge in circulation until it can be removed through blowdown. The amount of sludge depends upon the amount of hardness of feedwater introduced into the boiler. As has been noted, it is desirable to have the hardness of the feedwater as low as possible.

The phosphate treatment should be supplied to the boiler drum directly with a chemical pump. Most phosphates will react with the impurities in the water if introduced into the suction of the boiler feed pump, and cause deposits in the pumps, piping, feedwater regulators, and valves. Phosphate therefore, should be dissolved in the condensate to prevent a deposit in the chemical feed pump and lines. The amount of treatment is controlled by an analysis of the boiler water for excess phosphate. This analysis uses a color comparison of a treated sample matched against standards. An excess of 30 to 50 ppm is enough to ensure removal of the hardness. Since this phosphate treatment removes the hardness, it is not necessary to run a soap hardness test on boiler water if the specified excess is maintained.

Care must be taken in introducing phosphate into a boiler which contains scale. Old scale may be loosened from the tubes by the phosphate action and collect in a mass on the heating surface. This, in turn, can cause bags, overheating, and ultimate failure. When phosphate is introduced in a boiler which already contains scale, the boiler should be inspected frequently and the amount of excess maintained at about 20 ppm. In time the phosphate will remove the old scale, but it is best to start the treatment with a clean boiler.

Another method of internal boiler water conditioning is based on the use of chemicals which prevent the precipitation of scale-forming materials. These chemicals have chelating power to tie up calcium, magnesium, and other common metals in the water solution. This action prevents formation of scale and sludge in boilers, heat exchangers and piping, and is effective over the entire normal range of alkalinity encountered in boiler-plant operation. A compound referred to as EDTA (ethylene-diaminetetraacetic acid) is the active material in several products used for such treatment.

The treatment is introduced into the boiler feed line through a chemical feed pump. The pump and piping should be of corrosion-resistant stainless steel for high pressure conditions and of either stainless steel or plastic for low pressure conditions. A continuous feed is desirable, and a slight excess should be maintained in the boiler water at all times.

Even if there is a deficiency for a short time, however, the deposits will be removed when the excess is restored.

The choice between the use of chelating materials or phosphate depends upon the condition in the specific plant, the quantity of makeup water, and the amount and type of impurities which it contains. The relative cost of the two methods and anticipated results can be determined by a water-conditioning consultant.

CONDENSATE TREATMENT

Condensate usually does not require treatment before reuse. Makeup water is added directly to the condensate to form boiler feedwater. In some cases, though, condensate is contaminated by corrosion products. Steps must be taken to reduce corrosion and to remove undesirable substances before the condensate is recycled to the boiler as feedwater.

The presence of acidic gases in steam acidify the condensate, with consequent corrosion of metal surfaces. In such cases, the corrosion rate can be reduced by feeding chemicals to the boiler water which produce alkaline gases in the steam.

Many types of contaminants can be introduced to condensate in a variety of ways. These can include liquids, such as oil and hydrocarbons, as well as all sorts of dissolved and suspended materials. Each installation must be studied for potential sources of contamination. The recommendations of a water consultant should be obtained to assist in appropriate corrective treatment.

Several types of condensate purification systems are available from a variety of manufacturers. Some of these are capable of operation at temperatures as high as 300°F. A variety of condensate polishing systems, involving the application of ion exchange also are available.

ANALYTIC METHODS

Water treatment systems are subject to changes in operating cycles which can affect feedwater quality. For example, the resin bed of a demineralizer can become exhausted more quickly than expected, allowing impurities to leak through the demineralizer. Even small amounts of impurities in steam or water can damage equipment and reduce efficiency. Water tests made on a regular basis can alert operating personnel to such problems so that corrective action can be taken.

The kind of tests to be made depend on the type of impurities found in the water supply. Tests are recommended which determine the amounts of both impurities and treatment chemicals in the feedwater.

Impurity tests include checks on dissolved oxygen, silica, hardness, and alkalinity, plus pH value and conductivity. Treatment chemical tests check the level of phosphate and hydrazine to ensure proper supply.

Water tests can be made manually or with automatic monitoring devices. While the test methods vary with the type of equipment used, careful records of the readings must always be kept. A slight change in readings can indicate a minor problem which could become serious if not corrected immediately.

CHAPTER 5

Air Conditioning

THE GENERAL ACCEPTANCE of air conditioning for all types of occupancy has resulted in larger water chilling loads for individual buildings. From the viewpoint of the district heating and cooling industry, space cooling affords an opportunity to improve its annual load factor appreciably assuming generally that both heating and cooling will utilize the same thermal source(s).

Differing somewhat from district heating where users are supplied a source of heat via either steam or hot water distribution systems, cooling allows some design choices:

1. Low pressure steam or hot water is furnished to the users premises on a year round basis and absorption type chillers are incorporated into the heating and ventilating systems.
2. A central chilled water plant supplies cooling to the user via a separate distribution network.
3. One piping system transports hot water or chilled water from a central plant in relation to demand or in accordance with the season of the year.
4. A high pressure steam system is made available to drive turbines for air conditioning machinery.

STATISTICS

According to 1981 statistics distributed chilled water sales in the U.S. totaled 3,718M daily tons, an increase of 9.7% from the prior year. Total installed chiller capacity was 168,045 tons per hour, of which 105,500 was by steam turbine drive, 48,400 tons was electric motor drive, 140 tons gas engine drive and the balance absorption chillers.

The 45 companies responding to the IDHA statistics inquiry reported a steam air conditioning total tonnage of 66,222. However, a significant number of tons is not reported by the solicitated companies for a variety of reasons, among these being the objective to replace the steam units with electric drive compressors.

SYSTEM DESIGN CONSIDERATIONS

When designing an air conditioning system for a related group of buildings, such as found in factory complexes, college campuses, shopping centers, urban business districts, garden, and high rise apartments, it often becomes desirable to consider a central chilled water plant. The reasons for this are:

1. Initial cost is lower for a few larger water chillers than for many smaller ones.
2. Fuel or power costs are lower because the total capacity can be utilized more efficiently.

3. Operation and maintenance expenses are lower because less manpower is required.
4. More usable space is available because equipment is centralized and space is not required in each individual building.
5. Machinery noise and vibration problems are reduced.
6. Standby capacity is available at minimum cost.

Load Concentration

For central plants to be practical, experience indicates that the load concentration should be 150 to 250 tons per 100 lineal feet of distribution piping runs. Loads of this magnitude are usually found in factory complexes, college campuses, industrial complexes and shopping centers. Urban business districts and garden or high rise apartments need to be carefully analyzed to see if they qualify.

Piping System Cost

A basic consideration is the installed cost of the piping system. The ideal situation exists when the buildings are close together on a reasonably flat site. Conditions that contribute to prohibitive distribution costs are rocky subsoil, high water table and sharply variable ground contour. As a general guideline, if the cost of the piping system is less than one-third of the total chilled water system cost, consideration should be given to a central chilled water plants.

Size of Individual Water Chillers

It is evident that with a central plant fewer large tonnage water chillers can be used than would be practical in various individual buildings and as large water chillers generally will cost less per ton than the smaller units, this is a favorable influence to the overall cost of the project.

Space Utilization

The effective utilization of space is a factor that bears on the total cost of the equipment. The cost of space in a building designed for central plant purposes probably will be one-half to three-quarters of the cost of an equal amount of space within an air conditioned structure. With large tonnage machines, the space per ton required to house the larger chillers will be about ten percent less than for smaller units.

Diversity of Load

It has been found by tests on central plants that the maximum simultaneous load is considerably less than the sum of the maximum loads for all buildings in the system. The average value is around 60 percent of the maximum load. Diversity of load is, therefore, an important factor in the overall plant cost.

Determination of Load

The determination of the individual building loads is done in the normal manner. In order to fully evaluate the effect of diversity in system design, however, it is desirable to make an hour by hour analysis of each individual building so that the requirements of all the buildings can be integrated hour by hour to obtain the greatest advantage of this factor.

Design Chilled Water Temperature

The design chilled water temperature for a central plant project must be determined carefully. It must be selected to assure proper space conditions while achieving optimum balance between first cost and operating expense.

The water temperature must be low enough to provide the required dehumidification. On the other hand, it must be high enough to achieve a reasonable first cost and operating expense. Table 5.1 shows how the operating horsepower increases with lower chilled water design temperatures. The parameters used in this table include a rise of 6°F from the compressor to the chiller outlet and a 105°F condensing temperature. The brake horsepower per ton is based on refrigerant-11 properties.

Keeping the leaving chiller water temperature as high as practical will reduce the first cost of the compressor and driver. It will also result in lower operating expense because of the lower horsepower required. Both these points are clear from an examination of the table.

The logical approach to establishing the maximum design chilled water temperature is to determine the temperature required at each building and adjust in this temperature by the heat pickup in the piping and that added by the pumps. Minor adjustments may be required to obtain an optimum balance between pipe size and equipment operation.

Chilled Water Quantity

With the individual building load and the design chilled water temperature established, the amount of water that must be circulated may be determined. The dT differential temperature should be as high as possible without seriously penalizing the amount of the heat transfer surface in air handling units. The range should be from 12 to 18°F.

Piping

In considering the total central plant piping arrangement, there are a number of ways that the piping can be divided. In general whenever there is a pump or group of pumps that handle the chilled water in a separate circuit, such as in an individual building, this is termed a "loop". The distribution piping in a building is called the *building loop.*

If the project is widespread and handles a large area, it is generally desirable to provide a complete piping circuit with its pumps to distribute the water between the equipment and the individual buildings. This then becomes the *distribution loop.*

TABLE 5.1

RELATIONSHIP OF CHILLED WATER TO HORSEPOWER

Leaving Chiller Water Temperature °F	Compressor Conditions			Percent HP Increase
	Suction Temp °F	Condenser Temp °F	BHP/Ton	
44	38	105	1.014	0
42	36	105	1.054	4.0
40	34	105	1.090	8.5
38	32	105	1.129	11.1
36	30	105	1.170	15.4

The third piping system with its associated pumps handles the water flow between the water chillers and the distribution loop. This is called the *equipment loop*.

The three-loop system generally will be used on large tonnage projects, that is, above 5,000 tons. Smaller installations generally can be handled satisfactorily with the equipment and distribution loops combined.

Equipment Selection

CENTRIFUGAL CHILLER DRIVES

The centrifugal equipment may be electric drive or steam drive. Size and cost will dictate the specific type. Where there is steam available for heating, it may be used to drive a centrifugal compressor through a turbine if the pressure is 125 psig or higher and may exhaust at a pressure of 15 psig to an absorption unit or units. This efficient combination is known as a turbine-absorption combination water chiller.

It is also practical to drive compressors with either a natural gas engine or a gas turbine. For greatest efficiency, the heat normally wasted from the exhaust and jacket water of the engine or the exhaust of the turbine must be conserved. It is possible to convert this energy into steam that can be used to power an absorption type water chiller. Unless the waste heat is fully utilized, the direct gas-fired drivers are high in both operating expense and first cost.

COOLING TOWER SELECTION

The condenser water temperature will be determined from cooling tower performance in the normal manner. For best performance results there should be a separate tower for each chiller or at least a separate cell in a multi-cell tower.

PUMP SELECTION

The number and size of pumps in the distribution loop must be correlated with the increment size of the main plant water chillers. This is necessary in order to assure that the flow of water in the distribution loop is always less than the flow in the central plant loop. The flow in the central plant loop usually will fall in the range of 2.4 to 3 gallons per minute per ton of chilling.

Summary

In summary, the basic factors in the design of a central plant project are:
1. There must be sufficient load in a relatively confined area to justify a central plant. This must be concentrated to the point of 150 to 250 tons per 100 feet of distribution piping.
2. The size of the project and local conditions will dictate whether two or three piping loops are required.
3. When establishing water flows in the buildings, it is desirable to use as high a delta T as is practical, preferably in the range of 12 to 18 F.
4. Use two-way modulating valves for load control in the building so that the flow follows the load.
5. If a separate distribution loop appears desirable, it must be designed with a greater water flow than the building loop.
6. When an equipment loop is used, it must be designed for the greatest water flow.

7. Multiple pumps may be used in the distribution loop, but their size should be coordinated with the basic water chiller size.

ABSORPTION SYSTEM

An absorption system consists of an *evaporator, absorber, generator, condenser, two or three motor-driven pumps*, a *heat exchanger*, and a *purge unit*.

A sorbent solution in the refrigerant circuit absorbs refrigerant vapor from the cooler. This mixture then is heated in a generator to boil off the refrigerant and strengthen the sorbent. The refrigerant vapor is liquefied in the condenser and returned to the cooler; the strengthened sorbent solution is returned to the absorber.

Absorption systems generally are lithium-bromide salt-water systems or ammonia-water systems. Lithium bromide systems use lithium bromide to absorb refrigerant water vapor; ammonia-water systems use water to absorb the refrigerant ammonia vapor. In both, pumps are used to spray absorbent in the absorber and refrigerant in the cooler to increase efficiency of absorption and evaporation. A heat exchanger is used to conserve heat in the system and cooling water is used to remove heat to be rejected from the system. In some chillers the generator and condenser are combined in a high-pressure shell, with the absorber and cooler being combined in a second shell. In other chillers, all four elements are combined within a single shell. A purge unit is included with the absorber to remove any non-condensables from the system, thus assuring maximum efficiency and capacity at all times. The heat required by the generator may be obtained from flame, steam, hot water or other heated liquids. Absorption equipment is fully automatic from full load to no load. Performance does not vary greatly between 20% capacity and full load.

Basic Operating Cycle

The basic operating cycle of an absorption system using lithium bromide salt and water is described below. Components are added progressively to illustrate operation.

Figure 5.1 shows the evaporator or cooler which contains the refrigerant water, the absorber which contains the salt solution, and a pipe connecting the two vessels. Both vessels and the pipe are maintained at well below atmospheric pressure. The salt solution in the absorber has the affinity for water vapor and thus evaporates some of the water in the evaporator. The evaporative process cools the water remaining in the evaporator.

Figure 5.2 illustrates the addition of a recirculating system for each vessel and the coil which connects the evaporator to the refrigeration load in a closed circuit. The refrigerant water is sprayed over the coil by a pump and spray header so that each droplet provides more surface for evaporation. The evaporation and cooling effect of the spray on the coil surface chills the water, brine, or air circulating through the coil. The salt solution is sprayed into the absorber by a second pump and spray header to provide more solution surface for absorption.

The salt solution becomes diluted as it absorbs water vapor, thereby reducing its ability to absorb more. Accordingly, as shown in Figure 5.3, the solution is pumped into a generator to keep it at proper strength. Heat in the form of low-pressure steam (2 to 12 psig) or hot water (225 to 400°F) is applied in the generator to boil off absorbed water from the weak solution. The strong salt solution is then returned to the absorber to repeat its work.

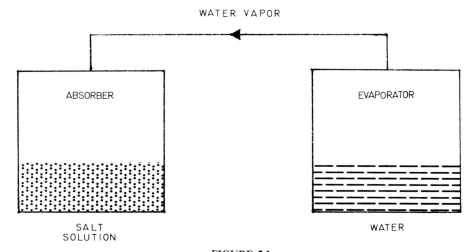

FIGURE 5.1

Absorption refrigeration cycle

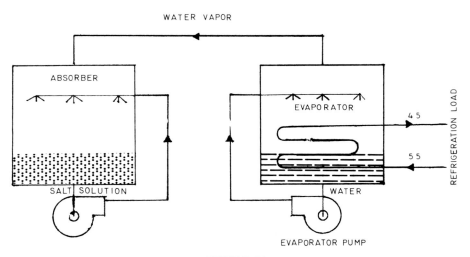

FIGURE 5.2

Absorption refrigeration cycle

The water which is boiled off in the generator turns into vapor which then is liquified in the condenser and returned to the evaporator where the cycle is repeated, as shown in Figure 5.4. A heat exchanger picks up heat from the hot concentrated salt solution and transfers it to the cooler, weak solution from the absorber for preheating. Condensing (or cooling) water from a cooling tower (or other source) is circulated through coils in the condenser and absorber to remove *heat-of-dilution* from the absorber and *heat-of-condensation* from the condenser. The waste heat is then rejected at the condensing water source.

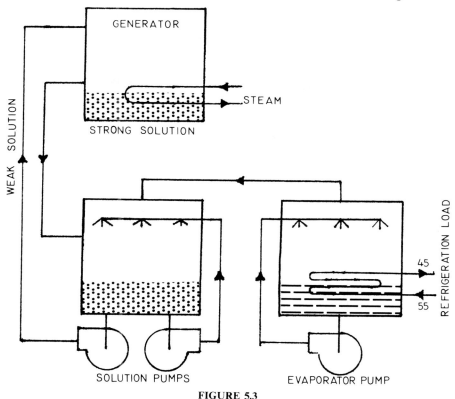

FIGURE 5.3

Absorption refrigeration cycle

Advantages

Some of the advantages of absorption systems include:
1. Small power requirement because power is required only to operate pumps, typically 20 hp total for nominal 1000-ton system.
2. Quiet operation thus eliminating any need for sound attenuation, and making them ideally suited for hospitals, libraries, churches, hotels, apartment buildings, and office buildings.
3. Vibration-free operation because the only moving parts are pumps and their small motors.
4. Lightweight making installation possible almost anywhere in any building. They range from 10,000 pounds for a 120-ton unit to just over 90,000 pounds for a 1,400-ton unit.
5. Efficient, economical part-load operation typically using less than 18.3 pounds steam/hr/ton at 12 psi pressure, and even less at part loads.
6. Low input energy because they are designed to operate on low-heat-energy sources such as low-pressure steam, hot water, or almost any hot fluid. Waste heat recovered from steam-turbine drives, natural-gas engines, gas turbines, and waste-heat boilers can be used.
7. Safe operation because no high pressure or volatile fluids are used.
8. Low-cost maintenance because there are few moving parts to service and refrigerant is inexpensive and readily available.

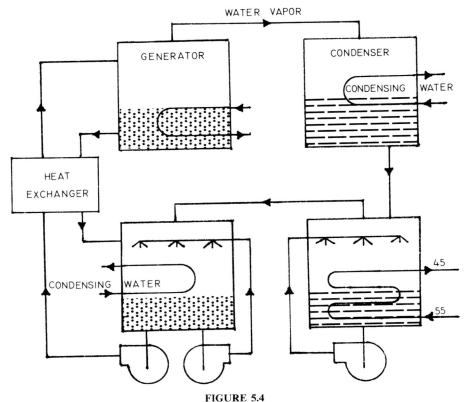

FIGURE 5.4
Absorption refrigeration cycle

Large Tonnage Absorption Machines

Large absorption machines are constructed in one, two or more shells or sections depending on the manufacturer or the application. They also come as single-stage or two-stage units. In a two-stage unit, heat derived from refrigerant vapor boiled from solution in the first stage concentrator (generator) is used to boil out additional refrigerant in the second concentrator.

CAPACITY CONTROL

Absorption machines meet load variations and maintain chilled water temperature control by varying the reconcentration rate of absorbent solution.

At any given load, the chilled water temperature is maintained by a temperature difference between refrigerant and chilled water. The refrigerant temperature is maintained in turn both by the absorber being supplied with a flow rate and concentration of absorbent and by the absorber cooling water temperature.

Load changes are reflected by corresponding changes in chilled water temperature. A load reduction, for example, results in less temperature difference being required in the evaporator and a reduced requirement for solution flow or concentration.

All units sense the chilled water temperature changes resulting from a load change with a thermostat in the leaving chilled water. In most units available today, the chilled water thermostat controls an automatic valve which regulates the heat input by reducing hot water flow or steam pressure.

A single-stage absorption machine operating at nominal conditions typically has a COP in the range of 0.65 to 0.70, when COP is defined as cooling effect divided by heat. For two-stage machines, the COP range typically is 0.90 to 1.02.

When chilled water temperatures are above nominal or when condensing water temperatures are below nominal, a COP higher than 0.70 can be reached. Reversing temperature conditions reduces the COP to below 0.60. A coefficient of performance of 0.68 corresponds to a steam rate of 18 pounds per hour per ton (pounds/h/ton).

Two-stage absorption machines achieve steam rates of approximately 12 pound/h/ton at full load operation. These units typically require steam gage pressure at the generator control valve inlet to be in the 125 to 150 range.

MULTIPLE UNIT APPLICATION

Multiple units may be specified for reasons of flexibility and economy, or when additional capacity is required. They may be arranged for either series or parallel operation. In either case, a return water sensor (RWT) may be used to cycle either the lead or the lag unit (number one or number two in parallel operation) when one unit can carry the load.

MAINTENANCE

All units built today use corrosion inhibitors to protect internal parts. Use of corrosion inhibitors does not eliminate the need for proper operation and maintenance with regard to purging and leak tightness.

Whenever a machine is opened to the atmosphere, vacuum should be broken with dry nitrogen. Further, as long as the machine is open, a sustained atmosphere of nitrogen should be provided in the unit to prevent corrosive attack.

Maintenance of the purge system is particularly important. Manufacturer's instructions should be followed and effectiveness of the purge system should be verified periodically. Periodic evaluation of machine leak-tightness should also be made. All manufacturers of this equipment describe procedures for measuring the leak rate, bubble count, or non-condensable accumulation rate of their machines. If the measured rate is excessive, indicating air leakage into the machine, it is very important to find the leak and repair it as soon as possible.

It is necessary to replace valve diaphragms, pump seals (where used), motor bearings, and other mechanical parts subject to wear and/or aging on a schedule recommended by the manufacturer.

Periodic cleaning of internal condensing or cooling water tube surfaces is usually required regardless of water treatment effectiveness. The more effective the water treatment, the longer the allowable period of time between tube cleanings.

MECHANICAL COMPRESSION SYSTEM

There are four basic types of mechanical compression systems, categorized on the basis of the device used to drive the compressor. The four basic types of devices are electric motors, gas engines, gas turbines, and steam turbines.

Electrically-Driven Cooling System Chillers

In the past, most compressors and chillers used for air-conditioning have been electrically-driven. A discussion of electrically-driven chillers, based on the type of compressor involved is therefore provided.

RECIPROCATING CHILLERS

The capacity of a reciprocating chiller is expressed in terms of cooling output at design conditions specified by Air-Conditioning and Refrigeration Institute (ARI) Standards in nominal tons. (One nominal ton is equivalent to 12,000 Btu of heat removed in one hour of steady-state operation.)

Hermetic reciprocating chillers are available in nominal capacities up to 185 tons with a water-cooled condenser and 165 tons with air-cooled condenser.

Open-drive type reciprocating chillers are available in nominal capacities ranging from 50 to 240 tons.

Nominal Full-Load Performance

Figure 5.5 identifies manufacturers' listed coefficient of performance (COP) values for various size hermetic-type reciprocating compressor packaged chillers at nominal full-load operating conditions, as specified by ARI Standard 590-76. These COP values do not include the electrical input for heat rejection fans or chilled-water or condenser-water pumps. As can be seen, water-cooled reciprocating packaged chillers average about a 30% higher COP (3.65) at full-load conditions than the same reciprocating chiller package coupled to an air-cooled condenser (2.85).

Open drive reciprocating packaged chillers show approximately 5–8% higher COPs, since the compressor motor is cooled by air surrounding the machine.

Capacity Control

Reciprocating chillers are available with simple on-off cycling control in small capacities with multiple steps of unloading down to 12.5% in the largest multiple compressor units. Most intermediate sizes provide unloading to 50,

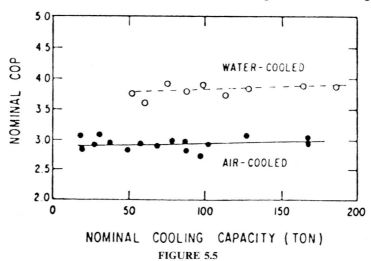

FIGURE 5.5

Full-load COP of a variety of reciprocating packaged chillers

33.3, or 25% capacity. When continuous operation below the minimum possible capacity is desired, hot-gas bypass can reduce capacity to almost 0%.

Multiple Unit Application

Reciprocating package chillers most commonly are used in parallel operation, with constant or variable water flow. Series applications also are employed, but far less frequently. The use of two or more smaller units as opposed to one larger unit provides far more operating flexibility. It results in energy conservation when capacity is matched to load by de-energizing units which are not needed. It also permits more convenient scheduling of maintenance and, should one unit break down, partial cooling can still be provided.

Economic Life

The economic life of reciprocating packaged chillers with nominal capacities of 15 tons or less is approximately 13 years. For larger units, economic life is estimated to be 20 years.

CENTRIFUGAL CHILLERS

The capacity of a centrifugal chiller is expressed in terms of the cooling output at design conditions as specified by ARI Standards in nominal tons.

Manufacturers and Available Size Ranges

Hermetic centrifugal packaged chillers currently are available in nominal capacities ranging from 80 to 2,000 tons.

Open-drive centrifugal packaged chillers are available in nominal capacities ranging from 90 to 1,250 tons. Large field-assembled, open-drive centrifugal chillers are available in sizes ranging from 700 to 5,000 tons. Multistage compressor models extend the range up to 10,000 tons.

Full-Load Performance

COP values for a variety of hermetic (from 90 to 2,000 tons) and open-type (from 90 to 1,250 tons) centrifugal chillers, at standards rating conditions (ARI Standard 550-77), are shown in Figure 5.6. An open-drive motor is air-cooled and does not require refrigerant motor winding cooling, improving the overall COP by 3 to 8%, as shown in the upper curve in Figure 5.6.

Part-Load Performance

Most centrifugal chillers can be operated down to 10% of design load. The part load COP and capacity of centrifugal chillers are dependent on both the condensing temperature and leaving chilled water temperature. Lower power input is needed with lower leaving condenser and leaving evaporator water temperatures.

Capacity Control

Centrifugal chillers can be operated down to 10 to 20% of the nominal rated capacity. Capacity control is normally provided by automatic devices that sense exiting chilled water temperature and adjust compressor capacity control devices such as variable inlet guide vanes or the suction dampers. If chilled water temperature continues to decrease after the capacity control has reached its minimum position, a low-temperature control will stop the compressor and then restart it when a rise in temperature indicates the need for cooling.

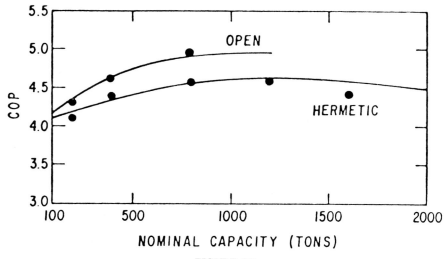

FIGURE 5.6

COP of various size centrifugal chillers

Centrifugal chillers also can be fitted with current limiting or demand limiting devices that limit compressor capacity during periods of possible high power consumption to prevent current draw from exceeding design value and to limit demand.

Multiple Unit Operation

Two or more centrifugal chillers can be applied with chilled and condenser water flowing in series through each. Assuming two units of equal size, each will shed capacity as the load decreases. When the load decreases to 40% of total capacity, one of the units will be shut down by a sequence control. If more than two units are installed, each should operate as near to 70% of full load as possible to obtain highest operating COP. (Most centrifugal machines use the least energy per ton at 60% to 80% of maximum rated capacity).

Economic Life

The economic life of a large centrifugal chiller ranges from 15 to 25 years.

SCREW CHILLERS

The capacity of a screw compressor chiller is expressed in terms of the cooling output at design conditions specified by ARI Standard 590-76; 95°F leaving condenser water temperature; 44°F leaving chilled water temperature, and 0.0005 fouling factor.

Screw compressor packaged chillers are available in nominal capacities ranging from 100 to 750 tons.

Full-Load Performance

The operating conditions used to display a nominal COP vs. chiller capacity curve are those stated by ARI Standard 590, and assume use of a normal two-pass chiller and condenser. The nominal COP values for several hermetic and open-type screw compressor chillers are shown in Figure 5.7.

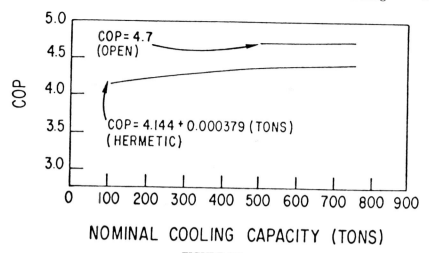

FIGURE 5.7

COP of various size screw compressor packaged chillers (hermetic)

Part-Load Performance

Part-load COP remains at or above the nominal COP down to 35% of full-load capacity. Below 35%, the COP drops relatively quickly, to about 77% of nominal value at 20% capacity.

Capacity Control

The leaving chilled water temperature of screw compressor chillers usually is sensed for capacity control. A hydraulically-actuated sliding valve arrangement controls the working length of the rotors and provides stepless capacity modulation from 100% down to 10% with complete system stability. Many screw compressor chillers are also fitted with a current limiter or demand limiter which limits compressor capacity during periods of high power consumption.

Economic Life

The economic life of a screw compressor packaged chiller is about 15 to 25 years.

Gas Engine-Driven Cooling Systems

Gas engines can be used to provide mechanical power to drive reciprocating, rotary screw or centrifugal refrigeration machines and may also indirectly supply steam to operate an absorption refrigeration machine by using the heat rejected from the engine cooling and exhaust system.

FUEL CONSUMPTION

Gas engines are from 20 to 30% efficient as converters of fuel to shaft energy. Fuel consumption of gas engines is customarily expressed in Btu per brake horsepower hour. Btu's are figured in terms of the "low heat value" of the fuel for this purpose. Two terms are associated with all hydrocarbon fuels and especially with natural gas, namely high heat value (HHV) and low heat value

(LHV). An understanding of heat value is an absolute essential when calculating or determining fuel consumption of gas prime movers.

Many local codes require use of standby fuels for natural gas engines. Most engines have this capability.

Manufacturers usually publish fuel consumption data at standard rating conditions. Manufacturers' "part-load" curves provide fuel consumption data for loads at several speeds.

HEAT RECOVERY

Because two-thirds of their input is dissipated as heat, gas engines offer significant opportunity for waste heat recovery. If waste heat is not recovered, cooling plant efficiency equals gas engine cooling system efficiency which, in turn, depends on the gas engine vs. load and load vs. heat balance curves. However, when heat is recovered and utilized, overall engine thermal efficiency can be as high as 80%.

Waste heat can be recovered from the engine jacket manifolds and exhaust in the form of hot water or low pressure steam. Additional heat can be recovered from the lubrication system, but this approach is not normally used unless maximum heat recovery is required. The amount of heat recoverable from the lubrication oil is relatively small, and the costs of large auxiliary oil coolers are high.

MAINTENANCE

Maintenance of gas engine-driven refrigeration compressors requires the services of competent, well-trained personnel.

Maintenance of the compressor section is similar to maintenance of electric-drive units except for the periodic gearbox oil changing and external lubricating pump care which may be required.

Engines require periodic servicing and replacement of parts depending on usage and type of engine. Actual maintenance intervals will vary according to cleanliness of the combustion air and engine room, the manufacturer of the engine, the number of engine starts and stops, and lubricating conditions as evidenced by oil analysis.

Maintenance contracts are offered by engine manufacturers and detailed data on costs and experience are available from them.

GAS ENGINE-DRIVEN HEAT PUMPS

An economic advantage is created when a gas engine-driven cooling unit is operated as a heat pump to also provide heat during winter months (using the same equipment both heating and cooling reduces capital investment). A gas engine-driven heat pump provides more heating cycle efficiency than motor-driven heat pumps by utilizing the recovered heat from the engine exhaust gas and jacket water.

Gas Turbine-Driven Cooling Systems

Gas turbines can be used directly to power centrifugal or screw chillers and, when their exhaust heat is used, can produce steam in a waste heat boiler for operation of an absorption machine or a steam driven centrifugal machine. Their waste heat can also be used directly to run an absorption machine.

Gas turbines are available in larger horsepower sizes. They normally are used with centrifugal refrigeration machines in applications ranging from 735 to 10,000 hp.

The gas turbine cycle consists of a compressor section where ambient air is compressed. The compressed air is passed into the combustion chamber where it is heated to 1450–1800°F by burning fuel directly in the air stream. The air and combustion products then flow into the expansion turbine section where they expand to atmospheric pressure. The energy released from the gas steam in the expansion process drives the compressor and produces output shaft power.

HEAT RECOVERY

Typical gas turbine efficiency ranges from 22 to 40% with exhaust gases from the turbine ranging from 806 F to 986 F. Overall thermal efficiencies can be increased to as much as 80% when exhaust heat is used as a source of preheated combustion air in a boiler or furnace, or to heat a process or working fluid such as the steam system. When exhaust is used directly as a source of heat to drive an absorption machine, efficiency can be increased to 90% or over.

MAINTENANCE

Industrial gas turbines are designed to operate 12,000 to 34,000 hours between overhauls with normal maintenance. However, when operated at part load, or under modulating load conditions as a chiller would normally operate, this life can be substantially extended. Normal maintenance includes operations such as checking filter and oil level and inspection for leaks. Specialized factory-trained service personnel are needed to conduct inspections for such engine components as combustors and nozzles. These inspections (depending on the manufacturer's recommendations) are required as frequently as every 4,000 hours of operation.

Steam Turbine-Driven Cooling Systems

Steam turbines are used for driving centrifugal refrigeration machines and condenser water circulating pumps. Steam turbines are usually selected to improve heat balance where exhaust or high pressure steam is available. Improved operating economies can be obtained by using steam turbines to drive a centrifugal refrigeration machine and an absorption chiller as well as fans or pumps.

A steam turbine may be operated as a condensing or non-condensing turbine. When steam is used for one application only, a condensing turbine drive produces power most economically. When steam is required for more than one application at different pressures, a non-condensing turbine (also called a backpressure turbine) provides power at the lowest cost.

Low pressure condensing turbines can be utilized where an abundance of low pressure steam is available. The exhaust steam from existing equipment can be used by the turbine to produce power from steam that otherwise would be wasted. Steam turbines are often used in the summer when available exhaust steam cannot be used for space heating.

Non-condensing turbines are most often used to drive centrifugal compressor chillers which share the cooling load with one or more absorption units. The turbine's 15 psig exhaust steam serves as the heat-energy source for the absorption unit's generator (concentrator). This dual use of heat energy generally lowers the energy input per unit of refrigeration output below that attainable from either the turbine-driven centrifugal or the absorption unit. To achieve good results, the combined system's turbine exhaust steam flow must be balanced with the absorption input steam requirements over the full range of anticipated load variations.

PERFORMANCE

A steam turbine's energy input is denoted in terms of its *steam rate* or *water rate*. Steam rate is expressed as pounds of steam per horsepower-hour. Actual steam rate (or design rate) is the theoretical steam rate of the turbine divided by its efficiency. Overall thermal efficiencies of steam turbines typically range from 55 to 80%. Manufacturers identify the turbine efficiencies and steam rates of their products.

The steam rate of a turbine is generally reduced with higher turbine speeds, greater number of stages, larger turbine size, and, a higher difference in heat content between entering and leaving steam conditions.

MAINTENANCE

Steam turbine maintenance concerns center on steam purity, steam flow control, and bearing lubrication systems that can affect internal turbine components. Steam path deposits, water ingestion, and lubrication system problems account for 87% of total forced outage hours. Case histories indicate that a maximum forced outage rate of 0.05% is realistically attainable. Outage hours for planned inspection and maintenance usually are double those of forced outage hours. In many installations, a complete inspection is scheduled after the first year of operation and thereafter at three-year intervals.

CHAPTER 6

Distribution Systems

THE THERMAL transmission and distribution system must be capable of conveying the thermal energy to consumers economically and efficiently. The final choice of a piping system to carry the transport media depended on the space heating and cooling requirements, the service hot water requirements, the transport media (chilled water, hot water or steam), and on total cost considerations.

The system which transmits and distributes thermal energy must provide it to consumers in an economic and efficient manner. A number of major considerations are involved in the decision on the piping system to be used to transport the medium. Such choices will depend on consumer space heating and cooling requirements, service hot water needs, type of transport medium (such as chilled water, hot water or steam), and on the cost factors related to each possible choice.

STEAM SYSTEMS

Planning for Distribution Network

When designing and extending a distribution system, a number of key decisions are necessary. The cumulative effect of these decisions on the system are as important as the most basic elements of design.

Before the process of designing a distribution system is undertaken, several prerequisite decisions must have been made and action taken. These include:
1. the amount of new business available should be accurately forecasted to determine if the system investment is justified,
2. the franchise for the district must be obtained,
3. a source of thermal energy (steam) for the system must have been obtained or decisions made as to its generation.
4. the proposed district must have been fully and properly surveyed.
5. in an area where there has been a pre-existing system, the decision to invest in new facilities must be carefully weighed.

Once these basic conditions have been fulfilled, the actual considerations of the system design itself become critical. At this stage, the following factors becomes important considerations in the design decision process:
1. The potential locations of additional plants, which may be needed in the future; they may be interconnected as needed in the most economical and efficient manner. One of the principal factors in system planning and design is the extent to which provisions should be made for future load growth. This consideration, depends on sound judgment of economic factors such as the rate of load growth.

Decisions based on such forecasts need detailed analysis of present and future worth of the proposed expansion. An estimate of the time schedule of load growth is a vital factor to be considered in this process.

2. The decision must be made as to whether or not the distribution system is to receive steam directly from the boilers or if by-product electricity is to be extracted first. If electrical generation is selected, means must be provided for delivering moisture-free steam to the system. In addition, the pressure of the exhaust or bled steam must be coordinated with the pressure demands of the steam consumers.

3. The nature of the energy requirements, particularly the characteristics of the demand are of necessity in the design of a distribution system.
   These requirements may include one or more of the following:
   a. immediate requirements at a given location,
   b. potential requirements along the route (i.e., potential new buildings), and
   c. the future capacities related to further extensions beyond the current pertinent service location.
   All are important in the system planning function.

4. Distribution pressure must be established. It must be determined if all consumer demands can be served from a single-piping system. Variations in consumer demand must be considered. After full analysis it usually happens that many consumers can be satisfactorily served with steam at pressures lower than the first request. This often occurs when consumers request high pressures in order to force steam through piping on their premises which is too small. If there are a sufficient number of legitimate high-pressure users to justify a two-pressure system, it may be economical to provide it or to set the pressure on a single-pipe system high enough to meet the peak high pressure demands.

5. The maximum distance from the plant where steam is to be distributed through a single-pressure piping system must be determined. This establishes the pressure drop per 100 ft for use in extending lines.

6. It must be decided if steam will be delivered to the system solely through distribution piping as an interconnected network, or if long-distance transmission feeders are to be used.

7. The percentage of total feedwater for the plant boilers which will be returned to the plants through condensate-return piping must be approximated and a corresponding allowance in plant design incorporated.

8. Whether the system will be routed through privately owned property or along public ways, space must be selected which will accommodate the system piping in a manner compatible with other existing or proposed underground facilities such as subway, sewer, water, electric, gas, telephone or other. Locations of these installations in public ways can usually be obtained from record plans either from the appropriate municipal department or from the pertinent utility.
   It should be remembered, however, that such records may not always be accurate or up to date. A physical inspection of the proposed route to check for manholes, vaults, valve boxes, and such is a good idea early in the system design process. In addition, a scale plan of the utility locations is of tremendous help in laying out the new route.

9. Knowledge of geological conditions along the proposed route is essential to the design and choice of materials to be employed in the system.

Factors such as the characteristics of rock or soil, ground water levels, or soil chemistry, can be determined by borings if not already known.

10. Some form of permit or grant from the local government is usually required for installation of facilities in public ways. To obtain such permits, the proposed installation usually must satisfy the requirements of the local agencies as to location and compliance with accepted engineering and safety practices.

    According to local practice, stipulations also may be imposed regulating work hours, removal of excavated material, police protection, safety measures, and other items. These can materially effect schedules and costs, and should receive adequate attention in the preparation of cost estimates.

11. System type, whether radial or loop is of major importance in the design of the system. Dependability and distribution investment usually require some trade-offs in this regard. From a marketing standpoint it may be necessary to develop load growth potentials of alternate or supplemental routes before the development of the relative economics of potential distribution systems.

12. Distribution piping may be planned radially outward from the boiler plant to the various points of usage. A high degree of reliability in supply may be achieved by cross-connecting the piping between two or more radial routes. This practice, called looping, ties the different sections of distribution piping together. This, in turn, allows consumers to be supplied with steam via alternate routes.

    Fully flexible loop service which can serve the maximum requirements of all buildings on a system is not always economically feasible. However, a temporary cutback in service for emergency repairs to distribution facilities can usually be arranged without significant inconvenience to consumers. Such situations should be allowed for in their service contracts.

    In addition, loop systems can reduce the number of customers which have to be shut down during maintenance operations on the different sections of the distribution system. Hospitals and hotels particularly benefit by having service from more than one main.

    Since looping provides more than one path for the flow of steam to any point, it greatly complicates calculation of the required supply pressures. Balancing the flow in all the loops within a reasonable range is possible but complicated. Programs have been developed which use digital computers to calculate flow, pressure drop and terminal pressures for looped steam system. Use of the digital computer has been an advantage in cases where the distribution system includes three or more interrelated loops.

13. The greatest volume of steam passes through the piping leaving the plant, as a result, the conduits for such piping may be large enough that they can be designed and constructed best as tunnels, whether or not additional space may be provided in them for a passageway alongside the piping.

    Steam tunnels are justified most appropriately as outlets for plant piping than for other purposes. Conditions which may justify their construction as opposed to closed conduits include cases where previously installed street facilities are so extensive as to force the location of the steam piping below all street obstructions, where the texture of soil is favorable, where a tunnel can be hydraulically-driven or jacked through without external shoring, where several pipe lines can be installed one above another in a rectangular conduit, and where the cost to widen the conduit about 18 in., to provide walking space, is considered justifiable, and where space for additional pipe lines or other facilities is required for future use.

14. Methods in installing underground distribution pipe lines too often follow precedent for the area. It is a better policy to have at least two or three approved designs from which the best can be selected based upon actual conditions.

15. The amount of spare capacity to be provided in extending a system depends on its type. If a network and feeder system is being built, deficiencies in distribution line capacity can be offset by installing feeders to the remote point.

    If a single-pressure system is used, the short looping of lines becomes more necessary to gain the advantage of load diversity. In all cases, long-range plants must be kept in mind for means and methods of supplying steam to increasingly remote locations.

16. If economic conditions are favorable, rental or acquired use of private plants may be more economical than extending the distribution piping into that locality.

    In such cases, it is advisable to use their private distribution lines temporarily and then to proceed to consolidate them with the new system.

    Types of underground construction best-suited for each location should be used regardless of what may appear to be a desirable universal standard.

17. An overhead route should be considered—even at a rental cost—if conditions justify it. An alternate route should be available in case the preferred right-of-way must be given up.

    Private rights-of-way through basements are a possibility. There is no requirement that district system piping be installed to follow the other utilities such as electric, water, and gas in placing lines exclusively in public thoroughfares. Large steam mains have been installed in building basements and across the intervening streets. Such a system can be extended considerably and in so doing there are advantages to the building owner as well as to the steam producer. Heat given off by the piping in winter usually returns a net advantage to the building, over and above the disadvantage of summertime radiation in northern climates. It may make possible less expensive interior piping for the building owner changing over to district steam. Use of building basements as locations for steam piping has been established by long tradition. A properly installed, insulated and painted steam main is usually not a disadvantage in a basement unless the basement space is used for purposes where such a line would be unsightly or interfere with other equipment.

18. It may be costly and wasteful if installations for future extensions of the piping go much further than the simple provision of excess carrying capacity of pipe lines to serve existing buildings or assured proposed buildings. While it may be economical to provide a reasonable amount of vault space for the offtake of future branch lines, valves, and traps, the outlets and valves should not be installed.

19. Sectionalizing valves on the mainline are necessary. It is not economical to attempt to save money by omitting them. The location of valves at approximately each city block or on each side of cross mains can often be justified.
20. A grid-type distribution system with large street mains enclosing relatively small areas does not always justify its cost. Designs are sometimes useful in which steam is distributed diagonally, thereby making use of pipes located at ninety degrees to each other, but unless they are actually used for this purpose, main lines on all four sides of a city block may not justify their existence.
21. In a large system it may become desirable to be able to monitor pressures from various points of the distribution system at operating headquarters. There are many types of telemetering devices which can be used to transmit the pressure readings to such a central point.

    As branchlines are extended in all directions the necessity of looping these become apparent. Relatively small loop connections at the extremities are generally sufficient since outages for repairs can usually be postponed for a few hours even on very cold days until the demand for steam is reduced. A limited amount of overtime repair work on nights or weekends should be balanced against the fixed cost of excessive investment in large loop piping.
22. A central-distribution operating headquarters is necessary when a system reaches a considerable size. Plant operations, distribution, and other operations are correlated and controlled on a twenty-four hour per day basis through these headquarters.

Steam System Design

A typical steam district heating piping system normally services customers within 3–5 miles of the sources. Usually single pipes have been used with systems in the U.S. For example, in the New York City system, power plant cogenerated steam is fed from back pressure turbines through three 24-inch diameter trunk lines at 190 psig. The steam, after heating or cooling downtown buildings, condenses and is conveyed to the city sewage system. The system is diagramed in Figure 6.1. Another example is the Baltimore system shown in Figure 6.2.

Possible disadvantages include:
1. increased requirements for boiler feedwater demineralization since the condensate is discarded,
2. reduced flexibility in the amount of steam provided, and
3. increased load on the city sewage or storm drain system.

The most widely used piping system design in the U.S. is the grid system with a main trunkline placed down the street and branches provided to each building. The Europeans, on the other hand, use a step-by-step branching system. This system is cheaper to construct and better utilizes the energy transfer medium.

DESIGN STEAM PRESSURE

Minimum design pressures should be compatible with those required to maintain minimum acceptable conditions of flow at various take-off points in the distribution system. In other words, the design steam supply pressure should not be lower than that which provides the saturated steam temperature required for the 100% heat transfer load.

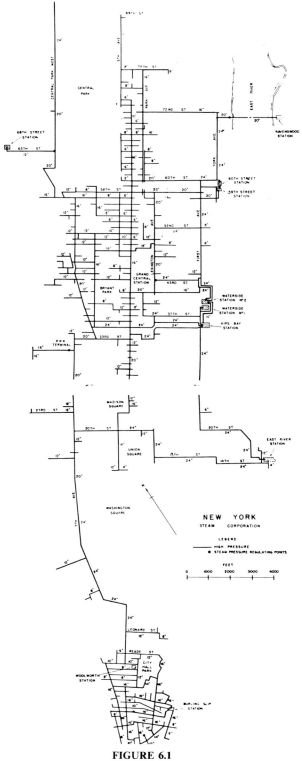

FIGURE 6.1
New York City steam system

FIGURE 6.2

Map showing steam distribution system Baltimore Gas and Electric Company

Drawn and distributed by the Map Development Unit, Distribution Engineering Department, June 1, 1979

Allowances must be made in piping design for pressure drops between the production sources and the key points in the system such as customer service connections.

DISTRIBUTION SYSTEM PRESSURES

Steam distribution systems generally can be classified according to set pressure ranges, low pressure systems range up to 30 psig; intermediate from 30 to 125 psig, and high pressure above 125 psig. Selection of the distribution system pressure is based on the minimum design pressure requirements of equipment served by the system.

CONDENSATE REMOVAL AND RETURN

Condensate is present in all systems using saturated steam because of inherent heat losses occurring in the system. Condensate also results from customer use of steam. The removal and return of condensate are two separate problems. Condensate *must* be removed from a distribution system to assure continued operation. Condensate may be returned to the generating facility if economics or other factors require it.

The decision to waste or return condensate basically is one of relative economics. Factors affecting this decision include savings related to heat in the condensate and the cost and availability of water and water treatment in comparison to the investment and operating costs of the facilities needed to return the condensate to the heat production plant.

Where heat for a system is derived from extraction or back pressure operations in an electric generation plant, demineralization and other water treatment requirements may be appreciable.

Accumulation of condensate in a distribution system has two major adverse effects: the condensate takes up space thus reducing the capacity of the system, and the condensate may be moved by fast-moving steam and act as a battering ram which can physically damage the system. This action is known as a water hammer that results in a short duration force which can be hundreds of times the force exerted by normal system pressure.

If economics indicate that condensate should be returned, in most cases pumping will be required to return the condensate. Service contracts should include provisions for the customer to provide such pumping facilities as may be necessary. In the case of larger buildings, this may be building system pumps. Care in the selection of these pumps is necessary to avoid high maintenance due to cavitation as a result of low mpsh.

Condensate return line sizing should be based on maximum flow rates and should allow for internal friction based on average operating conditions over extended periods of service.

Whenever it is practicable, return lines should be installed in close proximity to supply piping. The higher ambient created by heat loss from the latter may result in some degree of heat transfer to the returning condensate. In addition, the proximity of the two lines aids in the return of condensate removed from the supply lines by distribution system traps.

Provisions also must be made during design and construction phases to insure the removal of condensate from a system. A steam main should be constructed so as to grade the pipe not less than 1 inch in 500 feet. Where field conditions allow, the slope of the main should be in the directions of the steam flow. However, it is unrealistic to assume continuous grade for long distances, and condensate removal must be provided for at all low points where a water pocket would otherwise form. If a continuous grade can be maintained, provisions for drainage of condensate should be made every 300 to 400 feet.

Drip legs or collecting legs and steam traps must be provided at each condensate removal point. A collecting leg insures that condensate is delivered to the trap and provides a reservoir for the condensate, especially during a start-up, before the pressure rises sufficiently for the trap to operate. Drip legs should be the same size as the steam main. In theory, the drip leg should have a capacity equal to the volume of condensate formed in raising the steam pipe temperature to 212 F. In practice, collecting legs up to 3″ in diameter should hold one fourth the initial load (in smaller mains the weight of steam in the main at 0 psi is small); 4″ and larger legs should hold on half the initial warm-up load. Drip legs lengths may be calculated from these capacities and the drip leg diameter. See the example given in Figure 6.3.

The trap inlet must be connected to the side of the drip leg and should be one pipe size larger than the trap inlet connection and have an eccentric reducer at the trap to minimize dirt carry-over. The vertical distance between the main and the top of the trap should not be less than 12″, preferably more. The principal features of a recommended arrangement are illustrated in Figure 6.4.

Steam traps are automatic devices used to discharge condensate, air and other noncondensable gases from steam piping and equipment. They do this as soon as the unwanted gases or liquids accumulate without waste of live steam. A trap generally consists of a vessel in which the condensate, air and noncondensable gases are accumulated, an orifice through which these products are discharged, a valve to close the orifice part, mechanisms to operate the valve and inlet and outlet openings for the entrance and discharge of the condensate and gases from the trap vessel.

Steam traps can be classified by type based on operating principles. These fall into three main groups: mechanical, thermostatic, thermodynamic. There are also certain combinations of these basic types. Since no single trap is satisfactory for every application, it is important to select the appropriate type and the proper size for the location and intended use.

A mechanical trap differentiates between condensate and steam through the difference in density between the two fluids. The upright or open bucket trap is typical. In this type of trap (see Figure 6.5) the condensate enters the trap

---

What size and length drip leg should be used for a steam trap handling an effective length of 200 feet of 8″ Schedule 40, well-insulated, steel steam main? Assume initial main temperature to be 40°F.

Pertinent data:

        Cross-sectional metal area, $S = 8.40$ in.^{2}
        Steel pipe density, $R = 490$ lb./ft.^{3}
        Specific heat of steel pipe, $C = 0.12$ BTU/lb. per °F.
        Average heat of condensation for H_2O (40° to 212°F.), $H = 1020$ BTU/lb.

Volume of steel $= L \times S = 200$ ft. $\times 8.40/144$ ft.$^2 = 11.67$ ft.^{3}

Heat absorbed by pipe, $Q = C \times R \times V \times (T_2 - T_1)$
                   $= 0.12 \times 490 \times 11.67 \times (212\text{-}40)$
                   $= 118,000$ BTU's

Volume of water condensed $= Q/H = 118,000/1020 = 116$ lb.

Drip Leg shall accommodate $0.5 \times 116 = 58$ lbs. of H_2O, or $58/62.5 = 0.93$ ft.^{3}

For a 8″ drip leg with a cross-sectional flow area, $A = 50.0$ in.$^2 = 0.347$ ft.^{2}:

$$V = L \times A$$
$$L = V/A = 0.93/0.347 = 2.7 \text{ ft.}$$

FIGURE 6.3

Example: Drip leg sizing

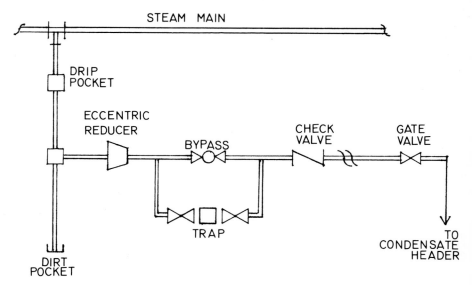

FIGURE 6.4
Recommended trap arrangement

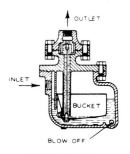

FIGURE 6.5
Upright bucket trap
(Courtesy of ASHRAE Handbook & Product Directory)

chamber and filling the space between the bucket and the walls of the trap. This causes the bucket to float and forces the valve against its seat. The valve and its stem usually are fastened to the bucket. When the condensate in the chamber rises above the edges of the bucket, it overflows into it and causes the bucket to sink. This action withdraws the valve from its seat. In turn, this permits the steam pressure acting on the surface of the condensate in the bucket to force the water to the discharge opening. When the bucket is empty, it rises and closes the valve and another cycle begins. The discharge from this type of trap is intermittent and it requires a definite differential pressure—usually one pound at least—between the inlet and outlet of the trap to lift the condensate out of the bucket to the return opening. Such a trap is particularly well suited for situations where there are pulsating pressures, since it is not influenced by pulsating or wide fluctuations in pressure. Upright bucket traps are available in sizes varying from ½ to 2½ inches and for pressures varying from partial vacuum to 1200 psi.

The thermostatic type of trap uses elements which expand and contract under the influence of heat and cold. In general, the modern type of thermostatic trap (see Figure 6.6) consists of thin corrugated metal bellows or disc enclosing a hollow chamber. The chamber either is filled with a liquid or a small amount of a volatile liquid, such as alcohol. The liquid expands or becomes a gas when steam comes in contact with the expansive element. The pressure created in either case expands the element and closes the valve of the trap against the escape of steam. When condensate or air comes in contact with the element, it cools and contracts. This opens the valve and allows the escape of water and air.

The discharge from these types of traps is intermittent. Thermostatic traps generally are used for the draining of condensate from radiators, convectors, pipe coils, drips, unit heaters, water heaters, cooking kettles and other equipment. Except for those thermostatic traps other than radiators requiring a cooling leg ahead of the trap, the trap must be installed as close to the equipment as possible. Thermostatic traps are made in sizes from ½ to 2 inches and for pressures ranging from partial vacuum conditions to 300 psi.

Operation of the thermodynamic trap depends on the thermodynamic properties of hot condensate or steam passing through an orifice. A typical thermodynamic trap is the impulse trap. Impulse traps (see Figure 6.7) depend on the property of condensate at a high pressure and temperature to flash into steam at a lower pressure. This flashing action is utilized to govern the movement of a valve by causing changes in pressure in a control chamber above the valve. The flow of condensate divides, the main part freely going out through the valve and the remainder—called the control flow—by-passing continuously up into the control chamber through an annular orifice around the control disc. From the control chamber, the condensate flows out through the control orifice in the valve stem. When the system is heating up the condensate is not yet at a high temperature and builds up in the control chamber. The flow through the control orifice does not change volume and the discharge through the orifice reduces the volume in the control chamber. Discharge through this orifice lowers the pressure in the control chamber and the valve opens to discharge air and condensate. When steam comes in contact with such a trap, the condensate is heated and the flow flashes in entering the control chamber and increases the volume of the control flow. Discharge

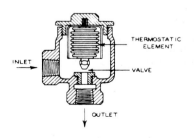

FIGURE 6.6

Thermostatic trap

(Courtesy of ASHRAE Handbook & Product Directory)

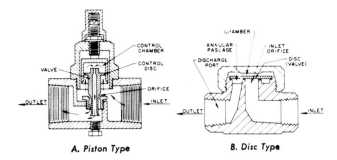

A. Piston Type   **B. Disc Type**

FIGURE 6.7

Thermodynamic trap, impulse trap

(Courtesy of ASHRAE Handbook & Product Directory)

through the control orifice is thereby choked and pressure in the control chamber builds up. This closes the valve and stops all discharge of hot condensate except for a small amount flowing through the control orifice.

The discharge from an impulse trap is pulsating or intermittent, but not as infrequent as with the bucket type of trap. It is nonadjustable. Impulse traps can be used for draining condensate from steam mains, unit heaters, laundry and kitchen equipment, water heaters, sterilizers, and other equipment where the pressure at the trap outlet is 25 percent or less than that of the inlet pressure. Impulse traps are made in sizes from ½ to 2 inches and for pressures ranging from 1 to 600 psi. Selection of the proper steam trap for the proper use allows a system to function at top efficiency without noises and water hammer, and with minimum loss of steam.

The following factors should be considered in selecting traps:

1. suitability to the application—mechanical, thermostatic or thermodynamic,
2. sufficient capacity to handle maximum head expected,
3. ability to discharge large volumes of air if necessary,
4. ease and cost of maintenance,
5. physical size and weight,
6. pressure limitations,
7. initial cost, and
8. ease of installations.

Proper sizing of steam traps also is very important. Too large a trap can create excessive back pressure and cause sluggish operation of equipment and the waste of steam. An undersized trap can result in improper drainage, loss of temperature, condensate backup and loss of efficiency.

CORROSION

Return piping often is subject to excessive corrosion from corrosive gases dissolved in the condensate or from free oxygen in the piping. Where such conditions exists, or are possible, the life of the return piping can be considerably shorter than the life of steam piping. Unless some arrangement is possible for the return piping to be replaced inexpensively, the saving possible by the return of condensate can not justify the replacement cost. The effect of corrosion may be minimized by selecting piping with a greater wall thickness than might be otherwise appropriate.

In dealing with and minimizing corrosion, the two primary solutions are use of noncorrodible materials or adequate corrosion control. Control of external corrosion is accomplished through use of protective coatings which will withstand the soil environment and operating conditions of the piping system and, where indicated, cathodic protection. Some consultants feel cathodic protection is advisable since corrosion can occur at any breaks in the coating. Internal corrosion can be controlled by the fluid treatment or special piping materials.

Most ferrous metal corrosion is the result of an electrochemical reaction caused by a difference in electrical potential due to nonhomogeneity of the soil or in the pipe wall itself. These homogeneous conditions may be due to oxygen differences (loose soil at top of pipe vs. packed soil in trench bottom), soil differences (clay at bottom vs. loam at top, or sand backfill vs. normal soil), moisture differences, new pipe vs. old, organic matter in the trench, or micro-differences in the pipe wall structure.

Connection of dissimilar metals also encourages corrosion. For example, if steel pipe is connected to copper pipe, the steel pipe will corrode. Road de-icing salts and some fertilizers can make soil very corrosive. Bacteria in some organic soils create strong corrosion cells. An additional source of corrosion is the presence of stray direct electrical currents in the ground. These may come from industrial welding operations, high voltage dc transmission lines, foreign cathodic protection installations, or from various other causes. Internal corrosion is affected by the chemistry of the fluid carried. Oxygen and carbon dioxide content are important factors. Internal corrosion often is a problem in steel condensate lines.

A number of tests can be made to help determine to what degree corrosion might occur in the soil. A corrosion survey should be made by a corrosion engineer prior to decisions on piping design. The survey should include an evaluation of soil conditions and the chemistry of the water or other fluid to be carried in the piping. The design engineer can then select proper materials, external corrosion control, fluid treatment, and inhibitors or internal lining to minimize costs and maximize system life and reliability.

One helpful test that is almost universally used is the resistivity test. This measures the electrical current carrying capacity of the soil. Since corrosion produces a small current flow in the soil from a corroding point on the metal pipe to a noncorroding point on the pipe, that current flow is inversely proportional to the soil's resistivity. The lower the soil resistivity, the greater the current flow and the faster the corrosion process will proceed. Resistivity often is a direct indicator of the rate of corrosion, and soils are often rated by their resistivity.

The U.S. Federal Construction Council Building Research Advisory Board lists the following soil classifications:

Corrosive

1. soil resistivity of 10,000 ohm per cm (100 Q per m) or less, or
2. detection of any stray current in the soil, or
3. where the water table is frequently above the bottom of the piping system, or
4. where the water table is occasionally above the bottom of the system and surface water is expected to accumulate and remain for long periods in the soil surrounding the system.

Mildly Corrosive

Soil resistivity is between 10,000 and 30,000 ohm per cm (100 and 300 Q per m).

Noncorrosive

Soil resistivity is 30,000 ohm per cm (300 Q per m) or greater. Corrosive conditions may be aggravated by an increased pH, sulfates, chlorides, bacteria, and possible stray current.

There are two basic types of cathodic protection systems. Both types generally are used with proper pipe coating materials. The two basic types are the galvanic anode system and the impressed current system. Cathodic protection systems should be tested annually to assure continued protection. Cathodic protection systems should be specially designed for each application by specialists in corrosion protection in accordance with prevailing standards. Soil investigation by a corrosion specialist should be conducted to determine whether cathodic protection be used for ferrous metal piping, conduits, and manholes.

Use of nonmetallic pipe of conduit often is a good means of combating corrosion. Some asbestos cement is subject to possible deterioration in soils with high sulfate content. Asbestos cement manufactured to AWWA Standards to Type II pipe (under 1% free-lime content) is resistant to sulfate reaction in any concentration found in any soils around the world. Asbestos cement pipe should be used with caution in soils with a pH below 4.5.

MAXIMUM AND RECOMMENDED VELOCITIES

The maximum weight flow rate of steam through any straight length of pipe of uniform diameter is limited by the sonic velocity. This limitation is applicable to all empirical formulae used in determination of the flow rates of compressible fluids through a pipe. Calculated sonic velocities of steam have been experimentally verified at about 1600 ft/sec and can exist even in pipe sizes several feet in diameter. However, for the steam conditions and long distances of interest in a district heating and cooling system, the pressure drop would have to be on the order of 80 to 90% of the initial pressure. Such high velocities would present many difficult engineering problems to system designers and fabricators of piping components.

Most steam distribution systems have design weight flow rates based on steam conditions and flow parameters which have proven satisfactory through many years of development. Reasonable maximum steam velocities recommended are 200 and 250 ft/sec. Factors, such as pulsating noise, wetness (or quality) of the steam, erosion of valve seats and orifices, and others eventually must be considered, but advances in thermal energy conveyance technology indicate that steam flow rates several times higher than those in current use may be worth assessment. Even if the noise levels must be kept low in submains, higher velocities may be acceptable in cross-country supply mains.

The flow rate of steam is determined in accordance with the general laws of gas flow, and is a function of the length and diameter of the pipe, the density of the steam, and the pressure drop through the pipe. Generally speaking, the higher the flow rate of steam through a pipe the shorter the distance that thermal energy can be conveyed efficiently. The power in the flowing steam supplies the pumping power required for conveyance by changing its state and reducing its deliverable energy. The pressure drop caused by each change of direction in steam flow also will lengthen the summation of equivalent pipe lengths, or lower the possible straight line distance of conveyance. The term "equivalent length" is a way of utilizing available test data on pressure drops through valves, orifices, and fittings. It is expressed as a ratio (L/D) and is equal to the length (in pipe diameters) of a straight pipe which will cause the same pressure drop as the piping component it would replace if tested under the same flow conditions. Equivalent lengths are used in the analyses of the "resistance coefficient," $(K = f L/D)$.

PIPE SIZING

Calculations for sizing piping for normal steam line extensions generally are a function of linear pressure drop. Where network systems are involved, computer analysis will save time and result in greater accuracy. Without use of a computer the solution of network piping using the linear pressure drop method becomes a matter of trial and error.

Several formulas based on straight line pressure drop have been developed for use in calculating the size of steam pipes for specified rates of flow. Unwin's formula is used widely because of the simplicity of its solution through means of a graphic chart. It has been a favorite in the district heating industry for many years. The formula is stated as:

$$P = \frac{0.0001306 \ W^2 L \left(1 + \frac{3.6}{d}\right)}{Yd^5}$$

where
- P = pressure drop, lb per sq. in.
- W = steam flow, lb per min.
- L = length of pipe, ft.
- Y = average density of steam, lb per cu. ft.
- d = inside diameter of pipe, in.

Individual solutions by the use of this formula are long and laborious, but can be shortened by means of a chart prepared from Unwin's formula.

Even further, the *ASHRAE Handbook and Product Directory, 1981 Fundamentals* presents several charts for weight-flow rate, pressure drop and velocity which consider the Reynold's number and its effect on friction loss, two items which are not considered using the Unwin formula. These charts are presented here as Table 6.1 and Figures 6.8 to 6.13.

WATER CONTENT OF STEAM

Moisture content of two percent or less generally is considered acceptable as commercially dry steam. Field tests assure that practically all steam in the district heating supplier's piping is well within this limit when its velocity is low.

Saturated steam continually condenses almost uniformly on the walls of steam piping even when the pipes are well-insulated. However, at higher steam velocities these drops of condensate may be scoured off and entrained in the flowing steam. Moisture on and near the bottom of the pipe may be scooped up and carried along. When there is no velocity the droplets run down to form a pool or stream at the bottom, leaving the steam in the interior of the pipe almost completely dry.

TABLE 6.1

WEIGHT FLOW RATE OF STEAM IN SCHEDULE 40 PIPE[a] AT INITIAL SATURATION PRESSURE OF 3.5 AND 12 Psig[b,c]

(Weight Flow Rate Expressed in Pounds per Hour)

Pressure Drop—Psi Per 100 Ft in Length

Nom. Pipe Size Inches	1/16 Psi (1 oz)		1/8 Psi (2 oz)		1/4 Psi (4 oz)		1/2 Psi (8 oz)		3/4 Psi (12 oz)		1 Psi		2 Psi	
	Sat. press. psig		Sat. press. psig		Sat. press. psig		Sat. press. psig		Sat. press. psig		Sat. press. psig		Sat. press. psig	
	3.5	12	3.5	12	3.5	12	3.5	12	3.5	12	3.5	12	3.5	12
1/4	9	11	14	16	20	24	29	35	36	43	42	50	60	73
1	17	21	26	31	37	46	54	66	68	82	81	95	114	137
1 1/4	36	45	53	66	78	96	111	138	140	170	162	200	232	280
1 1/2	56	70	84	100	120	147	174	210	218	260	246	304	360	430
2	108	134	162	194	234	285	336	410	420	510	480	590	710	850
2 1/2	174	215	258	310	378	460	540	660	680	820	780	950	1150	1370
3	318	380	465	550	660	810	960	1160	1190	1430	1380	1670	1950	2400
3 1/2	462	550	670	800	990	1218	1410	1700	1740	2100	2000	2420	2950	3450
4	640	800	950	1160	1410	1690	1980	2400	2450	3000	2880	3460	4200	4900
5	1200	1430	1680	2100	2440	3000	3570	4250	4380	5250	5100	6100	7500	8600
6	1920	2300	2820	3350	3960	4850	5700	5700	7000	8600	8400	10,000	11,900	14,200
8	3900	4800	5570	7000	8100	10,000	11,400	14,300	14,500	17,700	16,500	20,500	24,000	29,500
10	7200	8800	10,200	12,600	15,000	18,200	21,000	26,000	26,200	32,000	30,000	37,000	42,700	52,000
12	11,400	13,700	16,500	19,500	23,400	28,400	33,000	40,000	41,000	49,500	48,000	57,500	67,800	81,000

[a] Based on Moody Friction Factor, where flow of condensate does not inhibit the flow of steam.
[b] The weight-flow rates at 3.5 psig can be used to cover sat. press. from 1 to 6 psig, and the rates at 12 psig can be used to cover sat. press. from 8 to 16 psig with an error not exceeding 8 %.
[c] The steam velocities corresponding to the weight-flow rates given in this table can be found from the basic chart and velocity multiplier chart, Fig. 5.

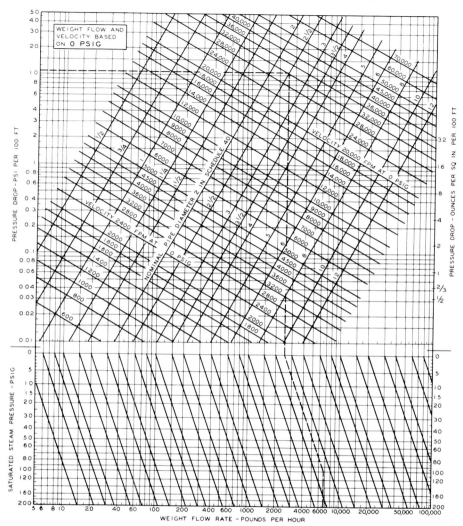

Based on Moody Friction Factor where flow of condensate does not inhibit the flow of steam.

FIGURE 6.8

Basic chart for weight-flow rate and velocity of steam in Schedule 40 pipe based on saturation pressure of Psig

(With Multiplier Charts for Obtaining Weight-Flow Rates and Velocities of All Saturation Pressures Between 0 and 200 Psig)

(Courtesy of ASHRAE Handbook & Product Directory)

Such conditions can be demonstrated with a calorimeter by taking steam samples at various velocities, and at various positions across the pipe diameter. Tests show moisture content as high as three percent periodically with moderate velocities up to five or six thousand ft per min., and measurements taken at five min. intervals show wide variations, indicating that the moisture is not uniformly distributed throughout the pipe in the form of a fog. The condition is

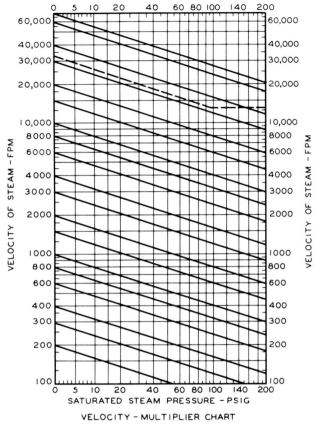

FIGURE 6.9

(Continued) Velocity multiplier chart

(Courtesy of ASHRAE Handbook & Product Directory)

best described as one of fast-moving drops of water carried along in a current of otherwise dry steam, and in all cases except with vertically upward flow, these drops are always falling to the bottom of the pipe. The condition appears similar to that of drops of rain swept horizontally in a high wind.

Quiescent steam does not include much moisture in distribution piping. Any small quantity that may exist is below the limits generally accepted as commercially dry.

Steam with a high moisture percentage with the water content distributed more or less uniformly in microscopic particles, is present in certain stages of steam turbines. However, by the time it reaches a low velocity such as where it is exhausted into the mains of a steam distribution system, the moisture has changed into drops which have fallen to the bottom of the pipe. When it has reached this stage there is no way to increase its moisture content at constant pressure. If the moisture content is raised by any induced velocity between the steam and its container, the condition is only temporary and vanishes as soon

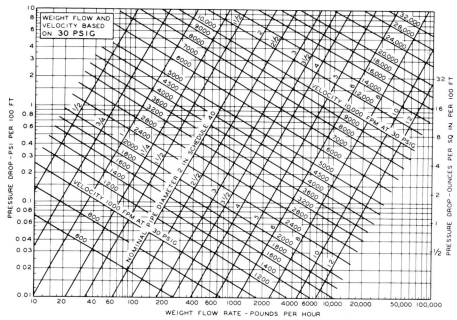

Based on Moody Friction Factor where flow at condensate does not inhibit the flow of steam.

FIGURE 6.10

Chart for weight-flow rate and velocity of steam in Schedule 40 pipe based on saturation pressure of 30 psig

(May be Used for Steam Pressures from 23 to 37 Psig with an Error Not Exceeding 9%)

(Courtesy of ASHRAE Handbook & Product Directory)

as quiescence is restored. In practice, then, the moisture content of steam is primarily a function of steam velocity. However, when velocities are reached at which the pressure drop along the pipe line, and the corresponding drop in total-heat content of the steam balances the radiation and friction factors, no more moisture will be added. If the drop in pressure becomes greater as a result of increased velocity, the moisture still entrained will be re-evaporated, and if the velocity is increased even further, superheat results.

Changes in the quality of the steam delivered to a consumer are important, since flowing steam picks up and carries forward droplets of condensate from the walls of pipes and part of that lying on the bottom. The amount entrained is proportional to velocity, and practical observations can be made to determine with a fair degree the accuracy of the amount of moisture so entrained.

Elimination of unwanted moisture in distribution steam piping is related to effective trapping. For this reason relatively large drain pockets should be included on steam lines to which steam traps are connected. In some cases deflector scoops or baffles may be placed in the line to direct the water into the trap pockets.

If water elimination at trap points is in effect, and water collects in pools, these may become the cause of dangerous water hammer either with steam in motion or with no velocity at all.

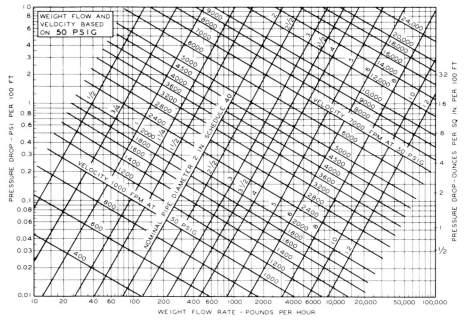

Based on Moody Friction Factor where flow of condensate does not inhibit the flow of steam.

FIGURE 6.11

Chart for weight-flow rate and velocity of steam in Schedule 40 pipe based on saturation pressure of 50 psig

(May Be Used for Steam Pressures from 40 to 60 Psig with an Error Not Exceeding 8%)

(Courtesy of ASHRAE Handbook & Product Directory)

SUPERHEAT

Superheaters are rarely installed in district heating plants unless it is necessary to transmit the steam over a considerable distance, or when by-product heat is extracted in some form before distribution.

High temperature or superheated steam is sometimes purchased from power companies and transmitted long distances. It is not unusual in such cases for the steam to be delivered with considerable superheat, especially if the velocity is high. In lowering the temperature of the transmitted steam the heat content of the superheat is used to evaporate injected water, thereby converting the mixture into saturated steam. This process is known as *de*-superheating.

A cross-sectional view of a desuperheater used for this purpose is shown in Figure 6.14. No spray heads are used in this apparatus. The mixing of the superheated steam with the water in the bottom of the tank is the result of the vortex and swirl action as the two fluids are forced upward through the contactor tubes into the center chamber of the tank. Solid particles of water still entrained in the steam are removed by the separators in the upper portion.

Temperature control of the desuperheated steam is achieved by by-passing a portion of the incoming steam directly to the outlet.

The water supply to this desuperheating unit amounts to about 10 percent of the incoming steam, and is purified by passing through softeners before use.

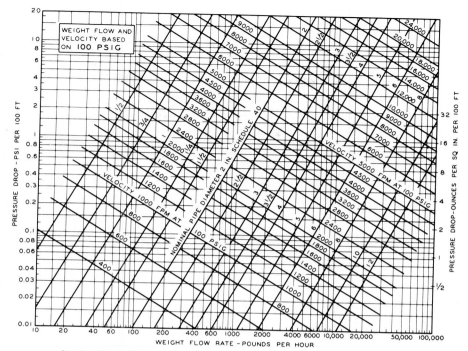

Based on Moody Friction Factor where flow of condensate does not inhibit the flow of steam.

FIGURE 6.12

Chart for weight-flow rate and velocity of steam in Schedule 40 pipe based on saturation pressure of 100 psig

(May Be Used for Steam pressures from 85 to 120 Psig With an Error Not Exceeding 8%)

(Courtesy of ASHRAE Handbook & Product Directory)

A simple pipe-line desuperheater using two atomizing type spray nozzles is shown in Figure 6.15. The two nozzles are inserted in a 14-in. line from opposite sides and, introduce the water in a spiral spray. The pipe walls are protected from direct contact with water particles by a liner 12 ft. long extended from the nozzles in the direction of steam flow.

Thermal Insulation

To minimize the heat loss of underground systems in order to reduce operating and maintenance problems, excessive condensate, and the undesirable heat effects on adjacent systems is important in system design.

The most important quality of any insulating material is its ability to resist the flow of heat through it. Substances with the greatest heat flow resistance per unit area and thickness are the best insulators. Good insulating characteristics alone are not sufficient however, if other properties are absent. Some essential properties of insulating materials are as follows.

Heat Conductivity Insulating materials commonly in use have K values in the order of 0.4–0.5 or less. Values beyond this range require too great a material thickness for economic operation.

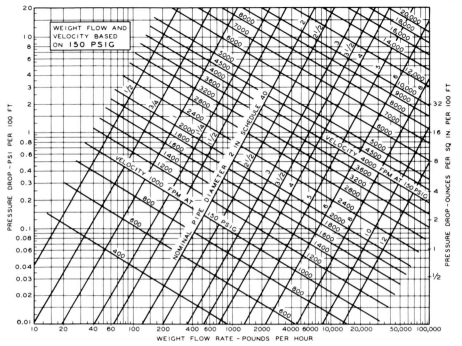

Based on Moody Friction Factor where flow of condensate does not inhibit the flow of steam.

FIGURE 6.13

Chart for weight-flow rate and velocity of steam in Schedule 40 pipe based on saturation pressure of 150 psig

(May Be Used for Steam Pressures from 127 to 180 Psig With an Error Not Exceeding 8%)

(Courtesy of ASHRAE Handbook & Product Directory)

Temperature Deterioration The insulating material must be within the temperature operating range required to maintain its insulating value for a long service life.

Low Moisture Absorption Moisture penetration into insulation reduces thermal resistance. The ability of the insulation to resist moisture penetration is especially advantageous in lines with a ground water problem.

Non-Corrosive to Pipe When water is in contact with a metal the probability of corrosion increases dramatically. To minimize corrosion, the insulation should not be an electrical conductor nor corrosive to the pipe, wet or dry.

Drying Characteristics Since water can be expected to enter a system sometime during its operating life, insulation should not be able to be permanently damaged by such water contact, and must be capable of in place rehabilitation. Proper rehabilitation includes lack of damage due to boiling of entrapped water and nonshrinking characteristics which might cause stress rupture.

Vermin Proofing The insulation should be vermin proof.

Electrical Insulation Since corrosion is essentially an electrical process, some form of insulation from stray electric currents should be provided around the pipe.

Low-Thermal Expansion Insulation, ideally, should have about the same coefficient of linear expansion as the carrier pipe, however this is rarely

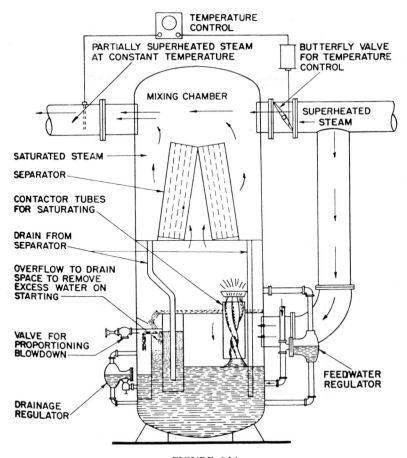

FIGURE 6.14

Mixing desuperheater

achieved. As a result, construction must incorporate a way of handling the difference in expansion rates. There are two designs for the application of insulation: one where the coefficients are different permits the pipeline to move through the insulation. In the other, where the coefficients are the same, the insulation is firmly attached and moves with the pipe.

TYPES OF INSULATION

Minerals of many types are used as insulating materials. Some are usable with very little processing while others require treatment. More recently, technology has provided a selection of man-made insulating materials. All have advantages and weaknesses. Table 6.2 provides information on characteristics of various insulating materials. This table includes the older types of insulating materials containing asbestos in many forms and is a guide to the servicing and removal of systems where protection from asbestos fibers is mandatory.

Calcium Silicate

Calcium silicate is a near-white rigid material suitable for temperatures up to 1200 F. It is manufactured in preformed slabs and pipe sections of various

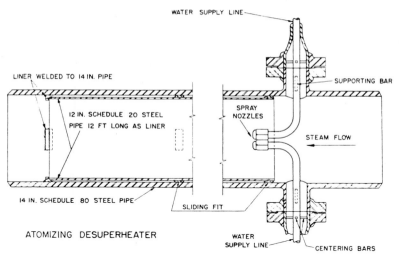

FIGURE 6.15
Atomizing desuperheater

thicknesses. Both synthetic silicas or silicates, as well as selected siliceous materials of natural origin are utilized. Reinforcing fibers such as amosite *asbestos,* chrysotile, mineral wool and glass fibers are used by different manufacturers. Some processes use steam induration in autoclaves where steam converts lime and diatomaceous silica into hydrous calcium silicate. Others use a reaction in boiling or hot water between the selected siliceous material and line in the presence of aluminumions. This results in a thick slurry in which reinforcing fibers may be added if not already introduced prior to the reaction. The mass is then molded into the desired shapes and dried in hot ovens under normal atmospheric.

Diatomaceous Earth

Diatomaceous earth is a special form of silica, with a high melting point (2930 F) and unique properties. It is comprised of minute silica skeletons of diatoms, which were microscopic plants that lived millions of years ago. Large deposits occur in California. A mixture of *asbestos* and diatomaceous earth forms an excellent high-temperature insulation (600 to 1900 F) and is manufactured under various trade names. Table 6.2 reflects the characteristics of the insulating materials discussed here as well as others of commercial importance. This summary is reproduced in the Table.

85% Magnesia

For lower temperatures, 85% magnesis insulation is composed of 85% magnesia and 15% *asbestos.* The asbestos fiber provides the reinforcing qualities necessary to permit molding and manufacture of pipe sections and other shapes. The magnesia component actually is a magnesium carbonate produced from dolomitic limestone by the action of carbon dioxide on slate dolomite. When properly installed, 85% magnesia maintains its excellent insulating properties for many years and is an economical material. It has the disadvantage of not being able to support any appreciable load and is adversely affected by water.

TABLE 6.2

CHARACTERISTICS OF THERMAL INSULATION MATERIALS

Materials	General forms	Strength	Resistance to water	Resistance to vapor	Composition	Advantages	Disadvantages	Temperature limits, °F		Conductivity Btu/(hr)(sq ft)(°F/in.)			
								min.	max.	32	70	212	500
Diatomaceous earth	Molded and formed pipe insulation, segments and blocks	Good compressive strength; limited flexural and tensile strength	Fair	Moderate	Diatomaceous earth blended with long asbestos fibers	Handles well, used as inner layer under 85% magnesia where operating temperature exceeds 575°F.	Not suitable for bridging under heavy load; non-flexible	212	1900		0.56	0.59	0.62
Glass fibers	Formed into pipe insulation and block	Soft, flexible fibers; will not break down under flexing	Excellent	Moderate	Glass fibers bonded	Lightweight, resilient, and flexible	Soft, will not resist mechanical abuse	32	450			0.25 to 0.30	
Glass cellular	Rigid, fabricated pipe insulation, lagging, segments and fitting covers	High compressive strength; fair tensile strength	Excellent	Excellent	Inorganic glass containing microscopic, hermetically sealed cells	Easily shaped and fitted; does not depend on vapor barrier for its vapor resistance; incombustible. High temperature limits.	Should be protected against abrasion. Design for expansion and contraction	−300	800	0.35	0.42	0.53	
Hydrous calcium silicate	Molded and formed pipe insulation, segments and blocks	Good compressive and flexural strength; limited tensile strength	Good	Moderate	Hydrous calcium silicate blended with long asbestos fibers	High shearing resistance; high compressive strength	Not suitable for bridging under heavy load; non-flexible	70	1200		0.400	0.450	0.540

TABLE 6.2—continued

Materials	General forms	Strength	Resistance to water	Resistance to vapor	Composition	Advantages	Disadvantages	Temperature limits, °F		Conductivity Btu/(hr)(sq ft)(°F/in.)			
								min.	max.	32	70	212	500
Mineral wool for high temp.	Molded into blocks and lagging	Limited compressive and tensile strength; fair flexural strength	Excellent	Moderate	Mineral fibers blended with binders	Flexible and withstands considerable expansion and contraction	Will not resist excessive mechanical abuse without indentation	70	1700		0.33	0.40	0.51
Glass fibers	Felted glass fiber blanket with various types of facings	Soft, flexible; little compressive resistance after application	Good	Moderate	Felted glass fibers fabricated with metal mesh or other facing	Flexible, light fibers will not break down under moderate impact; fibers respond to repeated compressing	Soft; little compressive strength	40	1000	0.26			
Mineral wool	Blankets with various types of facings	Fair compressive strength	Fair	Poor	Felted mineral wool	Withstands expansion and contraction	Soft	50	1200			0.35	0.45
Glass fibers	Felted into rolls	Soft, flexible; little compressive resistance after application	Good	Moderate	Fine glass fibers lightly bonded	Flexible; fibers respond to repeated compressing; good thermal cushioning	Pronounced depression under heavy loading	Not known	600				
Mineral wool	Semi-rigid felt	Fair compressive strength	Good	Poor	Mineral wool felted and bonded	Resilient; can withstand expansion and contraction	No mechanical abuse can be permitted	Not known	600	0.18 to 0.25	0.30 to 0.40	0.60 to 0.80	

Material										
Insulating Hydrocarbons	Loose, packaged in 100# bags	Similar to earth backfill. Will take normal bearing wads.	Will wash out if subject to water flow	—	Mined and sized high resin - content asphal-tile	Easy to install - poured in place but must be properly packed	Easily disturbed	Type A 220 Type B 300 Special B 365 Type C 420	300 365 420 520	Variable, dependent on thickness of sones and temperature. Average about 0.54 at 300°F. Varies from 0.45 to 0.6
Polyurethane Foam	Two liquid components usually supplied in 55 gal. drums for large usage	Fair compressive and tensile strength. Can be pierced easily and will not withstand abrasion.	Good	Good	Polyether based urethane	Outstanding thermal conductivity	Temperature limited. Special mixing equip. required.	0	250	0.14
Cell Concrete	Portland cement and foam solution	Good compressive strength	Can be wetted		Portland Cement	Good strength characteristics	Subject to wetting	0	1200	0.42 0.45 0.56 0.80

Mineral Wool

Mineral wool is created by blowing molten silica minerals into threads. These threads can be fashioned into insulating blankets or molded into blocks by adding suitable binders. When a water-proofing binder is used an effective low-temperature insulation can be produced which is highly moisture resistant and rot proof. In this form it is called mineral or rock cork.

Fiberglass

The low thermal conductivity, noncombustibility and inert nature of glass are desirable features for insulation. Molten glass can be spun into fibers similar to those of mineral wool and these fibers fashioned into blankets, molded pipe covering or blocks. Glass fiber insulation is normally good up to 600 F, with some special designs which can withstand 1000 F.

Since glass cannot absorb water, glass fibers molded into boards serve as low-temperature insulation when provided with a suitable warmside vapor seal. Cellular glass insulating material is made of thousands of glass bubbles molded into a lightweight rigid structure. This cellular glass material is suitable for temperatures from −350 F to +800 F. It is available in blocks and in shapes for pipe coverings.

Another insulating material made from materials very similar to glass is called hydrous calcium silicate. This material is effective up to 1200 F and is moisture resistant and may be found blended with small amounts of *asbestos fiber.*

Insulating Concrete

Some grades of Portland cement mixed with water and a glutinous soap solution will harden into a cellular form when the foamy combination is introduced into the cement mixture by means of a current of air and the entire mass properly agitated.

Vermiculite-Exploded Mica

Mica is a complex silicate of aluminum and other elements characterized by laminations of microscopic thinness. Some forms of this mineral have a small quantity of water between each of the laminations. When this is subjected suddenly to intensive heat it expands to form a large body of air cells, becoming a cellular insulation commonly known as vermiculite.

Insulating Hydrocarbons

A high resinous asphaltite has been mined and marketed in commercial quantities from the Uintah Basin of northwest Utah. Properly installed around a hot pipe, temperature effects create three zones of physical changes in the material. Closest to the pipe is a dense, semi-plastic coating, next is a "sintered" or partially consolidated zone, and finally, the unconsolidated zone of raw material unaffected by temperature.

Plastic Foam

Plastic foam is usually a two component polyether-based urethane resin foaming system which produces low density, rigid urethane foam. The foam is produced by the expansion of Freon-type gas. When properly mixed and introduced into a cavity, the liquid composition expands to fill the void space and cures into a rigid foam. The curing process takes place at ambient temperature without the application of external heat. However, at low ambients below about 50 F, the expansion process is impaired and the curing time extended.

The temperature range of polyurethane foam presently does not exceed about 250 F. Research work is in process which may lead to products which extend this limit, however.

While the closed cell content of the foam is generally 90–95%, some water absorption does occur. Normally, the monolithic form is sealed with a water barrier such as polyethylene film. One other disadvantage of the material is the fact that it burns when exposed to an open flame and is not self extinguishing.

Heat Losses From Insulated Buried Steam Lines

Heat loss from a pipe buried in soil occurs somewhat differently from that of a pipe in air, because of the soil's resistance to heat flow. Heat resistance of soil varies widely depending upon its composition and degree of dryness. Soil resistance when dry may be several times as great as when wet. Depth of burial makes very little difference in heat loss when the cover is at least two feet.

Efforts have been made to develop an optimum or economic thickness of insulation for steam mains. Such efforts attempt to balance the cost of steam, installed cost of insulation, capital investment, depreciation and heat losses for various K values and thicknesses of insulation at different temperature ranges so that overall cost is minimized. The heat loss factor, while important, becomes only one of the considerations.

Formulas for calculating heat loss from composite piping systems have been in existence for many years. Developed mathematically and confirmed experimentally, they are generally accepted as accurate.

For a complex system where the carrier pipe is covered with a layer of insulation and a casing without air space between them, the following formula applies:

$$H_p = \frac{t_i - t_2}{\dfrac{r_1 \log_e \dfrac{r_2}{r_1}}{K_1} + \dfrac{r_1 \log_e \dfrac{r_3}{r_2}}{K_2} + \dfrac{r_1}{r_3} \cdot \dfrac{1}{K_s}}$$

The terms used in this equation are defined as follows:

H_p = Heat loss in Btu per sq. ft. of pipe surface per hour
t_1 = Pipe temperature in °F
t_2 = Normal Soil Temperature in °F
r_1 = Radius of outer surface of pipe in inches.
r_2 = Radius of outer surface of insulation in inches
r_3 = Radius of outer surface of casing in inches
K_1 = Coefficient of thermal conductivity of the insulation in Btu per sq. ft. per degree F per inch thickness per hour
K_2 = Coefficient of thermal conductivity of the casing
K_s = Coefficient of thermal conductivity of the soil

Where an air space is involved, the added factor of thermal conductivity across the air space must be incorporated. This is handled as shown below in the heat loss formula for the rectangular concrete duct containing an insulated steam line.

$$H_p = \cfrac{t_1 - t_2}{\cfrac{r_1 \log_e (r_2/r_1)}{K_1} + \cfrac{A_1}{2}\left(\cfrac{1}{A_2} + \cfrac{1}{A_3}\right)\cfrac{1}{K_2} + \left(\cfrac{A_1}{\cfrac{A_3 + A_4}{2}}\right)\left(\cfrac{X}{K_3}\right) + \cfrac{A_1}{A_4}\cfrac{1}{K_s}}$$

where

H_p	=	Heat Loss in Btu per sq. ft. of pipe surface per hour
t_1	=	Pipe temperature in °F
t_2	=	Normal soil temperature in °F
r_1	=	Radius of outer surface of pipe in inches
r_2	=	Radius of outer surface of insulation in inches
K_1	=	Coefficient of thermal conductivity of the insulation
K_2	=	Coefficient of thermal conductivity of the air space
K_3	=	Coefficient of thermal conductivity of the concrete structure
A_1	=	Square feet of pipe surface per linear foot
A_2	=	Square feet of outer surface of insulation per linear foot
A_3	=	Square feet of inner surface of concrete duct per linear foot
A_4	=	Square feet of outer surface of concrete duct per linear foot
X	=	Thickness of concrete duct in inches
K_s	=	Thermal conductivity of soil

Providing for Pipe Expansion and Contraction

Any change in temperature of a thermal conduit such as steel pipe will either expand or contract. The magnitude of thermal expansion per 100 feet of length for carbon steel pipe from a base of 70°F is indicated by table 6.3.

The forces involved from the expansion of steel pipe are considerable and accommodation of this movement must be designed as part of any thermal distribution network. In exposed piping expansion loops, horseshoe shaped structure, may be positioned to absorb the changes in pipe length relative to the flowing temperature. There are numerous devices manufactured to accomplish the same result with lower space requirements, less fabrication and suitable for underground construction. In general these devices fall into one of three general categories, ball or hinge joints that permit flexing at a change in direction of the linve, slip joints that permit linear movement of one member in or out of a casing, and bellows devices that permit motion through the flexibility of an accordian-like element. Ball type joints are best utilized where there is a required change in direction of the pipe line. These devices in modern designs are generally maintenance free and are capable of relatively large pipe movement.

Slip type expansion joints can provide long travel and are very strong structurally. They do depend upon a packing/lubricant system and generally call for a manhole type housing in underground systems.

Bellows type expansion joints are made in a variety of types and styles often with innovative features for alignment, adjustment and reduction of differential pressure across the corregated portion. The most frequently used material for the bellows is stainless steel. There have been problems in certain environments with the stress corrosion of stainless steel elements. The movement of pipe under changes in temperature are defined as:

1. *Axial Movement:* The dimensional shortening or lengthening of an expansion joint parallel to its longitudinal axis, also referred to as extension, or traverse movement.

TABLE 6.3
THERMAL EXPANSION OF STEEL PIPE
eμ, inches per 100 ft.
from 70°F ambient temp.

Saturated Steam Vacuum in HG below 212°F., Pressure psig above 212°F	Temperature Degrees Fahrenheit	Carbon & Carbon Molybdenum Steel
	−20	−0.66
	0	−0.51
	20	−0.37
	32	−0.28
	40	−0.21
		.07
29.39	60	−0.07
29.18	70	0
28.89	80	.07
27.99	100	.24
26.48	120	.40
24.04	140	.55
20.27	160	.69
14.63	180	.85
6.45	200	1.01
0	212	1.10
2.5	220	1.17
5.0	227	1.22
10.3	240	1.33
20.7	260	1.51
25.0	267	1.56
34.5	280	1.67
50.0	298	1.82
52.3	300	1.84
74.9	320	2.02
103.3	340	2.10
125.0	353	2.30
138.3	360	2.37
150.0	366	2.42
180.9	380	2.55
200.0	388	2.61
232.4	400	2.72
250.0	406	2.77
293.7	420	2.91
300.0	422	2.92
366.1	440	3.08
400.0	448	3.11
451.3	460	3.27
500.0	470	3.36
550.3	480	3.44
600.0	489	3.53
664.3	500	3.64
795.3	520	3.83
945.3	540	4.01
1115	560	4.22
1308	580	4.42
1525	600	4.62
1768	620	4.82
2041	640	5.02
2346	660	5.24
2705	680	5.44
3080	700	5.65
	720	5.85
	740	6.06
	760	6.28
	780	6.49
	800	6.72

To determine the net expansion from a temp. below 70°F to a temp. above 70°F, the unit expansion at the lower temp. must be added to the unit expansion at the higher temp.

Example: expansion from 40 to 340°F = 2.19 −(−.21) = 2.40″/100ft.

2. *Lateral Deflection:* The relative displacement of the longitudinal axis of a pipe line perpendicular to that axis. This is also referred to as lateral offset, lateral movement, parallel misalignment, direct shear or transverse movement.

3. *Angular Rotation:* Movement producing angular displacement of the longitudinal axis of a pipe line. This is also referred to as rotational movement or radial movement.

Bellows and slip joints are illustrated in Figures 6.16 and 6.17. They may be shrouded and well protected against misalignment. Piping must be properly anchored and provided with alignment guides.

STEAM-LINE ANCHORS

Although many anchor designs are used, basic principles must always be included. One of the first of those is that the anchor be designed for the maximum possible pressure which could be placed on the line. If steam is to be fed from more than one plant, the design should be for the one carrying the highest pressure. If supplied through a pressure-reducing valve, the design should be for the upstream pressure unless other means are provided to limit the pressure. Anchors must be strong enough to withstand the full unbalanced pressure of the steam and expansion stresses.

Corrosion in underground steam-line construction is one of the most serious problems. An anchor with a safety factor of 10 when new may have this factor greatly reduced through corrosion during the years of use. The maximum years of service must be taken into account in designing any anchor.

It is often best to place expansion joints in manholes and to bury the anchors between them. In such cases, it is doubly important to design the anchors for maximum strength and life.

When anchors are attached to manhole walls, floors or ceilings by cinch bolts, they should be used in shear only. An even more desirable design is produced by concreting the steel members directly into the structure throughout the entire width of the walls and, if possible, avoiding cantilever anchors by

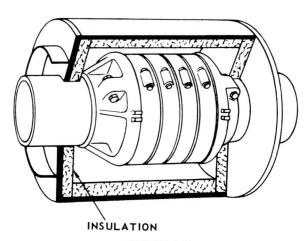

INSULATION

FIGURE 6.16

Bellows-type expansion joint absorbs linear pipe movement. Piping on both sides of joint must be guided to prevent buckling of bellows.

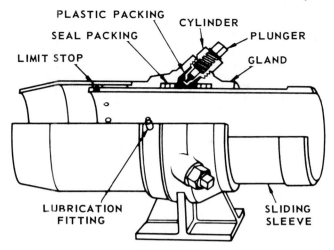

PLASTIC PACKING
SEAL PACKING
CYLINDER
PLUNGER
LIMIT STOP
GLAND
LUBRICATION
FITTING
SLIDING
SLEEVE

FIGURE 6.17

Slip-type expansion joint is installed on longitudinal axis of distribution piping system, usually in manholes.

(Courtesy of ASHRAE Handbook & Product Directory)

FIGURE 6.18
Steam-pipe anchor

using anchor beams supported at both ends. An anchor attached to only one side of a steam pipe is undesirable and becomes even more so as the distance of support from the center of the pipe line increases. In contrast to this, the simple anchor illustrated in Figure 6.18, and buried in concrete on opposite sides of the line is optimal.

Galvanized structural shapes are useful as anchors because of their resistance to corrosion. However, any welding should be done only where the galvanized coating is thoroughly removed in order to insure a perfect weld.

Designs which need metal members at the floor line of conduit or tunnel should be avoided since moisture exists in greater quantities there and the problem of corrosion is more serious.

The way to make use of tie rods as an anchor is to use four located in a plane passing through the longitudinal center of the pipe, one pair of rods extending from a common attachment point on one side at an angle of 30 degrees backward and forward, and another pair on the opposite side similarly attached. One of the most satisfactory anchors made with structural shapes uses a similar design, with the anchor securely welded on opposite sides of the line and embedded in massive concrete.

An anchor system where a pipe line passes through a wall strong enough to serve as an anchor is produced by imbedding a thimble in the wall and anchoring the pipe to it by a heavy plate welded to both pipe and thimble.

A stiffleg is an acceptable anchor, but it can only be used most effectively in its simplest form at a pipe offset. If a pipe line changes direction 20 degrees or more, one of the most desirable anchors is made by continuing a stiffleg of extra-heavy pipe or an extended structural member straight ahead at the bend, continuing on the center line of the pipe. This should be thoroughly embedded in concrete against thrust and pull. A similar stiffleg installed from the same contact point in line with the other run of pipe completes the anchor.

Light anchors are permissible where expansion bends are used. However, thin structural members present greater surface per unit of cross-sectional area than others and thereby increase the hazard of failure from corrosion proportionately.

Cast iron should be avoided in any anchor operating in excess of 125 psi. Expansion joints made of cast iron with an anchor base should have the flat surface of such base located at a distance from the center of the pipe, not greater than 1.5 times the pipe radius, unless massively built. There should be two anchor bases, one at the bottom and one at the top of the joint.

STEAM-LINE GUIDES

Lines which must be anchored, must also be guided. The design is simple enough that there should be no failures from this source if the same precautions are used in designing guides as in the design of the anchors. Simply supporting a line on rollers or other supports is not sufficient. In general, a straight line should be guided at every sixth or seventh support and precautions taken if the pipe deviates from a straight line between expansion joints. (See Figure 6.19).

PRESSURE-REDUCING VALVES

Single-seated pressure-reducing valves are used in distribution pressure-reducing stations, if a proper valve-operating mechanism is selected for the required pressure range. When pressure-reducing valves are located at the supply end of a feeder and it is necessary to control them automatically from the pressure at the remote end, specially constructed pressure-reducing valves must be used. Such valves cannot usually be operated well by extending the pilot line to remote points where a relatively large drop in pressure is placed between the pressure-reducing valve and the spill-in point. Such installations require a pressure-reducing valve with a design that incorporates a compensating device which positions and holds the valve regardless of its inlet and outlet pressures. This type of valve usually has some auxiliary source of power in connection with the valve position, such as water or compressed air.

FIGURE 6.19
Guide for 14 in. steam pipe

Double-seated valves or other types of pressure-reducing valves which permit some leakage of steam through them are not as good for distribution because of the possibility they may permit pressure to build up beyond the desired level.

Piston-operated pressure-reducing valves often have a greater discharge capacity for a given size valve seat than other designs since they conveniently can accommodate a higher lift. This holds true for both the single and double-seat designs.

Valves operated directly from a metal diaphragm have the least capacity for a given size seat due to limited valve-life, unless the diaphragm is constructed disproportionately large.

Valves directly operated by a flexible composition or rubber diaphragm have capacities between the two types discussed.

Tables of capacities for various satisfactory pressure drops are furnished by manufacturers. The size of a pressure-reducing valve should always be determined from the manufacturer's rating regardless of the size of the pipe line into which it is connected. Pipe sizes adjacent to pressure-reducing valves often are governed by factors other than the amount of steam which pressure-reducing valves can and should normally pass.

It is an unusual practice to install a pressure-reducing valve used for consumer's service in consumer's premises, but owned by the supplier. Reducing stations for the supplier's use should be located in space accessible by doorways or stairs. Manholes which can be entered only from a street opening and ladders may be used under some conditions, but are not often as satisfactory. Pressure-reducing valves in any location should be provided with convenient platforms for operation and maintenance.

Where a bypass is used and gate valves are required on each side of a pressure-reducing valve, these valves should be the same size as the end connections of the pressure-reducing valve.

A bypass is desirable where a single pressure-reducing valve owned by the supplier is used. The valve on the bypass line should be a globe pattern and one-pipe size smaller than the pressure-reducing valve. Where two or more pressure-reducing valves operate in parallel, the size of a common bypass is governed by several factors, but need not be larger (and, indeed, may be smaller) than would be required by the largest pressure-reducing valve of the group if installed singly.

When flanged pressure-reducing valves are used it is best to install a spool adjacent to the pressure-reducing valve on either the upstream or the downstream side. If gate valves are bolted directly to the pressure-reducing valve flanges, it is difficult if not impossible to remove the pressure-reducing valve body from the line without shutting steam off the entire pressure-reducing station.

An indicating or recording pressure gage should be installed on both the upstream and downstream side of each reducing valve. Neither gage should be connected to the pressure-reducing valve or to piping that must be closed off when the pressure-reducing valve is out of service for repairs.

Where steam use is great during the winter months but only a small amount is required through the summer, it is sometimes desirable to install a small pressure-reducing valve in parallel with the large one, both of the dead-end type. Even though very large single-seated valves will shut off tight with no demand, their operation is not recommended for very small loads.

Piping, Valves, Fittings and Accessories

The application of manufacturer's sizes, shapes, strengths, and composition of pipes, valves, fittings, and accessory equipment is set forth in detail in the "Code for Pressure Piping" of ANSI. The designer of a distribution system should use the information set forth in this Code. It covers piping, fittings and accessories at all temperatures and pressures for general and special applications.

Pipes

Steel or wrought-iron pipe in appropriate thicknesses are satisfactory materials for the distribution of steam. Pipe is best joined by welding. Flanges only should be used to connect piping to removable equipment, and then only when such equipment is located in easily reached places. If the welding of underground steel or wrought-iron pipe lines is properly done and tested, the conduits made watertight, the lines kept continuously hot, and not subjected to damaging water hammer, they can give service indefinitely. This is also true of stainless-steel and nonferrous piping.

When used for condensate return, steel or wrought-iron pipe has serious competition because of corrosion and other factors. Some steam distributors have replaced steel and cast-iron return piping with copper or brass pipe. Condensate return in the district heating industry in this country has become sufficiently widespread to determine the pipe material most economical for this purpose.

Valves

Flanged cast-iron valves, 2 in. to 30 in. with pressures up to 125 psi, give good service. Such valves should be accessible and protected from water, excessively moist vapors and other corrosive elements.

For pressures from 125 to 300 psi, flanged-steel and welded-end valves are widely used. Many steam suppliers prefer the performance of outside screw and yoke valves to the inside screw because of the assurance of the valve position indicated by the length of the protruding stem.

When by-pass valves are used with large gate valves up to 125 psi, flanged connections to the body are satisfactory, but for pressures above 125 psi, a completely independent by-pass line of steel pipe with by-pass valve included and welded to the main on opposite sides of the large valve is best. Globe valves are preferred for throttling service as in by-pass hand control around pressure-reducing valves. No drilled and tapped connection larger than ½ in. pipe size should be made into the body of a cast-iron gate valve. Drain connections for traps should not be made into the body of such valves, and should be made at the low points of the steel piping.

The location and number of distribution valves in a new district heating steam piping system is a decision to be made by the system design engineer after evaluating the following factors:

1. A drip pot and trap must always be installed at every low point and usually at the end of a steam main. Companies often build a manhole at these locations to house the trap. This also allows the opportunity for installation of a free-blow valve which can be very important in sectionalizing the steam main.

   If a trap manhole is built, a distribution valve also can be installed without greatly increasing the size of the manhole. However, if the distribution line profile means that several trap manholes have to be installed close together, a main line valve is not needed in each trap manhole.

2. Consideration should be given to installing main line valves at each tee or cross since it may be difficult to obtain outages for maintenance or new construction connections if large customers are connected to these branches.

   Manholes are sometimes built at tee and cross locations and main live valves installed in these manholes. This usually results in larger manholes with complicated auxiliary piping and pipe line anchors inside. Other options include installing the main line fitting in the ground at a street intersection and building separate valve manholes on each branch line as close as practical to the fitting. This results in more but smaller manholes, uncomplicated auxiliary piping and main line anchors outside of the manhole where deterioration of the anchor due to corrosion can be kept to a minimum. The method used depends upon policy, municipal requirements, quantity and location of foreign pipe, the depth of the steam main and the relative costs involved.

3. Line valves should be installed on each side of a service feeding a large or important customer to whom continuity of service is of paramount importance. (For example, a large industrial plant or a hospital) if this customer can be fed steam from two directions.

   If this type customer has separate services from two steam mains and interconnecting distribution piping within this building, such valving may not be necessary.

4. If a new steam main is being installed through an area where planned load growth is unpredictable enough main line valves should be installed to permit system changes without longer excessive outages of the steam main.

5. Enough valves must be installed to permit sectionalizing a piece of the steam main without excessive time for filling and free blowing and to

permit time for maintenance work or main line changes. The number needed is a function of the:

a. Size of the steam main
b. Length of main between distribution valves
c. Pressure at which the line is operated
d. Time required to operate the main line valves
e. Size and number of free blow and drip valves available for venting and filling the steam main
f. Maximum time it is expected that the steam main can be taken out of service
6. Manholes in which sectionalizing valves are installed are expensive to build and maintain. Therefore, the number of these manholes built should be minimized.

Fittings

Screwed malleable iron pipe fittings work well for most pressures up to 125 psi for sizes 2 in. or less. On higher pressures, fittings should be or forged or rolled steel. Welded piping with no screwed fittings in sizes up to 2 in. is useful in some special applications. For steel pipe in sizes 2½ in. and larger there is usually little justification for the use of flanged fittings where welding can be accomplished.

If pipe-line apparatus is to be removed at intervals, flanged connections have some use in preference to welded ones, especially in distribution work.

Tunnels and Underground Conduits

Unless already established by the existence of an existing system the choice of a type of distribution facility requires careful consideration of a wide variety of factors. One very important decision is the choice between a tunnel or an underground conduit system.

Tunnels are most often found in institutional systems where a tunnel is practical for the distribution of several utility services. This multiple use offsets the relatively high construction costs. Provisions must be made for future expansion of the tunnel structure for maintenance of its watertight integrity.

A tunnel allows easy access for inspection, testing and maintenance of facilities. Piping and insulation remain dry, which minimizes possible corrosion problems. Figure 6.20 shows the cross section of a typical tunnel constructed of reinforced concrete.

Underground conduits are used in almost all large scale systems, especially those installed in public rights of way. The conduit system used must be compatible with soil conditions and anticipated service. It should be built to maintain watertight integrity and should have sufficient insulation to restrict heat loss and minimize any effect on adjacent utility facilities. Conduit systems may be:

1. Box Type
2. Solid Pour
3. Prefabricated

A box-type concrete conduit is illustrated in Figure 6.21. The pipes are insulated in a conventional manner and supported by saddles or brackets. The air space around the pipe often is made large enough to take up pipe movement as well as to allow air changes for drying the insulation if it should become wet. However, such a large air space results in increased costs. The forms shown in

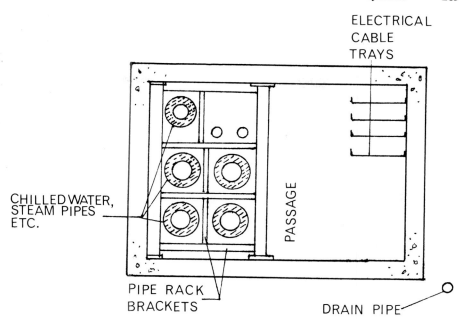

FIGURE 6.20

Reinforced concrete tunnel

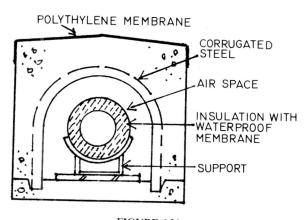

FIGURE 6.21

Box type concrete conduit

the illustration are corrugated steel sections. These forms never should be stacked on top of each other at the same site prior to installation. The toes of the form get bent outwards from such treatment and will not fit properly into the concrete chases.

Figure 6.22 shows a pipe trench made from concrete with removable covers. The pipe is insulated conventionally and is supported on saddles and brackets. Concrete covers must be fitted so that they remain watertight.

A solid pour conduit is shown in Figure 6.23. It is insulated with a hard

REMOVABLE COVER

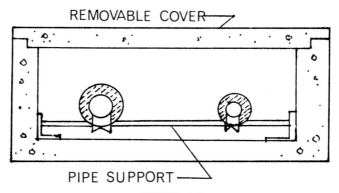

PIPE SUPPORT

FIGURE 6.22
Removable cover on box type conduit

6 MIL POLYTHYLENE MEMBRANE
LAID ON TOP OF EMULSION

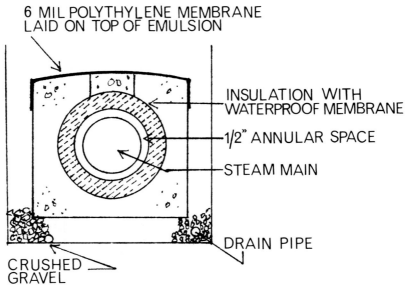

INSULATION WITH
WATERPROOF MEMBRANE

1/2" ANNULAR SPACE

STEAM MAIN

DRAIN PIPE

CRUSHED
GRAVEL

FIGURE 6.23
Solid pour conduit

calcium silicate insulation separated from the pipe by a ½-inch air space. This space allows the pipe to move logitudinally through the insulation and to clear pipe welds. The air space is increased to approximately 3 inches where lateral movement is encountered on expansion loops to allow for pipe movement. Insulation is wired on over wax-dipped corrugated paper strips which have been wired to the pipe to hold the insulation concentrically in place. Concrete is then poured around the insulated steam line.

In prefabricated conduit systems, sections are factory assembled complete with thermal insulation, pipe guides, expansion joints, anchor points, and

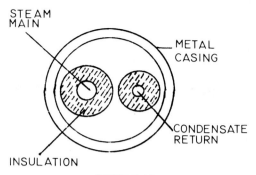

FIGURE 6.24
Metal casing, prefabricated conduit

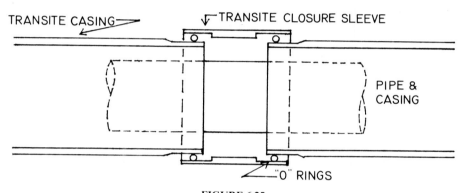

FIGURE 6.25
Cement pipe casing, prefabricated conduit

exterior casings. The casings may be metal (Figure 6.24) or cement pipe (Figure 6.25).

Field installation involves only joining the sections and providing anchors, end seals and glands at manholes or building terminals.

Metal casings normally are covered with asphalt or reinforced epoxy to help eliminate corrosion. These coatings must be protected from puncture or other mechanical damage during the construction period, especially during backfill operations. Sand is the substance most often used for backfill to a point at least a foot above the crown of the conduit. The remaining backfill must also be free of stones or other hard and potentially damaging constituents.

As further protection against corrosion, and especially in cases where soil resistivity is high, cathodic protection may be used in addition to the coatings. Such protective measures are very important, since any penetration of moisture through the metal casing can result in insulation damage, thermal loss and pipe corrosion.

Cement casing, on the other hand, is inert, insensitive to the resistivity of the soil and not subject to electrolytic corrosion.

SYSTEM TESTING

As many checks and tests as practical should be made before backfilling because of the difficulty of repairing underground systems. Tests on the system are certain to be required by local authorities, and may vary from one locality to the next. In addition to mandatory tests, all pipe welds should also be hydrostatically tested and flushed. If the conduit can be tested for leaks, this also should be done. Where a coating is applied to the conduit, the coating should be tested for pinholes and blemishes. During fabrication and installation the conduit should be continuously monitored and inspected.

Manholes

Manholes are needed in large underground distribution systems to provide access to and enclosures for expansion joints, line valves, pressure-reducing stations, traps, fittings, weld or gland seals, vent holes and vent telltales. They also provide a convenient location for changing elevations on one or more pipe branches or on the main. In addition, they can be used to house sumps, with or without pumps, for draining and removing water from the conduit system. Manholes, however, are expensive to construct and maintain. Their inclusion in a system therefore should be limited. Packless expansion joints, valves, vents and fittings may be successfully installed without manholes. Wherever possible, this practice should be followed to lower costs. Systems with short runs of piping between buildings may not require manholes if basements or crawl spaces can be utilized.

Matters for considerations in manhole design include:

1. *Size*—Adequate space should be provided for the installation and for maintenance and inspection of the included facilities.
2. *Location*—Within the limits set by its function and underground obstructions, consideration must be given to traffic density, flooding and access difficulties.
3. *Structural Requirements*—Manholes should be designed and built according to good structural engineering practice to meet the loads (traffic or pedestrian) which will be imposed upon them.
4. *Ventilation*—Proper ventilation manholes reduce conditions of temperature and humidity which will prolong the service life of the manhole and equipment. Where surface conditions allow, the best method of providing ventilation is to employ two pipes 4 inches or larger in diameter, venting to the atmosphere—one extending almost to the floor, the other ending flush with the ceiling. This produces a constant natural circulation of air. The disadvantages of this system are that it provides a way for surface water to enter the manhole and a means of escape for live steam which may be present from a leak in the system.
   If surface conditions do not allow continuous venting, construction should provide for rapid forced ventilation when needed. Two large openings from the manhole to the surface, with removable covers, can do this if used in conjunction with some mechanical air mover.
5. *Drainage*—Water in a manhole can cause corrosion and deterioration of insulation in the manhole and the adjacent system. In systems with conduit ends open at the manhole wall, flooding can force water back into the conduit. This dampens the insulation, increases heat losses and causes corrosion. To eliminate flooding, a variety of methods may be used.
   Gravity drains to storm sewer or drainage area must be lower than the floor of the manhole, however, so this method may not always be possible.

Drains of this type should contain a backwater trap to prevent the sewer system from rising and flooding the manhole.

Automatically operated electric pumps usually are the most effective method for removing water. The motor and electrical apparatus must be weatherproof, submersible or located in an area not subject to flooding, heat or high humidity. This can be achieved only by building a separate enclosure in the manhole for the motor. Installation of electrical equipment in hot manholes should be avoided because of the rapid deterioration of these facilities in a high temperature environment. Discharge lines should contain check valves.

Automatic steam-operated ejectors may be used; however, maintenance on this apparatus may be very expensive. Water operated ejectors are used more frequently and usually are more convenient because of easy access of water service to the manholes.

Dry wells may be used in areas with low rainfall (less than 25 inches per year) where soil permeability is relatively high. However, in areas which experience an occasional heavy rainfall, dry well action may be too slow to control flooding and may even contribute to the flooding by allowing ground water to enter the manhole.

A sump always should be provided in the manhole no matter which method is used for water removal. The sump location should allow for a portable suction hose to easily be run to it from the surface. Sumps placed directly below the access opening should be covered by removable gratings.

Raising the roof of the manhole above grade reduces the possibility of flooding from surface water, but this is generally not possible in metropolitan distribution systems.

Waterproofing exterior walls of a manhole to prevent seepage is effective in reducing flooding conditions. Exterior surfaces should be coated with creosote primer and coal tar. Suitable tapes and sheet wrappings may be substituted for enamel, bituminous materials, or asphalt coverings. Suitable waterproofing material for manholes should consider the following criteria:

a. Must retain original properties with age.
b. Resistant to chemical agents found in the soil.
c. Resistant to rodents.
d. Resistant to fungi and mildew.
e. Satisfactory for use at 200 F.

6. *Arrangement of Equipment*—Equipment should be arranged in a manhole to provide adequate space for installation, operation and maintenance. Planning must also include the possibility of mechanical damage resulting from objects falling from the surface. Electrical equipment should be located outside the manhole or be otherwise protected from the environment.

Manhole Types

Field poured manholes can be built of reinforced concrete with strength of up to 2500 pounds with adequate wall thickness and reinforcing sized for the structural dimensions, surface loading and soil conditions. Construction procedures are standard for any cast-in-place concrete structure. Manholes should be built in a way which will prevent the entrance of ground or surface water.

Wherever possible, the floor and walls should be formed from the same pour. The roof slab should contain access openings and allow for ventilation. The possible need for lifting heavy equipment in a manhole should be considered in the design. Heavy lifting eyes in the roof or openings to allow hoisting from the surface are good practice. Conduits entering the manhole should extend through the walls, without bonding, to prevent a convenient means for draining the conduit.

Field poured manholes have the advantage of being built in a variety of shapes but, the disadvantage of being relatively more expensive.

Prefabricated concrete manholes come in various combinations of floor, walls, and roof slab. Wall thicknesses and reinforcement are usually standardized by the manufacturer for specific types of loading. Where possible the manhole should be delivered to the job site with all piping, fittings, thermal insulation anchors, and other accessories completely installed. A bed of select fill should be laid to provide a firm bearing surface under the floor. The roof slab must contain all the needed openings. The provisions mentioned previously regarding waterproofing, duct entrances, and other conditions apply to prefabricated as well as to field poured concrete manholes.

When the prefabricated manhole arrives at the job site, it is merely lifted off the truck and lowered in place. The piping is then welded to the adjacent pipe units. The roof is set in place, joints sealed and the excavation is ready for backfilling. The installation of this type of manhole is faster and less costly than the construction of a field poured concrete manhole.

Prefabricated metal manholes can be built from heavy-gage, hot dip, galvanized, corrugated metal sheets. These are usually shaped into large diameter conduit sections which can be installed either in the horizontal or vertical position. Steel plates, similarly galvanized, installed at both ends of the conduit portion complete the basic fabricated unit. Access, ventilation and water removal must be provided as in any manhole installation. Cutouts are an integral part of the prefabricated unit. The unit may be coated inside and out with an asphaltic compound to assure a watertight corrosion resistant installation. Even with this coating, cathodic protection should be applied.

Installation is similar to that for prefabricated concrete manholes. Metal manholes generally are not as structurally strong as concrete. This limits their use to locations where heavy traffic loading is not a problem.

Corrosion in Concrete Manholes

Corrosion of exposed steel in manholes can be inhibited or prevented. On the other hand, corrosion of steel reinforcing members in concrete is not easily controlled.

In the hot, humid environment of a steam manhole, corrosion can be rapid and very damaging. The porosity of the concrete allows the corrosive agent to attack the steel. The corrosive agent may be oxygen, water, calcium chloride or a variety of other liquids or gases. As products of corrosion form, the volume of the original steel increases. This volume increase, in turn, causes stress in the concrete which lead to cracks and eventual spalling of the concrete. Once the reinforcing rods are exposed to corrosive agents, the corrosion process continues at an accelerated rate.

Some causes of possible corrosion may be designed into the manhole by accident or error. Some of these designed-in causes are:

1. Increased porosity in the concrete promotes corrosion of the reinforcement. A porosity of 9.5 percent or less, by volume, is optimum.

2. The addition of $CaCl_2$ to the concrete as a hardening agent can increase the rate of corrosion. The chloride does not appear to act as the corrosive agent, but instead seems to act as a corrosion catalyst. Calcium chloride in amounts greater than 2 percent of the cement, by weight, accelerates the rate of corrosion very rapidly.

3. Improper ventilation resulting in high heat and humidity accelerates corrosive action within the manhole.

4. Placing reinforcing steel close to the surface of the concrete decreases the barrier afforded by the concrete.
   Crackling and spalling occur more readily when the reinforcement covering is inadequate. A minimum covering of at least 2 inches is recommended.

5. Undesirable damp conditions may result from inadequate pumps, drains or waterproofing. The water acts as a carrier for the agent corroding the reinforcing steel.

Equipment corrosion located in a steam manhole is accelerated by water and high temperature conditions. The proper use of paints and coverings can provide protection for equipment installed in manholes, reducing the speed of corrosion. Equipment not specifically submersible should be installed in a location above the expected water level.

System Controls

Almost all steam distribution systems have started with only a small number of customers who were served at relatively low pressures. As these systems grew, operating pressures and system operating methods had to be revised. Today, almost all types and variations of system controls are in use in district heating systems. Some common control practices include:

1. Some companies distribute relatively high pressure steam to pressure reducing valves located in manholes. Groups of customers then are supplied from these pressure reducing valves.
   Another system uses basically the same setup except that the reducing valves are located in a station and their pilots electrically positioned from a dispatching center.

2. Several large companies which have many steam generating stations try to base-load selected stations with motor operated gate valves or parabolic disc valves using past experience and weather forecasts as guides. Reducing valves at the stations' they control the load swings as indicated by long distance recorders and telemeters carefully located throughout the system.

3. In yet another method, steam is distributed at varying sendout pressures which fluctuate with system demands, enough to maintain pressures at selected points on the system within predetermined limits. The company either supplies and maintains pressure reducing valves set to a utilization pressure or require that the customers provide these valves.

Another important aspect of steam system controls is protection. Steam distribution pressures and temperatures usually are controlled from the send-out plants. The instruments and controls used for this purpose normally are carefully maintained. In many systems, boiler design and safety valve settings also protect against excessive pressures.

Water hammer is another problem which must be taken into account particularly in box-type conduits. Water hammer can develop when steam mains become flooded from flash floods caused by rains, excessively high tides, water main breaks, or other causes. If the condensation rate of the steam in the main exceeds the installed trap capacity, such a potential exists. One solution involves installation of rupture discs in the drip piping in manholes at the ends of the steam main. A street controlled valve is installed on the high side of the rupture disc to shut off the flow of steam if the rupture disc breaks.

Another important aid in system control is metering. It is essential that all send-out points be accurately monitored for flow and pressure and for temperature if superheat is involved.

Metering stations should be installed on all major branch feeder lines. Information from these sources is most useful in determining where to add new capacity, additional feeder lines or control valve locations.

Temperature is another important consideration.

Steam tends to become superheated as the velocity increases. On a long feeder at high flow rates the superheat at the delivery point may far exceed the design temperature for the expansion bends or joints in the steam system. This is especially true if superheated steam is fed into the feeder lines from the generating station.

It becomes very important, then, to monitor and record the temperature of the steam at the send-out plant. The desuperheating station must also be controlled carefully if one is installed. A desuperheater station will always deliver superheated steam because there must be some superheat leaving the equipment for the controls to function.

Distribution System Efficiency

In steam systems energy losses during conveyance are indicated by the amount of condensate formed. The longer the distance the greater the energy loss. Even with a low enthalpy change (Δh), a significant loss of available energy occurs with each drop in steam pressure. The change of state of the steam during flow is like a throttling process through an orifice, and for pressure drops from moderately high initial pressures, droplets of steam form and drop to the bottom of the pipe. At very high velocities, the problem of water accumulation will be even more acute.

Another major cause of condensation is heat loss from the conduit which lowers the temperature of the steam in contact with the pipe wall. Such heat loss from a well insulated conduit system should only be 2 to 5% of the maximum energy deliverable at full design load conditions. Another energy loss from steam systems comes from energy in condensate released from the system, usually from steam traps. This loss must also be considered to include the energy involved in the addition of makeup water which must be heated when added to maintain inventory.

Condensate still retains some energy and is often collected and returned. Sometimes, however, it is rejected from the system. In cases where all of the condensate is released because no condensate return is installed, about 15% of the total energy delivered is lost. District heating systems often include condensate return piping and operating procedures which try to minimize steam trap losses.

The amount of change in heat loss or gain through conduit insulation after long-term exposure to widely differing underground conditions is probably the biggest variable in thermal energy conveyance. Once an outer conduit casing is penetrated by ground water and a sector of the distribution system becomes wet or deteriorated, the heat transfer loss from that sector may be several times the predicted loss. It even could be a full order of magnitude higher than the loss at design conditions.

Steam Turn-On Procedures

In initially turning on a steam main or service, the primary consideration is to take every precaution to prevent water hammer with the resulting hazards to personnel and property.

Because of the possibility of this danger, the initial turn-on of a steam main should always be supervised instead of an automatic warm-up. Before turning on a steam main it is necessary to know how the steam line pitches, where and how many low points exist, and the location of the sectionalizing valves.

All low points should be opened and any accumulated water drained out. If a steam service pitches into a building the service valve should be cracked open. If there are any trap manholes in the steam main, the free blow valves in those holes should be opened and the valve ahead of the traps shut off. This prevents any dirt in the main from entering the trap. If a section of steam main is to be turned on from one main line valve to another the drip piping in both manholes at the ends of the main should be so valved that the free blow valves in each manhole are left open.

Only then should steam be admitted to the new piping. This should be done at a very slow flow rate through partially opened by-pass piping on or around the main valve.

As the steam line warms, the flow of water will decrease and steam instead of water will come out of the freeblow valves. The free blow valve then can be shut off and the traps put into operation.

Circumstances may require some changes from this outline in actual operations.

The length of steam main which can be turned on at one time is determined by the size of the drip valve and by-pass valve piping, the diameter of the steam main, the pressure and quantity of steam available for filling the main, etc., and other less factors.

For example, if a large steam main were to be filled through a small by-pass valve at medium steam pressure, it is doubtful if it could ever be filled.

As soon as the steam main or service is up to pressure all the traps should be checked for operation. These traps will probably have to be checked for operation and the strainers blown down frequently during the first few months of operation.

After the traps have been checked, after any last minute testing for leaks has been done, and after the steam main is almost up to pressure the main line valves can be opened.

Maintenance

Maintenance in a steam distribution system cannot be overemphasized. Frequent meticulous and careful inspection, along with prompt repair work where needed are of paramount importance.

Steam can be injurious to persons and property and sometimes violently so. Steam outside the system can cause extensive damage to property, including walls, ceilings, floors and merchandise. Water hammer can cause similar damage with the added danger of personal injury through burns or asphyxiation. Water hammer can cause damage which results in the necessity of immediate shutdowns for repairs. This can cause interruption of services in hospitals, restaurant service, process lines, and other essential services. Once a leak or a break occurs, the steam will keep flowing and damages continue to mount until it is shut off. There can be no systemwide automatic safety devices for this medium.

The key to proper maintenance work is inspection. A good, accurate and careful inspection program can locate most small leaks and troubles before they become serious enough to require major repairs under emergency conditions.

Items in this category which are used in the operation of a steam system, and should be inspected frequently, include:

1. Steam or water siphons operated, their piping checked for leaks; street control valves checked for leaks and valve extension rods examined.
2. Accessible expansion joints checked for leaks.
3. Trap operation, leaks at traps or piping and the condition of associated valves.
4. Pressure reducing valves checked for leaks and operation.
5. All valve line and bonnet gaskets, packing, the condition of extension rods to street and valve operation.

Any electric driven sump pumps installed on the system should be inspected daily. Their counters should be read to note if any unusual conditions have developed. These could be such things as breaks or leaks in water or sewer lines. Sumps should be manually operated and a visual inspection made of all operating parts such as floats, pump stands, couplings and electrical wiring.

Items which require inspection on an annual basis when the manhole is cleaned or upon discovery of a possible hazardous condition are structural defects in manhole walls and roofs, the condition of anchor bases, bucking posts, ladders, manhole frames and covers.

Three modes generally exist for the handling of repairs on district heating systems:

1. Planned outage—2 to 4 day notification
   In this case formal notification is given to the send-out stations and to all customers involved and every attempt is made to do the necessary work with a minimum of inconvenience to all of the groups involved.
2. Unplanned outage—4 to 8 hour notification
   Valving is delayed until the send-out plants and the major customers have been notified. Repairs are made as soon as possible.
3. Emergency outage—No notification
   Valving is started immediately, the send-out plant and the customer notification group are notified and the repair is made as soon as possible.

When repairs, new service connections or system cutovers are made on a steam system and require customer outages, it should be planned to keep customer outages to an absolute minimum.

Several items can help to achieve minimum customer disruption if time is available. They include:

1. Assigning enough manpower and tools with each man knowing in advance the work to be accomplished and the part he is to play in the operation.
2. Having all the material and equipment available and ready to perform the work; doing all the piping prefabrication possible to keep welding time to a minimum.
3. Excavating enough of the area and breaking out enough concrete to allow sufficient working space.
4. Finding the exact location and severity of the leak.

It is desirable to have an extra welder as well as an extra truck and small crew available if an unexpected problem should develop on the job or an emergency call comes in from another location which would interfere with the completion of the primary job on schedule.

Good communications is important to an effective maintenance program. Communication between crews and between office and crew are very important. There are many situations where this sort of communication is critical such as during sectionalizing operations where crews are a distance apart, when an emergency arises and the office must reach a repair crew immediately, when crews must be rerouted and even for routine matters.

Frequent telephone calls are necessary when crews are working in buildings but radio is the most effective communications method when working in city streets. Walkie-talkies, citizen's band and commercial bands have all been used effectively, depending on transmission and reception conditions in the areas to be covered.

HOT WATER SYSTEMS

Hot water systems are gaining in popularity with U.S. Factors affecting their design, installation and cost are site specific. However, some basic considerations apply.

Design Features of Hot Water Networks

Temperature and Pressure: Most hot water systems in West European countries are designed for maximum supply temperatures of between 230 F and 266 F and return temperatures of 122 F to 158 F. Typical maximum design temperatures in the supply and return lines in East European block countries, including the USSR, are 300 F and 160 F, respectively. The reasons for using the lower temperatures are the smaller system sizes and the possible use of polyurethane insulation (with a temperature limitation of about 250 F). Some Japanese systems and one system in the Netherlands have supply temperatures up to 356 F to 419 F. Such systems are not cogeneration systems. The high temperature, therefore, does not affect the economics of the power plant.

Piping network pressure depends on the system's size and operating temperature and varies from 130 to 250 psig during the winter and between 60 and 150 psig during the summer. Only in district heating systems with high supply temperature (400 F) is the pressure in the newwork as high as 450 psig.

The pipe diameter and water velocity of the network is usually determined by an advance study, which considers piping cost, pumping power, and heat loss to provide the minimum annual cost of the system. Based on these data the water velocities may range from 1.6 to 13 feet per second.

District Heating Standards: Countries with hot water district heating have developed special standards to which the piping newworks are manufactured and tested. Special consideration is given to preinsulated, prefabricated, pipe-in-pipe type conduits. Finland, Denmark, Sweden, West Germany and the United Kingdom have set up special working groups within the District Heating Associations which are responsible for developing, improving and updating existing heating network standards.

Heat Carrier Pipe Materials: Metallic pipes commonly available for district heating systems normally are made of steel, copper or copper alloys. Low-carbon steel pipes, which may be seamless, longitudinally welded or spirally welded are the most widely used of the ferrous materials. The major disadvantage of low-carbon steel pipe is its poor corrosion resistance.

When the carrier pipe is steel, U.S. district heating systems usually use a thicker-walled pipe than comparable European systems. Some U.S. pipe fabricators utilize Schedule 40 or 80 pipes for hot water applications as their standard preinsulated pipes. On the other hand, pipes with thinner walls are used in European district heating networks. Usually a wall thickness equivalent to Schedule 10 or between Schedules 10 and 20 is utilized. The difference in Schedules of the steel pipe allows European district heating systems a lower initial piping capital cost than the U.S. The reduction in piping schedule does require special attention to network design and maintenance practices in order to prevent groundwater from penetrating the external pipe surfaces.

Most of the steel carrier pipes in West European district heating systems have no protective anti-corrosion coating except for some use of rust inhibiting paint. In the USSR protective coatings including heat resistant glass enamel, are used for pipe corrosion protection. This increases initial pipe installation costs.

Copper pipes frequently are used for district heating distribution systems in Europe and Japan. These copper pipes generally used with temperatures of up to 250 F and pressures up to 230 psi. For pipe diameters between ½ and 3 in, copper pipes are prefabricated in conduits and delivered in coils of about 80 feet. Larger sizes are supplied in straight lengths. Installation of long pipe sections reduces the number of joints and provides the possibility of bending the pipes in a sinusoidal pattern for thermal expansion purposes.

Stainless steel is sometimes used for small pipes and is available in conduit. These pipes are flexible and can be buried directly in long continuous lengths, following curves and slopes similar to electrical cable. Connections are made with standard fittings. The casing is corrugated steel with an extruded polyethylene jacket. Corrugated copper in small pipe sizes is also utilized as a carrier in pipe cable fashion.

Piping Installations: District heating pipes usually are installed underground, and a variety of different designs are used to protect the insulation and pipe from groundwater damage which would deteriorate the insulating material. Piping installation requirements could be summarized as:

1. prevention of water penetration to the piping surface;
2. retention of efficient heat insulation, and
3. design for a reasonable installation cost.

Most European systems utilize concrete culverts for pipe installations. The main advantages of such culverts are strength, durability and the prevention of water penetration.

Concrete culverts fabricated on site are the most expensive, but when properly built, are the most watertight. Such culverts are often a requirement in exceptionally wet ground or in places where extreme strength is needed. To reduce installation costs, partially prefabricated culvert is sometimes utilized.

Concrete culverts usually are used for pipes of 10 in. in diameter and larger, and conduit designs for smaller diameter pipe installations. Smaller Japanese district heating systems predominantly use steel cased conduits. Tunnels are used for large pipes whenever possible, such as in the Stockholm district heating system.

From the standpoint of reliability, it is important that the piping installation be drainable and dryable. Most of the utilities surveyed provided for this with an air gap between the insulation and the culvert. However, some pre-insulated systems do not utilize that feature.

A majority of utilities build their piping systems to resist groundwater infiltration and the spread of water. The installation with the best resistance to water damage, corrosion and mechanical or structural damage is considered the concrete culvert. Groundwater drainage along the piping network is an important factor in insuring system reliability. However, 70 percent of foreign networks have no drainage system. Some of these utilities rely on the culvert itself for water drainage. The concrete culvert design is considered by most utilities to be the simplest for installation and repair work.

A leak detection system installed with the piping system can be useful, since it saves time in identifying the leak location. The sooner a leak is detected, the lower the potential damage to the piping system. It also reduces the time of disruptions in service.

Polyurethane foam is used commonly as an insulating material for conduit installations. The popular use of polyurethane in the United States and Europe is a result of its low thermal conductivity of 0.18 Btu/in/hr/ft^2/F. However, the age and operating temperature of the material also affects the resultant thermal conductivity. To avoid significant deterioration, polyurethane is used for pipes with operating temperatures less than 250 F, in order to retain its insulating quality.

Polyurethane foam components must be accurately weighed or metered, and thoroughly mixed at closely controlled temperatures to produce a foam with optimum physical properties. Polyurethane foam, while offering high thermal efficiency as an insulating material, has certain characteristics requiring that it be protected. For example, moisture penetrating the foam results in a significant increase in thermal conductivity. Although the polyurethane foam is not hygroscopic due to its closed cells, it cannot withstand damage from water vapor. Proper casing is also needed to protect the foam from chemicals, mechanical abuse, vermin, ultraviolet degradation, and other on-site hazards.

Since the systems' pipes carry hot water, expansion must be taken into consideration. Typical methods of absorbing the thermal expansion are through installation of an expansion loop, elbow, or offset, where space permits, or through use of mechanical expansion devices in limited spaces.

To reduce installation and maintenance costs, new methods of allowing for thermal expansion have been suggested. One such method eliminates standard expansion devices from the system. Copper pipes are laid in a sinusoidal curve giving it a built-in expansion allowance. When the temperature of the carrier pipe rises, the amplitude of the curve increases if the end points are fixed. The increase in amplitude is very small, since the expansion is uniformly distributed across the entire arc. About a 3% additional length must be added to the pipe when this piping system is used because of the wave pattern.

Thermal expansion stress may be minimized by prestressing the pipe. This allows for easy, compensation-free laying and achieves an installation free from any fixed points without any concrete structures. The prestressed pipe lengths are designed in accordance with the planned temperature differences and dimensioned so that the lines are kept free from thermal stresses during normal operating conditions. Pipe is prestressed when both the carrier and casing pipes are metallic. Prestressing pipe by cold drawing or heating to a predetermined installation temperature before the pipes are backfilled, however, requires large piping right-of-way areas to be open for long periods, since the prestressing can be done only with completely uncovered pipes in relatively large sections. To eliminate this disadvantage, a method of accommodating thermal expansion has been developed in Denmark for conduits with steel carrier pipe, polyurethane insulation and polyethylene casing. Conduits are installed in the ground in the usual way using this method, but with an "E-muff" element welded into the system instead of the conventional expansion devices. Before the E-muffs are fixed into the system, they are adjusted by prestressing according to the actual distance between the two E-muffs for the maximum operating temperature of the network.

Pipe failure has been experienced in almost all hot water district heating networks. Even in the most recently constructed systems, corrosion failures and increased heat losses have occurred.

The average rate of failure seems to depend on the duration of service and the age of the system. However, some utilities have not found a direct relationship between the failure rate and piping age. Age may have only a small impact when the system is well maintained.

The piping failure rate or actual breaks of pipes in hot water sytems is reported to be between 0.048 and 0.32 per mile per year. The average annual failure rate for the district heating system in Moscow during 1968 and 1971 was 0.43. The failure rate for the Kiev district heating system was between 0.48 and 0.64. One European system reported 0.68 leaks per mile in 1978, primarily as a result of external corrosion.

The major failure elements appear to be the water carrier pipes, expansion bellows, and pipe connections to valves in manholes and piping joints.

The location of pipe failures varies dramatically for different utilities. Failures occur in straight piping, joints, expansion devices, manholes, valves, pipe anchors and supports, and near crossings with other utilities.

Major causes of failures include:
1. electrochemical corrosion, usually related to the casing coating failure and ground water infiltration into the conduit,
2. mechanical and structural damage resulting from vibration from vehicles and leaking manhole covers under thermal stresses, as well as infiltration of hot water from leaking valve gland packings,
3. insulation failure and damage of the insulation joints which brings about pipe corrosion, and
4. failure of other utility systems using the same pathways.

An analysis of failures in these systems leads to a conclusion that intensive local corrosion takes place because of periodic contact of an unprotected external piping surface with groundwater. This process takes place in both directly buried and culvert type installations when flooded with water or mud. Cyclic wetting and drying of the pipe insulation causes external pipe corrosion. The wetting of insulation also increases the heat loss from pipes because of the increase in the coefficient of heat transfer of the insulation. It also brings about rapid mechanical disintegration of the insulation.

The source of this unwanted water may be penetration from above the pipe as a result of rain or melting snow, failure of a co-located potable water line, sewer or drainage system, or groundwater penetrating the area beneath the pipe.

Dry insulation is a reliable means of insuring that pipe remains in good condition. In a concrete culvert, favorable conditions are provided for drying insulation, including the existence of convection in the air gap along the pipe, a decrease in relative humidity of the air with sweeping of the hot surface of the insulating cover, and considerable time intervals between successive wettings of the insulation.

The insulation must be protected from destruction and aging due to cyclic conditions of wetting and drying. Therefore, the extensive use of insulation materials, such as calcium silicate, with its low coefficient of thermal conductivity, and which are resistant to aging during periodic wetting and drying is very important to the reliable service life of the network.

Installations with such an air gap have a corrosion rate of less than 0.004 inches per year. However, maintaining the air gap in a concrete culvert and protecting it from mud flow is difficult and requires close and constant control of trench conditions. This can be especially difficult for small diameter piping where mud ingress can occur often and the culvert size does not allow for maintenance. Complete or even partial mud ingress into the culvert changes its configuration to that of a directly buried installation. Concrete culverts, therefore, should be used with a reliable water drainage system.

Unlike steam systems, the prime area for failure in a hot water network is the supply line. The return line does not experience such severe problems. The external conditions of both pipes are identical, but internally there is a significant difference in operating pressure and temperature. The internal pressure cannot affect the external corrosion process; however, a pipe damaged by corrosion may rupture at this spot as a result of the pressure. Practically all European and some Japanese systems operate on a continuous year-round basis. The systems may be out of service only for short periods of time. The major influence on the corrosion rate in these systems is the average temperature in the supply pipe which operates throughout the year at water temperatures of between 165 F and 180 F.

With free access of moisture and oxygen to the piping surface, a pipe wall temperature of between 155 F and 185 F sets up the most damaging intensity of corrosion. The supply line operates most of the time at these unfavorable temperatures. Underground pipes operating at higher temperatures are less affected by external corrosion. The external corrosion rate of steam piping networks is substantially lower than that of hot water networks. In contrast, condensate return lines in steam systems with fluid temperature below 200 F are subject to high corrosion rates.

Total heat losses in most hot water system transmission and distribution piping range from 4 to 15 percent of the annual energy delivered. The average heat loss figure is about 8.8 percent based on data reported from utilities in Europe and Japan. The reliability of an underground hot water piping system appears to be determined by the following factors: quality of anti-corrosion protection; average annual water temperature in the piping network; age of the network; thickness of the pipe walls; types of installation (especially the provision of an air gap during service life of the pipe); site hydrological conditions; and the condition of adjacent utility systems.

CHILLED WATER DISTRIBUTION SYSTEMS

Experience has shown that distribution piping can run up to 50 percent of the total installed cost of the chilled water district heating system, so careful planning of the installation is very important.

Layout

In the distribution loop the pumps circulate the water between the central plant equipment and the individual buildings. Warm return water from each building is delivered to the return side of this loop.

Basically the distribution piping layout can be either direct return or reverse return. Figure 6.26 compares a reversed-return circuit with a direct-return circuit. In the direct-return system, the length of supply and return piping

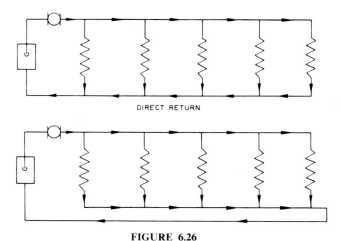

FIGURE 6.26
Direct-and reversed-return two-pipe systems
(Courtesy of ASHRAE Handbook & Product Directory)

through the several subcircuits are unequal. This may cause unbalanced flow rates and require careful balancing to provide each subcircuit with design flow. The reversed-return system provides nearly equal total lengths for all terminal circuits.

Generally, the most economical distribution system layout will result if the mains are run by the shortest and most convenient route to the terminal equipment in a building or a group of buildings having the largest flow rate requirements, and branch or secondary circuits are then laid out to connect with these mains.

Chilled Water Flow

The water flow in the distribution loop must always be greater than the total flow in all the building loops. This is necessary to assure a constant supply temperature to each building. By the same token, the total flow in the building loops must be less than in the distribution loop to insure a constant supply temperature. In other words, the ΔT in the distribution loop must be intermediate between the building loops and the equipment loop. This ΔT will then usually fall into the range of 12 to 14 F.

Pipe Sizing

The amount of water to be circulated will have a significant bearing on whether the loop costs are on the high or low side. Basically, it is desirable to have the minimum water quantity with the smallest practical pipe size.

While the temperature rise in the loop is a determining factor in the water quantity circulated, pressure drop and pumping cost must also be considered. Further, the estimated long range usage and growth of the system must also be evaluated.

Table 6.4 shows the gmp flow required for various loads from 2,000 to 10,000 tons at water temperature rises from 8 to 22 F. With a given tonnage it is readily apparent how the water quantity will vary as the ΔT changes.

Table 6.5 correlates water flow with pipe sizes. Also tabulated is velocity

TABLE 6.4

GPM FLOW AT WATER TEMPERATURE

Temp Rise F (ΔT)	2,000 Tons GPM	3,000 Tons GPM	4,000 Tons GPM	5,000 Tons GPM	6,000 Tons GPM	7,000 Tons GPM	8,000 Tons GPM	9,000 Tons GPM	10,000 Tons GPM
22	2,180	3,280	4,370	5,450	6,550	7,650	8,720	9,800	10,900
20	2,400	3,600	4,800	6,000	7,200	8,400	9,600	10,800	12,000
18	2,670	4,000	5,340	6,670	8,000	9,325	10,670	12,000	13,330
16	3,000	4,500	6,000	7,500	9,000	10,500	12,000	13,500	15,000
14	3,430	5,150	6,870	8,570	10,300	12,000	13,700	15,420	17,150
12	4,000	6,000	8,000	10,000	12,000	14,000	16,000	18,000	20,000
10	4,800	7,200	9,600	12,000	14,400	16,800	19,200	21,600	24,000
8	6,000	9,000	12,000	15,000	18,000	21,000	24,000	27,000	30,000

pressure drop per 1,000 feet of run and theoretical pumping horsepower per 1,000 feet equivalent length.

This data is useful for making rapid pipe size evaluations relating to load, water velocity and horsepower.

Pressure drop data is based on the Williams and Hazen formula:

$$S = \left(\frac{V}{1.318 \, CR} \, 0.63 \right)^{1.85}$$

where,

S = fraction loss in feet per foot
V = velocity in feet per second
R = hydraulic radius
C = constant, relating to the king and interior condition of the pipe. The value for C was taken as 100 which is applicable to ordinary wrought iron pipe or 13- to 20-year old cast iron.
Vel = Velocity in feet per second
ΔP = Pressure drop in feet of water
HP = Theoretical water horsepower based on

$$HP = \frac{Ft \, Head \times GPM \times 8.33 \times 60}{33,000}$$

$$= \frac{Ft \, Head \times GPM}{3,960}$$

Horsepower data is theoretical, and actual pump horsepower will be greater in accordance with pump efficiency. For a preliminary evaluation, divide the tabular horsepower by 0.75 to obtain the estimated pump horsepower. If runs are other than 1,000 feet, use a direct ratio between 1,000 feet and the actual length of run. In a system of this type having a minimum number of fittings, the added equivalent length for fittings can be ignored in preliminary calculations.

Pipe Materials

Several piping materials are used in chilled water thermal distribution systems including low-carbon steel, fiberglass, reinforced plastic and polyvinyl chloride. The selection will depend primarily on the soil type and the site. Black steel or wrought iron pipe is usually chosen because of cost factors. The

TABLE 6.5
GPM FLOW RATE OF PIPE SIZES 8 TO 30 INCHES

GPM		8″	10″	12″	14″	16″	18″	20″	24″	30″
2,000	Vel	12.78	8.16	5.68	4.17	3.19	2.52	2.04	1.42	
	ΔP	107.10	35.90	14.90	7.05	3.68	2.06	1.24	0.51	
	HP	54.10	18.10	7.52	3.56	1.86	1.04	0.63	0.26	
2,500	Vel		10.40	7.00	5.25	3.98	3.16	2.56	1.77	
	ΔP		54.25	22.80	10.10	5.53	3.10	1.88	0.70	
	HP		34.20	14.40	6.39	3.49	1.96	1.19	0.44	
3,000	Vel		12.24	8.40	6.30	4.79	3.80	3.08	2.13	1.36
	ΔP		76.20	31.50	14.70	7.74	4.30	2.70	1.00	0.36
	HP		57.75	23.90	11.20	5.86	3.26	2.05	0.76	0.27
3,500	Vel			9.95	7.35	5.59	4.43	3.59	2.49	1.56
	ΔP			41.60	18.10	10.40	5.40	3.50	1.40	0.40
	HP			36.80	16.00	9.20	4.76	3.09	1.24	0.35
4,000	Vel			11.35	8.40	6.38	5.06	4.10	2.85	1.81
	ΔP			53.20	24.70	13.40	7.40	4.50	1.80	0.60
	HP			53.70	25.00	13.55	7.48	4.55	1.82	0.61
4,500	Vel			12.78	9.45	7.18	5.67	4.60	3.20	2.05
	ΔP			69.00	32.20	16.40	9.20	5.55	2.26	0.77
	HP			78.40	36.60	18.65	10.47	6.31	2.57	0.88
5,000	Vel			14.20	10.50	7.96	6.33	5.13	3.54	2.26
	ΔP			84.00	39.20	20.00	11.30	6.80	2.70	0.90
	HP			106.00	49.50	25.30	14.30	8.58	3.41	1.14
6,000	Vel			17.05	12.60	9.58	7.60	6.15	4.25	2.72
	ΔP			115.00	55.00	27.80	15.60	9.60	3.80	1.30
	HP			174.00	83.20	42.10	23.60	14.55	5.75	1.97
7,000	Vel			19.89	14.60	11.18	8.85	7.18	4.97	3.18
	ΔP			152.50	70.80	37.00	21.00	12.80	5.20	1.70
	HP			269.00	125.00	65.40	37.10	22.60	9.20	3.00
8,000	Vel				16.70	12.78	10.02	8.17	5.68	3.63
	ΔP				93.20	47.40	26.50	16.30	6.60	2.20
	HP				202.00	95.80	53.60	33.00	13.35	4.45
9,000	Vel				18.80	14.37	11.40	9.20	6.35	4.08
	ΔP				118.00	59.00	33.50	20.40	8.10	2.70
	HP				268.00	134.10	76.20	46.40	18.40	6.14
10,000	Vel					15.96	12.67	10.40	7.07	4.54
	ΔP					71.90	41.00	25.30	9.80	3.30
	HP					181.50	103.80	63.90	24.80	8.33
12,000	Vel						15.30	12.25	8.55	5.47
	ΔP						56.50	34.10	14.00	4.73
	HP						171.00	103.00	42.40	14.32
14,000	Vel						17.75	14.30	9.95	6.40
	ΔP						75.00	45.40	18.60	6.30
	HP						266.00	161.00	66.00	22.35
16,000	Vel								11.38	7.30
	ΔP								24.00	8.10
	HP								97.00	32.70
18,000	Vel								12.80	8.20
	ΔP								29.80	10.00
	HP								135.50	45.50
20,000	Vel								14.20	9.12
	ΔP								36.10	12.20
	HP								182.50	61.60
24,000	Vel									10.09
	ΔP									17.20
	HP									105.00

standard weights and sizes available in both types can readily tolerate the working pressures involved.

Black steel is the least expensive and is generally satisfactory where ground conditions are basically dry and sandy. The supply pipe must be properly protected and insulated.

Insulation

Only minimal insulation is required on chilled water lines. Polyurethane foam insulation is preferred because it does not become waterlogged. One inch of polyurethane foam insulation is usually satisfactory when ground temperatures remain about 55 to 66 F. All insulation should be wrapped with glass fabric and then coated to insure watertight integrity.

Heat Gain

Even with insulation, there will be heat gains in the supply pipe that must be anticipated when establishing the design chilled water temperature for the central plant. Heat gains can be approximated from Figure 6.27. The values in this chart are conservative. For runs other than 10,000 feet, proportion the values directly.

Pipe Burial Method

If the soil is basically sandy and without ground water problems, piping usually can be buried directly in the ground. As shown in Figure 6.28, a gravel

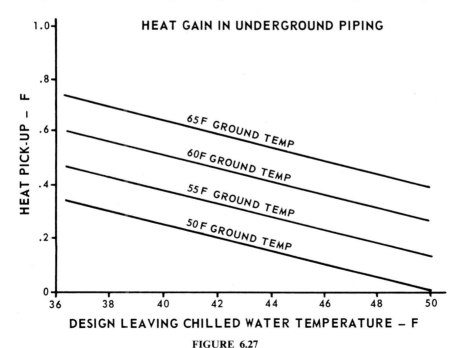

FIGURE 6.27

Heat gain in underground piping. Based on 10,000 feet of run insulated with one inch polyurethane foam and moderately wet soil

(Courtesy of the TRANE Co.)

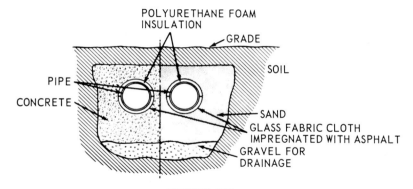

FIGURE 6.28
Buried pipe with sand or concrete fill
(Courtesy of the TRANE Co.)

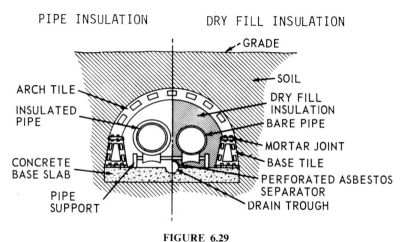

FIGURE 6.29
Buried pipe with vitreous tile conduit
(Courtesy of the TRANE Co.)

bed for drainage is laid with a sand or concrete fill around the pipe. A poured concrete shroud, as shown on the left of Figure 6.28, provides better pipe support.

Where the soil is corrosive or where ground water is a problem, a more elaborate installation is necessary. Vitrified tile with a concrete base arrangement is shown in Figure 6.29. The base slab or concrete with a formed water trough is laid in the bottom of the trench. The pipe is supported on rollers with arched tile placed over the pipe. Insulation is optional. If used, it is applied to the pipe or used as loose fill. Figure 6.29 shows insulation omitted on the return line.

Pipe Expansion (Bellows and Slip Joints)

Expansion is not a serious problem with chilled water piping runs because of small temperature differences between the piping and the ground. Steel pipe expands or contracts approximately 0.0795 inches per degree F for each 1,000 feet.

If a temperature difference of 20 F exists, expansion or contraction will be 1.6 inches per 1,000 feet. This is easily compensated for with expansion joints every 200 to 500 feet, depending on the local conditions.

GENERAL CONSIDERATIONS FOR DISTRIBUTION LOOP INSTALLATION

Soil Characteristics

Distribution loop piping is usually installed underground. This may or may not cause problems depending on local ground conditions. The follow-up was taken from a Federal Government study of existing installations:

The character of the soil in which piping will be placed is extremely important. A soil survey should provide definite answers to the following questions:

1. Water table location?
2. Soil perviousness? Will water remain around underground piping even though the water table is below the piping?
3. Will the piping trench become a drainage ditch for the area?
4. If ferrous pipe is used, will cathodic protection against corrosion be required?
5. Will soil stability allow normal trenching and backfilling without damaging piping?

Preliminary Soil Investigation

Ground water must be carefully evaluated. A survey should be conducted when the water table is at its peak during the spring season. Explorations at a depth well below pipe burial depth should be made every 100 to 150 feet along the proposed piping run. The location of any impermeable strata and its distance from pipe burial depth must be found. Seepage collecting on such a layer would eventually flood the piping.

Percolation tests can help determine if the soil above the trench depth will become saturated at any time. The test is made by digging a one-foot square hole to a depth two feet below the trench depth. The hole is then filled with water to the bottom of the trench. The water is allowed to seep away and the hole is immediately refilled to the same level. The time required for the water level to drop two inches is then observed. If it takes 20 minutes, or less, the soil is considered permeable. If it takes longer than 20 minutes, the soil can be saturated, and a Class A water-tight arrangement as defined by Technical Report No. 30R-64 must be installed.

Soil resistivity tests also must be made along with the distribution piping run. If these readings are less than 2,000 ohms per cubic centimeter, cathodic protection should be installed. Cathodic protection may be required if readings are between 2,000 to 10,000 ohms per cubic centimeter. Above 10,000 ohms, cathodic protection should not be needed.

STANDARDS AND CURRENT INSTALLATION PRACTICES

The American National Standards Institute (ANSI) code B 31.1 on Power Piping is the principal code applicable to district heating piping systems and the piping systems of their customers. This power piping code includes high pressure steam, over 15 psi, HTW and chilled water systems. The code generally is followed on a voluntary basis, and most states do *not* make it mandatory.

The B 31.1 code prescribes minimum requirements only for the design, materials fabrication, testing, and inspection of piping systems.

CONSTRUCTION PROCEDURES

Some general considerations in construction of district heating distribution systems are as follows:

Company versus Contractor Forces: The use of company or contractor work forces for the distribution system in construction work is a matter each company must consider for itself based on local conditions.

The quantity of distribution system construction work varies over wide limits depending on the system. There will be periods when these distribution systems are expanding rapidly and other times when minimal construction work will be available.

Unless a company has a relatively constant construction work load or has a regularly available supply of labor which can be rotated from other jobs to system construction work when necessary, building of mains with company forces is not economically justified for the following reasons:

1. A contractor can sublet parts of the job to meet a completion date or to bring to the job some needed specialized equipment or workmen with specific skills.
2. The variety of jobs involved would result in the creation of many new job titles with corresponding difficulties in the work coordination especially if organized employees are involved.
3. Pieces of equipment necessary to the specific job, but uneconomical for the company to own, can be contracted for only as required.

Construction work should always be coordinated and directed by competent company inspectors to safeguard the company's interests. These job supervisors not only must demand the strictest adherence to plans and specifications but must closely coordinate and discuss field changes with the maintenance forces who have to service the completed installation.

Scheduling: Regardless of who does the work, the company must be able to anticipate a completed job in accordance with a predetermined schedule. The company often furnishes the contractor with the pipe, insulation, and the major pieces of equipment required for the job.

A control group should be established to oversee and report on job progress and the scheduling and procurement of material and equipment for the job. This group often is responsible to the highest levels of management.

Realistic completion schedules are established for the component parts of the job, in conference with the various departments involved and in coordination with the contractors on the job.

Conducting the Job: One of the main considerations in the construction of a distribution system whether by contractor of company forces, is *safety*. This includes not only the workmen and other individuals connected with the installation job but also the general public such as pedestrians, vehicles and children.

Every person involved in the progress of the job, directly or indirectly, should be alert, have enough knowledge and use enough foresight to protect both himself, any other persons, or public and private property from injury or damage.

Safety on jobs which must be performed in the presence of the general public becomes of the highest importance. Since these individuals are not acquainted with construction methods or procedure, they must be protected from themselves and the work.

In addition to observing all standard safety procedures and using all approved safety clothing and equipment provided or stipulated by the company, the workmen and their supervisors must be sure that all protective devices such as warning barriers, rope, extended sheathing, or other type of protective devices for open excavations, suitable street and sidewalk bridging and adequate lighting when necessary, are used to minimize all hazards connected with the work. Federal laws affect this aspect of the job as well.

Minimizing Public Nuisance: Since any work done in the street or sidewalk inconveniences or aggravates motorists, area businesses, and the general public to some degree, ill feeling and aggravation should be kept to a minimum.

Work normally prohibited often can be done by keeping the police and other municipal agencies informed of the details, reasons for and the urgency of the contemplated work. If this does not suffice, a police officer should be obtained to direct vehicular or pedestrian traffic while the work is in progress.

Hauling away all dirt, sheathing if necessary, and covering the trench each night with steel plates to permit rush hour traffic to flow may be required. Working the job at night, and on weekends can also assist in completing the job.

Inconvenience to persons conducting businesses abutting or in close proximity to the work may be kept to a minimum by providing temporary access to the premises or scheduling the work so as not to interfere with access to either customer entrances or to receiving or delivery entrances.

Testing Procedures: After the distribution system is built, but before it is turned on, it should be tested using a non-destructive test method.

ASA Standard B 31.1, Section 4, District Heating Piping Systems, P422, requires that a hydrostatic test be made after erection if practicable. On jobs where envelope or box type construction is employed and all welds and expansion joints can be exposed this test can still be used.

However, in much of the construction used at the present time where welds are not left exposed or where it is necessary to backfill the trench as soon as possible after the pipe is installed, some other method must be used for inspecting the welds. This can include use of:

1. Ultrasonic: This system employs sound reflection.
2. Zyglo: A fluid carrying a fluorescent dye in conjunction with an electric light or an ultraviolet ray lamp for detecting flaws in non-magnetic steels.
3. Magna flux: Magnetic particle inspection for surface flaws in magnetic steels.
4. X-Ray: Photographs taken of welds through film sensitized by gamma rays from isotopes or radium.

The method or methods used for weld examination best can be decided upon by each company since the test and the examination of the test results are usually performed by a local testing laboratory knowledgeable in this work.

Some systems which are installed within steel sleeves may deteriorate due to corrosion or electrolytic action unless protected. These steel sleeves should be wrapped to provide corrosion protection and tested after wrapping to insure that the insulation is effective, protected by cathodic protection or both. Periodic checking for the adequacy of corrosion protection should be performed.

Cleaning of Pipes Prior to Turn On: Cleanliness of the inside of piping and equipment prior to turn on is essential. The best method to insure a clean steam main is by not permitting dirt or foreign matter to get into the pipes during construction. Dirty pipes can cause plugged traps or trap lines and result in damaging water hammer, make valves in the distribution system inoperable or cause dirt to get into meters, reducing valves or other control equipment.

Dirt in pipes can come from two sources:

1. Foreign matter in the pipe such as stones, sand, welding pellets, tools, clothing, timber and many other things.
2. Mill scale or a rust coating inside of pipes.

Mill scale should not be a great problem with the manufacturing procedures in use at the present time. In the forming process most mill scale is cracked off on electric or butt welded steel pipe. On hot formed seamless or butt welded steel pipe the inside of the pipe is cleaned after fabrication by brushing or other method to remove the loose mill scale.

However, if mill scale must be removed by chemical treatment, it can be done; this is a time consuming and expensive method. For short lines of small diameter, flushing can be used. Large pipes must have each length treated individually in separate tanks. The process consists of tank immersion or flushing with a picking solution for several hours, flushing with water and a tank immersion or flushing with a neutralizing solution.

Attempts have been made to remove mill scale by allowing the steam main to operate for a period of time with a relatively large opening. This method may remove some foreign matter, but the effectiveness for mill scale removal is low. In addition, this method can be very difficult to use in a congested area.

Foreign matter is kept from entering steam pipes by carefully cleaning pipes before installation, being careful that dirt or foreign matter does not get into the pipe after it is laid in the trench, by taking care that the trench is always dry and any pipe openings well protected, by using end caps each night and by preventing welding pellets from entering the pipe or removing them if they do. Another method is to clean the pipe with an air operated wire brush.

Backfill, Repaving, Cleanup: Backfill material and procedures for this work are usually specified by the municipality. Some localities permit backfilling with the removed material, others require special materials.

Some engineers prefer water flushing to settle the backfill. However, it usually is tamped with air driven tools, particularly when the steam line is hot.

After the excavation has been backfilled it is paved in accordance with local regulations. However, in the winter, on a heavily traveled road, a cement patch will stand up much better than hot top.

Special Mechanical Equipment: Many new tools have been developed and in common use in construction work. Progressive contractors are all familiar with these labor saving devices and engineers and construction supervisors must have a working knowledge of this equipment and the conditions under which it can be used advantageously.

A partial list of such equipment includes:

1. paving saws,
2. boring machines,
3. all types of digging machines,
4. cranes and boom trucks,
5. electric driven hoists and platforms,
6. ram set equipment,
7. hole and circular saws for concrete,

8. air driven brushes,
9. all types of pumps and pumping equipment, and
10. prefabricated structural items.

Proper use of this equipment can result in:

1. An ability to do the work without extensive preparations or prolonged outages.
2. A reduction in the number of job hazards by substituting mechanical for physical effort.
3. An improvement in the quality of the finished job.
4. A reduction in the time necessary to perform the work, whether or not it is a maintenance or construction project. This can reduce costs and improve public relations.

In some cases projects would be difficult to complete were it not for the modern tools and equipment available.

Maps and Records: Lack of knowledge of company and customer responsibility or of the design and location of structures in the street is expensive and wastes time.

Five types of drawings and sketches should be maintained and constantly updated for all design, construction and operating personnel connected with steam distribution system. These personnel must be informed about the exact status of all major and auxiliary piping in order to perform their jobs effectively.

1. Sets of plans with views of parts of the system, keyed to an index map, show the location of manholes, the size and location of line valves, as well as the location of services and service valves. These are prepared in sizes suitable to be carried by repair crews, and should be coded to show all the distribution piping and valves owned by and maintained by both the company and the customer.
2. General plans of various sizes show the streets when the piping is located as well as the locations of the major send out stations. These give a quick but accurate overall picture of the distribution system.
3. A field construction inspectors notebook or similar record is prepared in the field at the time the work is done shows where access to pertinent information is readily available.
4. Detailed street maps show steam main construction in both plan and profile. These plans show anchors, guides, expansion joints, manholes and valves, discharge lines, and other useful information, as well as foreign pipe in the excavated area.
5. Small schematic drawings show auxiliary piping within each manhole. These looseleaf notebooks should be given to each person responsible in charge of or performing maintenance work on the system sections. They are also useful for describing leak locations and showing the approximate location of all auxiliary equipment in manholes such as ladders, drip valves, siphon valves, freeblow valves, main line valves, by-pass valves, and manhole floor drains, if in case there happens to be a leak in the manhole and it cannot be readily "blown down."

LEAK LOCATION

Evaluating heat leakage from buried lines is done using infrared scanning equipment. More detailed location often is made using temperature probes in the earth over the piping to develop a temperature change profile. Checking for hot spots and observation of test excavations are most generally used for non-pressure-tight systems.

Air-space system leaks often can be found by introducing an odor into the conduit. The conduit is then pressurized and the line is walked for detection of the odor at a specific location. Injecting refrigerant gas or helium into the system under air pressure is another method. Refrigerant leaks may be located at the surface with a halide torch. With helium, a probe is inserted into the ground along the system to detect the leak. Without such equipment, a systemized search by excavation can be made by starting at the middle of the line and determining the direction of the leak from that point. The suspect section is then inspected at its mid-point. This is done until the leak is located. Vapor emission from conduit vent telltales will indicate whether there is a possible leak in a particular segment or run of pipe.

CHAPTER 7

Metering

THE METER is the most important single piece of apparatus in any facility engaged in the distribution of thermal energy. In the Third Edition of the District Heating Handbook metering was considered only in regard to utilities selling steam, and the steam customer. Current commodities also include hot and chilled water as well as steam. The utility has expanded its horizons to include all types of suppliers of the service, and the customer has become the user. This change has occurred because of increased emphasis on conservation of energy resulting from ever-escalating costs for fuels and services. The strongest deterrent to wasteful fuel and energy is the meter, with its resultant allocation of costs.

It goes without saying that meters be "sturdy", "reliable" and "accurate". However, a more specific definition of the required accuracy of measurement is necessary. These measurement systems must be capable of sustained operation at a prescribed accuracy level to qualify as a measuring device in commercial service for transfer of a commodity. For example, it is not equitable and possibly unlawful to install at one user's premises a meter known to maintain 1% accuracy range, while in another area using one which may vary by 5%.

No meter or metering system should be used in the commerial sale of thermal energy if its accuracy cannot be tested and proved in accordance with standards that are traceable to the U.S. National Bureau of Standards.

This chapter examines "state-of-the-art" thermal measurement, excluding some of the older systems, but including technology that improves established concepts and leads to the development of better measurement.

PHYSICAL PROPERTIES

The physical properties of all substances are described in terms of space, time, temperature and mass. The following units have been adopted for use in the United States.

Space. By an executive order dated April 15, 1893, in the United States a yard was defined as 3600/3937 of a meter, with 39.37 inches (in.) equal to one meter; more recently, the value was altered very slightly, making the U.S. yard equal to 0.9144 meters. This makes one inch equal 2.54 centimeters (cen), exactly. One foot (ft) contains 12 inches, and one mile (mi) 5,280 feet.

Time. The unit of time is a second (sec). There are 86,400 seconds in a mean solar day. One minute (min) contains 60 seconds, and one hour (hr) 3,600 seconds.

Temperature. The measure of the intensity of heat is usually determined by a mercurial thermometer, in which a small amount of mercury in a bulb expands in a tube of uniform bore. On the Fahrenheit (F) scale, the temperature of melting ice is assumed as 32 degrees and the boiling point of water as 212 degrees. The increase in volume between these reference points is divided into 180 parts, or degrees, each of which represents an equal increase in volume, since—with slight deviations—nearly all substances increase proportionately in volume for equal rises in temperature. On the celsius (C) scale, the melting point of ice is zero and the boiling point of water is 100 degrees. All reference points are set at standard atmospheric pressure.

Mass. In the United States the unit of mass is a pound (lb); one pound is equal to 453.59 grams. In very accurate scientific measurements there are slight discrepancies that may arise because of the general practice of using the pound both for the unit of mass and weight. Under general conditions, however, mass differs only very slightly from weight. Weight is the measure of the intensity of the force of attraction of the earth acting upon a mass; whereas, mass is the actual quantity of material a body contains. The unit of mass does not vary with the change in attraction due to gravity.

Density. Density is the mass of substance per unit volume. This generally is expressed in pounds per cubic foot.

Matter

Matter is made up of exceedingly small particles, called molecules—making every body the sum of its molecules. Every molecule is separated from its neighbors, on all sides by inconceivably small spaces and is in quivering motion in its little space, moving back and forth among its neighbors, and rebounding from them. When a body is heated it causes the molecules to move more rapidly through their respective spaces, so they strike harder blows on their neighbors, and usually push them a tiny bit further away. Thus, with increased temperature, the size of a body increases. This theory accounts for most of the known phenomena related to matter.

Matter exists in three distinct states—solid, liquid, and gaseous. Liquids and gases are fluids. A liquid is a fluid of a nature such that if a certain volume is introduced into a vessel of greater volume, it occupies a portion of the vessel equal only to its own volume. A gas is a fluid of a nature such that if a certain volume is introduced into a vessel, whatever the volume of the vessel may be, the gas will distribute itself throughout the vessel.

Compressibility

Pressure increases with depth in both liquids and gases because the lower layers of fluids sustain the weight of all the layers above. Consequently, if the body of fluid is of uniform density, as is nearly always the case in liquids, the

TABLE 7.1

UNITS OF CONVERSION

1 meter (m) =	39.370 inches		1 kilogram (kg)	=	2.2046 pounds
	=	3.2808 feet	1 pound (lb)	=	453.59 grams
	= 1000 millimeters			=	0.45359 kilogram
	= 100 centimeters		1 cubic meter	=	35.315 cubic feet
1 foot (ft)	=	30.480 centimeters	1 liter	=	1000.03 cubic centimeters
	=	304.80 millimeters	1 cubic centimeter (cc) =		0.061024 cubic inch
1 inch (in.)	=	2.5400 centimeters	1 cubic foot (cu ft)	=	1728 cubic inches
	=	25.400 millimeters	1 cubic inch (cu in.)	=	16.387 cubic centimeters

pressure increases directly as the depth increases. Gaseous matter is much more compressible. As one result of the extreme compressibility of gaseous matter, the atmosphere is far from being of uniform density. The contrast between water and air (liquid and gas) may be seen in the fact that if water at a pressure of one atmosphere is subjected to a pressure of two atmospheres, it contracts one part in 22,000, while under the same circumstances, the return of air contracts one-half.

Elasticity

Closely allied to compressibility is the elasticity of gases. This is the ability of gases to recover their former volume after compression. The elasticity of all fluids is perfect. In other words, the force exerted in expansion is always equal to the force used in compression. However much a fluid is compressed, it will always completely regain its former volume when the pressure is removed. Liquids are perfectly elastic; but, inasmuch as they are perceptibly compressed only under tremendous pressure, they are regarded as practically incompressible. As a result, it is rarely necessary to consider their elasticity. Matter in a gaseous state expands indefinitely, unless restrained by external force. The atmosphere is confined to the surface of the earth by the force of gravity.

Pascal's Law

External pressure applied to a fluid is transmitted equally in all directions. The pressure on each unit of area exercised inward upon a mass of fluid is transmitted undiminished in all directions, and acts with the same force upon all surfaces in a direction at right angles to those surfaces; hence the pressure applied to any area of a confined fluid is transmitted, without reduction, to every other equal area through all the fluid to the walls of the containing chamber.

According to this law, the gas pressures in the various parts of a "continuous and connected reservoir" are nearly equal. The total pressure acting upon any portion of the surface is equal to the pressure exerted by the depth of fluid plus the effect of the external pressure, which is transmitted by the fluid.

Liquid Pressure

Since the weight of water at 60°F is 62.367 pounds per cubic foot, a column of water one foot high and one square foot in area exerts a pressure of 62.367 pounds on one square foot of surface, or 0.43310 pound per square inch. Therefore, a column of water one foot high and one square inch in area is equivalent to a pressure of 0.43310 pound per square inch, and one pound per square inch equals 2.3089 feet of water head, or 27.707 inches of water. One inch of water head exerts a pressure of 0.03609 pound per square inch. The average atmospheric pressure in midcontinent areas is about 14.4 pounds per square inch. It may be expressed as equal to 14.4 × 27.707 or 399 inches of water head. In the same manner, one inch of mercury at 32°F is equivalent to 0.4912 pound per square inch, since one cubic inch of mercury weighs 0.4912 pound.

Table 7.2 contains accurate values of the physical properties of water and mercury for various temperatures. Failure to realize that changes of volume occur on account of the temperature has led to many different values being used for similar computations. Although these changes in volume are small and do not materially affect results, whenever differing values are used for the

TABLE 7.2

PHYSICAL PROPERTIES OF WATER AND MERCURY

WATER

Properties of Water			Multipliers for Inches of Water			
Water Temperature °F	Density, lb per cu ft	Specific gravity	Lb per sq in. psi	Inches of water for 1.0 psi	Inches of mercury at 32°F	Inches of water at 39.2°F
39.2	62.427	1.0000	0.03613	27.680	0.07355	1.0000
40	62.426	1.0000	0.03613	27.680	0.07355	1.0000
45	62.422	0.9999	0.03612	27.683	0.07355	0.9999
50	62.410	0.9997	0.03612	27.688	0.07353	0.9997
55	62.391	0.9994	0.03611	27.696	0.07351	0.9994
60	62.367	0.9990	0.03609	27.707	0.07348	0.9990
65	62.337	0.9986	0.03607	27.720	0.07345	0.9986
70	62.302	0.9980	0.03605	27.736	0.07341	0.9980
75	62.262	0.9974	0.03603	27.754	0.07336	0.9974
80	62.217	0.9966	0.03600	27.774	0.07331	0.9966
85	62.167	0.9958	0.03598	27.796	0.07325	0.9958
90	62.114	0.9950	0.03595	27.820	0.07318	0.9950
95	62.056	0.9941	0.03591	27.846	0.07312	0.9941
100	61.994	0.9931	0.03588	27.874	0.07304	0.9931
105	61.930	0.9920	0.03584	27.903	0.07297	0.9920
110	61.861	0.9909	0.03580	27.934	0.07289	0.9909

MERCURY

Properties of Mercury			Multipliers for Inches of Mercury			
Mercury Temperature °F	Specific gravity	Lb per sq in. psi	Inches of mercury for 1.0 psi	Inches of water at 39.2°F	Inches of water at mercury temperature	Inches of mercury at 32°F
32	13.596	0.4912	2.026	13.596	13.597	1.0000
40	13.584	0.4908	2.038	13.584	13.584	0.9992
45	13.578	0.4905	2.039	13.578	13.579	0.9987
50	13.571	0.4903	2.040	13.571	13.574	0.9982
55	13.564	0.4900	2.041	13.564	13.572	0.9977
60	13.557	0.4898	2.042	13.557	13.570	0.9972
65	13.550	0.4895	2.043	13.550	13.570	0.9967
70	13.544	0.4893	2.044	13.544	13.571	0.9962
75	13.537	0.4890	2.045	13.537	13.572	0.9957
80	13.530	0.4888	2.046	13.530	13.576	0.9952
85	13.523	0.4885	2.047	13.523	13.580	0.9947
90	13.516	0.4883	2.048	13.516	13.584	0.9942
95	13.510	0.4881	2.049	13.510	13.590	0.9937
100	13.503	0.4878	2.050	13.503	13.597	0.9932
105	13.496	0.4876	2.051	13.496	13.604	0.9927
110	13.489	0.4873	2.052	13.489	13.613	0.9922

same condition or the same value for differing conditions, similar results cannot be obtained.

As indicated in Table 7.2 it is unreasonable to expect final results correct to five significant figures from data obtained with commercial instruments. In order to obtain constants or coefficients which will check to four significant figures, experiments must be conducted with a great degree of scientific accuracy.

Absolute Pressure

The absolute pressure is defined as the total pressure acting upon a surface. The solution of problems in measurement is simplified by expressing all pressures in absolute units. To express gage pressures above atmospheric pressure in absolute units, the atmospheric pressure must be added to the gage pressure. For example, if the gage pressure is 10 psig and the atmospheric pressure is 14.7 psia, the absolute pressure is equal to 10 ± 14.7 or 24.7 psia. Altitude and mean atmospheric pressure for different cities is provided in Table 7.3.

Standard Atmosphere. The value adopted by the National Weather Service is defined as a pressure of 1013.250 millibars, established by the International Committee on Weights and Measures. This corresponds to 760 millimeters of mercury at 32°F, which is equivalent to 29.9213 inches of mercury at 32°F or 14.696 psia. The "bar" is a scientific unit of pressure. The "bar" is defined as a force equal to 1000 dynes per square centimeter and corresponds to a pressure of 14.504 psi; the millibar equals 0.001 bar.

Pressure Gages

The pressure acting upon or exerted by gases and liquids is expressed in pounds per square inch, inches of mercury, inches of water, and feet head of fluid. It is indicated by spring-gages, siphon-gages or U-gages.

Vacuum

The term "vacuum" is usually used to mean a partial reduction of pressure below the normal atmospheric pressure, or zero gage pressure. This is the engineering conception of the term as used in this publication. The greatest vacuum attainable with engineering appliances in general use is about 29 inches of mercury below atmospheric pressure.

Absolute Temperature

Absolute temperature is obtained by adding 460 degrees to the ordinary Fahrenheit scale; 80°F = 80 + 460 = 540°F absolute; −190°F = −190 + 460 = 270°F absolute. Experimenters have determined the absolute zero at various values from 459.2 to 459.6 degrees below zero, but 460 degrees has been used in nearly all calculations.

METHODS OF METERING

The statistics of operating steam distribution companies which report annually to IDHA, show that in 1981 there were 12,300 customers billed for service. Of these, 10,200 utilized condensate meters and 2,200 were reported using flow-meters. Condensate meters can be grouped into two general types, each having a range of seven capacities, but at the present time only one type is manufactured in the U.S. Flow-meters, are available in many types, designs,

TABLE 7.3

ALTITUDE AND ATMOSPHERIC PRESSURE

Location	Elevation in feet above sea level	Average atmospheric pressure, psia	Location	Elevation in feet above sea level	Average atmospheric pressure, psia
Abilene, Tex.	1738	13.85	Las Vegas, Nev.	1869	13.74
Albany, N.Y.	97	14.70	Lincoln, Nebr.	1189	14.12
Albuquerque, N.M.	4972	12.30	Los Angeles, Cal.	512	14.46
Amarillo, Tex.	3676	12.90	Louisville, Ky.	525	14.48
Asheville, N.C.	2253	13.62	Madison, Wis.	974	14.23
Atlanta, Ga.	1173	14.16	Memphis, Tenn.	399	14.56
Atlantic City, N.J.	52	14.72	Miami, Fla.	25	14.74
Austin, Tex.	605	14.42	Milwaukee, Wis.	681	14.38
Baker, Ore.	3471	12.98	Minneapolis, Minn.	919	14.24
Baltimore, Md.	123	14.70	Montgomery, Ala.	218	14.65
Binghamton, N.Y.	871	14.29	Nashville, Tenn.	546	14.48
Birmingham, Ala.	700	14.41	New Orleans, La.	53	14.73
Bismarck, N.D.	1677	13.86	New York, N.Y.	314	14.58
Boise, Idaho	2739	13.35	North Platte, Nebr.	2787	13.30
Boston, Mass.	124	14.67	Oklahoma City, Okla.	1214	14.11
Brownsville, Tex.	57	14.71	Omaha, Nebr.	1105	14.16
Buffalo, N.Y.	706	14.37	Parkersburg, W.Va.	637	14.43
Burlington, Vt.	403	14.51	Philadelphia, Pa.	114	14.70
Cairo, Ill.	357	14.57	Phoenix, Ariz.	1107	14.12
Charleston, S.C.	48	14.74	Pittsburgh, Pa.	842	14.31
Charlotte, N.C.	779	14.36	Pocatello, Idaho	4477	12.52
Chattanooga, Tenn.	762	14.38	Portland, Me.	63	14.70
Cheyenne, Wyo.	6141	11.77	Portland, Ore.	154	14.68
Chicago, Ill.	673	14.39	Providence, R.I.	159	14.66
Cincinnati, Ohio	627	14.43	Pueblo, Colo.	4690	12.42
Cleveland, Ohio	762	14.35	Rapid City, S.D.	3259	13.06
Columbia, S.C.	347	14.58	Reno, Nev.	4532	12.51
Columbus, Ohio	822	14.33	Richmond, Va.	164	14.69
Concord, N.H.	289	14.58	Roanoke, Va.	1176	14.11
Corpus Christi, Tex.	20	14.72	Rochester, N.Y.	523	14.46
Dallas, Tex.	512	14.47	Roswell, N.M.	3566	12.95
Davenport, Iowa	606	14.43	Sacramento, Cal.	66	14.70
Dayton, Ohio	900	14.28	St. Louis, Mo.	568	14.45
Denver, Colo.	5292	12.14	Salt Lake City, Utah	4357	12.58
Des Moines, Iowa	860	14.29	San Antonio, Tex.	693	14.38
Detroit, Mich.	730	14.36	San Diego, Cal.	87	14.68
Duluth, Minn.	1133	14.12	San Francisco, Cal.	155	14.67
Elkins, W.Va.	1947	13.73	Santa Fe, N.M.	7013	11.44
El Paso, Tex.	3778	12.85	Saulte Ste. Marie, Mich.	614	14.40
Erie, Pa.	714	14.37	Seattle, Wash.	125	14.69
Evansville, Ind.	431	14.53	Shreveport, La.	249	14.62
Fort Smith, Ark.	463	14.51	Sioux City, Iowa	1138	14.14
Fort Wayne, Ind.	857	14.30	Sioux Falls, S.D.	1427	13.99
Forth Worth, Tex.	679	14.39	Spokane, Wash.	1929	13.74
Grand Rapids, Mich.	689	14.37	Springfield, Ill.	636	14.42
Harrisburg, Pa.	378	14.56	Springfield, Mo.	1324	14.06
Hartford, Conn.	159	14.66	Syracuse, N.Y.	596	14.43
Helena, Mont.	4123	12.67	Toledo, Ohio	628	14.42
Houston, Tex.	138	14.68	Topeka, Kans.	986	14.22
Indianapolis, Ind.	823	14.32	Tucson, Ariz.	2555	13.41
Jackson, Miss.	331	14.58	Tulsa, Okla.	676	14.39
Kansas City, Mo.	963	14.24	Washington, D.C.	112	14.70
Keokuk, Iowa	614	14.42	Wichita, Kans.	1358	14.03
Knoxville, Tenn.	995	14.25	Winston-Salem, N.C.	978	14.26
Lander, Wyo.	5352	12.10	Yuma, Ariz.	142	14.68

and utilizing several operational theories. There are so many types and varieties that no single volume has ever documented all the variations. This chapter, therefore, is limited essentially to a discussion of condensate measurement and major varieties of flow metering—the conventional head type, the shunted flow design and the insertion turbine.

Condensate Measurement

Condensate usually is measured by a meter unit consisting of a case enclosing a compartmentalized water wheel device called a "rotor". Condensate enters the center of the rotor through an inlet tube called a "spout" which directs the water flow to the rotor compartments. The filling and emptying of the compartments results in rotation which is transmitted through the case to a "counter" or "register". The meter generally is an atmospheric pressure device but may be operated under vacuum with minor modifications.

The meters used in the U.S. are sturdy machines characterized by great accuracy over a measurement range from drops of water to full rated capacity. Depending on the condition of the condensate, these meters will hold this accuracy over a two or three year period. After this time the rotor and spout must be cleaned and the rotating parts serviced. With reasonable maintenance, the service life of a U.S. built condensate meter will be more than 25 years.

Condensate meters, even with their high accuracy and broad range, only can record the water delivered to their inlet. This may not be a true indication of the volume of steam furnished the user. In large, older structures, which often are extensively remodeled, diversion of steam condensate can easily occur (intentionally or otherwise), or water from other sources can be misdirected to condensate returns and be included in the measurement. A common point of failure is leaks in water heating coils. The simplest method of checking is the maintenance and examination of meter records so as to alert personnel to changes in usage patterns.

TABLE 7.4
WATER TEMPERATURE CORRECTION FACTORS TO BE APPLIED WHEN TESTING CONDENSATE-TYPE METERS

Condensate-type meters are normally calibrated for water at 140°F, and a correction factor should be applied when testing these meters with water at a lower temperature. The correction factors are shown in the following table:

Temp., Deg. F	Correction Factor	Temp., Deg. F	Correction Factor
36	.9832	80	.9865
38	.9832	82	.9868
40	.9832	84	.9872
42	.9833	86	.9875
44	.9833	88	.9879
46	.9834	90	.9882
48	.9834	92	.9886
50	.9835	94	.9890
52	.9836	96	.9894
54	.9837	98	.9898
56	.9838	100	.9902
58	.9840	102	.9906
60	.9842	104	.9910
62	.9843	106	.9914
64	.9845	108	.9918
66	.9847	110	.9923
68	.9849	112	.9928
70	.9851	114	.9932
72	.9853	116	.9937
74	.9856	118	.9941
76	.9858	120	.9945
78	.9862	140	1.000

Condensate meters are calibrated for water at 140°F which is relatively close to the maximum allowable entering temperature for drain systems under most municipal plumbing codes. Higher temperatures will shorten the life of the meter, and installation of some cooling procedure is necessary. Cooler water, however, causes a change in accuracy that should be accounted for if billing errors of more than ±0.5% are developed. Table 7.4 lists the water temperature correction factors.

Condensate meters must be intalled in full accord with the manufacturer's specifications. Figure 7.1 is typical of the present line of meters manufactured in the U.S.

The testing and calibration of condensate meters must be on an "as-found" and "as-left" basis. That is, the meter removed from service must be tested without alterations to its mechanism. Following the reconditioning process, the meter must again be tested and approved for installation. In general, a meter that, when tested "as-found" is *more* than 3% inaccurate by over-registration, the customer is due a refund, or if inaccurate through under-registration, the supplier should have authorization to negotiate for unbilled service. In servicing U.S. built condensate meters particular care must be taken not to interchange counters or registers between sizes. Accepted practice is for more than one person to check the installation of registers. It should be noted that the type of meter currently produced in the U.S. is essentially non-adjustable as to the accuracy of registration. The other type having a bolted-together, compartmentized rotor and *is* adjustable by redirecting the angle of the spout. These adjustable meters must be serviced as complete units. The non-adjustable type of meter, however, may be serviced by returning only the rotor and spout to the shop. This practice saves transportation of the heavy case but does require more sophisticated testing equipment.

Steam condensate meters can be equipped with contact devices built into the registers for remote registration or for connection to demand metering instruments. Manifolding of condensate meters is an acceptable practice, provided the inlet is of adequate size and properly vented so that flow into the meters is by gravity. Outlets in single or multiple installations should have an air gap device to avoid flooding. The exception is for meters in vacuum service. Condensate meters made and used in Europe utilize essentially the same principle, but are constructed with fewer compartments in the rotor. A Japanese condensate meter which has been tested in the U.S. operates on a teeter-board principle. It has alternating trays, one filling as the other discharges. It is made with stainless steel construction and is reportedly capable of in-line applications at pressures up to 250 PSIG. However, at the time of test, its accuracy was not suitable for revenue billing.

One method of condensate measurement for very large consumption of steam uses a fluid turbine meter with electronic read-out. These meters are accurate if operated under positive pressure in a full line. In application, condensate enters a receiving tank; when it nears the "full" position, a float switch fully opens a discharge valve allowing the tank to drain through the meter. When a lower float switch is activated, flow through the meter is stopped. A modestly sized tank and a small meter will measure very large loads with little sensitivity to high temperature, pressure or corrosive fluids.

Flow Meter Measurement—Conventional Orifice

The conventional steam flow meter consists of a primary device which creates a differential pressure relative to the rate of flow and a secondary device which

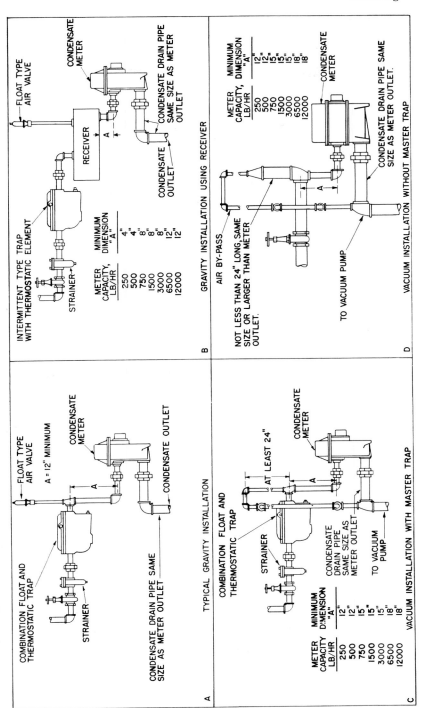

FIGURE 7.1

Typical condensate meters

translates the differential into useable data. There are certain terms associated with flow meters which must be defined.

Linearity. The state of conforming to a straight line, generally defined in terms of percentage (*i.e.*, the linearity is ±0.5 percent of the reading through the range of the meter).

Repeatability. The quality of performing with the same results again and again.

Rangeability. This is not a proper word, but it is used extensively. It involves the definition of the range of an instrument (*i.e.*, 10 gpm to 100 gpm).

Turndown ratio. Another way of explaining range (*i.e.*, 10 gpm to 100 gpm would equal a 10 to 1 turndown).

Beta ratio. A term used to define the relationship between the inside diameter of a pipe or conduit to the bore of an orifice, nozzle, or venturi throat (*i.e.*, 4 in. schedule 40 pipe has a diameter of 4.026 in.). If an orifice has a bore diameter of 2.21 in., the beta ratio would equal $2.21/4.026 = 0.549$.

Accuracy of range. Accuracy is presented as a percentage of full range of the instrument (*i.e.*, ±1 percent equals ±1 unit in 100). This means at 25 percent of meter range, there is ±1 unit in 25, or a true accuracy of ±4 percent.

Accuracy. Accuracy is presented as a percentage of actual readout of the instrument (*i.e.*, ±1 percent equals 1 unit in 100). It also means at 25 percent of meter range, there is ±0.25 units in 25, or a true accuracy of ±1 percent.

Reynolds number. A mathematical factor used to express the relationship among the velocity, viscosity, density, and dimensions of a fluid in a system of flow. The formula is: R_N = average velocity × pipe diameter/kinematic viscosity.

In considering the use of flow meters with steam, it is important that the pressure, temperature, flow rate and pipe specifications be clearly understood. Flow meters cannot be selected properly without these parameters having been well defined. In selecting the meter the primary device must be the first consideration. A wide choice is available. Some of the most commonly used types include:

Orifice Plate

This is the most widely used meter. It is a flat piece of metal, usually ⅛ in. stainless steel with a hole bored in it, installed between two flanges. Pressures are taken both upstream and downstream of the plate, measuring the pressure drop caused across it by the fluid passing through the restrictive hole in the plate. The fluid flow is related to the pressure drop according to the following formula:

$$Q_d/Q_a = (\Delta P_d/\Delta P_a)^{\frac{1}{2}}$$

where

Q_d = maximum design flow rate
Q_a = actual flow rate
ΔP_d = maximum design differential pressure
ΔP_a = actual differential pressure

The upstream and downstream pressure taps come in several configurations: corner, flange, vena contracta, and radius. Flange tapped is the most common, but the others are also acceptable.

This type of meter is adaptable to most fluids, moderately priced, has good accuracy at design flow rates, easy range change; no moving parts; simple differential pressure readout; easy to maintain.

The weaknesses are: limited range (can be increased with additional electronics at increased price); high permanent pressure loss; accuracy (depreciates as flow rate decreases); transfer piping (the connection between the pipeline and the readout instrumentation) causes added inaccuracies.

Flow Nozzle

A smooth tapered throat distinguishes the nozzle from the orifice. It is installed between flanges or welded directly to a pipe section. Otherwise, the principle of operation is the same as an orifice. Strengths and weaknesses are similar. It costs more than an orifice, but would have applications for high pressure superheated steam systems where high pipe velocities are common.

Venturi

As with the nozzle there is a tapered throat, but the exit is elongated and smooth as shown in Figure 7.2. The venturi can be provided with flanged, welded, or threaded end fittings. The principle of operation is basically the same as an orifice.

The strengths are: adaptable to most any fluid; high accuracy at design flow rate; no moving parts; simple differential pressure readout; easy to maintain; low permanent pressure loss.

The weaknesses are: expensive; limited range (can be increased with additional electronics at an increased price); accuracy depreciates as flow rate decreases; transfer piping causes added inaccuracies.

Averaging Pitot

The averaging pitot meter is shown in Figure 7.3. Based on the principle of comparing total pressure (velocity pressure plus static) to static pressure to obtain the velocity of the fluid through a pipe, use the formula:

$$V = (2gh)^{\frac{1}{2}}$$

where
  V = velocity, fps
  g = acceleration due to gravity, 32 ft per sec^2
  h = velocity head, ft

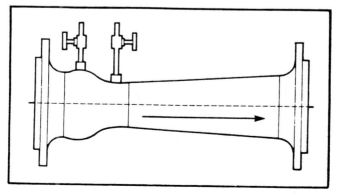

FIGURE 7.2
Venturi

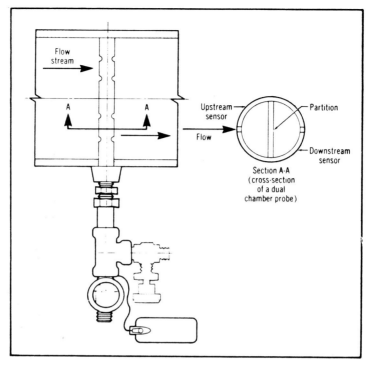

FIGURE 7.3

Averaging pitot meter

To find the volume, the expressed formula would then be:

$$Q = AV$$

where
Q = volume per unit of time
A = cross-sectional area of the pipe
V = velocity

The results provide the same square root relationship as with an orifice plate, nozzle, and venturi. The meter comprises two chambers, one facing upstream with multiple holes to establish an average velocity, and one facing downstream (sometimes with multiple holes) to sense the static pressure. The unit generally is installed by welding a coupling on the pipe and inserting the probe through the coupling. The probe may be a single tube with partition separating the upstream and downstream sides, or it may consist of two parallel tubes aligned along the longitudinal axis of the pipe.

The strengths are: adaptable to most fluids; low cost; no moving parts; simple differential pressure readout; easy to maintain; easy to install; minimum pressure drop.

The weaknesses are: low readout amplifies inaccuracies; unit can clog; limited range; accuracy depreciates as flow rate decreases; viscosity limit of 300 centipoises. Transfer piping causes added inaccuracies.

The secondary element of a flow metering system offers more choices than the primary. The mercury sealed manometer generally is giving way to the bellows-type unit which displaces less fluid for a given movement of the meter. The fully electronic meter, receiving signals from pressure, temperature and differential transducers, also is gaining acceptance. Meters which integrate fully, (that is, those which extract the square root and make the correction for steam density through a pressure relationship) are stock items. The daily round chart recorder has been a good instrument. However, chart changing and interpretation costs are becoming prohibitive. At the present time thirty day charts are not unusual, and long running strip chart recorders are gaining favor. Use of digital readouts and the multiplexing of electronic modules are accepted practices.

In installing the two elements of a conventional steam flow meter, certain precautions have proved to be important. These include:

1. Wherever possible install the secondary element below the line and grade the instrument lines away from the primary device. Minimum tube size for sensing lines should be ½" inside diameter.
2. Make provisions for cleaning the tap points of the orifice section, preferably without having to take the line out of service.
3. Use the American Gas Association Report No. 3 for orifice meters in locating the primary element with respect to pipe configuration.
4. Use caution in metering immediately down-stream of a pressure reduction valve. In addition to turbulence, a super-heat factor may be created.
5. Verify factors and relationship of plate diameter to meter reading constants.
6. Check plates to insure the sharp edge of the orifice. There are instruments available for this task. However in a field inspection light must not be reflected from any point on the sharp edge.

Orifice meters are made accurate only by the application of known constants. Small deviations in these constant factors can lead to a major loss of revenue. Tests indicate that an orifice section flooded with water to the edge of the orifice is more than 8% in error. The sharp edge of an orifice plate nicked moderately may cause a 3% error. In general, the meter and all its auxiliary devices must be assembled and maintained in original condition by competent personnel.

Flow Meter Measurement—Shunt Type

In shunt flow meter operation, a proportion of the flow through the meter is diverted by an orifice plate through nozzles onto a small turbine situated in the shunt circuit.

Turbine rotation is controlled at a speed proportional to the bypass flow by the action of a damping fan rotating in water. Since the bypass flow is proportional to main flow rate, the turbine speed is a measure of the total flow through the meter.

Turbine speed is geared down by a reduction train, the final stage of which is coupled to a driving magnet. This influences a similar magnet in the counter box, both magnets locking into step to enable the turbine rotation to be totalized on the counter. In smaller sizes, the meters are single piece in-line. Larger sizes require a piped bypass.

Experience shows:

  Maintenance: moderate to high
  Piping requirement: moderate
  Turndown ratio: 7 to 1
  Accuracy: ±2 percent of reading

Linearity: ±2 percent
Repeatability: ±0.20 percent
Cost: moderate to high

The strengths are: reasonable range; no power required for totalization.

The weaknesses are: high maintenance; not easy to calibrate.

The shunt flow meter described in the Third Edition of the District Heating Handbook is essentially the same as one of the meters available in the U.S. today. However, two additional types of shunt flow meters are now being marketed. The original meter is made in 1″, 2″, 3″ and 4″ pipe sizes, but one of the newer designs is made in only a 2″ size. The most apparent change in the newer design is relocation of the counter mechanism to the uppermost part of the assembly. The third meter being marketed is very similar to the original shunt flow design.

There are several points to be considered in selecting a conventionally designed shunt flow meter for measuring steam, since this type meter differs from the orifice-recorder systems. These meters are designed to withstand overloads of up to 200% for short periods of time. By anticipating the maximum load of a user and the load's duration, it is usually possible to select a lower rate flow meter and thus improve rangeability. These meters can be fabricated with a by-pass arrangement with line sizes of six inches or more allowing a single meter measurement with very high capacity. Some precautions must be observed with all shunt flow meters:

1. Meters must be installed strictly in accordance with manufacturer's instructions. (See Table 7.5 and Figure 7.4).
2. The meter records steam use only at the name-plate conditions. Any variation in pressure or quality must be corrected by application of a compensating factor to the meter reading.
3. A pressure (density factor) correcting counter is available for these meters but must be of the proper range and carefully calibrated.
4. The meters are made accurate by adjustment of the gear ratios and any change in the mechanism requires careful inspection.
5. These are essentially orifice type flow meters and should be serviced at the same interval.

Testing shunt flow steam meters for accuracy is an expensive and demanding operation. The manufacturers will supply drawings of a test stand that uses air pressure as a test medium and standard orifice plates as references. Present day

TABLE 7.5
SHUNT FLOW METER INSTALLATION

Meter Type and Size	Fittings Upstream	Pipe Diameters Upstream	Pipe Diameters Downstream
In-Line (1, 2, 3, 4 inch)	Any	12	6
By-Pass (5 inch and larger)	1 elbow or 2 elbows same plane	10	5
	2 or more elbows not in same plane	25	5
	Gate Valve (if not kept wide open)	25	5

Main Size	Main Flg.	B
5"-18"	150 Lbs.	1 Pipe Dia.
5"-18"	300 Lbs.	1 Pipe Dia.
5"-16"	600 Lbs.	1 Pipe Dia.
18"	600 Lbs.	¾ Pipe Dia.
20"-24"	All	½ Pipe Dia.

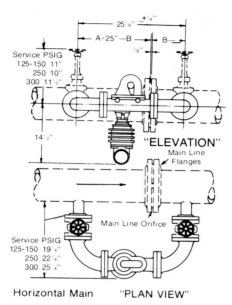

FIGURE 7.4

By-pass installation

construction of a test unit for the full range of sizes and which has its own air source will cost in excess of $50,000. The factory will test and service meters at the plant on a fixed-fee basis. Such testing, however, must be acceptable to the public regulatory commission having jurisdiction over meter tests.

In recent years, the manufacturer of one line of shunt flow meters has developed a computer program to greatly simplify the extensive calculations involved in testing. The program is used in documenting the registration of new meters and in retesting of meters returned for service. The program can be purchased for those operators which have in-house test facilities.

Flow Meter Measurement—Turbine Type

The insertion turbine meter for measuring steam is a relatively new development. The turbine is simply a set of blades in a housing approximately one inch in diameter. It is inserted through the pipe wall into the stream and the speed of blade rotation becomes a linear readout of the flow rate within the stated flow range. It is sensed by means of an electronic mechanism. The output is fed to a steam flow computer along with the output of temperature and pressure transducers. The computer normally displays the mass flow rate and totalized flow. The computer module is capable of making many self-checks and displaying faults. The more advanced units accept inputs from multiple turbine units.

The rotor or turbine unit has the advantage of installation and removal from the steam line without interruption to service. The initial installation can be made on an active line using the "hot tapping" technique developed by the natural gas industry. Figure 7.5 shows various styles of rotors and insertion probes.

A variety of rotors are available with blades pitched to suit the velocity of the flow stream. When components are aligned properly, the state-of-the-art turbine meters have greater rangeability than conventional flow devices. Line sizes are from 3″ to 48″ and temperatures to 750°F can be measured.

The meters can be factory tested, as their small dimensions make shipping easy. For in-house testing a test unit using sonic nozzles is available. The test procedure is relatively uncomplicated (reference IDHA Proceedings, 1981, "Facility for the Sonic Calibration of Flowmeters").

Flow Meter Measurement—Developments

Flow measurement of all fluids is improving through the availability of better, more reliable data, and through the development of more advanced materials. Meters of the future apparently will be electronic in nature and very compact. They also may be more expensive than present day versions.

One principle of measurement gaining attention for steam metering is "Vortex Shedding." This is a principle of measurement that has been around for years. Vortex shedding is the name given to the natural effect occurring when a gas or a liquid flows around a blunt or nonstreamlined object (See

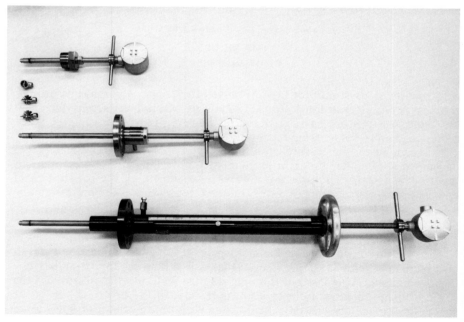

FIGURE 7.5

Various styles of rotors and insertion tubes
Courtesy of Engineering Measurements Co.

Figure 7.6). The flow, unable to follow the shape on its downstream side, separates from the surface of the object, leaving a highly turbulent wake that takes the form of a continuous series of eddies forming and being swept downstream.

Each eddy or vortex first grows and then becomes detached or shed from the object. If the vortex generating object is correctly shaped and placed in a pipeline with the correct relative dimensions, it forms a primary flow element that generates pulse signals over very wide flow ranges at a frequency directly related to the volumetric flow rate approaching it.

The meter generally is installed between two standard ANSI flanges up through 8 in. Above 8 in., it is inserted in the flow stream.

Experience indicates:

    Maintenance: low to moderate
    Piping requirements: moderate
    Turndown ratio: 10 to 1 or better
    Accuracy: ±1 percent of reading
    Linearity: ±0.5 percent
    Repeatability: ±0.5 percent
    Cost: moderate to high

The strengths are: excellent range; good accuracy over entire range; no or minimal moving parts; easy to maintain; easy to install.

The weaknesses are: higher cost; not good for viscous fluids.

The use of ultrasonic principles in steam flow measurement has gained some attention. In most systems of this type an ultrasonic beam is transmitted diagonally across the steam line. As the flow causes a bending of this path, the flow is determined electronically. Using this system, pressure and temperature are supplied to the small computer by line mounted transducers. Such systems may have the ability to report accurate flow without any perforation of the pipe wall.

A similar system exists where a critical tone signal is imposed at the inner pipe wall and received several feet down stream. The velocity of the flowing stream has a measurable effect on the time-distance relationship of the signal and can be calculated as mass flow. An important consideration is that this system does not intrude into the pipe and thus there is no pressure loss.

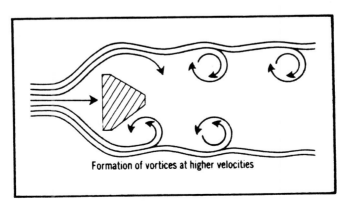

Formation of vortices at higher velocities

FIGURE 7.6
Vortex shedding—principle of operation

HOT AND CHILLED WATER METERING

Hot and chilled water-heat meters are essential to measuring changes in flow, differences in the temperature change between the inlet and outlet of the system, and to calculate the volume of heat change. Metering devices combining these measurements are called Btu meters, where Btu (British thermal unit) is defined as the quantity of heat required to raise the temperature of one pound of water by one degree Fahrenheit.

Figure 7.7 illustrates the components of a typical Btu meter.

Water Meter Classification

Water meters are available in two main categories:
1. displacement- and propeller-type meters, and
2. head-type meters.

Table 7.6 lists the types of elements used for measuring flow and temperature and also the types of output indication provided. The meter components may use pneumatic, mechanical, electronic, magnetic, solid state devices, or any appropriate combination.

The propeller and displacement types will be described first, since they are generally simpler and less expensive than the head types.

DISPLACEMENT- AND PROPELLER-TYPE METERS

Water meters used with indicating-type Btu meters either may be the displacement type, containing a rotating disk for line sizes up to 4-inch, or the propeller type, available in 4-inch through 30-inch sizes. Displacement water

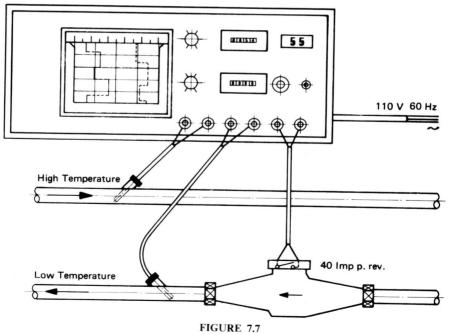

FIGURE 7.7

Btu metering system
Courtesy of Sonceboz Corp.

TABLE 7.6

TYPES OF ELEMENTS USED FOR MEASURING FLOW AND TEMPERATURE AND TYPES OF OUTPUT INDICATION

Flow	Temperature	Remarks[a]
Displacement disk or propeller	Liquid expansion capillary	Indicates Δt, totalizes gals. and BTU
Differential head	Gas filled or resistance	Records flow, Δt, and BTU's
Differential head D.P.—transmitter	Liquid expansion or resistance	Records flow, Δt, and records and totalizes
Differential head	Liquid expansion or resistance	Records flow, Δt, and records and totalizes
Differential head	Resistance bulbs	Records flow, Δt, and records and totalizes
Differential head ring balance	Resistance bulbs	Records flow, Δt, and records and totalizes
Differential head D.P.—transmitter	Resistance bulbs	Records flow, Δt, and records and totalizes
Differential head	Resistance, liquid or gas expansion	Records flow, Δt, and records and totalizes
Displacement disk	Liquid expansion capillary	Indicates Δt, totalizes gals. & BTU's
Differential head	Liquid expansion capillary	Records flow, Δt, and records and totalizes
Differential head	—	Indicates and totalizes
Propeller type	Platinum sensors	Totalizes BTU's and gals.

[a] Symbol Δt represents differential temperature.

meters are essentially standard water meters with some parts modified to increase meter life in handling the continuous flow encountered in Btu metering. Water flow through the meter supplies the power necessary to operate the Btu computer mechanism, which is mounted on the water meter and contains the differential pressure system, the integrator, and the readouts.

Readouts generally provided include:

1. The total Btu's of heat absorbed by the water (provided by a counter).
2. The total quantity of water circulated (provided by a counter).
3. The temperature difference between the water supply and return lines (shown on the indicating scale).

These meters provide acceptable accuracy when applied to reasonably constant flow rates in cases where temperature differences are significant. However, many sophisticated systems require flow rate adjustment from 0 to 100%, and it is not uncommon to see a low load temperature difference of only 1 or 2 degrees F. In such applications, a precision orifice-type flow meter with electronic or pneumatic temperature-sensing and transmitting is essential. The signals from the flow transmitter and the temperature differential transmitter then are fed to an integrating calculator for totalizing energy. Such instrumentation is dependent on skilled installation and careful continued maintenance.

Description of Operation

In the meter shown in Figure 7.8, the temperature sensing system consists of sensing bulbs, sheathed capillary tubing, and bourdon spirals, all completely filled with mercury. The bourdon spirals are attached, through suitable linkages, to a shaft in a manner where their opposing forces establish a shaft position

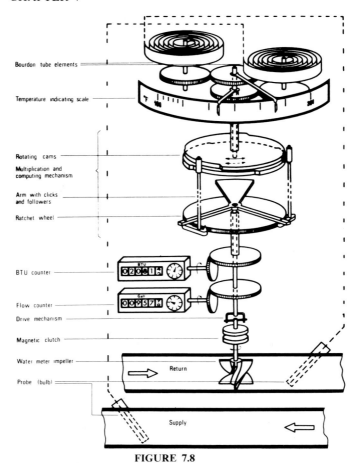

Bourdon tube elements

Temperature indicating scale

Rotating cams

Multiplication and computing mechanism

Arm with clicks and followers

Ratchet wheel

BTU counter

Flow counter

Drive mechanism

Magnetic clutch

Water meter impeller

Probe (bulb)

Return

Supply

FIGURE 7.8
Temperature sensing system
Courtesy of Sonceboz Corp.

which indicates the temperature difference between the supply and return water flow. This differential is indicated on a scale by means of a pointer affixed to the shaft. A movable cam also is attached to the shaft adjacent to a fixed cam. The relative positions of both cams are determined by the temperature differential. The cams are designed to expose a gap into which a spring-loaded pawl can drop. The pawl is continuously rotated around both cam surfaces by the water meter. When the pawl drops into the gap it engages a ratchet which in turn drives a Btu counter. The length of the gap is proportional to the temperature differential and the speed of pawl rotation is proportional to the water flow rate. Consequently the meter mechanism continuously integrates the product of temperature differential and water flow rate to provide Btus.

HEAD-TYPE METERS

A number of manufacturers provide head-type meters together with either liquid expansion or resistance-type temperature bulbs for obtaining temperature differential. These meters record water flow, temperature differential, and totalized Btu use.

Description of Operation

In a typical head-type meter, differential pressure across the primary element is piped to a manometer within the recorder. This measurement then is converted into a flow record. The temperature differential between the water supply and return lines may be measured with resistance bulbs, thermocouples or liquid or gas expansion capillary type systems. Resistance bulbs are used more generally and have an advantage over an expansion type system since thermometers can be located at greater distances from the recording meter. The receiver for measurement of temperature differential may be an a-c servo motor amplifier operating from an error voltage developed across a modified Wheatstone bridge. When this measurement is incorporated in the flow meter through the addition of multiplying linkages, the flow meter becomes a Btu meter.

Meter Selection

In selecting a meter, consideration must be given to the size of the cooling load, the revenues to be obtained, or the economies that may be achieved if the Btu usage is known. All have a strong bearing on the justifiable meter cost. In addition, it is necessary to know the volume of water flow to be measured, the temperatures and temperature differentials of the chilled water, the relative locations of the supply and return lines, and the maximum water pressure. Provision must be made for a suitable location for the meter, for an electric power supply if needed and, for the required straight runs of pipe upstream and downstream from the primary flow element. Consultation with manufacturer's representatives is advisable.

Installation Requirements

General installation requirements for Btu meters are as follows:
1. The Btu meter should be installed in the supply line. The meter should be installed so that it is accessible easily for reading. Adequate space should be available to open the meter for maintenance work.
2. A by-pass line should be installed around the Btu meter (and strainer, if used) to permit filling and flushing the line without damaging the meter. The by-pass allows maintenance work to be done without interrupting flow. When the meter is to be used for billing, the operating company may either lock or eliminate the by-pass.
3. A strainer should be installed ahead of the meter, or at least one strainer installed for the entire system. The strainer should be installed so that adequate space is available for opening and cleaning it.
4. Both temperature capillaries should be the same length and must be exposed to the same ambient temperature.
5. Thermometer wells: at least the bottom 2½″ of the well should be in the flowing stream.
6. Manufacturer's instructions should be followed for more specific requirements concerning the position of the meter, straight runs of pipe, or fittings upstream or downstream from the meter.

START-UP PROCEDURE

The following is a general procedure for start-up of these meters:
1. Flush the line thoroughly before putting the meter into service. Most difficulties with new meters are caused by pipe cuttings, welding slag, pipe scale, and other debris carried into the meter with the first rush of liquid.

A by-pass is recommended to permit this flushing operation. If a by-pass is not used, a section of pipe should be installed in place of the meter and the line flushed before the meter is installed.

2. Do not install the temperature bulbs in the wells at this time, to prevent a false temperature differential from damaging the equipment.
3. Start the meter slowly especially when starting a displacement meter. A sudden flow of water into an empty meter can damage the measuring disk. With a by-pass, use this procedure:
   a. Start flow through the by-pass and flush the line thoroughly.
   b. Open the meter inlet valve slightly and allow the meter to fill with liquid slowly. Then open this valve completely.
   c. Open the meter outlet valve slightly and allow the compressed air to bleed out slowly. Then open this valve completely.
   d. Slowly close the by-pass valve.
   Without a by-pass, use this procedure:
   a. Install a section of pipe in place of the meter.
   b. Flush the line thoroughly.
   c. Install the water meter.
   d. Open the upstream valve slightly and allow the line to fill with liquid. Then open this valve completely.
   e. Open the downstream valve slightly and allow the compressed air to bleed out. Then open this valve slowly.
4. Insert the temperature bulb in the chilled water return line temperature well and immediately insert the other one in the supply line temperature well. Installing both bulbs at nearly the same time will prevent a large temperature overrange.
5. Check the maximum flow rate through the meter by setting the control valve wide open and reading the gallon counter for one minute. If the maximum flow rate is above the capacity of the meter, it must be reduced and some suggested methods are:
   a. Partially close a manual balancing valve, if available.
   b. Shorten the stroke of the control valve so that it will pass only the desired rate when wide open.
   c. Install a restricting orifice downstream of the meter.

ACCURACY

The accuracy of a Btu meter using either a displacement- or propeller-type water meter is the sum of the accuracy of its components as shown in Table 7.7. If all components in the illustration were in error to the limit of the manufacturer's tolerances, and all errors were in the same direction, the integrated total Btu reading could be in error by 3.6 percent at 25°F temperature differential, or 5.1 percent at 10°F temperature differential when using a propeller meter. This is unacceptable for billing meters in utility service where installed accuracy must be as close to zero error as practical, and calibrated meters must be accurate to ±2.0% over the expected range of flow. It is critical, therefore, for the supplier of thermal service to select the most accurate components and to have in-house facilities that will assure the installation of meters proving to be less than ±2% inaccurate. No company should enter into the sale of hot or chilled water based on meter measurement without adequate in-house facilities to make a full range of comprehensive tests on meters before installation and periodically thereafter. Without such facilities a supplier cannot resolve customer complaints of overcharging or inequitable service.

TABLE 7.7

ACCURACY- PROPELLER- AND DISPLACEMENT-TYPE BTU METERS

Component	Tolerance[a]	Average Accumulated Error[b]
Water meter, displacement type	1%	½%
Water meter, propeller type	2%	1%
Temperature differential	¼°F	Less than ¼°F
@25°F full scale differential	1%	Less than 1%
@10°F	2½%	Less than 2½%
BTU computer	0.6%	0.3%

Sum of component errors[c]	Displacement Meter	Propeller Meter	Displacement Meter	Propeller Meter
@25° temp. diff.	2.6%	3.6%	1.8%	2.3%
@10° temp. diff.	4.1%	5.1%	3.3%	3.8%

[a] Tolerances are manufacturers' guarantees, computed over the recommended range of flow rates or temperature differentials.
[b] This is based on average operating conditions, at flows varying throughout the recommended ranges.
[c] Some errors would usually cancel out, and the actual final error would be less than these limits.

Head Type

When the primary element is engineered and manufactured in accordance with ASME recommendations for flow measurement, the overall error should not exceed 2 percent at flow rates between 100 percent and 25 percent of rated capacity and with an error not greater than that at 25 percent at flows between 10 percent and 25 percent of rated capacity. The error in measuring temperature difference should not exceed 2 percent of the full scale range and the error in Btu measurement should not exceed 2 percent.

An inaccuracy in head-type meters stems from the mathematical relationship between flow rate and the differential pressure signal. The square root proportionality relating flow and differential pressure is denoted by the following formula:

$$Q_m/Q_d = (\Delta P_m/\Delta D_d)^{\frac{1}{2}}$$

where

Q_m = measured flow rate
Q_d = maximum design flow rate
ΔP_m = differential pressure measured
ΔD_d = maximum design differential pressure

As an example, in a 1000 gpm water system with an instrument purchased to have 100 inches water column (W.C.) equal to the maximum flow rate of 1000 gpm, when the flow is at 500 gpm or half the design, the meter will register 25 inches W.C. and at 300 gpm a reading of only 9 inches W.C. can be realized. If the instrument has a specified ±1% of full scale range accuracy, the deterioration of accuracy at 300 gpm or translates to an 11% error in flow. This is unacceptable when systems must be cost-effective.

OTHER METERING CONSIDERATIONS

Hot or chilled water can be accounted for in commercial sales without the requirement for Btu integration. Systems, particularly in Denmark, measure only the volume of water used by the consumer. The systems are designed to provide a relatively uniform inlet temperature to each subscriber. The heat extracted by the customer's equipment is not related to the revenue producing process, and it is wise for the user to install as effective a means of heat extraction as possible. Such systems are less costly to install and maintain.

A simple device used in Europe for approximating the use of energy in hot water radiation systems is the "Evaporation Meter." These devices are modified "U" shape tubes containing a fluid with a known rate of evaporation, and are calibrated so that fluid is displaced in proportion to the quantity of heat sensed by the device. Results are used more in allocation of costs than in actual billing.

CONCLUSION

Central energy systems in the U.S. must obtain their revenue on the basis of meter readings. These meter readings must be accurate and meet local utility regulations. In non-commercial situations meters are essential to effective energy saving efforts. The selection of meters is critical to the financial stability of the enterprise, whether it be profit or non-profit. Progress in steam, and hot and chilled water measurement in the past decade has not been outstanding due principally to the lack of good markets. If district heating and cooling moves forward it will be a challenge for the instrument community to keep pace.

REFERENCES

1. *ASHRAE Handbook & Product Directory, 1977 Fundamentals*, American Society of Heating, Refrigerating and Air-Conditioning Engineers, Inc.
2. *Fluid Meters, Their Theory and Application*, American Society of Mechanical Engineers (ASME).
3. Cheremisinoff, Nicholas P., *Fluid Flow Measurement*, Marcel Dekker.
4. Dowdell, Roger B., *Flow: Its Measurement and Control in Science and Industry*, Vol. 2, 1981, Instrument Society of America.
5. Hayward, T. J., *Flow Meters*, John Wiley & Sons, Inc.
6. Spink, L. K., *Principles and Practice of Flow Meter Engineering*, 9th Edition, 1975, The Foxboro Co.
7. C. R. Griesbach, *Facility for the Sonic Calibration of Flowmeters*, Proceedings of IDHA, 1981.

CHAPTER 8

District Heating Service to the User

ESTIMATING STEAM REQUIREMENTS

THE AMOUNT of steam consumed during a given period is actually the summation of all the variable hourly steam uses during that period.

The uses for steam may be divided into three general classes:
1. space heating,
2. process, and
3. air-conditioning.

Steam Requirements for Space Heating

There are five accepted methods of estimating space-heating requirements in common use today:
1. the degree-hour method,
2. the degree-day method,
3. the calculated heat-loss method,
4. the fuel-use method, and
5. computer-analysis method.

DEGREE-HOUR METHOD

The degree-hour method is more accurate than most other methods in that the heating requirements for building occupied hours and unoccupied hours are considered separately, and the two combined for total seasonal requirements. Also, all internal heat gains are taken into account. The total annual Btu requirements can be estimated from the following equation:

$$\frac{HLo}{\Delta To} \times DHo \times \frac{to}{t} \times (1 - C_f) + \frac{HLn}{\Delta tn} \times DHn \times \frac{tn}{t} \times (1 + C_f)$$

where:

HLo = Calculated heat losses during occupancy.

HLn = Calculated heat losses during non-occupancy.

ΔTo = Difference between indoor and outdoor design temperature during occupancy.

Δtn = Difference between indoor and outdoor design temperature during non-occupancy.

DHo = Degree-hours at balance or change over temperature during occupancy.

DHn = Degree-hours at balance temperature (usually the inside set-back temperature) during non-occupancy.

to = Time of occupancy in hours per week.

tn = Unoccupied hours.

t = 168 hours per week.

C_f = Compensation factor. This factor is introduced into the equation to weigh daytime and nighttime consumptions to compensate for daily temperature ranges. It is of necessity an approximation, since available weather data is not broken down according to time of day. Compensation factors vary with period of occupancy, as shown in the following table.

Daily Hours of Operation	C_f
24	0
18	.10
12	.20
9	.25

Balance or change over temperature can best be shown graphically as in Figure 8.1.

Degree hours at balance temperatures can be determined for various cities by plotting the number of hours at which various temperatures are recorded. This is obtained from the U.S. Weather Bureau Summary of Hourly Observations for your city. A sample of this is shown in Figure 8.2.

The calculation of annual energy consumption, for example, can be shown as follows:

	Occupied	Unoccupied
All Heat losses (Transmission ventilation infiltration)	5300 M Btu	4000 M Btu
Hours Operation	73	95
Balance temperature	30 F	60 F (setback)
Degree hours	9000	113,000

It should be noted here that the losses for the unoccupied hours take into account less ventilation air during nighttime and weekend operation and that higher daytime temperatures generally prevail over nighttime and this situation should be taken into account when determining weekend losses.

$$\frac{5300 \text{ M Btu}}{70\text{-}0} \times 9000 \times \frac{73}{168} (1 - .20)$$

$$+ \frac{4000 \text{ M Btu}}{60\text{-}0} \times 113{,}000 \times \frac{95}{168}$$

$$\times (1 + .20) = 236{,}862 + 5{,}272{,}806 = 5{,}509{,}668 \text{ M Btu/year}$$

$$\frac{5{,}509{,}668 \text{ M Btu}}{970 \text{ Btu/lb. Steam}} = 5680 \text{ M lbs. of Steam/year}$$

DEGREE-DAY METHOD

This method, sometimes referred to as one of the short-cut methods, consists of comparison of the structure to be estimated with a similar structure, the actual steam use of which is known. It assumes that steam usage of buildings

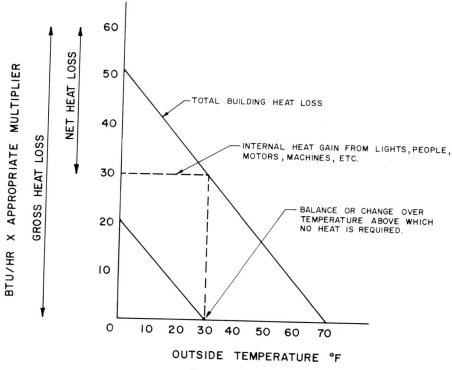

FIGURE 8.1

Balance or change over temperature

of the same general type of occupancy, such as hotels or office buildings, will be governed by similar overall factors which determine heat loss, such as inside temperature, hours of service, and ventilation, provided adjustment is made for any difference in size and outside weather conditions.

This method of estimating steam requirements utilizes a simplified means of measurement of temperature differential and time, the unit of which is known as the *degree-day*. It has been learned from experience that when the daily mean temperature is 65 F, generally no heat is required for space heating; and, furthermore, that as the daily mean temperature falls below 65 F, heating requirements tend to vary directly in proportion to the difference between the mean outside temperature and 65 F.

The number of degree-day units (generally referred to as degree-days) for any day may be calculated by subtracting the mean outside temperature from 65 F, and the total degree-days for any longer period is the sum of the degree-days of the individual days in that period.

On a day having a maximum temperature of 40 F and a minimum temperature of 20 F there would be

$$65 - \frac{(40 \text{ to } 20)}{2} = 35 \text{ degree-days.}$$

The normal degree-days for various cities in the United States and Canada are tabulated in Table 8.1.

BALANCE OR CHANGE OVER TEMPERATURE

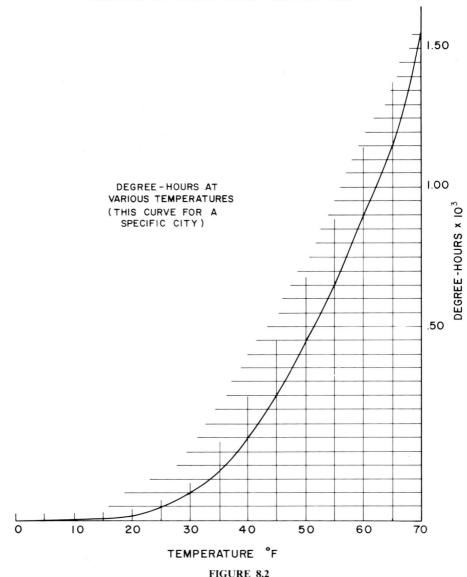

FIGURE 8.2

Degree-hours at various temperatures (this curve for a specific city)

Although 65 F is the base for calculating degree-days, recent research indicates that a lower base temperature may accurately reflect the impact climatic conditions upon energy consumption in new buildings; due to more energy building envelopes.

The degree-day is thus a means for measurement of heating requirements as affected by outside temperature. For any given structure it may also be utilized to check relative efficiency of operation, as the steam consumption in pounds of steam per degree-day may be compared for various periods of operation to determine whether the rate of use is increasing or decreasing.

The degree-day method of estimating steam requirements may be expressed by the equation:

$$S = N \times R \times D$$

where:

S = Steam consumption for the estimate period, lb.
N = Number of load units expressing the size of the heating load, such as
    (a) MBtu of calculated hourly heat loss
    (b) M cu. ft. of heated content, or
    (c) Sq. ft. of connected equivalent direct radiation.
    (d) Sq. ft. of heated floor area.
R = Rate of steam consumption in pounds per degree-day, per load unit as expressed by N.
D = Number of degree-days in the estimate period.

The application is, therefore, quite simple in that, if the rate of use or R factor of a given building has been established at, say 0.5 pounds of steam per degree-day per M cu. ft. of space heated, the requirements of a similar building of the same type of occupancy may be estimated as:

Pounds Steam = (M cu. ft. of space heated) × 0.5 × Degree-days.

The same procedure would be followed in case the R factor has been established as lb. steam per degree-day per M Btu hourly heat loss, per square foot of equivalent direct radiation, or per square foot of heated floor area.

Many suppliers of district heating use some form of the degree-day method for estimating steam requirements, or at least for quick spot checks. Their general practice is to establish average R factors for buildings of various types of occupancy, such as office buildings, hotels, etc., from actual metered uses. From these records of actual consumption established for average conditions, it is possible to adjust for maximum variation from that average and, in many cases, to find a building which is practically identical to the one to be estimated.

CALCULATED HEAT-LOSS METHOD

This method is theoretical and assumes that the hourly rate of heat loss as calculated for design of a given structure may be adjusted in accordance with the variation in temperature difference between inside and outside to obtain all other hourly heat losses for any estimating period. Expressed mathematically:

$$\text{Lb steam} = H \frac{(t - t_a) N - (Q \times N)}{(t_i - t_o) S} \tag{1}$$

where:

H = Calculated hourly heat loss
t = Average inside temperature maintained during estimating period
t_a = Average outside temperature during estimating period
N = Number of hours in estimating period
t_i = Inside temperature usually taken as that used in calculation of H
t_o = Outside temperature used to establish H
S = Number of Btu utilized in each pound of steam
Q = Heat gain from all sources (lighting, people, motors, cooking, etc.)

TABLE 8.1

AVERAGE MONTHLY AND YEARLY DEGREE DAYS FOR CITIES IN THE UNITED STATES AND CANADA[a,b,c] (BASE 65 F)

State	Station		Avg. Winter Temp[d]	July	Aug.	Sept.	Oct.	Nov.	Dec.	Jan.	Feb.	Mar.	Apr.	May	June	Yearly Total
Ala.	Birmingham	A	54.2	0	0	6	93	363	555	592	462	363	108	9	0	2551
	Huntsville	A	51.3	0	0	12	127	426	663	694	557	434	138	19	0	3070
	Mobile	A	59.9	0	0	0	22	213	357	415	300	211	42	0	0	1560
	Montgomery	A	55.4	0	0	0	68	330	527	543	417	316	90	0	0	2291
Alaska	Anchorage	A	23.0	245	291	516	930	1284	1572	1631	1316	1293	879	592	315	10864
	Fairbanks	A	6.7	171	332	642	1203	1833	2254	2359	1901	1739	1068	555	222	14279
	Juneau	A	32.1	301	338	483	725	921	1135	1237	1070	1073	810	601	381	9075
	Nome	A	13.1	481	496	693	1094	1455	1820	1879	1666	1770	1314	930	573	14171
Ariz.	Flagstaff	A	35.6	46	68	201	558	867	1073	1169	991	911	651	437	180	7152
	Phoenix	A	58.5	0	0	0	22	234	415	474	328	217	75	0	0	1765
	Tucson	A	58.1	0	0	0	25	231	406	471	344	242	75	6	0	1800
	Winslow	A	43.0	0	0	6	245	711	1008	1054	770	601	291	96	0	4782
	Yuma	A	64.2	0	0	0	0	108	264	307	190	90	15	0	0	974
Ark.	Fort Smith	A	50.3	0	0	12	127	450	704	781	596	456	144	22	0	3292
	Little Rock	A	50.5	0	0	9	127	465	716	756	577	434	126	9	0	3219
	Texarkana	A	54.2	0	0	0	78	345	561	626	468	350	105	0	0	2533
Calif.	Bakersfield	A	55.4	0	0	0	37	282	502	546	364	267	105	19	0	2122
	Bishop	A	46.0	0	0	48	260	576	797	874	680	555	306	143	36	4275
	Blue Canyon	A	42.2	28	37	108	347	594	781	896	795	806	597	412	195	5596
	Burbank	A	58.6	0	0	6	43	177	301	366	277	239	138	81	18	1646
	Eureka	C	49.9	270	257	258	329	414	499	546	470	505	438	372	285	4643
	Fresno	A	53.3	0	0	0	84	354	577	605	426	335	162	62	6	2611
	Long Beach	A	57.8	0	0	9	47	171	316	397	311	264	171	93	25	1803
	Los Angeles	A	57.4	28	28	42	78	180	291	372	302	288	219	158	81	2061
	Los Angeles	C	60.3	0	0	6	31	132	229	310	230	202	123	68	18	1349
	Mt. Shasta	C	41.2	25	34	123	406	696	902	983	784	738	525	347	159	5722
	Oakland	A	53.5	53	50	45	127	309	481	527	400	353	255	180	90	2870
	Red Bluff	A	53.8	0	0	0	53	318	555	605	428	341	168	47	0	2515
	Sacramento	A	53.9	0	0	0	56	321	546	583	414	332	178	72	0	2502
	Sacramento	C	54.4	0	0	0	62	312	533	561	392	310	173	76	0	2419
	Sandberg	C	46.8	0	0	30	202	480	691	778	661	620	426	264	57	4209
	San Diego	A	59.5	9	0	21	43	135	236	298	235	214	135	90	42	1458
	San Francisco	A	53.4	81	78	60	143	306	462	508	395	363	279	214	126	3015
	San Francisco	C	55.1	192	174	102	118	231	388	443	336	319	279	239	180	3001
	Santa Maria	A	54.3	99	93	96	146	270	391	459	370	363	282	233	165	2967

State	Station	Type	Temp	Jul	Aug	Sep	Oct	Nov	Dec	Jan	Feb	Mar	Apr	May	Jun	Annual
Colo.	Alamosa	A	29.7	65	99	279	639	1065	1420	1476	1162	1020	696	440	168	8529
	Colorado Springs	A	37.3	9	25	132	456	825	1032	1128	938	893	582	319	84	6423
	Denver	A	37.6	6	9	117	428	819	1035	1132	938	887	558	288	66	6283
	Denver	C	40.8	0	0	90	366	714	905	1004	851	800	492	254	48	5524
	Grand Junction	A	39.3	0	0	30	313	786	1113	1209	907	729	387	146	21	5641
	Pueblo	A	40.4	0	0	54	326	750	986	1085	871	772	429	174	15	5462
Conn.	Bridgeport	A	39.9	0	0	66	307	615	986	1079	966	853	510	208	27	5617
	Hartford	A	37.3	0	12	117	394	714	1101	1190	1042	908	519	205	33	6235
	New Haven	A	39.0	0	12	87	347	648	1011	1097	991	871	543	245	45	5897
Del.	Wilmington	A	42.5	0	0	51	270	588	927	980	874	735	387	112	6	4930
D.C.	Washington	A	45.7	0	0	33	217	519	834	871	762	626	288	74	0	4224
Fla.	Apalachicola	C	61.2	0	0	0	16	153	319	347	260	180	33	0	0	1308
	Daytona Beach	A	64.5	0	0	0	0	75	211	248	190	140	15	0	0	879
	Fort Myers	A	68.6	0	0	0	0	24	109	146	101	62	0	0	0	442
	Jacksonville	A	61.9	0	0	0	12	144	310	332	246	174	21	0	0	1239
	Key West	A	73.1	0	0	0	0	0	28	40	31	9	0	0	0	108
	Lakeland	C	66.7	0	0	0	0	57	164	195	146	99	0	0	0	661
	Miami	A	71.1	0	0	0	0	0	65	74	56	19	0	0	0	214
	Miami Beach	C	72.5	0	0	0	0	0	40	56	36	9	0	0	0	141
	Orlando	A	65.7	0	0	0	0	72	198	220	165	105	6	0	0	766
	Pensacola	A	60.4	0	0	0	19	195	353	400	277	183	36	0	0	1463
	Tallahassee	A	60.1	0	0	0	28	198	360	375	286	202	36	0	0	1485
	Tampa	A	66.4	0	0	0	0	60	171	202	148	102	0	0	0	683
	West Palm Beach	A	68.4	0	0	0	0	6	65	87	64	31	0	0	0	253
Ga.	Athens	A	51.8	0	0	12	115	405	632	642	529	431	141	22	0	2929
	Atlanta	A	51.7	0	0	18	124	417	648	636	518	428	147	25	0	2961
	Augusta	A	54.5	0	0	0	78	333	552	549	445	350	90	0	0	2397
	Columbus	A	54.8	0	0	0	87	333	543	552	434	338	96	0	0	2383
	Macon	A	56.2	0	0	0	71	297	502	505	403	295	63	0	0	2136
	Rome	A	49.9	0	24	24	161	474	701	710	577	468	177	34	0	3326
	Savannah	A	57.8	0	0	0	47	246	437	437	353	254	45	0	0	1819
	Thomasville	C	60.0	0	0	0	25	198	366	394	305	208	33	0	0	1529

a Data for United States cities from a publication of the United States Weather Bureau, *Monthly Normals of Temperature, Precipitation and Heating Degree Days, 1962,* are for the period 1931 to 1960 inclusive. These data also include information from the 1963 revisions to this publication, where available.

b Data for airport stations, A, and city stations, C, are both given where available.

c Data for Canadian cities were computed by the Climatology Division, Department of Transport from normal monthly mean temperatures, and the monthly values of heating degree days data were obtained using the National Research Council computer and a method devised by H.C.S. Thom of the United States Weather Bureau. The heating degree days are based on the period from 1931 to 1960.

d For period October to April, inclusive.

e The data for these normals were from the full ten-year period 1951–1960, adjusted to the standard normal period 1931–1960.

TABLE 8.1—Continued

State	Station	Avg. Winter Temp[d]		July	Aug.	Sept.	Oct.	Nov.	Dec.	Jan.	Feb.	Mar.	Apr.	May	June	Yearly Total
Hawaii	Lihue	72.7	A	0	0	0	0	0	0	0	0	0	0	0	0	0
	Honolulu	74.2	A	0	0	0	0	0	0	0	0	0	0	0	0	0
	Hilo	71.9	A	0	0	0	0	0	0	0	0	0	0	0	0	0
Idaho	Boise	39.7	A	0	0	132	415	792	1017	1113	854	722	438	245	81	5809
	Lewiston	41.0	A	0	0	123	403	756	933	1063	815	694	426	239	90	5542
	Pocatello	34.8	A	0	0	172	493	900	1166	1324	1058	905	555	319	141	7033
Ill.	Cairo	47.9	C	0	0	36	164	513	791	856	680	539	195	47	0	3821
	Chicago (O'Hare)	35.8	A	0	12	117	381	807	1166	1265	1086	939	534	260	72	6639
	Chicago (Midway)	37.5	C	0	0	81	326	753	1113	1209	1044	890	480	211	48	6155
	Chicago	38.9	C	0	0	66	279	705	1051	1150	1000	868	489	226	48	5882
	Moline	36.4	A	0	9	99	335	774	1181	1314	1100	918	450	189	39	6408
	Peoria	38.1	A	0	6	87	326	759	1113	1218	1025	849	426	183	33	6025
	Rockford	34.8	A	0	9	114	400	837	1221	1333	1137	961	516	236	60	6830
	Springfield	40.6	A	0	0	72	291	696	1023	1135	935	769	354	136	18	5429
Ind.	Evansville	45.0	A	0	0	66	220	606	896	955	767	620	237	68	0	4435
	Fort Wayne	37.3	A	0	9	105	378	783	1135	1178	1028	890	471	189	39	6205
	Indianapolis	39.6	A	0	0	90	316	723	1051	1113	949	809	432	177	39	5699
	South Bend	36.6	A	0	6	11	372	777	1125	1221	1070	933	525	239	60	6439
Iowa	Burlington	37.6	A	0	0	93	322	768	1135	1259	1042	859	426	177	33	6114
	Des Moines	35.5	A	0	6	96	363	828	1225	1370	1137	915	438	180	30	6588
	Dubuque	32.7	A	12	31	156	450	906	1287	1420	1204	1026	546	260	78	7376
	Sioux City	34.0	A	0	9	108	369	867	1240	1435	1198	989	483	214	39	6951
	Waterloo	32.6	A	12	19	138	428	909	1296	1460	1221	1023	531	229	54	7320
Kans.	Concordia	40.4	A	0	0	57	276	705	1023	1163	935	781	372	149	18	5479
	Dodge City	42.5	A	0	0	33	251	666	939	1051	840	719	354	124	9	4986
	Goodland	37.8	A	0	6	81	381	810	1073	1166	955	884	507	236	42	6141
	Topeka	41.7	A	0	0	57	270	672	980	1122	893	722	330	124	12	5182
	Wichita	44.2	A	0	0	33	229	618	905	1023	804	645	270	87	6	4620
Ky.	Covington	41.4	A	0	0	75	291	669	983	1035	893	756	390	149	24	5265
	Lexington	43.8	A	0	0	54	239	609	902	946	818	685	325	105	0	4683
	Louisville	44.0	A	0	0	54	248	609	890	930	818	682	315	105	9	4660

State	City															Total
La.	Alexandria	A	57.5	0	0	0	56	273	431	471	361	260	69	0	0	1921
	Baton Rouge	A	59.8	0	0	0	31	216	369	409	294	208	33	0	0	1560
	Lake Charles	A	60.5	0	0	0	19	210	341	381	274	195	39	0	0	1459
	New Orleans	A	61.0	0	0	0	19	192	322	363	258	192	39	0	0	1385
	New Orleans	C	61.8	0	0	0	12	165	291	344	241	177	24	0	0	1254
	Shreveport	A	56.2	0	0	0	47	297	477	552	426	304	81	0	0	2184
Me.	Caribou	A	24.4	78	115	336	682	1044	1535	1690	1470	1308	858	468	183	9767
	Portland	A	33.0	12	53	195	508	807	1215	1339	1182	1042	675	372	111	7511
Md.	Baltimore	A	43.7	0	0	48	264	585	905	936	820	679	327	90	0	4654
	Baltimore	C	46.2	0	0	27	189	486	806	859	762	629	288	65	0	4111
	Frederick	A	42.0	0	0	66	307	624	955	995	876	741	384	127	12	5087
Mass.	Boston	A	40.0	0	9	60	316	603	983	1088	972	846	513	208	36	5634
	Nantucket	A	40.2	12	22	93	332	573	896	992	941	896	621	384	129	5891
	Pittsfield	A	32.6	25	59	219	524	831	1231	1339	1196	1063	660	326	105	7578
	Worcester	A	34.7	6	34	147	450	774	1172	1271	1123	998	612	304	78	6969
Mich.	Alpena	A	29.7	68	105	273	580	912	1268	1404	1299	1218	777	446	156	8506
	Detroit (City)	A	37.2	0	0	87	360	738	1088	1181	1058	936	522	220	42	6232
	Detroit (Wayne)	A	37.1	0	0	96	353	738	1088	1194	1061	933	534	239	57	6293
	Detroit (Willow Run)	A	37.2	0	0	90	357	750	1104	1190	1053	921	519	229	45	6258
	Escanaba	C	29.6	59	87	243	539	924	1293	1445	1296	1203	777	456	159	8481
	Flint	A	33.1	16	40	159	465	843	1212	1330	1198	1066	639	319	90	7377
	Grand Rapids	A	34.9	9	28	135	434	804	1147	1259	1134	1011	579	279	75	6894
	Lansing	A	34.8	6	22	138	431	813	1163	1262	1142	1011	579	273	69	6909
	Marquette	C	30.2	59	81	240	527	936	1268	1411	1268	1187	771	468	177	8393
	Muskegon	A	36.0	12	28	120	400	762	1088	1209	1100	995	594	310	78	6696
	Sault Ste. Marie	A	27.7	96	105	279	580	951	1367	1525	1380	1277	810	477	201	9048
Minn.	Duluth	A	23.4	71	109	330	632	1131	1581	1745	1518	1355	840	490	198	10000
	Minneapolis	A	28.3	22	31	189	505	1014	1454	1631	1380	1166	621	288	81	8382
	Rochester	A	28.8	25	34	186	474	1005	1438	1593	1366	1150	630	301	93	8295
Miss.	Jackson	A	55.7	0	0	0	65	315	502	546	414	310	87	0	0	2239
	Meridian	A	55.4	0	0	0	81	339	518	543	417	310	81	0	0	2289
	Vicksburg	C	56.9	0	0	0	53	279	462	512	384	282	69	0	0	2041
Mo.	Columbia	A	42.3	0	0	54	251	651	967	1076	874	716	324	121	12	5046
	Kansas City	A	43.9	0	0	39	220	612	905	1032	818	682	294	109	9	4711
	St. Joseph	A	40.3	0	6	60	285	708	1039	1172	949	769	348	133	15	5484
	St. Louis	A	43.1	0	0	60	251	627	936	1026	848	704	312	121	15	4900
	St. Louis	C	44.8	0	0	36	202	576	884	977	801	651	270	87	0	4484
	Springfield	A	44.5	0	0	45	223	600	877	973	781	660	291	105	6	4900

TABLE 8.1—Continued

State	Station		Avg. Winter Temp[d]	July	Aug.	Sept.	Oct.	Nov.	Dec.	Jan.	Feb.	Mar.	Apr.	May	June	Yearly Total
Mont.	Billings	A	34.5	6	15	186	487	897	1135	1296	1100	970	570	285	102	7049
	Glasgow	A	26.4	31	47	270	608	1104	1466	1711	1439	1187	648	335	150	8996
	Great Falls	A	32.8	28	53	258	543	921	1169	1349	1154	1063	642	384	186	7750
	Havre	A	28.1	28	53	306	595	1065	1367	1584	1364	1181	657	338	162	8700
	Havre	C	29.8	19	37	252	539	1014	1321	1528	1305	1116	612	304	135	8182
	Helena	A	31.1	31	59	294	601	1002	1265	1438	1170	1042	651	381	195	8129
	Kalispell	A	31.4	50	99	321	654	1020	1240	1401	1134	1029	639	397	207	8191
	Miles City	A	31.2	6	6	174	502	972	1296	1504	1252	1057	579	276	99	7723
	Missoula	A	31.5	34	74	303	651	1035	1287	1420	1120	970	621	391	219	8125
Neb.	Grand Island	A	36.0	0	6	108	381	834	1172	1314	1089	908	462	211	45	6530
	Lincoln	C	38.8	0	6	75	301	726	1066	1237	1016	834	402	171	30	5864
	Norfolk	A	34.0	9	0	111	397	873	1234	1414	1179	983	498	233	48	6979
	North Platte	A	35.5	0	6	123	440	885	1166	1271	1039	930	519	248	57	6684
	Omaha	A	35.6	0	12	105	357	828	1175	1355	1126	939	465	208	42	6612
	Scottsbluff	A	35.9	0	0	138	459	876	1128	1231	1008	921	552	285	75	6673
	Valentine	A	32.6	9	12	165	493	942	1237	1395	1176	1045	579	288	84	7425
Nev.	Elko	A	34.0	9	34	225	561	924	1197	1314	1036	911	621	409	192	7433
	Ely	A	33.1	28	43	234	592	939	1184	1308	1075	977	672	456	225	7733
	Las Vegas	A	53.5	0	0	0	78	387	617	688	487	335	111	6	0	2709
	Reno	A	39.3	43	87	204	490	801	1026	1073	823	729	510	357	189	6332
	Winnemucca	A	36.7	0	34	210	536	876	1091	1172	916	837	573	363	153	6761
N.H.	Concord	A	33.0	6	50	177	505	822	1240	1358	1184	1032	636	298	75	7383
	Mt. Washington Obsv		15.2	493	536	720	1057	1341	1742	1820	1663	1652	1260	930	603	13817
N.J.	Atlantic City	A	43.2	0	0	39	251	549	880	936	848	741	420	133	15	4812
	Newark	A	42.8	0	0	30	248	573	921	983	876	729	381	118	0	4589
	Trenton	C	42.4	0	0	57	264	576	924	989	885	753	399	121	12	4980
N.M.	Albuquerque	A	45.0	0	0	12	229	642	868	930	703	595	288	81	0	4348
	Clayton	A	42.0	0	6	66	310	699	899	986	812	747	429	183	21	5158
	Raton	A	38.1	9	28	126	431	825	1048	1116	904	834	543	301	63	6228
	Roswell	A	47.5	0	0	18	202	573	806	840	641	481	201	31	0	3793
	Silver City	A	48.0	0	0	6	183	525	729	791	605	518	261	87	0	3705

State	City															
N.Y.	Albany	A	34.6	0	0	19	138	440	777	1194	1311	1156	992	564	239	45	6875
	Albany	C	37.2	0	0	9	102	375	699	1104	1218	1072	908	498	186	30	6201
	Binghamton	A	33.9	22	22	65	201	471	810	1184	1277	1154	1045	645	313	99	7286
	Binghamton	C	36.6	0	0	28	141	406	732	1107	1190	1081	949	543	229	45	6451
	Buffalo	C	34.5	19	19	37	141	440	777	1156	1256	1145	1039	645	329	78	7062
	New York (Cent. Park)	C	42.8	0	0	0	30	233	540	902	986	885	760	408	118	9	4871
	New York (La Guardia)	A	43.1	0	0	0	27	223	528	887	973	879	750	414	124	6	4811
	New York (Kennedy)	A	41.4	0	0	0	36	248	564	933	1029	935	815	480	167	12	5219
	Rochester	A	35.4	9	9	31	126	415	747	1125	1234	1123	1014	597	279	48	6748
	Schenectady	C	35.4	0	0	22	123	422	756	1159	1283	1131	970	543	211	30	6650
	Syracuse	A	35.2	6	6	28	132	415	744	1153	1271	1140	1004	570	248	45	6756
N.C.	Asheville	C	46.7	0	0	0	48	245	555	775	784	683	592	273	87	0	4042
	Cape Hatteras		53.3	0	0	0	0	78	273	521	580	518	440	177	25	0	2612
	Charlotte	A	50.4	0	0	0	6	124	438	691	691	582	481	156	22	0	3191
	Greensboro	A	47.5	0	0	0	33	192	513	778	784	672	552	234	47	0	3805
	Raleigh	A	49.4	0	0	0	21	164	450	716	725	616	487	180	34	0	3393
	Wilmington	A	54.6	0	0	0	0	74	291	521	546	462	357	96	0	0	2347
	Winston-Salem	A	48.4	0	0	0	21	171	483	747	753	652	524	207	37	0	3595
N.D.	Bismarck	A	26.6	34	28	222	577	1083	1463	1708	1442	1203	645	329	117	8851
	Devils Lake	C	22.4	40	53	273	642	1191	1634	1872	1579	1345	753	381	138	9901
	Fargo	A	24.8	28	37	219	574	1107	1569	1789	1520	1262	690	332	99	9226
	Williston	A	25.2	31	43	261	601	1122	1513	1758	1473	1262	681	357	141	9243
Ohio	Akron-Canton	A	38.1	0	9	96	381	726	1070	1138	1016	871	489	202	39	6037
	Cincinnati	C	45.1	0	0	39	208	558	862	915	790	642	294	96	6	4410
	Cleveland	A	37.2	9	25	105	384	738	1088	1159	1047	918	552	260	66	6351
	Columbus	A	39.7	0	6	84	347	714	1039	1088	949	809	426	171	27	5660
	Columbus	C	41.5	0	0	57	285	651	977	1032	902	760	396	136	15	5211
	Dayton	A	39.8	0	6	78	310	696	1045	1097	955	809	429	167	30	5622
	Mansfield	A	36.9	9	22	114	397	768	1110	1169	1042	924	543	245	60	6403
	Sandusky	C	39.1	0	6	66	313	684	1032	1107	991	868	495	198	36	5796
	Toledo	A	36.4	0	16	117	406	792	1138	1200	1056	924	543	242	60	6494
	Youngstown	A	36.8	6	19	120	412	771	1104	1169	1047	921	540	248	60	6417
Okla.	Oklahoma City	A	48.3	0	0	15	164	498	766	868	664	527	189	34	0	3725
	Tulsa	A	47.7	0	0	18	158	522	787	893	683	539	213	47	0	3860

TABLE 8.1—Continued

State	Station		Avg. Winter Temp[d]	July	Aug.	Sept.	Oct.	Nov.	Dec.	Jan.	Feb.	Mar.	Apr.	May	June	Yearly Total
Ore.	Astoria	A	45.6	146	130	210	375	561	679	753	622	636	480	363	231	5186
	Burns	C	35.9	12	37	210	515	867	1113	1246	988	856	570	366	177	6957
	Eugene	A	45.6	34	34	129	366	585	719	803	627	589	426	279	135	4726
	Meacham	A	34.2	84	124	288	580	918	1091	1209	1005	983	726	527	339	7874
	Medford	A	43.2	0	0	78	372	678	871	918	697	642	432	242	78	5008
	Pendleton	A	42.6	0	0	111	350	711	884	1017	773	617	396	205	63	5127
	Portland	A	45.6	25	28	114	335	597	735	825	644	586	396	245	105	4635
	Portland	C	47.4	12	16	75	267	534	679	769	594	536	351	198	78	4109
	Roseburg	A	46.3	22	16	105	329	567	713	766	608	570	405	267	123	4491
	Salem	A	45.4	37	31	111	338	594	729	822	647	611	417	273	144	4754
Pa.	Allentown	A	38.9	0	0	90	353	693	1045	1116	1002	849	471	167	24	5810
	Erie	A	36.8	0	25	102	391	714	1063	1169	1081	973	585	288	60	6451
	Harrisburg	A	41.2	0	0	63	298	648	992	1045	907	766	396	124	12	5251
	Philadelphia	A	41.8	0	0	60	297	620	965	1016	889	747	392	118	40	5144
	Philadelphia	C	44.5	0	0	30	205	513	856	924	823	691	351	93	0	4486
	Pittsburgh	A	38.4	0	9	105	375	726	1063	1119	1002	874	480	195	39	5987
	Pittsburgh	C	42.2	0	0	60	291	615	930	983	885	763	390	124	12	5053
	Reading	C	42.4	0	0	54	257	597	939	1001	885	735	372	105	0	4945
	Scranton	A	37.2	0	19	132	434	762	1104	1156	1028	893	498	195	33	6254
	Williamsport	A	38.5	0	9	111	375	717	1073	1122	1002	856	468	177	24	5934
R.I.	Block Island	A	40.1	0	16	78	307	594	902	1020	955	877	612	344	99	5804
	Providence	A	38.8	0	16	96	372	660	1023	1110	988	868	534	236	51	5954
S.C.	Charleston	A	56.4	0	0	0	59	282	471	487	389	291	54	0	0	2033
	Charleston	C	57.9	0	0	0	34	210	425	443	367	273	42	0	0	1794
	Columbia	A	54.0	0	0	0	84	345	577	570	470	357	81	0	0	2484
	Florence	A	54.5	0	0	0	78	315	552	552	459	347	84	0	0	2387
	Greenville-Spartanburg	A	51.6	0	0	6	121	399	651	660	546	446	132	19	0	2980
S.D.	Huron	A	28.8	9	12	165	508	1014	1432	1628	1355	1125	600	288	87	8223
	Rapid City	A	33.4	22	12	165	481	897	1172	1333	1145	1051	615	326	126	7345
	Sioux Falls	A	30.6	19	25	168	462	972	1361	1544	1285	1082	573	270	78	7839

State	City		Temp													
Tenn.	Bristol	A	46.2	0	0	51	236	573	828	828	700	598	261	68	0	4143
	Chattanooga	A	50.3	0	0	18	143	468	698	722	577	453	150	25	0	3254
	Knoxville	A	49.2	0	0	30	171	489	725	732	613	493	198	43	0	3494
	Memphis	C	50.5	0	0	18	130	447	698	729	585	456	147	22	0	3232
	Memphis	A	51.6	0	0	12	102	396	648	710	568	434	129	16	0	3015
	Nashville	A	48.9	0	0	30	158	495	732	778	644	512	189	40	0	3578
	Oak Ridge	C	47.7	0	0	39	192	531	772	778	669	552	228	56	0	3817
Tex.	Abilene	A	53.9	0	0	0	99	366	586	642	470	347	114	0	0	2624
	Amarillo	A	47.0	0	0	18	205	570	797	877	664	546	252	56	0	3985
	Austin	A	59.1	0	0	0	31	225	388	468	325	223	51	0	0	1711
	Brownsville	A	67.7	0	0	0	0	66	149	205	106	74	0	0	0	600
	Corpus Christi	A	64.6	0	0	0	0	120	291	291	174	109	0	0	0	914
	Dallas	A	55.3	0	0	0	62	321	524	601	440	319	90	6	0	2363
	El Paso	A	52.9	0	0	0	84	414	648	685	445	319	105	0	0	2700
	Fort Worth	A	55.1	0	0	0	65	324	536	614	448	319	99	0	0	2405
	Galveston	A	62.2	0	0	0	6	147	276	350	263	189	33	0	0	1274
	Galveston	C	62.0	0	0	0	0	138	270	360	258	189	30	0	0	1235
	Houston	A	61.0	0	0	0	6	183	307	363	258	192	36	0	0	1396
	Houston	C	62.0	0	0	0	0	165	288	384	258	174	30	0	0	1278
	Laredo	A	66.0	0	0	0	0	105	217	267	134	74	0	0	0	797
	Lubbock	A	48.8	0	0	18	174	513	744	800	613	484	201	31	0	3578
	Midland	A	53.8	0	0	0	87	381	592	651	468	322	90	0	0	2591
	Port Arthur	A	60.5	0	0	0	22	207	329	384	274	192	39	0	0	1447
	San Angelo	A	56.0	0	0	0	68	318	536	567	412	288	66	0	0	2255
	San Antonio	A	60.1	0	0	0	31	204	363	428	286	195	39	0	0	1546
	Victoria	A	62.7	0	0	0	6	150	270	344	230	152	21	0	0	1173
	Waco	A	57.2	0	0	0	43	270	456	536	389	270	66	0	0	2030
	Wichita Falls	A	53.0	0	0	0	99	381	632	698	518	378	120	6	0	2832
Utah	Milford	A	36.5	0	0	99	443	867	1141	1252	988	822	519	279	87	6497
	Salt Lake City	A	38.4	0	0	81	419	849	1082	1172	910	763	459	233	84	6052
	Wendover	A	39.1	0	0	48	372	822	1091	1178	902	729	408	177	51	5778
Vt.	Burlington	A	29.4	28	65	207	539	891	1349	1513	1333	1187	714	353	90	8269
Va.	Cape Henry	C	50.0	0	0	0	112	360	645	694	633	536	246	53	0	3279
	Lynchburg	A	46.0	0	0	51	223	540	822	849	731	605	267	78	0	4166
	Norfolk	A	49.2	0	0	0	136	408	698	738	655	533	216	37	0	3421
	Richmond	A	47.3	0	0	36	214	495	784	815	703	546	219	53	0	3865
	Roanoke	A	46.1	0	0	51	229	549	825	834	722	614	261	65	0	4150

TABLE 8.1—Continued

State	Station	Avg. Winter Temp[d]	July	Aug.	Sept.	Oct.	Nov.	Dec.	Jan.	Feb.	Mar.	Apr.	May	June	Yearly Total
Wash.	Olympia	A	44.2	68	71	198	422	636	753	834	675	645	450	307	177	5236
	Seattle-Tacoma	A	44.2	56	62	162	391	633	750	828	678	657	474	295	159	5145
	Seattle	C	46.9	50	47	129	329	543	657	738	599	577	396	242	117	4424
	Spokane	A	36.5	9	25	168	493	879	1082	1231	980	834	531	288	135	6655
	Walla Walla	C	43.8	0	0	87	310	681	843	986	745	589	342	177	45	4805
	Yakima	A	39.1	0	12	144	450	828	1039	1163	868	713	435	220	69	5941
W. Va.	Charleston	A	44.8	0	0	63	254	591	865	880	770	648	300	96	9	4476
	Elkins	A	40.1	9	25	135	400	729	992	1008	896	791	444	198	48	5675
	Huntington	A	45.0	0	0	63	257	585	856	880	764	636	294	99	12	4446
	Parkersburg	C	43.5	0	0	60	264	606	905	942	826	691	339	115	6	4754
Wisc.	Green Bay	A	30.3	28	50	174	484	924	1333	1494	1313	1141	654	335	99	8029
	La Crosse	A	31.5	12	19	153	437	924	1339	1504	1277	1070	540	245	69	7589
	Madison	A	30.9	25	40	174	474	930	1330	1473	1274	1113	618	310	102	7863
	Milwaukee	A	32.6	43	47	174	471	876	1252	1376	1193	1054	642	372	135	7635
Wyo.	Casper	A	33.4	6	16	192	524	942	1169	1290	1084	1020	657	381	129	7410
	Cheyenne	A	34.2	28	37	219	543	909	1085	1212	1042	1026	702	428	150	7381
	Lander	A	31.4	6	19	204	555	1020	1299	1417	1145	1017	654	381	153	7870
	Sheridan	A	32.5	25	31	219	539	948	1200	1355	1154	1051	642	366	150	7680
Alta.	Banff	C	—	220	295	498	797	1185	1485	1624	1364	1237	855	589	402	10551
	Calgary	A	—	109	186	402	719	1110	1389	1575	1379	1268	798	477	291	9703
	Edmonton	A	—	74	180	411	738	1215	1603	1810	1520	1330	765	400	222	10268
	Lethbridge	A	—	56	112	318	611	1011	1277	1497	1291	1159	696	403	213	8644
B.C.	Kamloops	A	—	22	40	189	546	894	1138	1314	1057	818	462	217	102	6799
	Prince George*	A	—	236	251	444	747	1110	1420	1612	1319	1122	747	468	279	9755
	Prince Rupert	C	—	273	248	339	539	708	868	936	808	812	648	493	357	7029
	Vancouver*	A	—	81	87	219	456	657	787	862	723	676	501	310	156	5515
	Victoria*	A	—	136	140	225	462	663	775	840	718	691	504	341	204	5699
	Victoria	C	—	172	184	243	426	607	723	805	668	660	487	354	250	5579
Man.	Brandon*	A	—	47	90	357	747	1290	1792	2034	1737	1476	837	431	198	11036
	Churchill	A	—	360	375	681	1082	1620	2248	2558	2277	2130	1569	1153	675	16728
	The Pas	C	—	59	127	429	831	1440	1981	2232	1853	1624	969	508	228	12281
	Winnipeg	A	—	38	71	322	683	1251	1757	2008	1719	1465	813	405	147	10679

N.B.	Fredericton*	A	—	78	68	234	592	915	1392	1541	1379	1172	753	406	141	8671
	Moncton	C	—	62	105	276	611	891	1342	1482	1336	1194	789	468	171	8727
	St. John	C	—	109	102	246	527	807	1194	1370	1229	1097	756	490	249	8219
Nfld.	Argentia	A	—	260	167	294	564	750	1001	1159	1085	1091	879	707	483	8440
	Corner Brook	C	—	102	133	324	642	873	1194	1358	1283	1212	885	639	333	8978
	Gander	A	—	121	152	330	670	909	1231	1370	1266	1243	939	657	366	9254
	Goose*	A	—	130	205	444	843	1227	1745	1947	1689	1494	1074	741	348	11887
	St. John's*	A	—	186	180	342	651	831	1113	1262	1170	1187	927	710	432	8991
N.W.T.	Aklavik	C	—	273	459	807	1414	2064	2530	2632	2336	2282	1674	1063	483	18017
	Fort Norman	C	—	164	341	666	1234	1959	2474	2592	2209	2058	1386	732	294	16109
	Resolution Island	C	—	843	831	900	1113	1311	1724	2021	1850	1817	1488	1181	942	16021
N.S.	Halifax	C	—	58	51	180	457	710	1074	1213	1122	1030	742	487	237	7361
	Sydney	A	—	62	71	219	518	765	1113	1262	1206	1150	840	567	276	8049
	Yarmouth	A	—	102	115	225	471	696	1029	1156	1065	1004	726	493	258	7340
Ont.	Cochrane	C	—	96	180	405	760	1233	1776	1978	1701	1528	963	570	222	11412
	Fort William	A	—	90	133	366	694	1140	1597	1792	1557	1380	876	543	237	10405
	Kapuskasing	C	—	74	171	405	756	1245	1807	2037	1735	1562	978	580	222	11572
	Kitchener	C	—	16	59	177	505	855	1234	1342	1226	1101	663	322	66	7566
	London	A	—	12	43	159	477	837	1206	1305	1198	1066	648	332	66	7349
	North Bay	C	—	37	90	267	608	990	1507	1680	1463	1277	780	400	120	9219
	Ottawa	C	—	25	81	222	567	936	1469	1624	1441	1231	708	341	90	8735
	Toronto	C	—	7	18	151	439	760	1111	1233	1119	1013	616	298	62	6827
P.E.I.	Charlottetown	C	—	40	53	198	518	804	1215	1380	1274	1169	813	496	204	8164
	Summerside	C	—	47	84	216	546	840	1246	1438	1291	1206	841	518	216	8488
Que.	Arvida	C	—	102	136	327	682	1074	1659	1879	1619	1407	891	521	231	10528
	Montreal*	A	—	9	43	165	521	882	1392	1566	1381	1175	684	316	69	8203
	Montreal	C	—	16	28	165	496	864	1355	1510	1328	1138	657	288	54	7899
	Quebec*	A	—	56	84	273	636	996	1516	1665	1477	1296	819	428	126	9372
	Quebec	C	—	40	68	243	592	972	1473	1612	1418	1228	780	400	111	8937
Sasks	Prince Albert	A	—	81	136	414	797	1368	1872	2108	1763	1559	867	446	219	11630
	Regina	A	—	78	93	360	741	1284	1711	1965	1687	1473	804	409	201	10806
	Saskatoon	C	—	56	87	372	750	1302	1758	2006	1689	1463	798	403	186	10870
Y.T.	Dawson	C	—	164	326	645	1197	1875	2415	2561	2150	1838	1068	570	258	15067
	Mayo Landing	C	—	208	366	648	1135	1794	2325	2427	1992	1665	1020	580	294	14454

For purposes of clarification, the previous formula may be rearranged

$$\text{lb steam} = \frac{\dfrac{H}{t_i - t_o} \times (t - t_a) \times N - (Q \times N)}{S} \qquad \text{(1-a)}$$

Practical application of this formula may be demonstrated by the following example:

The maximum hourly heat loss of a building has been calculated at 2,400,000 Btu when the outside temperature is zero F and the inside temperature is 70 F.

The inside temperature during the heating season will be maintained at 72 F from 7 A.M. to 5 P.M. Monday through Saturday. A minimum temperature of 65 F will be maintained during the non-business hours.

Calculate the steam requirements from September 1 to June 1, during which period the average mean outside temperature is 40 F.

Solution

Rate of heat loss as per design condition

$$= \frac{H}{t_i - t_o} = \frac{2,400,000}{70-0}$$
$$= 34,286 \; Btu \; per \; degree \; difference.$$

Where variable inside temperatures are maintained, the average temperature may be calculated from the formula.

$$\frac{t_1 N_1 + t_2 N_2 + - - - - t_n N_n}{N_1 + N_2 + - - - - - N_n} \qquad \text{(1-b)}$$

Where:

$t_1 N_1$ = Temperature maintained $\times$ N_1 hours.
$t_2 N_2$ = Different temperature maintained $\times$ N_1 hours.
Business hours   =   2,340 (temperature maintained 72 F)
Nonbusiness hours = Sunday 936 (assumed temperature 65 F)
                               Night 3,276 (estimated temperature 67 F)
                               6,552

From formula 1-b,   then average inside temperature

$$= \frac{(72 \times 2,340) + (65 \times 936) + (67 \times 3,276)}{2,340 + 936 + 3,276} = 68.5 \; F$$

The average mean outside temperature as obtained from Weather Bureau records for locality of building = 40 F.
Average temperature difference for period = 68.5 − 40 = 28.5 F
Number of hours in period, N = 6,552
Number of Btu utilized per lb of steam, S, usually can be assumed as 1,000.
Heat gain was established as follows:

$$Q = A + B + C \qquad \text{(1-c)}$$

A = Lighting load kW $\times$ Btuh/kW $\times$ 80% use factor
B = Miscellaneous Power Equipment kW $\times$ Btuh/kW $\times$ 50% use factor
C = People Load Number persons $\times$ Btuh/Person

From formula 1-c, Q was estimated as follows:

A = 14.65 kW × 3,413 × 80%
B = 30 kW × 3,413 × 50%
C = 120 Persons × 200 Btuh
A = 40,000 Btuh
B = 51,000 Btuh
C = 24,000 Btuh
Q = 115,000 Btuh

From formula 1-a,   we have:

$$\text{lb steam} = \frac{34{,}286 \times 28.5 \times 6{,}552 - 753{,}480{,}000}{1{,}000}$$

$$= 5{,}648{,}813 \text{ lb per season}$$

The calculated heat-loss method provides a means for a specific approach to the rather complex problem of estimating steam requirements and permits a separate analysis of the many factors which determine heat loss. In the case of structures of unusual design and operation, it is sometimes the only method applicable. It is emphasized, however, that the accuracy must depend on the ability to estimate average rate of heat loss and average temperature difference. It is pointed out that the method assumes constant rate of heat loss, therefore constant conditions of sun effect, wind velocity, amount of ventilation, relative humidity, and all other factors which affect the hourly heat loss excepting the variable of temperature differential. Any change in these assumed constants must, therefore, be considered. It should also be noted that sun effect is usually not included in heat-loss calculations.

FUEL USE METHOD

Records of fuel uses of a plant are frequently the most reliable source of data in making district steam estimates, especially where numerous complicated steam-process loads are supplied in conjunction with space heating.

The ratio of the annual amount of district steam to the former fuel uses of a given plant may be expressed as lb. of steam per unit of fuel such as lb. of coal, gal. of oil, or cu. ft. of gas, and average ratios thus established for estimating purposes. Any comparison should be made only between plants using the same type of fuel as the respective ratios are affected by the relative boiler efficiencies and flexibilities of operation normally attained with various types of fuels. This ratio, even for the same type of fuel, is further subject to variation in the method of operation and utilization of the district steam service as well as the design and former method of operation of the plant, and, at best, these ratios can only be used as a means of determining average conditions.

Ratios of district steam to fuel are generally lower than those indicated by boiler efficiency tests. Such tests usually are based on short periods of operation under favorable conditions of loading and maintenance. Numerous savings are reflected in the district steam-fuel ratio, such as elimination of boiler-plant losses, lower steam use due to more effective and flexible methods of control, utilization of heat in condensate, and elimination of banking losses.

COMPUTER ANALYSIS METHOD

The digital computer provides an economical, high speed calculation capability. When applied to the problem of estimating heating requirements, it allows more sophisticated methods to be used. For accurate energy determinations, the hour-by-hour method is mandatory. The computer provides a method of evaluating the effects of wind, sun, cloud cover, internal heat sources, etc., on the total heating load. Such items are now either ignored or considered by an adjustment factor. The application of a computer increases the need for accurate input data if meaningful output data is to be obtained.

COMMERCIAL AND INDUSTRIAL PROCESSES

District steam service is widely used in a great many commercial and industrial applications. A number of tables and informative data are presented to assist the design engineer in obtaining a better understanding of steam requirements for the process equipment listed. The net steam consumption of the appliances in the tabulation is estimated, based upon requirements and the average allowances for line and other losses that normally occur between the steam source and the load. These losses increase as the demand is smaller and the operation of device is more intermittent as indicated below:

Where hourly load is less than   34.0 lb/hr   losses 25%
Where hourly load is from   34–170 lb/hr   losses 15%
Where hourly load is over   170 lb/hr   losses 10%

This variation in losses is based upon the fact that smaller appliances have greater relative lengths of supply piping, and the ratio of exposed surface to the inside flow capacity is greater (see Table 8.2).

STEAM REQUIREMENTS FOR AIR-CONDITIONING

Steam use for summer air-conditioning varies widely due to methods of application. The general type of system, whether absorption, steam turbine driven compressor or steam jet, the cost of electricity and availability of adequate cooling water in general, determine the specific method of design and limit data on steam usage to specific installations.

BUILDING SPACE CONDITIONING

No two buildings are identical. As a result, every heating and space conditioning system must be designed to meet the needs of a unique situation. A designer, with knowledge of the particular needs of the building in question, is best equipped to determine the specifics of HVAC for a building. This discussion of building heating, ventilating and air-conditioning systems will be of a generally descriptive nature for this reason.

Traditional Steam Systems

Although heating systems using direct radiation are still found in many older buildings, they are seldom employed in modern systems. These direct radiation systems have been classified by pressure, method of condensate return and piping arrangement. Operating pressures for such systems may be low pressure (0 to 15 psig), high pressure (over 15 psig), vapor and vacuum systems (atmospheric and below).

When steam is introduced into the distribution piping at a low point, the system is called an upfeed system, when the steam is introduced at a high level it is a downfeed system. The piping distribution of these older systems was either one-pipe or two-pipe.

In the one-pipe system, steam and condensate flow in the same direction in a single main but in opposite directions in risers and radiator connections.

TABLE 8.2

STEAM CONSUMPTION OF INDUSTRIAL AND COMMERCIAL APPLIANCES

	Operating Pressure lb	Lb per hr	
		In Use	Maximum
Bakeries			
Dough room trough, 8 ft long	10.0	3.6	
Proof boxes, 500 cu ft capacity		7.1	
Ovens: Peel or Dutch Type	10.0		
White bread, 120 sq ft surface		29.3	
Rye bread, 10 sq ft surface		58.6	
Master baker ovens		29.3	
Century Reel, w/pb per 100 lb bread		29.3	
Rotary ovens, per deck		29.3	
Bennett 400, single deck		44.0	
Hubbard (any size)		58.6	
Middleby-Marshall, W/pb		58.6	
Baker-Perkins travel ovens, long tray (per 100 lb)		13.0	
Baker-Perkins travel ovens, short tray (per 100 lb)		29.3	
General Electric		20.1	
Fish Duothermic Rotary, per deck		58.6	
Revolving ovens:			
8–10 bun pan		29.3	
12–18 bun pan		58.6	
18–28 bun pan		87.9	
Bottle Washing	5.0		
Soft drinks, beer, etc.			310.0
Milk quarts, per 100 cases per hr			58.6
Candy and Chocolate	70.0		
Candy cooking, 30 gal. cooker, 1 hr, 325 deg.		46.9	
Chocolate melting, jacketed, 24″ dia.		29.3	
Chocolate dip kettles, per 10 sq ft tank surface		29.3	
Chocolate tempering, tops mixing, each 20 sq ft active surface		29.3	
Candy kettle per sq ft of jacket	30.0		60.0
Candy kettle per sq ft of jacket	75.0		100.0
Creameries and Dairies			
Creamery cans 3 per min			310.0
Pasteurizer, per 100 gal heated 20 min			232.5
Laundry Equipment	100.0		
Vacuum stills, per 10 gal		16.0	
Spotting board, trouser stretcher		29.3	
Dress finisher, overcoat shaper, ea.		58.6	
Jacket finisher, Susie Z, ea.		44.0	
Air vacuum finishing board, 18″ Mushroom Topper, ea.		20.1	
Steam irons, each		4.3	
Flat Iron Workers			
48″ × 120″, 1 cylinder		248.0	
48″ × 120″, 2 cylinder		310.0	
4-Roll, 100 to 120″		217.0	
6-Roll, 100 to 120″		341.0	
8-Roll, 100 to 120″		465.0	
Shirt Equipment			
Single cuff, neckband, yoke No. 3 ea.		7.1	
Double sleeve		13.0	
Body		29.3	
Bosom		44.0	
Dry Rooms			
Blanket		20.1	
Conveyor, per loop. approx.		7.1	
Truck, per door, approx.		58.6	
Curtain, 50 × 114		29.3	
Curtain, 64 × 130		58.6	
Starch cooker, per 10 gal. cap.		7.5	
Starcher, per 10″ length, approx.		5.2	
Laundry pressers, per 10″ length, approx.		7.1	
Collar equipment: Collar and Cuff Ironer	100.0	21.6	
Deodorizer		87.9	
Wind Whip, Single		58.6	
Wind Whip, Double		87.9	

TABLE 8.2—*Continued*

	Operating Pressure lb	Lb per hr	
		In Use	Maximum
Tumblers:			
Huebsch, 36″ per 12″ length		29.3	
Vorcone, 42″ per 15″ length		44.0	
Vorcone, 30″ × 40″		73.3	
Vorcone, 46″ × 120″		310.0	
Presses, central vacuum, 42″		20.1	
Presses, steam 42″		29.3	
Puff Irons, ea.		7.1	
Tumblers, General Usage			
Other Source			
36″, per 10″ length, approx.		29.3	
40″, per 10″ length, approx.		38.1	
42″, per 10″ length, approx.		52.7	
Dishwashers	10–30		
2-Compartment tub type			58.6
Large conveyor or roller type			58.6
Autosan, colt, depending on size		29.3	117.2
Champion, depending on size		58.6	310.0
Hobart Crescent, depending on size		29.3	186.0
Fan Spray, depending on size		58.6	248.0
Crescent manual steam control	30.0		
Hobart model AM-5	10.0		
Dishwashing machine	15–20	60–70	
Hospital Equipment	40–50		
Stills, per 100 gal distilled water		102.6	
Sterilizers, bed pan		2.9	
Sterilizers, dressing, per 10″ length, approx.		7.1	
Sterilizers, instrument, per 100 cu in approx.		2.9	
Sterilizers, water, per 10 gal approx.		5.8	
Disinfecting Ovens, Double Door:			
Up to 50 cu ft, per 10 cu ft approx.		29.3	
50 to 100 cu ft, per 10 cu ft		21.6	
100 and up, per 10 cu ft		16.0	
Sterilizers, Non-Pressure Type	40.0		
For bottles or pasteurization		51.0	69.0
Start with water at 70 F maintained for 20 minutes at boiling at a depth of 3″			
Instruments and Utensils:	40.0		
Start with water at 70 F, boil vigorously for 20 min:			
Depth 3½″: Size 8 × 9 × 18″		27.0	27.0
Depth 3½″: Size 9 × 20 × 10″		30.0	30.0
Depth 4″: Size 10 × 12 × 22″		39.0	39.0
Depth 4″: Size 12 × 16 × 24″		60.0	60.0
Depth 4′: Size 10 × 12 × 36″		66.0	66.0
Depth 10″: Size 16 × 15 × 20″		92.0	92.0
Depth 10″: Size 20 × 20 × 24″		144.0	144.0
Average steam cables	50.0	102.0	
Tire Shops			
American, Bacon, Lodi Machines	60.0		
Truck molds, large		87.9	
Truck molds, medium		58.6	
Passenger molds		29.3	
Sections, per section		7.1	
Plastic Molding			
Each 12 to 15 sq ft platen surface	125.0	29.3	
Paper Manufacture			
Corrugators per 1,000 sq ft	175.0	29.3	
Wood pulp paper, per 100 lb paper	50.0	372.0	
Restaurant Equipment (kitchen equipment)			
Standard steam tables, per ft length		36.6	
Standard steam tables, per 20 sq ft tank		29.3	
Bain Marie, per ft length, 30″ wide		13.0	
Bain Marie, per 10 sq ft tank		29.3	
Coffee urns, per 10 gal., cold make-up		13.0	
3 compartment egg boiler		13.0	

TABLE 8.2—*Continued*

	Operating Pressure lb	Lb per hr	
		In Use	Maximum
Oyster steamers		13.0	
Clam or lobster steamer		29.3	
Steam Jacketed Kettles	5–20		
10 gal capacity		13.0	
25 gal stock kettle		29.3	
40 gal stock kettle		44.0	
60 gal stock kettle		58.6	
Plate and Dish Warmers			
Per 100 sq ft shelf		58.6	
Per 20 cu ft shelf		29.3	
Warming ovens, per 20 cu ft		29.3	
Direct vegetable steamer, per compartment		29.3	
Potato steamer		29.3	
Morandi Proctor, 30 compartment, no return		87.9	
Pot sink, steam jets, average use		29.3	
Silver burnishers, Tahara		58.6	

There must be a continuous slope to the main in the direction of steam flow. Air vent valves are necessary with this system. A typical one-pipe system diagram is shown in Figure 8.3.

In the two-pipe system, separate mains are used for the steam supply and for the condensate. This system may use traps or employ a vacuum pump for operation at or below atmospheric pressure. A diagram of a basic two-pipe system is shown in Figure 8.4 and one for a vacuum system is shown in Figure 8.5. When equipped with thermostatic traps, the two-pipe system is referred to as a vapor systems.

Commercial building design over the past decade has included significant increases in lighting levels and an associated growth in internal heat gain. Coupled with a trend towards higher population density, increased fenestration and the resultant requirement for added ventilation increased lighting load has brought about major changes in the heating function.

Heating has become a part of total space conditioning which has to include all phases of environmental control—heating, ventilating, cooling, humidification, dehumidification, and air cleaning. The higher internal heat gains have greatly altered the characteristics of energy requirements for heating. In many cases, such inherent gains are adequate to supply all the heating needed during normal occupancy periods.

In practice, however, it is common to have an excess of heat in one area of the building and a deficiency in another. Consequently, a variety of systems have been developed to redistribute the excess to the area of deficiency.

The recent rise in concern for energy conservation has brought with it the development of a vast array of new products designed to maximize energy efficiency. New system concepts and configurations are evolving rapidly which incorporate these products, passive use of solar energy and more efficient heat recovery equipment.

Basic HVAC Systems

Several basic types of heating, ventilating and air-conditioning (HVAC) systems exist for use in commercial buildings. A wide variety of system combinations and variations are currently in operation. One multi-story building may use all the basic systems in various forms and may also have

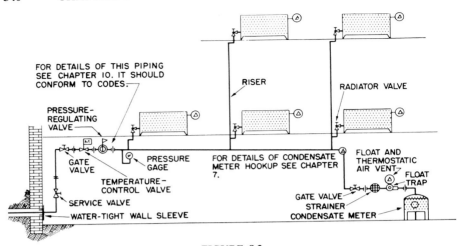

FIGURE 8.3

One-pipe gravity heating system using condensate meter

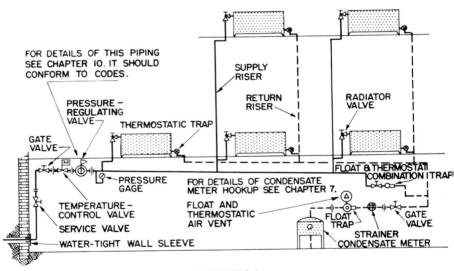

FIGURE 8.4

Two-pipe gravity heating system using condensate meter

unconditioned space. There is no one best system or combination of systems. Each installation must be appraised individually.

A general discussion of some of these systems is provided below.

All Air Systems

An all-air system is defined as a system providing complete sensible heating and cooling and latent cooling utilizing only air to the conditioned space. The piping between the refrigerating and/or heat producing devices and the air handling device is generally ignored in this context. No additional cooling is

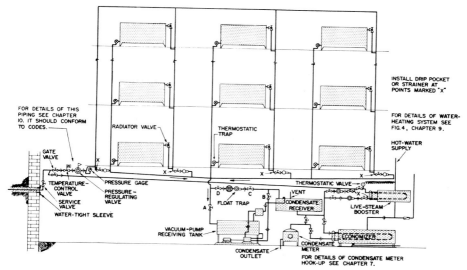

FIGURE 8.5

Vacuum system

required at the zone. Heating may be accomplished by the same air stream either in the central system or at a particular zone. In some applications, heating is accomplished by a separate air, water, steam, or electric heating system. The term zone implies a provision or the need for separate thermostatic control, while the term room implies a partitioned area which may or may not require separate control.

All-air systems may be briefly classified and are discussed here-in in two basic categories, single-path systems and dual-path systems. Single-path systems are those which contain the main heating and cooling coils in a series flow air path, using a common duct distribution system at a common air temperature to feed all terminal apparatus. Dual-path systems are those which contain the main heating and the cooling coils in a parallel flow, or series-parallel flow air path, using either: a separate cold and warm air duct distribution system, which is blended at the terminal apparatus (dual-duct systems); or, a separate supply duct to each zone, with blending of warm and cold air at the main supply fan.

System characteristics may be broken down as follows:
1. Single-path
   a. Single duct, constant volume,
   b. Single duct, variable volume,
   c. Single duct, reheat.
2. Dual-path
   a. Dual-duct (including dual-duct, variable volume),
   b. Multizone.

The air-air system may be adapted to all types of air-conditioning systems for comfort or process work. It is applied in buildings requiring individual control of conditions and having a multiplicity of zones, such as office buildings, schools and universities, laboratories, hospitals, stores, hotels, and shops. Air systems are also used for many special applications where a need exists for close control of temperature and humidity.

Single-Zone HVAC Systems

A single-zone HVAC system is designed for only one set of space conditions. Its use is limited to situations where variations occur almost uniformly throughout the zone served or where the load is stable. To handle diversified conditions, it must be installed in multiple. A single-zone system is usually applied to small department stores, small individual shops in a shopping center, individual classrooms of a small school, computer rooms, and similar applications. For example, a rooftop unit complete with refrigeration system, serving an individual space is an example of a single-zone system. The refrigeration system, however, could be remote and serve several single-zone units in a larger installation.

In a typical single-zone central unit the return fan is necessary if only outdoor air is used for cooling purposes. It could be eliminated if air could be relieved from the space with little pressure loss through the relief system.

Single-zone system control can be achieved by varying the quantity of cooling medium, providing reheat, face and bypass dampers or a combination of these. Single-duct systems with reheat satisfy variations in load by providing independent sources of heating and cooling. Complete humidity control for the space can be obtained by including a humidifier in the system. Since control is directly from space temperature and humidity, close regulation of system conditions may be achieved. Single-duct systems without reheat have cooling flexibility but cannot control summer humidity independent of temperature.

Terminal Reheat System

The terminal reheat system is a modification of the single-zone system. Its purpose is to permit zone or space control for areas of unequal loading; or to provide heating or cooling of perimeter areas with different exposures; or for process or comfort applications where close control of space conditions is desired. As the word "reheat" implies, the application of heat is a secondary process, being applied to either pre-conditioned primary air or recirculated room air. A single low pressure reheat system is produced when a heating coil is inserted in the duct system. The more sophisticated systems utilize higher pressure duct designs and pressure reduction devices to permit system balancing at the reheat zone. The medium for heating may be hot water, steam, or electricity.

The system is generally applied to hospitals, laboratories, office buildings or to spaces where wide load variations are expected. Terminal units are designed to permit heating of primary air, or secondary air induced from the conditioned space. Units are located either under the window or in the duct system overhead. Conditioned air is supplied from a central unit at a fixed cold air temperature designed to offset the maximum cooling load in the space. The control thermostat simply calls for heat when the temperature falls below the upper limit of the controlling instrument's setting.

A schematic arrangement of the components for a typical terminal reheat system is shown in Figure 8.6.

The usual arrangement is to draw through the cooling coil as this permits use of low pressure casings and possible standard air handling units. A slight penalty occurs, however, as fan heat raises the cold air temperature a few degrees F after cooling, requiring an increased air volume to offset load conditions. The induction type reheat unit is shown schematically in Figure 8.7. Full cooling capacity is provided in the primary air stream and supplied by

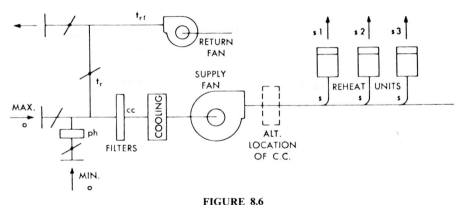

FIGURE 8.6

Reheat system components in typical arrangement

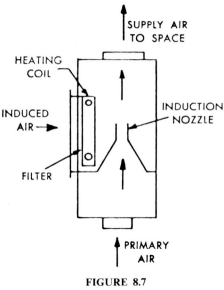

FIGURE 8.7

Induction reheat unit

the central equipment to the terminal. Zone temperature control is accomplished by heating the secondary or induced air stream. This type of terminal is used where it is desirable to introduce supply air to the space at a higher temperature, or to permit higher space air movement without increasing the quantity of primary air over the amount of air required for cooling.

Induction type units are generally located under the window to offset winter downdrafts. Overhead installations are limited, as ductwork installed to the unit supply decreases induction air volume and unit capacity. When installed under the window, this unit has the advantage of providing gravity heating during off-hour operation, permitting shutdown of the air system.

A modification of the induction reheat system provides for a very low supply air temperature for cooling at high load conditions, with resetting of supply air to a higher temperature for lighter load conditions.

The reheat coil is located in the primary air system. Room air is induced but not heated. For maximum cooling, cold air is supplied at approximately 40 F. The basic reason for design of this system is to permit reduction of equipment and duct sizes. Room air is induced at a fixed ratio to raise the supply air temperature in order to prevent condensation on supply grille surfaces. With air volume selected for a high temperature difference between supply air and space air, total air volume for the system is reduced considerably. All primary air is exhausted eliminating the need for return ductwork.

The low temperature induction type of reheat unit is shown schematically in Figure 8.8.

Supply air temperature may be reset from 40 to 50 F or higher (depending upon space load conditions) as the outdoor temperature rises. Solar loads must be checked carefully when selecting reset schedules.

The variable volume concept when applied to reheat systems permit flow reduction as a first step in control, thereby suspending the application of heat until flow conditions reach a predetermined minimum. This reheat system may be designed to permit initial cost savings as well as operating cost savings. With air volume selected for maximum instantaneous peak loads rather than the sum of all peaks, the total system air volume (CFM_s) is reduced. Also, any additional system diversity, such as areas with intermittent loads (conference rooms, office equipment rooms, etc.) may be included in the total volume reduction.

With volume reduction as a first step in control, reheat is not applied until the minimum volume is reached. This procedure reduces system operating cost for summer and intermediate weather appreciably.

Some overlapping of energy requirements may still occur at intermediate loads, depending upon the amount of flow reduction selected or permitted.

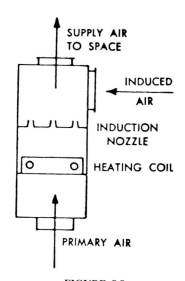

FIGURE 8.8
Low temperature reheat unit with induced room air.

Approximate performance of the variable volume reheat system for a complete season is shown in Figure 8.9. For interior areas, such as conference rooms where a minimum flow setting is necessary, or top floors of buildings with roof loads, a heating means should be provided at the terminal.

Single duct reheat systems are highly flexible; they can provide a narrow variation of temperature in rooms or zones having a wide range of load requirements. The refrigeration machine can be shut down when the temperature of outdoor air is below the required supply air temperature, thus providing low cost cooling in winter.

Variable Volume System

The variable volume system compensates for varying cooling load by regulating the volume of cooling air supplied through a single duct. Special zoning is not required because each space supplied by a controlled outlet is a separate zone. Figure 8.10 shows schematically a true variable air volume (VAV) system.

Significant advantages of the variable volume system are low initial cost and low operating costs. The system is far lower in first cost in comparison with other systems that provide individual space control, because it requires only single runs of duct and a simple control at the air terminal. Also, where diversity of loading occurs, smaller equipment can be used.

Operating costs generally are lowest of all air systems, with savings of as much as 35 percent in energy costs realistically possible. Since the volume of air is reduced with a reduction in load, the refrigeration and fan horsepower closely follow the actual air-conditioning load of the building.

The type of controls for variable volume units will vary with the terminal device. Most types are designed to use either pneumatic or electric controls. Action of the controller simply reduces flow. The one exception is the ceiling dump (bypass) type. To conserve horsepower and limit system noise, especially in larger systems, some means of controlling fan-operating characteristics and system static pressure should be used. Many methods of doing this are available, including use of a fan speed control, variable inlet vane control, fan bypass, fan discharge damper, and variable pitch fan control.

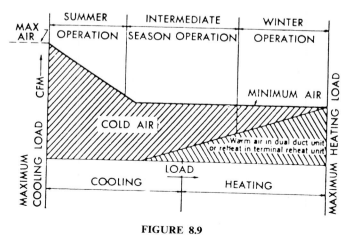

FIGURE 8.9

Performance of VAV dual-duct and VAV terminal reheat units

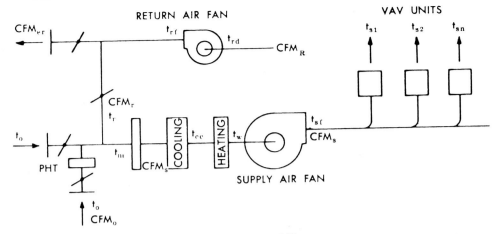

FIGURE 8.10

VAV system

Dual-Duct System

The dual-duct or double-duct system is an exclusively all-air system after the air has left the central air handler. In this arrangement, air from both a hot duct and a cold duct is supplied to a mixing terminal in the space to be conditioned. The mixing unit calls for the correct proportion of hot and cold air in response to demands from a room thermostat.

Figure 8.11 shows the outside air entering the central air handler, where it is filtered, humidified or dehumidified, and finally conditioned (by either a heating coil or a cooling coil) as it enters the appropriate duct. Varying amounts of cold, dehumidified air from the cold duct and either neutral or warm air from the hot duct, as required by the room thermostat, are supplied to the room through the room terminal unit.

A fan for return air and exhaust air is often necessary to exhaust excess air outside and to return air to the central unit to balance the volume of outdoor air that is metered into the system. The double-duct system can use 100% outside air for cooling during seasons when the outside temperature is equal to or less than the supply air temperature (usually 50 to 55 F). Thus the refrigeration unit can be shut down, and free cooling is obtained.

Dual-duct systems commonly have been used in office buildings, hospitals and large laboratories, because of the great flexibility they provide in satisfying multiple loads and in providing prompt and opposite temperature response on demand as required. Because they provide availability of simultaneous cold and warm air, they are also inherently inefficient in use of energy.

Multi-Zone System

The multi-zone central station units provide a single supply duct for each zone and obtains zone control by mixing hot and cold air at the central unit in response to room or zone thermostats. For a comparable number of zones, this system provides greater flexibility than the single-duct and involves lower cost than the dual-duct system, but it is physically limited by the number of zones which may be provided by the equipment.

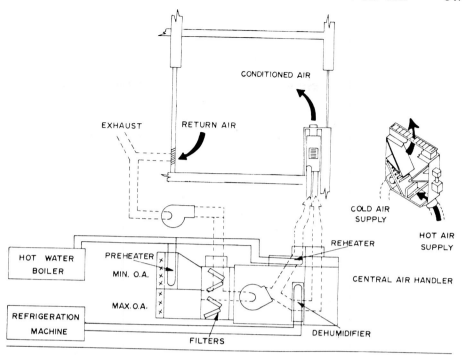

FIGURE 8.11
Dual-duct system

The typical multi-zone equipment is similar in some respects to the dual-duct system but the two air streams are proportioned within the equipment, instead of being mixed at each space served, and the proper temperature air is provided as it leaves the equipment. From central station (built up or packaged) apparatus, the multi-zone system distributes a single air stream to each room or zone through separate ducts. The central station apparatus includes dampers that pre-mix the proper amounts of cold and warm air for each duct and is controlled by room and apparatus thermostats. The system conditions groups of rooms or zones by means of a blow-through central apparatus having heating and cooling coils in parallel downstream from the fan.

In summer, if heat is maintained on the heating coil, the unit may function as a zoning reheat unit. The heating coil may also be made inoperative and a face and bypass control may be utilized. In this case, the path through the heater coil serves as a coil bypass.

Since the blow-through fan unit may be used either as a centrally located zoning reheat unit or zoning face and bypass unit, it is well adapted to multi-room applications. Properly engineered and installed, it gives excellent control of temperature and humidity in individual spaces.

In typical summer operation, the minimum outside damper is open, the refrigeration is on, the maximum outdoor and exhaust air dampers are closed and the return air damper is open.

Normally, the chilled water temperature is maintained at a constant level and the full design quantity of water is continuously circulated through the cooling coils. This allows the apparatus dewpoint temperature to fall at partial load conditions, and the reduced temperature helps to maintain better humidity conditions as the zone loads and sensible heat ratios fall.

As the outdoor temperature drops below room temperature, there is the probability that a perimeter space may need heat although interior spaces still require cooling. Some provision should be incorporated for activating the heating coil at outdoor temperatures around 60–65 F. Alternately, the controls can be set up to activate the heating coil if any perimeter zone calls for heating.

When outdoor air temperatures are below the design cold deck supply temperatures, the refrigeration source is shut down. A thermostat modulates the outdoor, return and exhaust air dampers to maintain the desired cold plenum temperature. The cool outdoor air is thus used to provide economical cooling during marginal and winter weather.

Air- and-Water Systems

In an air-and-water system, both air and water are distributed to each space to perform the cooling function. In virtually all air-water systems, both cooling and heating functions are carried out by changing the air or water temperatures (or both) to permit control of space temperature during all seasons of the year. There are several basic reasons for the use of this type of system.

Because of the greater specific heat and much greater density of water compared to air, the cross-sectional area required for the distribution pipes is markedly less than that required for duct-work to accomplish the same cooling task. Consequently, the quantity of air supplied can be low compared to an all-air system, and less building space needs to be allocated for the cooling distribution system when a substantial part of the heat gain can be removed directly from the conditioned space by a recirculating water system.

The reduced quantity of air is usually combined with a high velocity method of air distribution to minimize the space required. If the system is designed so that the air supply is equal to the air needed to meet outside air requirements or that required to balance exhaust (including exfiltration) or both the return air system can be eliminated for the areas conditioned in this manner.

The pumping horsepower necessary to circulate the water throughout the building is usually significantly less than the fan horsepower to deliver and return the supplanted air. Thus, not only space but also operating cost savings can be realized.

The water side, by complementing rather than totally replacing the air side, retains for air-water systems many of the major performance capabilties of more versatile all-air systems, including positive ventilation, central dehumidi-fication and winter humidification, and good temperature control over widely fluctuating sensible cooling and heating load conditions for a large number of control zones.

All air-and-water systems in common usage are designed for both heating and cooling. Advantage is made of the dual distribution to provide the availability, at least through the intermediate seasons, of both sources of heating and cooling.

Systems of this type have been commonly applied to office buildings, hospitals, hotels, schools, better apartment houses, research laboratories, and other buildings where system capabilities can be properly utilized to satisfy performance criteria.

The air side of the air-and-water systems is comprised of central air-conditioning equipment, a duct distribution system, and a room terminal. The air supply is constant volume and often referred to as primary air, to distinguish it from room air which is recirculated over the room coil. It functions to provide filtered outdoor air for ventilation. In the cooling season, the air is dehumidified in the central conditioning unit sufficiently to achieve comfort humidity conditions throughout the spaces served, and to avoid condensation on the room cooling coil. In winter, moisture is frequently added centrally to limit dryness. As the air is dehumidified, it is also cooled to offset a portion of the room sensible heat loads. The air source may be from outdoors, or it may be a mixture of outdoor and return air. When air is returned, the proportion compared to the outdoor air quantity is generally small. Thus, where freezing temperatures are encountered, a preheater is usually essential.

The water side in its basic form consists of a pump and piping, to convey water to heat transfer surface within each conditioned space. The heat exchange surface in the form of a coil may be an integral part of the air terminal (as with induction units) a completely separate component within the conditioned space (radiant panel), or either (as can be the case with fan-coil units). The water is cooled either by direct refrigeration or, more commonly, by the introduction of chilled water from the primary cooling system or by heat transfer through a water-to-water exchanger. To distinguish it from the primary chilled water circuit, the water side is usually referred to as the secondary water loop or system.

Individual room temperature control is obtained by varying the capacity of the coil (or coils) within the room by regulation of either the water flow through it or the air flow over it. The coil may be converted to heating service during the winter, or a second coil or heating device within the space may provide heating capacity depending upon system type.

Air-and-water systems are categorized as two-pipe, three-pipe, and four-pipe systems. They are basically similar in function and all incorporate both cooling and heating capabilities for all-season air-conditioning. However, arrangements of the secondary water circuits and control systems differ greatly.

AIR-WATER INDUCTION SYSTEMS

The basic arrangement for air-water induction units is shown in Figure 8.12.

Centrally conditioned primary air is supplied to the unit plenum at high pressure. The plenum is acoustically treated to attenuate part of the noise generated in the duct system and in the unit. A balancing damper is used to adjust the primary air quantity within limits.

The high pressure air flows through the induction nozzles and induces secondary air from the room and over the secondary coil. This secondary air is either heated or cooled at the coil depending on the season, the room requirement, or both. Ordinarily, no latent cooling is accomplished at the room coil, but a drain pan is provided to collect condensed moisture resulting from unusual latent loads of short duration. The primary and secondary air is mixed and discharged to the room.

A lint screen is normally provided at the inlet to the secondary coil. Induction units are installed in custom enclosures designed for the particular installation, or in standard cabinets provided by the unit manufacturer. These enclosures must permit proper flow of secondary air and discharge of mixed air without imposing excessive pressure losses. They also must be arranged to allow easy access for servicing.

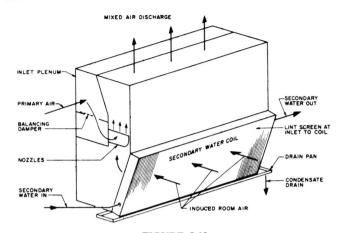

FIGURE 8.12
Air-water induction unit

Induction units are usually installed at a perimeter wall under a window, but units designed for overhead installation are available.

During the heating season, the floor-mounted induction unit can function as a convector during off hours with hot water to the coil and without a primary air supply.

A wide variety of induction unit configurations is available, including units with low overall height or with extremely large secondary coil face areas, to suit the particular needs of space or load.

FAN-COIL CONDITIONER SYSTEM

The fan-coil conditioner unit is a versatile room terminal which is applied to both air-water and water-only systems. Despite the shortcomings in the quality of air-conditioning achieved with water-only systems, the fan coil units have been more commonly associated with that class of system than with air-water. Many of the standard features of the units are accordingly incorporated into it for water-only applications.

The basic elements of fan-coil units are a finned-tube coil and a fan section. The fan section recirculates air continuously from within the perimeter space through the coil which is supplied with either hot or chilled water. In addition, the unit may contain an auxiliary heating coil which is usually of the electric resistance type but which can be of the steam or hot water type. Thus, the recirculated room air is either heated or cooled.

Fan-coil unit capacity can be controlled by regulation of coil water flow, air bypass, fan speed, or a combination of these.

Water flow can be thermostatically controlled by either return air or wall thermostats. Two-position valves are often used for fan-coil applications instead of modulating valves because of their lower cost.

Water valves should not be used for control where aperture outdoor intakes are used unless freezing of the coils is prevented if the fans are operating when water flow stops.

Bypass dampers are available on some conditioners. Capacity control is achieved by modulation of a damper to bypass all or part of the air around the unit coil.

Fan speed control may be automatic or manual. Automatic control is usually on-off with manual speed selection.

All-Water Systems

All-water systems are those with fan-coil, unit ventilator, or valance-type room terminals, with unconditioned ventilation air supplied by an opening through the wall or by infiltration. Cooling and humidification is provided by circulating chilled water or brine through a finned coil in the unit. Heating is provided by supplying hot water through the same or a separate coil, using 2-, 3-, or 4-pipe water distribution from central equipment. Electric heating or a separate steam coil may also be used. Humidification is not practical in all-water systems unless a separate package humidifier is provided in each room.

Seasonal changeover is required in most climates, with a two-pipe system, and zoning of piping is required to reduce operating difficulties during intermediate seasons, when a sun-exposed zone may need cooling while other zones need heat. When heating, units cannot be used as convectors in unoccupied rooms and fans must be kept running.

If a two-pipe system has only one pump, the same quantity of hot and cold water is circulated even though the requirements for each may be different. With 3- and 4-pipe systems, hot and cold water may be required year-round.

FAN-COIL UNITS (UNIT VENTILATORS)

Figure 8.13 shows a typical air-conditioning unit ventilator equipped with a combination hot-chilled water coil for use in a two-pipe system. This type of unit is usually provided with face-and-bypass dampers for capacity control.

Figure 8.14 shows a typical air-conditioning unit ventilator with two separate coils, one used for heating and the other for cooling with a four-pipe system. The heating coil may be hot water, steam or electric. The cooling coil can be either a chilled water coil or a direct expansion refrigerant coil. Heating and cooling coils are sometimes combined in a single coil by providing separate tube circuits for each function. In such cases, the effect is the same as having two separate coils.

Because a unit ventilator has a dual function of introducing outdoor air for ventilation and maintaining a specified room condition, the heating capacity required is the sum of the heating required to bring outdoor ventilation air up to room temperature and the heat required to offset room losses. The ventilation cooling capacity of a unit ventilator is determined by the air volume delivered by the unit and the temperature difference between the unit discharge and the room temperature.

VALANCE UNITS

A valance unit is a device which cools or heats room air by convection, without the use of a fan or motor. It is a proprietary system. In this system a finned coil is mounted in an insulated sheet metal enclosure so that air can pass over the coil by convection, as shown in Figure 8.15. It usually is hung at the junction of the wall and ceiling. In the cooling mode, the cooled and dehumidified air at the coil drops downward, drawing warm air through the coil. When in the heating mode, the heated air rises to the ceiling. Supplemental heating may be required under windows in cold climates. Ventilation must be provided separately.

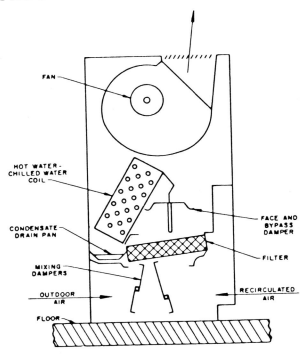

FIGURE 8.13

Typical air-conditioning unit ventilator with combined hot-chilled water coil

PANEL HEATING AND COOLING

Radiant panel systems combine controlled temperature room surfaces with central plant heating and cooling. The controlled temperature surfaces may be located in the floor, walls, or ceiling, and the temperature maintained by circulating water or air. The central station air system can be basic, one zone, constant temperature, constant volume system; or the air system can encompass some or all of the features used in properly designed dual-duct, reheat, multizone, or variable volume systems. A controlled temperature surface is referred to as a radiant panel if 50 percent or more of the heat transfer is by radiation to other surfaces served by the panel.

Modern hot water panel heating has been applied to residences for over 50 years, and large-scale applications of panel heating and cooling systems to commercial and institutional buildings have been used within the last 25 years. Residential heating applications usually consist of pipe coils embedded in masonry floors or plaster ceilings. This construction serves well where loads are relatively stable and where solar effects are minimized by building design. However, in buildings where glass areas become greater and load changes occur more rapidly, the slow response, lag, and override effect of masonry panels has proven to be unsatisfactory. Lightweight metal panel ceiling systems provide quick response to load changes and can be used for cooling as well as heating.

Radiant panel systems are similar to other air-water systems in the arrangement of system components. Room thermal conditions are maintained primarily

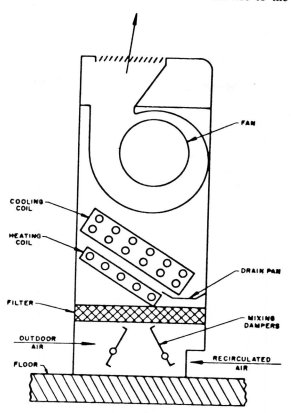

FIGURE 8.14

Typical air-conditioning unit ventilator with separate coils

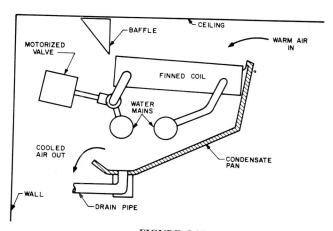

FIGURE 8.15

Section through valance unit

(Courtesy of ASHRAE Handbook & Product Directory)

by direct transfer of radiant energy, rather than by convective heating and cooling. Room heating and cooling loads are calculated in the conventional manner. Manufacturers' ratings generally are noted in terms of total performance which can be applied directly to the calculated room load.

The most common forms of panel applications in heating and cooling systems are as follows.

Metal Ceiling Panels

Metal ceiling panels are normally integrated into a system that both heats and cools. In such a system, a source of dehumidified ventilation air is required in summer, and the system is classed as one of the combination air-water systems. In such a system, various amounts of forced air are supplied year-round. When metal panels are applied for heating purposes only, a ventilation system may or may not be required, depending upon local codes.

Metal ceiling panels have successfully employed two-pipe, three-pipe, and four-pipe distribution systems. It is common to design for a 20 F differential in temperature across a given grid and a 5 F rise for cooling, but higher temperature drops may be employed if applicable.

Some ceiling installations require active grids to cover only a portion of the room, and consequently, compatible matching standard acoustical panels are normally used for the remaining ceiling area. Esthetic considerations may dictate the use of any inactive panel which fits the ceiling grid system.

Embedded Piping in Ceilings, Walls, and Floors

When piping is embedded in ceilings, the construction used is generally one of the following:

1. Pipe or tube is embedded in the lower portion of a concrete slab, generally within an inch of its lower surface. If plaster is to be applied to the concrete, the piping may be placed directly on the wood forms. If the slab is to be used without plaster finish, then the piping should be installed not less than 0.75 in. above the undersurface of the slab. The minimum coverage must be in compliance with the local building code requirements.
2. Pipe or tube is embedded in a metal lath and plaster ceiling. If the lath is suspended to form a hung ceiling, both the lath and the heating coils are securely wired to the supporting members in such a way that the lath is below but in good contact with the coils. Plaster is then applied to the metal lath, care being taken to embed the coil.
3. Copper tube of the smaller diameters is attached to the underside of wire lath or gypsum lath. Plaster is then applied to the lath to embed the tube.
4. Other forms of ceiling construction are composition board, wood paneling, etc., having warm water piping, tube, or channels built into the panel sections.

Coils are usually of the sinuous type, although some header or grid-type coils have been used in ceilings. Coils may be of plastic, ferrous, or nonferrous pipe or tube, with coil pipes spaced from 4.5 to 9 in. on centers, depending on the required output, pipe or tube size, and other factors.

Although not so universally used as ceiling panels, wall panels may be constructed by any of the methods outlined for ceilings.

The construction for piping embedded in floors will depend upon whether (a) the floor is laid on grade, or (b) the floor is above grade.

1. Plastic, ferrous, and nonferrous pipe and tube are used in floor slabs

which rest on grade. The coils are constructed as either sinuous-continuous pipe coils, or arranged as heater coils with the pipes spaced from 6 to 18 in. on centers. The coils are generally installed with 1½ to 4 in. of cover above the coils. It is recommended that insulation be used to reduce the perimeter and reverse losses.

2. Where the coils are embedded in structural load-supporting slabs above grade, construction codes may affect their position. Otherwise, the coil piping is installed in the same manner as described for slabs resting on grade.

Air-Heated Floors

Several methods have been devised to warm the interior room surfaces by circulating heated air through passages in the floor. In some cases, the heated air is recirculated in a closed system. In others, all or a part of the air is passed through the room on its way back to the furnace to provide supplementary heating and ventilation. Care must be exercised to assure compliance with any building codes that might apply.

Heat Pump Systems

The term heat pump as applied to a year-round air-conditioning system, commonly denotes a system in which refrigeration equipment is used in such a manner that heat is taken from a heat source and given up to the conditioned space when heating service is wanted, and is removed from the space and discharged to a heat sink when cooling and dehumidification are desired. The thermal cycle is identical with that of ordinary refrigeration, but the application is equally concerned with the cooling effect produced at the evaporator and the heating effect produced at the condenser. In some applications, both the heating and the cooling effects obtained in the cycle are utilized.

While the heat source and sink for heat pumps can be air, earth or solar energy, water is the source and sink of heat pumps used with district heating and cooling systems.

Two types of water source heat pumps are used: A *water-to-air* heat pump which relies on *water* as a heat source and sink, and uses *air* to transmit heat to or from the conditioned space, and a *water-to-water* heat pump uses *water* as the heat source and sink, and *water* for both cooling and heating operations.

Water source heat pumps are growing in market importance because of their adaptability to water based heating systems, to multi-zone or multi-unit applications where energy recovery is a possibility, and because of other technically attractive features which include:

1. Water source equipment, which offers higher COPs and smaller variation of COP with source temperature, since the source temperature is maintained at 32 F or higher.

2. Water source equipment, which is compatible for use with a thermal storage system, thus permitting better load management.

A water-to-air heat pump cycle which is commonly used in commercial buildings requiring simultaneous heating and cooling is shown in Figure 8.16. Each module has one or more water-to-air heat pumps. The units are connected hydronically with a two-pipe system. Cooling is achieved by each unit in a conventional manner, supplying cooling air to the individual module and rejecting the heat thus removed to the two-pipe system by means of a shell-and-tube condenser. The total heat gathered by the two-pipe system will be

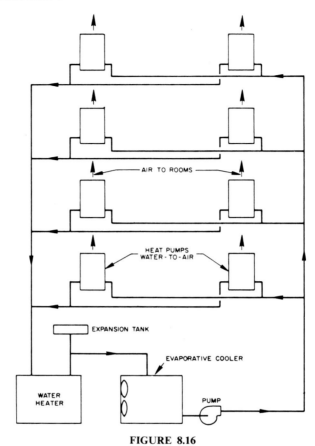

FIGURE 8.16
Heat transfer system using water-to-air unitary heat pump
(Courtesy of ASHRAE Handbook & Product Directory)

rejected to an evaporative cooler usually mounted on the roof. If and when some of the modules, particularly on the northern side, require heat, the individual units will switch (by means of four-way refrigerant valves) into the heating cycle. The units derive their heat source from the two-pipe water loop, thereby basically obtaining heat from a relatively high source, namely, the condenser water of the other units. Naturally, when only heating is required, all units will be in the heating cycle and, consequently, a heat exchanger must be added to provide 100% heating capability. The water loop is usually kept between 70 to 90 F temperature and, therefore, needs no insulation.

WASTE HEAT RECLAMATION SYSTEMS

Waste heat reclamation is the recovery and utilization of heat energy which otherwise would be discarded. Reclaiming waste heat saves energy, reduces operating costs, and reduces peak loads.

There are several major uses for recovered waste heat.

Using recovered hot gases to preheat boiler makeup water is almost always cost-effective, especially when there is a large continuous flow of makeup water.

The engineering needed to retrofit an economizer (feed-water preheater) onto an existing boiler is fairly straight forward.

Preheating combustion air is another heat reclamation option that can greatly reduce fuel costs. In this case, however, major ductwork modifications often are needed and burners usually must be modified as well.

Another popular method of using waste heat involves the application of heat exchangers to heat or cool the make-up air introduced into a building by its mechanical system. Several types of heat exchangers are available for this purpose.

Although the basic principles in heat recovery are the same, there are many methods to implement it by using different devices applicable to different systems or situations. Heat recovery devices reduce the peak heating and cooling loads when used with outdoor air systems and many reduce or completely eliminate the requirements for heating and/or cooling equipment in major building expansions. The following are some of the most frequently used methods for heat recovery.

Rotary Heat Exchanger

A rotary heat exchanger, Figure 8.17, uses a cylindrical drum or wheel as the heat-transfer medium. The wheel rotates slowly between the supply-air and exhaust-air streams. The wheel absorbs sensible heat from the warmer air stream, and rotates to the other air stream, where the heat is picked up by the cooler air. When the wheel is hygroscopically treated with a desiccant, it can also transfer latent heat, in the form of water vapor being transferred from the humid air stream to the drier air stream. Nonhygroscopic wheels transfer water vapor when the temperature of one air stream is below the dew-point temperature of the other, and when there is direct condensation of water vapor. When temperatures are below 32 F, the supply air usually is preheated to prevent freezing.

Rotary heat exchangers usually are economical for applications where ventilation air rates exceed 4000 cfm. When operated at approximately 8 to 10 rpm with a face velocity of 550 fpm, a nonhygroscopic rotary exchanger recovers 70% to 80% of the sensible heat and 40% to 60% of the latent heat. Hygroscopic or enthalpy exchangers recover 70% to 80% of the total heat.

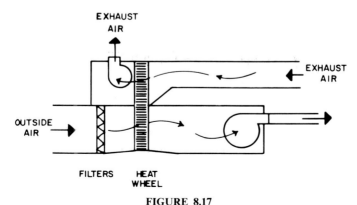

FIGURE 8.17

Rotary heat exchanger

(Courtesy of The Electrification Council)

To apply a rotary heat exchanger, the supply and exhaust ductwork must be located in close proximity to each other. This can be an obstacle in some applications. Another problem occurs when one of the air streams is contaminated. In such cases, purge sections must be added to the wheel, and special filtration may be needed in the supply air as well.

Air-to-Air Heat Exchangers

Air-to-air heat exchangers transfer heat from one air stream to another through direct contact on either side of a metal heat transfer surface. The surface may be either a plate with fins (more common for low temperature use in HVAC systems), or a tube as shown in Figure 8.18 (more common for boiler flue-gas heat transfer).

Preheating primary and secondary air increases boiler efficiency by reducing the cooling effect when the air enters the combustion chamber. As shown in Figure 8.19, a 100 F increase in the temperature of the combustion air entering the boiler produces approximately a 2% reduction in boiler loss for natural gas and light oil.

Combustion air can be preheated up to 350 F for stoker-fired coal, oil, and gas. The maximum temperature permissible is determined by the type of construction involved and the materials of the firing equipment. Manufacturer's recommendations should be followed in all cases.

Air-to-air heat exchangers transfer sensible heat only. They are not designed for cooling applications. Size is limited only by the physical dimensions of the space available. They may be purchased as packaged units or they can be custom designed for the application.

Although the efficiency of air-to-air heat exchangers generally is less than 50%, their low cost often justifies their use. In addition, they offer low resistance to air flow, require no motive power input, and are reasonably trouble free and durable.

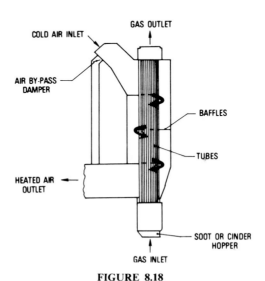

FIGURE 8.18

Flue-gas air-to-air heat exchanger

(Courtesy of The Electrification Council)

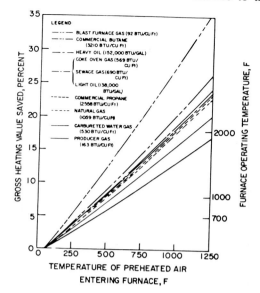

FIGURE 8.19

Fuel savings resulting from use of preheated combustion air
(Courtesy of The Electrification Council)

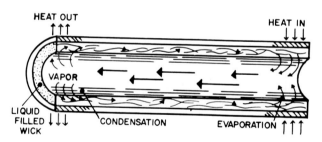

FIGURE 8.20

Heat pipe
(Courtesy of The Electrification Council)

Heat Pipe

A heat pipe, Figure 8.20, is a passive heat exchanger consisting of closed fluid within a sealed tube. Cool air passing over one end of the tube is heated when the fluid enclosed in the tube condenses. The warmer air stream passing over the other end of the tube is cooled when the adjacent fluid contained in the tube evaporates. The action is reversible and operates whenever there is a temperature difference between the ends of the tube.

A heat pipe can be used for heat recovery only when the air intake and air exhaust ducts of a building's HVAC system are located close to each other. Heat recovery is achieved by installing a group of heat pipes between the air intake and the air exhaust ducts.

Run-Around System

A run-around system generally is used to recover sensible heat, Figure 8.21. It consists of finned-tube water coils located in the exhaust and supply air streams, and a pump that circulates water or a water/antifreeze solution between the coils. The system is seasonably reversible, preheating in the winter and precooling in the summer.

Coils and pump normally are selected to achieve sensible recovery efficiencies of 40% to 60%. Greater efficiencies can be achieved by adding more coils in the heat exchangers to increase their capacity. When finned tubing is added, the pressure drop across the coil increases, requiring more power for supply and exhaust systems, as well as more pumping energy. As a result, gains in efficiency are partially offset by increased energy requirements.

If latent recovery is necessary, water coils can be replaced with a cooling-tower surface, and an additional solution pump is used. This provides total heat (enthalpy) transfer as the solution absorbs heat and water vapor from the air streams, and also acts as an air washer or scrubber.

Twin Tower Sprays

A twin tower spray system, Figure 8.22, is an air-to-air enthalpy recovery system used to reduce the energy consumed for cooling. The outside air entering

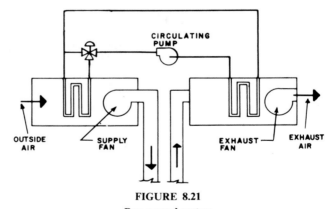

FIGURE 8.21

Run-around system

(Courtesy of The Electrification Council)

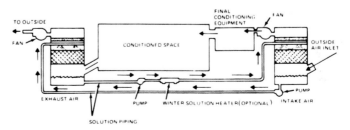

FIGURE 8.22

Twin tower sprays

(Courtesy of The Electrification Council)

the cooling system is preconditioned by utilizing the energy available in the air being exhausted from the building. During the summer, hot, moist outside air is pre-cooled and dehumidified by utilizing the cool, dry air being exhausted to the outside. During the winter, cold, dry outside air is heated and humidified by utilizing the warm, moist air being exhausted to the outside.

The energy transfer between airstreams is accomplished when a hygroscopic solution contacts the air streams. The solution is continuously circulated between the intake and exhaust, transporting heat and moisture from one air stream to the other.

Boiler Stack Economizer

High flue gas temperature is an indicator of fuel waste in central heating plants. For example, when natural gas is used, flue gas temperature of 1000 F indicates a loss equivalent to 179 ft^3 of gas for each 1000 ft^3 of gas burned. If the flue gas temperature is reduced to 500 F, the loss is reduced to 98 ft^3 for each 1000 ft^3 of gas burned, for a savings of 81 ft^3 for each 1000 ft^3 burned.

One of the most effective methods of reducing boiler stack losses is through use of a boiler stack economizer, which generates savings in two ways. The economizer reduces the temperature of the flue gas—and associated losses—and uses the heat which is removed to pre-heat boiler feed water.

A boiler stack economizer, Figure 8.23, consists of a heat exchanger placed inside an exhaust stack to pre-heat boiler feed water. Heat captured from the exhaust gases increases the temperature of the feed water which is returned to the boiler. The volume of feed water passing through the transfer coils is

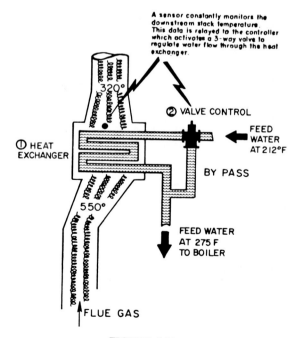

FIGURE 8.23

Schematic of a boiler stack economizer with stack temperature controls

(Courtesy of The Electrification Council)

controlled to prevent sulfur released by the fuel into the exhaust stack from reaching its dew point and condensing. This condensate can corrode the chimney or stack.

As a general rule, when an economizer is installed to pre-heat boiler feed water, every 10 F to 11 F increase in feed-water temperature produces approximately 1% increase in boiler efficiency.

A *word of caution*: if the temperature of the flue gases is reduced too much, sulfur trioxide (SO_3) will combine with moisture in the flue gas to produce sulfuric acid mists. The temperature at which this happens is called the *acid dew point temperature*. When sulfuric acid mist occurs, it will adhere to cooler surfaces (such as recuperator tubes), entrap fly carbon and other particles in the flue gas, and initiate low temperature corrosion. (Minimum stack temperatures for trouble free operation when burning oil are given in Table 8.3.) In most cases, the corrosion problem will not be serious if the temperature of the metal is kept above 240 F. Exposed metal ductwork can be protected through insulation, which will keep temperatures higher. A metal stack can be protected by an aluminum outer shroud which provides an air space, or it can be left bare and replaced as necessary. Masonry stacks also are exposed to such corrosive action and may be protected by a glazed tile liner. National Fire Protection Association (NFPA) code books should be consulted for more details.

Shell and Tube Heat Exchangers

Shell and tube heat exchangers are commonly used devices. They consist of a tubular shell with a flange, in which a tube bundle of "U" bend construction is inserted. This device transfers heat between two physically separated fluids, one circulating through the tubes while the other passes through the shell. The difference in the leaving temperatures of the two liquids is called the "approach."

Shell and tube heat exchangers can be used to capture energy from hot condensate, hot refrigerant gas, condenser water, and hot drain lines from kitchens and laundries and use it by transferring it to heating domestic hot water or convert it into other useful forms of energy.

Heat exchangers should be insulated to prevent unnecessary heat loss and should be constructed of materials to suit the application.

Shell and tube exchangers can be used to exchange heat in the following configurations:

1. Liquid-to-liquid
2. Steam-to-liquid
3. Gas-to-liquid

TABLE 8.3

MINIMUM STACK TEMPERATURES FOR TROUBLE-FREE OPERATION

Fuel	Sulfur (%)	Minimum Stack Temperature	
		°C	°F
Diesel type	1.0	138	280
Heavy oil	2.5	155	310
Heavy oil	3.5	160	320

All three configurations are commercially available in a wide range of sizes and outputs with reliable heat exchange data.

Hot-Gas Heat Exchanger

A typical refrigeration machine with a water cooled condenser rejects approximately 15,000 Btu/h for each 12,000 Btu/h of refrigeration. An air cooled condenser rejects up to 17,000 Btu/h. Up to one-third of the heat of compression can be recaptured by installing a heat exchanger in the hot-gas line between the compressor and condenser of the chiller. A typical arrangement used in conjunction with a domestic hot water system is shown in Figure 8.24. Hot-gas temperature depends on head pressure, but usually is on the order of 120 F to 130 F.

Hot-Drain Heat Exchanger

Kitchens, laundries, and other service facilities which utilize large quantities of hot water often discharge hot waste water to drains. A heat exchanger can recapture this waste heat, and use it to preheat service hot water. A typical system is shown in Figure 8.25.

In general, special equipment to preheat water from 50 F to 105 F usually is

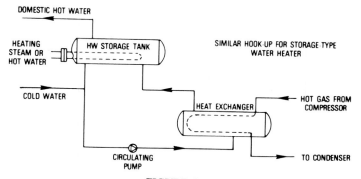

FIGURE 8.24

Schematic of hot-gas heat exchanger heat-recovery system

(Courtesy of The Electrification Council)

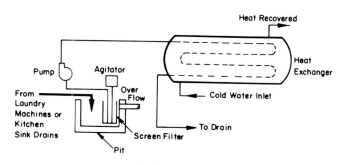

FIGURE 8.25

Schematic of laundry and kitchen hot-water heat-recovery system

(Courtesy of The Electrification Council)

cost effective. The warmer water can then be fed into the service hot water tank at 105 F for further heating to the required utilization temperature.

Hot Condensate Heat Exchanger

The condensate return portion of many steam systems exhausts large quantities of flash steam when the hot condensate is reduced to atmospheric pressure in the condensate receiver. The heat contained in the flash steam can be recovered by installing a heat exchanger in the condensate-return main ahead of the receiver, Figure 8.26, to reduce condensate temperature to approximately 180 F. The recovered heat can be used in many ways, as to preheat water.

The quantity of heat recovered depends on the quantity and temperature of the condensate. Consider the following example:

Example:

Condensate return volume is equal to 6 gpm at 260 F. A heat exchanger is installed to reduce the condensate temperature from 260 F to 180 F. The quantity of heat recovered is:

$$Q = 6 \times (260 - 180) \times 500 = 240,000 \text{ Btu/h}$$

where 500 converts gpm to pounds per hour.

In each case, the feasibility of a waste heat recovery system depends upon being able to use the recovered heat.

Refrigeration Equipment Condenser Heat Recovery

Refrigerated and frozen food cases usually have multiple compressor and condenser installations which generate large quantities of heat. The heat can be captured and used to provide space heating and humidity control.

A system for recovering heat energy from service refrigeration equipment is shown in Figure 8.27. Hot refrigerant gas from the individual compressors is fed into a common manifold. When the store is to be heated, the manifold gas

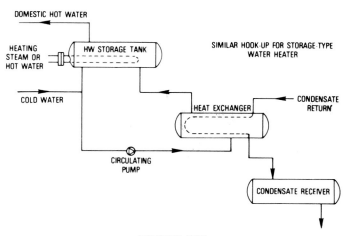

FIGURE 8.26

Waste-heat recovery using a hot-condensate heat exchanger

(Courtesy of The Electrification Council)

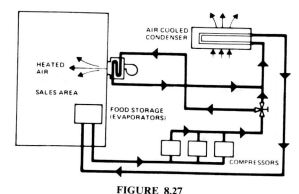

FIGURE 8.27

Refrigeration equipment heat recovery system
(Courtesy of The Electrification Council)

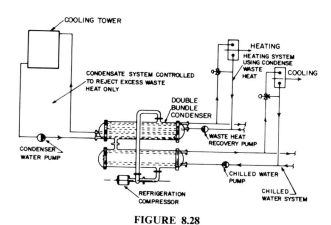

FIGURE 8.28

Waste-heat recovery from central chiller using double bundle condenser
(Courtesy of The Electrification Council)

is piped to heat exchangers, located in the air supply ducts. These may be arranged in two or more independent zones depending on the store's needs. In warm weather hot gas from the manifold is routed directly to an outside condenser where its heat content dissipates into the atmosphere. Sales area cooling is performed by condensing units which supply direct-expansion or chilled-water coils in ducts.

Another type of heat recovery system designed for supermarkets employs a closed hot water loop to transfer energy from the refrigerant manifold to the duct coils or closed-circuit cooling tower. Air-to-water heat pumps and duct heaters, singly or in combination, supplement recovered heat in this system.

Double Bundle Condenser System

A double bundle condenser is constructed with a building water circuit and a cooling tower circuit enclosed in the same shell, Figure 8.28. Hot refrigerant gas from the compressor is discharged into the condenser shell where its heat is absorbed by either one of the water circuits or by both simultaneously depending on the requirements of the system at a given time.

The condenser is split into two independent hydronic circuits to prevent contamination of the building water system with cooling tower water, which may contain dirt and chemicals. When a double bundle condenser is used in conjunction with a standard refrigeration machine, the heat rejected by the compressor is made available to the building water circuit.

In some heat recovery applications, the amount of heat reclaimed during occupied hours may exceed daytime heating requirements of perimeter zones. In these cases, the excess heat can be stored for release during times when the building is unoccupied.

The cost of installing a double bundle condenser system is such that, as a replacement, it probably will be most feasible for a system which already is at or near the end of its useful life.

Heat Pump As Heat Exchanger

Heat pumps are actually heat transfer devices and, unlike those previously described, upgrade the temperature by as much as a factor of 3:1. This feature makes them particularly attractive for use with low temperature heat sources. They also have the capacity to transfer latent heat as well as sensible heat.

Heat pumps are available in the following configurations, each having particular application:
1. Air-to-air (very limited applications).
2. Water-to-air.
3. Water-to-water.
4. Air-to-water.

Heat pumps make heat available from low-temperature sources. For example, heat can be extracted from cold drain water at approximately 50 F to produce temperatures high enough for use by domestic hot water systems, air pre-heating and other similar applications. When selecting heat pumps, choose equipment that has the highest COP over the range of expected operating conditions.

Kitchen Exhaust Heat Recovery

A kitchen exhaust heat recovery unit can recover 70% of the heat from hood exhaust air. The air from the exhaust hoods goes through a water wash cycle which separates up to 94% of the grease, and then is discharged through a duct designed to recapture 70% of the heat. The recaptured heat is transferred to the kitchen fresh air make-up. In some tests, use of this procedure has eliminated the need to heat kitchen make-up air. Return on investment is projected at approximately three years. Close analysis is required to determine how practical this is for a given kitchen, especially in light of other energy management options which may be applied, such as reduction of kitchen exhaust air.

Any range of supply air quantities can be handled by the addition of more tubes to the heat exchanger rack. They contain no moving parts so there is minimal leakage between air streams. Mechanical energy is not used except in the form of increased fan energy to overcome static pressure losses.

Incinerators

Incinerators burning solid waste produce 6,000 Btu/lb of common trash. Special heat recovery incinerators are now available in sizes down to approximately 450 F. They can be used in a heat exchanger as a source of high and low temperature heat.

In employing incinerators for heat recovery, the heat should be used at the highest practical temperature. Typical applications are absorption refrigeration, heating, and domestic hot water.

Waste-Heat Boilers

Waste-heat boilers are used in conjunction with high-temperature heat recovery as from engine exhaust and exhaust from gas turbines used to drive refrigeration equipment or electric generators. In the case of the turbine, a duct, similar to a breeching, is connected directly from the exhaust of the turbine to the boiler. After passing through the boiler the gases are discharged to the atmosphere. Gas turbines produce about twice as much recoverable heat as reciprocating engines of the same size. Generally, a turbine yields 7 to 13 pounds of steam per hour (15 psi steam) per kilowatt generated. An overall system efficiency of slightly over 65% is possible in total energy plants, if all the recoverable heat is used. (A total energy plant is a plant which utilizes recovered heat from electrical power generators to provide a portion of the energy requirement for space heating, domestic hot water, and space cooling.)

Heat-of-Light System

The major advantage of a "heat-of-light" system lies in its reduction of heating, cooling, and HVAC system and distribution loads, rather than in savings in electrical energy for lighting. However, slightly higher lamp efficiencies will result as the cooling effect on the lamps increases their output.

Both systems require special fixtures. Wet systems require a completely new water circulating system and connections to a cooling tower. Wet heat of light systems are thus not particularly suitable for retrofitting, unless a complete remodeling of the existing HVAC and electrical systems of a building is contemplated.

With a dry heat-of-light system, room air is extracted through the lighting fixture, is passed over the lamp and ballast, and is either ducted to a fan or drawn into the ceiling plenum space. The heated air from the lamp and fixture can be supplied to cooler perimeter zones during the heating season or recirculated back to an existing air handling unit or discharged outdoors during the cooling season. If a ceiling plenum system is used, a separate fan is necessary to draw the warm air from the ceiling plenum to deliver it to cooler zones or to discharge it outdoors.

When ceiling plenums are used as collection chambers, each zone must be isolated from the other by a vertical barrier, and ceilings over conditioned areas should be insulated to a "U" valve of .1 or better to limit reradiation to the occupied spaces. (Consult all codes to comply with fire protection requirements.)

Wet heat-of-light systems have special lighting fixtures which include built-in water passages and air extract inlets. Air is extracted through the fixture and water is circulated through passages to the cooling tower where the heat is removed and the cool water piped back to the fixtures. The heat removed from fixtures can be used for reheat purposes in the cooling system instead of being rejected to the outdoors. The circulating water system can also be used to pick up heat from special water-cooled louvered venetian blinds to reduce solar heat gain at the windows, as well as to make the heat available for other uses.

The two types of systems provide the following advantages:
1. Excess heat from interior areas of the building can be collected and distributed to perimeter areas.
2. The sensible room heat component of the cooling load is decreased, permitting a reduction in the quantity of air required for cooling (thus saving fan horsepower).
3. In the case of wet heat-of-light systems, the cooling load is reduced and less power is required for the refrigeration units.

Application Guidelines

Table 8.4 is a matrix which indicates sources of waste heat, the applications for which it can be applied, and the devices which can be used for the application. Situations which usually justify use of a waste heat reclamation system are as follows:
1. Exhausted air quantity exceeds 4,000 cfm.
    When more than 4,000 cfm is being exhausted and when there are more than 3,500 heating degree days and more than 8,000 cooling degree hours above 78 F db, consider thermal wheels, heat pipes and other devices to transfer energy between exhaust and outdoor air ducts. Where supply and exhaust ducts are remote from each other and cannot be brought together, consider systems other than heat pipes and thermal wheels.
    Install a thermal wheel or heat pump to recover both sensible and latent heat in locations with more than 12,000 wet-bulb degree hours above 66 F, wb.
    When justified for the heating mode only, install an air-to-water-to-air heat pump to transfer energy from the exhaust air stream to the fresh air stream.

TABLE 8.4
APPLICATIONS OF HEAT RECLAMATION DEVICES

Energy Source	Temper Ventilation Air	Preheat Domestic Hot Water	Space Heating	Terminal Reheat	Temper Make-Up Air	Preheat Combustion Air	Heavy Oil Heating	Internal to External Zone Heat Transfer
Exhaust air	1a, 1b, 1c, 2, 3, 4, 5				1a, 1b, 1c, 2, 3, 4, 5	Direct		5, Direct
Flue gas	1b, 3, 4		3.4		1b, 3, 4	1b, 2, 3, 4		
Hot condensate	3, 6	3, 6	3, 5, 6	3, 6	3, 6	3, 6	6	
Refrigerant hot gas	6	6		6	6			
Hot condenser water	3, 6	3, 6	3, 5, 6	6	3, 5, 6	3, 5, 6	6	5
Hot water drains		6						
Solid waste	7	7	7	7	7	7	7	
Engine exhaust & cooling system	6, 8	6	6, 8	6	6, 8	6, 8	6	
Lights	5, 9		5, 9	5, 9	5, 9			5, 9

Device
1. Thermal Wheel 2. Run-around coil 5. Heat Pump 7. Incinerator 9. Heat-of-Light
  a) Latent 3. Heat pipe 6. Shell/Tube 8. Waste Heat
  b) Sensible 4. Air-to-Air   Heat Exchange   Boiler
  c) Combination   Heat Exchanger

Utilize exhaust-air heat energy to temper make-up air and preheat combustion air, or use this system for space heating via heat pumps.

2. Stack temperature exceeds 350 F.

When stack temperature exceeds 350 F, install a heat pipe or an air-to-air exchanger to transfer energy from the hot flue gas to temper ventilation air, pre-heat domestic hot water, heat space, or pre-heating combustion air.

Take into account the corrosive effect of flue gas when selecting materials.

Provide an alternative source of combustion air when heat exchanger dampers are closed for cleaning.

3. There is laundry and/or kitchen waste water.

When more than 30,000 gal/week of water at temperature above 120 F is discharged to waste, use as a heat source for heat pump or other HVAC system requirements.

Consideration must be given to the characteristics of the waste water, particularly the soap/detergent content of laundry waste water and the grease content of kitchen waste water. Piping and/or material modifications may be necessary to enable the heat exchanger to handle water with high concentrations of these impurities. In addition a holding tank may be required to maintain a steady flow rate through the heat exchanger when water is being sporadically discharged.

Waste heat thus recovered may be used by any system requiring hot water, such as domestic hot water and heating systems.

4. Engines larger than 50 hp; combustion turbine exhaust and cooling systems:

Exhaust gas heat recovery is restricted by the partial limitations of the heat exchanger plus the prevention of flue gas condensation. The recommended minimum exhaust temperature is approximately 250 F. Depending on the initial exhaust temperature 50% to 60% of the available exhaust heat can be removed.

5. Incinerators:

Consider recovering waste heat from incinerators if the quantity of solid waste exceeds 1,000 lbs/day.

6. Steam Condensate:

Recover heat from condensate return systems when district heat steam condensate is discharged to waste, or when steam condensate from equipment supplied by on-site boilers is at a temperature of 180 F or greater.

7. Refrigeration Systems:

Recover heat from refrigeration system hot gas where there is a steady and concurrent demand for refrigeration and waste heat, and when the refrigeration systems operate 1,000 hours or more per year.

Condensing in the heat exchanger must be limited to a value that permits adequate pressure differential for the expansion device operation.

The heat exchanger must be located after the hot gas bypass or other unloading devices. If located outdoors, drains must be provided to prevent freezing.

8. Condenser water systems.

Install a heat exchanger or heat pipe in the hot condenser water line to temper outdoor air, pre-heat domestic hot water, or modify the piping in air handling units to utilize hot condenser water to heat air.

Install a coil to extract heat from the hot condenser water line to heat intake air in an air-cycle heat pump which can then transfer its condenser heat to the space requiring it.

Generally, it is not economical to replace existing condensers with double-bundle condensers. If a replacement is being contemplated due to age or the installation of new refrigeration equipment, give considerations to a double-bundle condenser.

9. Air-cooled condensers:

In any building with 15 hp or more of refrigerated display cases or storage boxes, and heating degree days exceeding 3,000, recover heat from air-cooled condenser.

When air-cooled condensers are located away from spaces requiring condenser, or cascade condensers, to recover heat that is otherwise dissipated by the cooling tower.

Install tanks to store hot condenser water from daytime cooling for night-time heating. This water can be used directly for space heating or as a heat source for a heat pump system.

Estimating Energy and Cost Savings

Energy savings will vary with the type of energy recovery equipment. Actual or net savings will be influenced by additional energy required due to pressure drops across the coils or wheel, runaround circulating pump, and design of the equipment as well as climate conditions. Recovery efficiencies of different systems also vary; those for the three most commonly used of these systems are given here, and should be used in calculating energy savings. A sample calculation for one of these systems also follows:

RUNAROUND SYSTEM

Estimate approximately 60% net outside air heating energy savings and 20% net outside air cooling energy savings.

HEAT PIPE SYSTEM

Due to no external power required estimate the net recovery efficiency of the heat pipe is slightly higher than a runaround system. Estimate approximately 70% net outside air heating energy savings and 25% net outside air cooling energy savings.

THERMAL WHEELS

For metallic material wheels (sensible heat transfer only) estimate approximately 70% net outside air heating energy savings and 25% net outside air cooling energy savings.

Example—Thermal Wheel

Given

1. 10,000 cfm outside air for ventilation and exhaust
2. Operating hours 72 hrs/week
3. Space temperature 68 F heating, 50% relative humidity design for cooling
4. 6,000 annual heating degree days
5. 2,000 annual degree hours wet bulb above 66 F
6. No. 2 fuel oil, 138,700 Btu/gal, efficiency 75%
7. Cooling system COP—3.5

Heating Cost Savings

Heating Btu/year/1,000 cfm (Figure 3-2) 72 × 10⁶ Btu

$$\text{Energy Savings} = \frac{10,000}{1,000} \times 72 \times 10^6 \text{ Btu} \times 0.7 = 504 \times 10^6 \text{ Btu/yr.}$$

$$\text{Fuel Savings} = \frac{504 \times 10^6 \text{ Btu/yr}}{138,700 \text{ Btu/gal} \times 0.75} = 4,845 \text{ gal/yr}$$

Annual Heating Cost Savings = 4,845 gal/yr × \$1.00/gal
= \$4,845

Cooling Cost Savings

Cooling Btu/yr/1,000 cfm (Figure 3-2) 32 × 10⁶ Btu

$$\text{Energy Savings} = \frac{10,000}{1,000} \times 32 \times 10^6 \text{ Btu} \times 0.25 = 80 \times 10^6 \text{ Btu/yr}$$

$$\text{Electricity Savings} = \frac{80 \times 10^6 \text{ Btu/yr}}{3.5 \times 3,413} = 6,697 \text{ kWh/yr}$$

Annual Cooling Cost Savings = 6,697 kWh/yr × \$0.05/kWh
= \$335

Total Savings

Heating Cost Savings \$4,845
Cooling Cost Savings   335
                                                    \$5,280

Note: If extra fan energy is used due to the thermal wheel, this must be deducted from the savings.

STEAM REFRIGERATION AND AIR CONDITIONING

Steam is an important direct-energy source for many refrigeration applications including use in oil refining, food processing, and the manufacture of chemicals, synthetic rubber, and synthetic textiles. The single most widely applied use, however, is in comfort and industrial air conditioning.

Air conditioning is recognized as a necessity for most commercial and industrial buildings. Businesses which cater to a transient public trade would find it difficult to meet competition unless their buildings were air-conditioned. Air conditioning is required in many industrial plants to insure continuous operation through summer months for the efficient production of uniform quality products and to improve working conditions and maintain worker efficiency.

Steam used for refrigeration and for summer seasonal air conditioning is especially desirable for a district heating utility. Refrigeration applications often are a year-round use, while air-conditioning applications complement winter heating uses of the steam system to improve the year-round load factor.

The following illustration shows how steam air conditioning can improve the steam load factor for a department store.

Annual steam consumption for space heating, water
heating, and process equipment .... 2,247,000 lb
Steam demand .... 1.300 lb per hr
Annual load factor .... 19.7 per cent
After adding a 150-ton steam-absorption air-condition-
ing system, comparable figures are:
Annual steam consumption .... 3,597,900 lb
Steam demand (based on heating) .... 1.300 lb per hr
Annual load factor .... 31.5 per cent

In comparing steam with electricity and gas as the primary source of energy for refrigeration, a favorable result depends upon a number of factors in each case. An economic feasibility analysis must be undertaken to determine which particular type of energy is the most desirable for each individual installation.

Factors which are significant in selection of the energy source and related equipment include:

1. Capacity of plant
2. Nature of air-conditioning requirements
   a. Length and time of peaks
   b. Sensible to latent heat ratio
3. Available equipment space
4. First cost
5. Annual cost of
   a. Gas
   b. Steam
   c. Electricity
   d. Labor
   e. Water and other materials
   f. Taxes, interest, and depreciation

Refrigeration equipment using steam may be an absorption machine type, a steam jet machine type, steam turbine-driven centrifugal compressor, or a steam engine-driven reciprocating compressor.

Absorption Refrigeration

Absorption refrigeration is a process by which the necessary energy for operation is derived directly from heat in the form of steam or hot water. In contrast, in a vapor or mechanical compression process, the energy required for operation of the vapor or mechanical compression cycle is the mechanical energy that drives the compressor.

In a vapor compression cycle liquid refrigerant is evaporated, then condensed at two separate and distinct pressure levels within the system. The difference between the low-side pressure and the high-side pressure is obtained with the compressor.

Evaporation and condensation of a liquid refrigerant is also the process which is used in the absorption cycle, also with a high side and a low side pressure within the system. The absorption cycle, however, uses the application of heat to increase pressure from the low-side to the high-side. The vapor compression cycle, on the other hand, uses the purely mechanical pumping of the compressor to obtain the pressure differential.

To develop a pressure differential by use of heat, the absorption cycle uses two substancers. One of these must be able to be readily absorbed in the other through physical and chemical reactions. One of these substances is called refrigerant, the other is called an absorbent. The choice of the substance used for the refrigerant depends upon its physical properties such as its pressure-temperature characteristics and its latent heat in Btu per pound. For such use, a substance must be suitable and efficient given the operating pressures and temperature in the absorption cycle. The primary characteristic of an absorbent is that it must have a strong attraction for the refrigerant so the refrigerant will be readily absorbed.

Absorption equipment currently manufactured in the U.S. is either water cooled equipment using lithium bromide water, where water is the refrigerant, or air cooled equipment using ammonia water, where ammonia is the refrigerant.

Figure 8.29 is a typical schematic diagram of an absorption machine using a lithium bromide absorption cycle for capacities from 50–1500 tons.

COMPONENTS

The major components of an absorption system are comprised of the following:

1. Evaporator section—the chilled water is cooled by the evaporation of the refrigerant which is sprayed over the chilled water tubes.
2. Absorber section—evaporated water vapor is absorbed by the absorbent. The heat of absorption is removed by condenser water circulated through this section.
3. Generator section—heat is added in the form of steam or hot water to boil off the refrigerant from the absorbent to reconcentrate the solution.
4. Condenser section—the water vapor produced in the generator is condensed by condenser water circulated through this section.
5. Evaporator pump—the refrigerant is pumped over the tube bundle in the evaporator section.
6. Solution pumps—the salt solution is pumped to the generator and also to the spray header in the absorber.
7. Heat exchanger—the dilute solution being pumped to the generator from

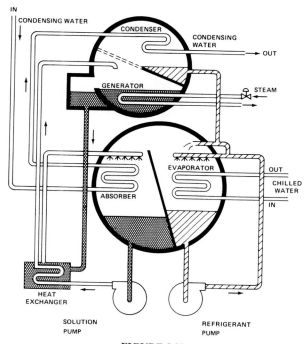

FIGURE 8.29

Diagram of two-shell lithium bromide cycle water chiller

(Courtesy of ASHRAE Handbook & Product Directory)

the absorber is heated by the hot concentrated solution which is returned to the absorber.

8. Purge unit—noncondensables are removed from the machine and low pressure is maintained in the machine.

CAPACITY CONTROL METHOD

Lithium bromide-water cycle absorption machines meet load variations and maintain chilled water temperature through a control varying rate of reconcentration of the absorbent solution.

The chilled water temperature at any constant load is maintained by a temperature difference between refrigerant and chilled water. In turn, the refrigerant temperature is maintained by the absorber being supplied at a specific flow rate and at a specific concentration of solution, and by the absorber cooling water temperature.

Load changes bring about corresponding changes in chilled water temperature. For example, a load reduction results in less of a temperature difference required in the evaporator and a reduced requirement for solution flow or concentration. The resultant chilled water temperature drop is met by adjusting the rate of reconcentration to match the reduced requirements of the absorber.

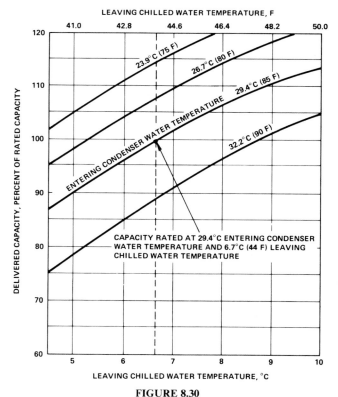

FIGURE 8.30

Performance characteristics of lithium bromide cycle water chiller

(Courtesy of ASHRAE Handbook & Product Directory)

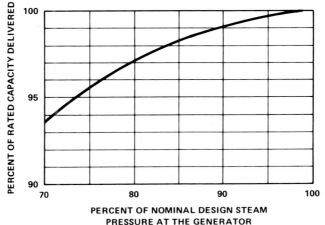

FIGURE 8.31

Effect of steam pressure on capacity

(Courtesy of ASHRAE Handbook & Product Directory)

TABLE 8.5

RATING CONDITIONS FOR HEAT-OPERATED UNITS

Leaving chilled water temperature	44 F
Chilled water temperature differential	10 F
Entering condenser water temperature	85 F
Steam pressure at control valve inlet	9–12 psig
Scale factor for evaporator, condenser, and absorber	0.0005

The normal performance characteristics of a lithium bromide-water cycle absorption machine with an indirect heat source generator are shown in Figure 8.30. The effect of steam pressure on maximum available capacity is shown in Figure 8.31.

The coefficient of performance (COP) of a lithium bromide-water cycle absorption machine operating at nominal conditions (Table 8.5) is usually in the range of 0.60 to 0.70. When chilled water temperatures are above the nominal or when condensing water temperatures are below the nominal, a value of COP as high as about 0.70 can be reached. Reversing these temperature conditions reduces the COP to below 0.60. A coefficient of performance of 0.60 is just about equivalent to a steam rate of 20 lb/(hr) (ton); 0.65 to 18.5 lb/(hr)(ton); 0.70 to 17 lb/(hr) (ton).

Use of two-stage generation in absorption machines improves the COP. Such units may achieve steam rates of approximately 12 lb/(hr) (ton) at full load operation. These dual effect units usually require steam gage pressure at the generator control valve inlet in the 125 to 150 psig of range.

EQUIPMENT SELECTION

Factors which influence the selection of an absorption machine are load, quantity of chilled water, temperature of the chilled water, source of condenser water, temperature of condenser water, quantity of condenser water, fouling factor allowance, and heat source. The final selection is usually based on the least expensive combination of machine and cooling tower combined with a reasonable machine operating cost. An absorption machine can be used with any conventional open or closed circuit chilled water system.

Load, chilled water quantity, and temperature rise are all related, so that when any two are known, the third can be found using the formula:

$$\text{Load (tons)} = \frac{\text{water quantity (gpm)} \times \text{temp. rise}}{24}$$

Tables in manufacturers literature usually will provide ratings in tons based on various leaving chilled water temperatures, entering condenser water temperatures and steam pressures for a particular machine size.

Chilled water temperature should be selected very carefully rather than simply assumed. The use of two machines piped in series may be an economic advantage when low water quantities and a high rise (15 to 20 degrees) are required for the chilled water system, since one machine operates at a higher level and requires less heat input.

Suitable condenser water can come from almost any source for use in an absorption machine, provided it is of good quality. Generally, cooling towers are used, but lake, river or even well water can be used if available in sufficient quantity at the right temperature.

If a lake, river, well or existing process water is to be used for condensation, the maximum expected water temperature should be the key factor in selecting the machine. The quantity of water required will depend on the load and temperature. When a cooling tower is to be used with the absorption machine, the tower should be matched carefully to the machine to provide the most economical combination. In many cases the best choice of a tower will indicate a condenser water temperature higher than that normally estimated (which is usually 7 to 10 degrees above the design wet-bulb temperature). This can mean a major saving in cooling tower cost by reducing the size of the tower needed. Since this machine is heat-operated, the heat rejection to the cooling tower is about twice that of a motor-driven refrigeration machine. A cooling tower for use with an absorption machine usually is about three quarters larger than that used with the motor-driven machine. The condenser water temperature drop through the tower usually runs about 17 to 20 degrees.

The fouling factor allowances to be used for the chilled and condenser water systems in the selection of the machine generally are a minimum factor of .0005 for both.

Usually absorption machines use low pressure steam or high temperature water as an energy source. The pressure or temperature limits usually are defined by the manufacturer. However, 12 psig steam pressure or a leaving hot water temperature of 240 F and a temperature drop of 160 degrees usually are considered as maximum values.

When the pressure or temperature of the energy source exceeds the machine design limits, a steam pressure reducing valve, a water-to-water heat exchanger, a steam-to-hot water converter, a hot water-to-steam converter, a run-around system, or blending of return water with supply water can be used to reduce the energy source to the acceptable limits.

When the system's capacity requirements are less than the capacity of the machine a lower operating steam pressure should be considered. This permits a lower steam rate and a lower total steam consumption. The condenser water quantity must be maintained at full nominal flow for this condition.

Machines now are available which provide "free cooling" when condensing water is available below 50 F. Capacity levels up to 60% of nominal are available by storing solution out of circulation and condensing refrigerant vapor directly on cold absorber tubes.

CONDENSATE RETURN SYSTEMS

Steam-operated absorption machines require a steam trap or a direct return to a receiver through a wet return arrangement. If adequate capacity single traps are not available, multiple traps in parallel may be used. Either an inverted bucket or float and thermostatic trap may be used. The operating steam pressure should be used as the inlet pressure to the trap, and the small pressure loss in the generator tubes is neglected. The trap discharge pressure depends on the type of return system and must be determined on the basis of each individual application.

Usually it is not practical to utilize an existing vacuum pump condensate return system for an absorption machine, since the condensate is much higher in temperature than that for which the return pump may have been selected. This hot condensate can flash and cause vapor binding of the piping or vacuum return pump. A separate wet return system is best where possible. Where not possible, the condensate may be discharged to an atmospheric vent receiver through a steam trap. The condensate also may be cooled to an acceptable level in a heat exchanger then discharged to the vacuum pump condensate system. Any cold water source which can utilize the rejected heat may be used.

CONTROLS

Chilled Water Temperature Control

For an absorption machine to perform satisfactorily under partial load, a capacity reduction is required in proportion to the instantaneous load. Capacity reduction can be achieved by steam throttling, controlling condenser water flow, or controlling the reconcentrated solution. Capacity reduction for some hot water machines can be achieved through hot water throttling.

All these methods are used to control the ability of the machine to reconcentrate solution returned to the absorber. The more dilute the concentration is in the absorber, the less capacity the machine has to chill the water. Solution control gives the best steam rate at partial loads since this is where the machine is operated most often. Such a lowered steam rate is possible because only enough solution must be reconcentrated to match the load. Scaling is minimized because the condensing temperature is maintained at the lowest possible level.

Energy Source Control

Pressure must be maintained within one pound of the design pressure when using steam as the energy source by a pressure reducing valve if high pressure steam is used.

A control valve is usually required when high temperature hot water is the energy source to control the hot water flow through the machine. A two-way throttling or three-way mixing valve is controlled either by a thermostat in the hot water leaving the machine or by means of a chilled water thermostat through a high limit thermostat located in the leaving hot water. The two-way valve should be used only if it does not adversely affect the hot water boiler circulation or the circulating pump. The three-way valve provides for constant flow and is the one most often used.

Multiple Machine Control

Absorption machines may be applied to coolers in parallel and series arrangements. Installations of machine coolers in parallel may utilize two or more machines. If connected in series for chilled water flow, pressure loss through the coolers is cumulative and may become excessive if more than two machines are installed in series.

Parallel Arrangement

When two or more machines are installed with the coolers in the chilled water circuit connected in parallel, each machine should control its own leaving chilled water at design temperature as in a single machine installation. The same throttling range should be used for each machine. As the load on the system is reduced, each machine automatically reduces capacity simultaneously, thus producing the same leaving chilled water temperature.

Operating all machines simultaneously down to minimum load provides the best total steam consumption and the most economical operation when using solution control. There is no economic advantage to shutting down any of the machines at partial load since the steam consumption for two machines operating at partial load is less than for one machine operating at full load. Since there is a minimum of moving parts, there is no reason to shut down a machine to prevent its wearing out.

Each machine cooler should be provided with a separate chilled water pump in a normal air conditioning applicator. The pump and pump motors should be selected to avoid pump motor overload if one or more of the machines and their pumps are shut down.

If separate pumps are not provided and a machine must be shut down, something must be done to shut off the chilled water and condenser water flow after the shutdown cycle is completed.

Series Arrangement

When the coolers are connected in series, equal reduction in loading of each machine produces the best steam consumption. The throttling range of the high stage machine must be adjusted to make certain each machine handles the same percentage of the system load at design and part load conditions.

In any series selection, the range required on the high stage machine must equal the chilled water temperature drop through the low stage machine plus the throttling range of the low stage machine.

CONDENSER WATER TEMPERATURE CONTROL

Some absorption machines and certain process applications require condensing (cooling) water temperature variance from design be limited to ± 5 F. This usually is accomplished by using a three-way valve between the cooling tower and the machine which is controlled by the water temperature to the absorber. The valve permits recirculation and mixing of tower and return water to control the temperature within specific limits.

Where the application allows, some newer absorption machines may accept considerable condensing water temperature variation, permitting absorber inlet temperatures down to 45 F. This is done through use of one or more of the following control methods:

1. An override control limits the opening of the steam valve.
2. A control valve permits liquid refrigerant to transfer from the absorbent circuit.

3. A control valve permits absorbent to transfer from the absorbent to the refrigerant circuit.

At the low limit of water temperature and refrigeration load conditions the unit may be permitted to cycle on and off. This ability of modern machines to use colder condenser water when available, can mean reduced energy demand and improved seasonal operating economics over older machines.

SAFETY CONTROL

Safety controls for the absorption machine should be provided to prevent damage to the machine.

These controls should include:
1. Flow switches or auxiliary contacts of chilled and condenser water pumps should shut down the machine when water flow is interrupted in either circuit.
2. Solution pump and evaporator pump auxiliary contacts should shut down the machine when either pump becomes inoperative.
3. Low temperature cutout should shut down the machine to prevent ice formation and tube damage when the chilled water temperature falls below the minimum allowable temperature.

Steam Turbine-Driven Equipment

Steam turbines are used in air-conditioning and refrigeration systems to drive centrifugal compressors as well as chilled-water and condenser-water pumps and serve as prime movers for electrical generators in total energy systems.

Steam turbines are desirable as drives for large water chilling systems of 200 tons or over employing centrifugal compressors.

High or low-pressure steam may be used with the turbine, operating condensing or noncondensing, depending on the availability of the steam and the economics of each particular installation. Since the cost of steam is a major part of the total operating cost, the steam rate of the turbine is an important factor. Usually the lower the steam rate, the higher the first cost of the equipment, with the exception of the cooling tower. Each installation requires careful economic study to determine the most suitable equipment.

Steam turbines generally can be divided into two principal categories: condensing and noncondensing. The definitions of these, and further subdivisions of these basic families are:
1. Noncondensing turbine—A steam turbine designed to operate with an exhaust steam pressure equal to or greater than atmospheric pressure.
2. Condensing turbine—A steam turbine designed to operate with an exhaust steam pressure below atmospheric pressure.
3. Automatic-extraction turbine—A steam turbine which has both an opening (or openings) in the turbine casing for the extraction of steam and means for directly regulating the steam flow to the turbine stages below the extraction opening.
4. Non-automatic-extraction turbine—A steam turbine which has an opening (or openings) in the turbine casing for the extraction of steam but does not have means for controlling the pressure of the extracted steam.
5. Induction (mixed-pressure) turbine—A steam turbine with separate inlets for steam at two pressures, has an automatic device for controlling the pressure of the secondary steam inducted into the turbine, and means for directly regulating the flow of steam to the turbine stages below the induction opening.

An additional variant is the induction-extraction turbine which has the capability of either exhausting or admitting a supplemental flow of steam through an intermediate port in the casing. This acts to maintain a process heat balance.

Turbines and the extraction and induction-extraction type may have several casing openings, each passing steam at a different pressure.

A vast majority of the steam turbines driving centrifugal compressors for air conditioning are the multistage condensing type. Such turbines give good steam economy at reasonable initial cost. Steam usually is available at a gage pressure of 50 psig or higher with no demand for exhaust steam. Turbines also may be effectively utilized where an abundance of low pressure steam is available.

Aside from rather wide industrial use, the noncondensing or back pressure turbine is most often used in water-chilling plants for driving a centrifugal compressor which shares the cooling load with one or more absorption unit. The exhaust steam from the turbine is usually at a gage pressure of about 15 psig and serves as the heat-energy source for the absorption unit's concentrator. This dual use of the heat energy in the steam results in a lower energy input per unit of refrigeration effect output than can be attained by operating alone with either the turbine-driven centrifugal or the absorption unit.

Important in the design of such combined systems is the need to balance turbine exhaust steam flow with absorption input steam requirements to the greatest extent possible over the full range of anticipated load variations.

Extraction and mixed-pressure turbines are used principally in industry or in large central plants. Extracted steam often is used for boiler feedwater heating or where steam with lower heat content is needed.

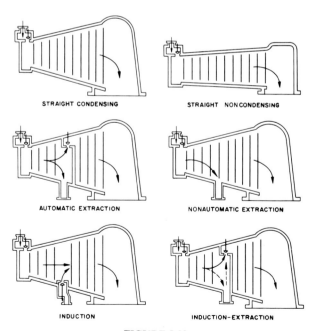

STRAIGHT CONDENSING   STRAIGHT NONCONDENSING

AUTOMATIC EXTRACTION   NONAUTOMATIC EXTRACTION

INDUCTION   INDUCTION-EXTRACTION

FIGURE 8.32
Basic turbine types
(Courtesy of ASHRAE Handbook & Product Directory)

PERFORMANCE

The energy input to a steam turbine is figured in terms of its steam rate, commonly known as water rate. The steam rate is expressed in terms of pounds of steam per horsepower-hour.

The steam rate of a turbine generally is reduced with higher turbine speeds, greater number of stages, larger turbine size, and, always with a higher difference in heat content between entering and leaving steam conditions. Often improvement of one or more of these factors can be achieved with only a minimal increase in initial capital cost. The payback rate, in reduced cost of motive steam due to the lowered steam rate, should always be considered in light of this incremental capital cost.

The trend in steam turbines seems to be toward higher unit power output and speeds, keeping pace with similar changes in the machines they are called upon to drive. Current requirements for centrifugal water-chilling compressor applications range from approximately 100 to 10,000 hp and 3,000 to 10,000 rpm, with the higher speeds associated with lower power outputs and vice versa.

Typical characteristics of steam driven centrifugal water chillers are shown in Tables 8.6 to 8.9.

CONTROLS

Steam turbine controls include the speed governing controls and certain safety devices.

TABLE 8.6
EFFECT ON STEAM RATE OF INLET PRESSURE AND SUPERHEAT[a]

Inlet Pressure (psig)	Inlet Superheat (deg F)	Exhaust Pressure (in. Hg vac.)	Design Output (hp)	Design Speed (rpm)	Design Steam Rate (lb/hp-h)	Steam Rate (%)
125	0	26	500	6000	16.5	100
125	100	26	500	6000	15.5	93
125	200	26	500	6000	14.6	88
250	0	26	500	6000	14.5	87
250	100	26	500	6000	13.6	82
250	200	26	500	6000	12.7	77
400	0	26	500	6000	13.6	82
400	100	26	500	6000	12.5	75
400	200	26	500	6000	11.7	70

[a] Number of stages and efficiency are constant.

TABLE 8.7
EFFECT ON STEAM RATE OF POWER AND SPEED[a]

Inlet Pressure (psig)	Inlet Superheat (deg F)	Exhaust Pressure (in. Hg vac.)	Design Output (hp)	Design Speed (rpm)	Design Steam Rate (lb/hp-h)	Steam Rate (%)
250	0	26	500	3600	18.5	100
250	0	26	500	6000	14.5	78
250	0	26	1500	3600	16.0	86
250	0	26	1500	5000	13.5	73
250	0	26	3500	4000	12.5	68
250	0	26	3500	6000	11.5	62

[a] Number of stages is constant.

TABLE 8.8

EFFECT ON STEAM RATE OF EXHAUST PRESSURE[a]

Inlet Pressure (psig)	Inlet Superheat (deg F)	Exhaust Pressure	Design Output (hp)	Design Speed (rpm)	Design Steam Rate (lb/hp-h)	Steam Rate (%)
250	0	26 in. Hg vac.	1000	5000	14.0	100
250	0	28 in. Hg vac.	1000	5000	12.7	91
250	0	5 psig	1000	5000	24.8	177
250	0	20 psig	1000	5000	32.4	231
250	0	50 psig	1000	5000	41.2	294

[a] Number of stages is constant.

TABLE 8.9

EFFECT ON STEAM RATE OF NUMBER OF STAGES

Inlet Pressure (psig)	Inlet Superheat (deg F)	Exhaust Pressure	Design Power (hp)	Design Speed (rpm)	Number of Stages	Design Steam Design Rate Steam (lb/hp·h)	Steam Rate (%)
125	0	26 in. vac.	1000	5000	5	16.0	100
125	0	26 in. vac.	1000	5000	7	15.1	94
125	0	26 in. vac.	1000	5000	9	14.4	90
150	0	5 psig	500	6000	2	36.0	225
150	0	5 psig	500	6000	3	31.0	194
150	0	5 psig	500	6000	5	29.5	184

The principal function of a speed governing control system is to maintain constant turbine speed in spite of load fluctuations or minor variations in supply steam pressure. The speed governing control system consists of these basic parts:

1. A speed governor (mechanical, electrical or hydraulic);
2. a speed control mechanism (relays, pressure of power amplifying devices, levers and linkages, servo-motors);
3. governor-controlled valve or valves;
4. a speed changer, and
5. external control devices as required.

The safety devices most commonly provided include an overspeed mechanism which acts through a quicktripping valve, independent of the main governor valve, to shut off the steam supply to the turbine, and a pressure-relieving valve in the turbine casing. Overspeed trip devices may act directly through linkages to close the steam valve or hydraulically by relieving oil pressure, allowing the valve to close. It is also essential that the turbine be shut down should other safety devices, such as oil pressure failure or any of the refrigeration protective controls, so dictate. These devices usually act through an electrical interconnection to mechanically or hydraulically close the turbine trip valve.

To shorten the coastdown time of a tripped condensing-type turbine, a vacuum breaker often is installed in the turbine exhaust and opens to admit air on receiving the trip signal.

Steam-Jet Refrigeration Equipment

The steam-jet refrigeration cycle is similar to the more conventional refrigeration cycles which use an evaporator. Basic components of the steam-jet system are a compression device, a condenser and a refrigerant. Instead of a mechanical compression device, however, a steam ejector or "booster" is used to compress the refrigerant to the condenser pressure level.

Water is used as the refrigerant. The cooling effect is achieved in the steam-jet refrigeration cycle by continuous vaporization of a part of the water in the evaporator at a low absolute pressure level.

Steam-jet refrigeration equipment primarily is used in comparatively high-temperature water cooling and air conditioning. For use in air-conditioning systems, its advantages include the complete safety of water as a refrigerant, freedom from vibration, and ability to adjust quickly to load variations. Disadvantages include the difficulty of maintaining the high-vacuum condition necessary for optimal operation and the large amount of condenser water required.

In usual practice, steam-jet refrigeration systems produce chilled water at temperatures between 35 to 70 F which includes the ranges used for comfort air conditioning. In process work, however, where the processed substance is directly evaporated, vaporization at higher temperatures is common.

Since water is the refrigerant in a steam-jet unit, it cannot be operated at evaporator temperatures below 32 F due to freezing. Since evaporator temperatures above 50 F are impractical in comfort cooling applications due to inability to adequately control humidity in the conditioned space, with water as a refrigerant, the useful range of evaporator temperature is thermodynamically restricted.

Steam-jet refrigerator systems are available commercially in 10 to 1,000 ton capacities, although they may be found or built in both smaller and larger sizes.

SYSTEM COMPONENTS

A steam-jet refrigeration system includes an evaporator (or flash tank), a steam-jet ejector (or booster ejector), a condenser, and a two-stage ejector noncondensable pump. Auxiliary components include a chilled water circulating pump, a cooling water circulating pump, a condenser condensate pump, valves and control elements. The pumps and valves are the only components containing moving parts. Figures 8.33 and 8.34 show two of the most common basic systems and their component arrangements.

The steam jet refrigeration equipment can be equipped with capacity control to take full advantage of the lower water temperature from the cooling tower when available, and, as a result, operate more efficiently under partial load.

Heat Rejection Equipment

Without an adequate supply of low cost cooling water, a cooling tower must be provided. Cooling towers are the most commonly used devices to dissipate heat from water-cooled refrigeration and air-conditioning. The water consumption rate of a cooling tower is only about 5% that of a once-through system, making it far less expensive to operate with purchased water supply.

A cooling tower uses a combination of heat and mass transfer to cool water. The water to be cooled is distributed in the tower by spray nozzles, splash bars, or filming-type fill in a way which exposes a very large water surface area to the atmosphere. Fans, convective currents, natural wind currents, or induction

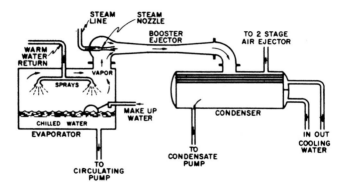

FIGURE 8.33

Steam-jet refrigeration system with surface condenser

(Courtesy of ASHRAE Handbook & Product Directory)

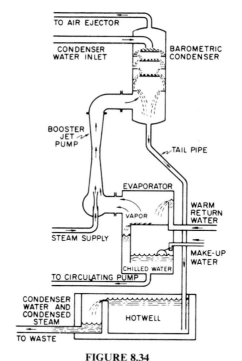

FIGURE 8.34

Steam-jet refrigeration system with barometric condenser

(Courtesy of ASHRAE Handbook & Product Directory)

effect from sprays are used to circulate the air. The relative heat levels of the water and air cause some of the water to evaporate. Since water must absorb heat to change from a liquid to a vapor at constant pressure, this heat is taken from the water remaining in the liquid state. In this manner, the heat of vaporization at atmospheric pressure is removed from the circulating water and transferred to the airstream.

Atmospheric water cooling equipment includes spray ponds, spray-filled atmospheric towers, natural draft atmospheric towers, and mechanical draft towers. Except for relatively small installations on which the spray-filled atmospheric tower may be used, the mechanical draft tower is the most widely used in air-conditioning applications. The mechanical draft tower is the most compact, the lowest in silhouette, the lightest and the best suited to meet exacting conditions of water temperature.

Mechanical draft towers are classified either as induced draft or forced draft.

An induced draft tower fan draws air through the tower (Figure 8.35). The fan in a forced draft tower pushes air through the unit.

Mechanical draft towers are also classified by airflow direction: crossflow, counterflow, or parallel flow.

With a crossflow design (Figure 8.35 B) air flows at 90° to the falling water. In a counterflow tower (Figure 8.35 A), air flows upward through the tower opposite the falling water. With parallel flow air flows downward through the tower parallel to the water.

Most induced draft towers rely on crossflow or counterflow circulation. For counterflow, the fan is placed on top of the tower or near the top, on a side. For crossflow, the fan is located on a side to draw air through the tower, perpendicular to water flow.

Few induced draft towers use parallel flow, because the fan must be located near the bottom of the tower. This pulls water droplets through the tower, increasing waterfall speed, thus shortening the period for which the water is exposed to air.

Forced draft towers rely mostly on the counterflow principle. The fan is located on the side of the tower, near the bottom. It forces air upward through the water.

Mechanical draft towers use either spray or splash deck water distribution. Some use both spray and decking to expose more surface area to air.

COOLING TOWER PERFORMANCE

The relation between the enthalpy of the air and the water temperature is illustrated in Figure 8.36 for a counterflow tower. Heat transfer rate from the water to the air depends on the enthalpy of the air, represented by wet-bulb

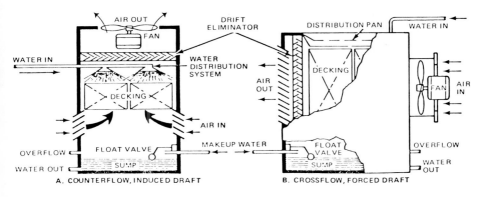

FIGURE 8.35
Types of mechanical draft cooling towers

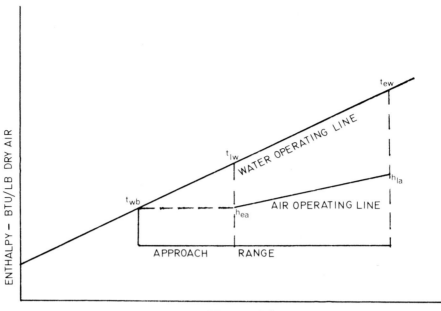

h_{ea} = entering air enthalpy
h_{la} = leaving air enthalpy
t_{ew} = entering water temperature
t_{lw} = leaving water temperature
t_{wb} = wet-bulb temperature

FIGURE 8.36
Water cooling process, counterflow cooling tower

temperature, and is independent of the air dry-bulb temperature. For a given air and water quantity thru a tower, the rate of heat transfer "rated tower capacity" is increased by lowering entering air wet-bulb temperature or by raising the temperature of the water entering the tower.

Tower performance is specified in terms of water *range* and *approach*. "Cooling range" is the difference between water entering and leaving temperatures and is equal to the temperature rise thru the condenser. "Approach" is the difference between the water temperature leaving the tower and the entering air wet-bulb temperature.

SELECTION CONSIDERATIONS

Selection of a cooling tower suitable for a specific application requires consideration of several major factors: cooling duty, economics, required services and environment conditions. Because there are a wide variety of cooling tower types available today which can meet the required cooling duty, such items as size, height, length, width, plan area, volume of air flow, fan and pump energy consumption, materials of construction, water quality, and availability are all important considerations which influence the final equipment selection.

The optimum choice is generally made based on an economic evaluation. Two common methods of such economic evaluation are life-cycle costing and payback analysis. Each of these procedures provides a method of comparing alternative equipment possibilities on the basis of total owning, operating, and maintenance costs.

Other factors to be considered are safety features and codes; operating flexibility for economical operation at varying loads or during seasonal changes, experience and reliability of manufacturers; availability of spare parts; effects of corrosion, scale, or deterioration on service life; general design and rigidity of structures; and conformity to building codes. In addition, equipment vibration, sound levels, acoustical attentuation, and compatibility with the architectural design are also important.

SERVICE WATER HEATING

A service water heating (SWH) system usually consists of a means for generating hot water, storing it, distributing it, and using it. There are many different configurations. The interrelationships involved between components can affect the operating efficiency and economics of the entire system.

Water Heater Types

Steam and hot water are used as the heating medium in a variety of indirect water heaters. The steam or hot water from the district heating plant transmits its heat by means of a heat exchanger (indirect water heater).

Live steam or hot water is sometimes also injected directly into the volume of water to be heated. A description of some of the common types of service water heating systems and equipment follows.

INSTANTANEOUS HEATER

The instantaneous indirect water heater is used to provide a steady, continuous supply of hot water. This type of heater is, in essence, a shell and tube heat exchanger. The shell is usually of ferrous metal and contains a nest of nonferrous tubes. Water flows through the non-ferrous tubes and is heated to the proper temperatures between its inlet and outlet.

Numerous configurations of shell and tube exchangers may be found. In some, the water makes only one pass whereas, multipass arrangements are available in others. Tubes may be straight through, "U" shaped, helical or spiral in design.

In all cases, the heat transfer capability between the water and the steam must be at least the equivalent of the heat required for desired discharge temperature under the maximum instantaneous usage rate.

Another type of instantaneous heater is the steam injection heater. It provides hot water by mixing cold water and steam under some method of proportional control. Such heaters are apt to be noisy and the condensate from the steam is not returned. Their application is limited to scattered areas of industrial plants where a supply of hot water from a central system is not feasible.

Instantaneous water heaters have a lower first cost and smaller physical dimensions compared with storage-type heaters. They are less susceptible to corrosion because the water is confined to the inside of the tubes and the head, both of which are generally made of non-ferrous metals. Instantaneous water heaters with straight-through tubes are more desirable for heating water that contains unusually large amounts of scale-forming materials because of the ease with which the tubes can be cleaned.

TANK HEATER

A tank heater is a modified instantaneous water heater. It offers a highly sophisticated design of exchanger surface housed within a vertical shell or tank. In this heater, water is in the shell and steam flows through the tubes.

A temperature sensor controls a modulating steam flow regulator that matches the steam input to the hot water demand. The rapid response of this system to large changes in hot water use eliminates any need for external storage.

As with an instantaneous heater, the input steam and/or water capacity of the tank heater must be adequate to meet the maximum short interval water heating demand.

STORAGE WATER HEATER

The main advantage of the storage heater is its lower steam demand and its adaptability to automatic temperature control. The lower steam demand is of benefit to those district steam users who purchase steam under a load factor type of rate schedule.

Storage water heaters are made in several types. The most common form is a closed horizontal steel tank with a horizontal nest of copper tubes inserted from one end near the bottom of the tank.

Cold water is admitted to the tank through a bottom connection and hot water is drawn off at the top. Steam is admitted to the tubes and condensate is removed through a head casting at the end of the nest of tubes. The tubes are usually U shaped but, in some heaters, they are straight with cast-iron heads at both ends of the nest of tubes. Storage heaters are also available with vertical tanks.

Another type employs an external instantaneous heater. Still another form of storage water heater uses an open tank. The water in this tank may be heated by an open-end steam pipe immersed in the water or via a pipe coil exchanger.

HELIFLOW WATER HEATER

A heliflow heater consists of one or more spiral shaped coils held between two flat surfaces. One of these surfaces is the base plate and the other is called the casing. When bolted together, these parts form a closed, spiral shaped fluid circuit outside of the coil and in between the two surfaces. Flow external to the coil is counterflow to the companion circuit inside of the coil. The coil itself acts as a baffle in directing the external flow.

In multiple coil units, coils are stacked on top of one another and held together by the base plate and casing. At the end of the coil, a manifold is attached. These manifolds are then bolted to the base plate matching up with the piping connections to and from the coil side of the unit. The connections that admit the fluids to the outside of the coil are located on the base plate or the casing and introduce these fluids at the proper point outside of the coil.

Sizing Storage Water Heaters

The size of a water heater is determined by the hot water demand and load characteristics. For a storage-type water heater, both the size of the storage tank and the capacity of the heating coil must be considered. But, in the case of an instantaneous water heater, only the capacity of the heating element need be

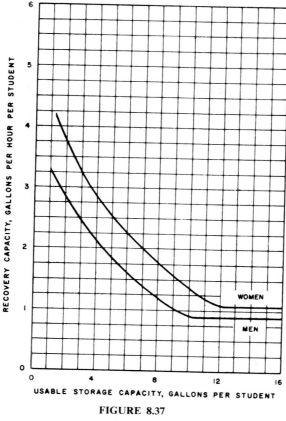

FIGURE 8.37

Dormitories

(Courtesy of ASHRAE Handbook & Product Directory)

determined. Physical dimensions must be considered so that the water heater will fit into the space allotted to it.

Hot water requirements in most commercial and industrial buildings vary in total volume flow rate, duration or peak load period, and with temperature needed. Peak hourly and daily demands for various categories of buildings are shown in Table 8.10. These demands only apply to central storage type hot water systems and represent maximum and average consumption for these types of buildings. Averages for schools and food service establishments are based on actual days of operation, while all others are based on total days. Monthly consumption estimates can be derived from use of averages.

Figures 8.37 through 8.42 show relationships between recovery and storage capacity for several types of buildings. Any combination of storage and recovery capacity that falls on the proper curve will satisfy the requirements of the building. Selecting the minimum recovery rate and the maximum storage capacity on the curves will identify the smallest hot water capacity capable of supplying building requirement. The higher the recovery capacity, the greater the heating capacity and the smaller the storage capacity needed.

The following curves may be used to select water heaters having fixed storage

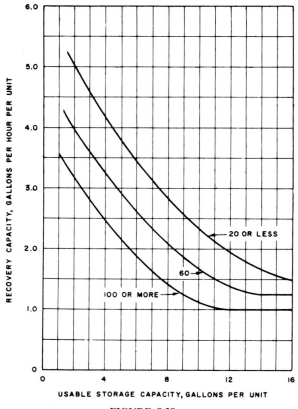

FIGURE 8.38

Motels

(Courtesy of ASHRAE Handbook & Product Directory)

or recovery capacities, by trading recovery for storage requirements. Where hot water demands are not coincident with steam or purchased hot water demands, water heater inputs can be selected to avoid additional energy demands, and the corresponding storage tank size can be selected from the curves.

Recovery capacities shown in Figures 8.39 to 8.44 represent the actual hot water flow required without considering system heat losses. Heat losses from storage tanks and recirculating hot water piping should be added to the recovery capacities shown on the graphs. With large uninsulated storage tanks and extensive lengths of uninsulated hot water piping, it is necessary to increase the recovery capacity substantially.

The storage capacities shown are considered net usable requirements. Based on the assumption that only 60 to 80% of the hot water in a storage tank is usable, the actual storage tank size should be increased by 25 to 66% to compensate for unusable hot water.

EXAMPLE 1:

Determine the water heater size and monthly hot water consumption for an office building to be occupied by 200 people:

TABLE 8.10

TYPICAL HOT WATER DEMANDS FOR VARIOUS TYPES OF BUILDINGS

Type of Building	Maximum Hour	Maximum Day	Average Day
Men's dormitories	3.8 gal (14.4 l)/student	22.0 gal (83.4 l)/student	13.1 gal (49.7 l)/student
Women's dormitories	5.0 gal (19 l)/student)	26.5 gal (100.4 l)/student	12.3 gal (46.6 l)/student
Motels: no. of units[a]			
20 or less	6.0 gal (22.7 l)/unit	35.0 gal (132.6 l)/unit	20.0 gal (75.8 l)/unit
60	5.0 gal (19.7 l)/unit	25.0 gal (94.8 l)/unit	14.0 gal (53.1 l)/unit
100 or more	4.0 gal (15.2 l)/unit	15.0 gal (56.8 l)/unit	10.0 gal (37.9 l)/unit
Nursing homes	4.5 gal (17.1 l)/bed	30.0 (113.7 l)/bed	18.4 gal (69.7 l)/bed
Office buildings	0.4 gal (1.52 l)/person	2.0 gal (7.6 l)/person	1.0 gal (3.79 l)/person
Food service establishments:			
Type A—full meal restaurants and cafeterias	1.5 gal (5.7 l)/max meals/h	11.0 gal (41.7 l)/max meals/h	2.4 gal (9.1 l)/avg meals/day[b]
Type B—drive-ins, grilles, luncheonettes, sandwich and snack shops	0.7 gal (2.6 l)/max meals/h	6.0 gal (22.7 l)/max meals/h	0.7 gal (2.6 l)/avg meals/day[b]
Apartment houses: no. of apartments			
20 or less	12.0 gal (45.5 l)/apt.	80.0 gal (303.2 l)/apt.	42.0 gal (159.2 l)/apt.
	10.0 gal (37.9 l)/apt.	73.0 gal (276.7 l)/apt.	40.0 gal (151.6 l)/apt.
	8.5 gal (32.2 l)/apt.	66.0 gal (250 l)/apt.	38.0 gal (144 l)/apt.
100	7.0 gal (26.5 l)/apt.	60.0 gal (227.4 l)/apt.	37.0 gal (140.2 l)/apt.
200 or more	5.0 gal (19 l)	50.0 gal (195 l)/apt.	35.0 gal (132.7 l) apt.
Elementary schools	0.6 gal (2.3 l)/student	1.5 gal (5.7 l)/student	0.6 gal (2.3 l)/student[b]
Junior and senior high schools	1.0 gal (3.8 l)/student	3.6 gal (13.6 l)/student	1.8 gal (6.8 l)/student[b]

[a] Per day of operation.
[b] Interpolate for intermediate values.

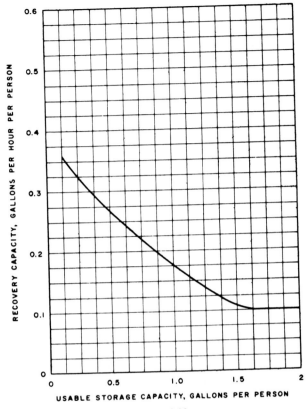

FIGURE 8.39

Office Buildings

(Courtesy of ASHRAE Handbook & Product Directory)

1. Storage system with minimum recovery rate.
2. Storage system with 1.0 gal per person storage.
3. Additional minimum recovery rate requirement for a luncheonette, open 5 days a week, serving a maximum of 100 meals in one hour, and an average of 200 meals per day.

SOLUTION:

1. With minimum recovery rate of 0.10 gph person from Figure 8.39 for office buildings, 20 gph recovery is required, while the storage is 1.6 gal per person, or $200 \times 1.6 = 320$ gal storage. On a 70% net usable basis, the tank size will be $1.43 \times 320 = 458$ gal.
2. The curve also shown 1.0 gal storage per person at 0.175 gph per person recovery, or $200 \times 0.175 = 35$ gph. The tank size will be $1.43 \times 200 = 286$ gal.
3. The hot water requirements for a luncheonette are contained in the recommendations for food service establishments (Figure 8.40). The recovery vs. storage curve shows that with minimum recovery capacity of 0.25 gph per maximum meals per hour, 100 meals would require 25 gph

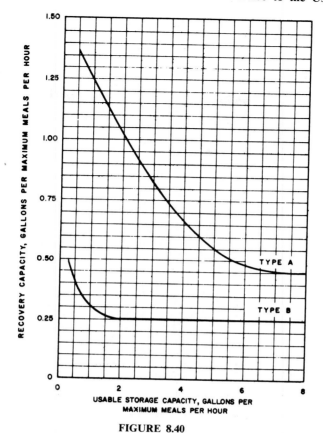

FIGURE 8.40

Food Service

(Courtesy of ASHRAE Handbook & Product Directory)

recovery, while the storage would be 2.0 gal per meal, or $100 \times 2.0 \times 1.43$ = 286 gal. storage. The combined requirements with item a would then be 45 gph recovery and 744 gal. storage.

4. From Table 8.39, the office building will consume an average of 1.0 gal. per person per day $\times$ 30 days $\times$ 200 people = 6000 gal. per month, while the luncheonette will consume 0.7 gal. per meal $\times$ 200 meals per day $\times$ 22 days per month = 3080 gal. per month, for a total of 9,080 gal. per month.

Note: Recovery capacities shown are for heating water only. To these capacities, additional capacity must be added to offset the system heat losses.

Another method of sizing storage type water heaters takes the number of outlets or fixtures into account rather than the number of persons. The estimated hot-water demand per fixture for various types of buildings is given in Table 8.11.

The amount of hot water drawn from most fixtures depends upon the number of persons using them and the habits of these persons. Since personal habits have so many variables, it is difficult to devise a formula for determining the exact demand.

Table 8.11 can be used to size either storage or instantaneous water heaters

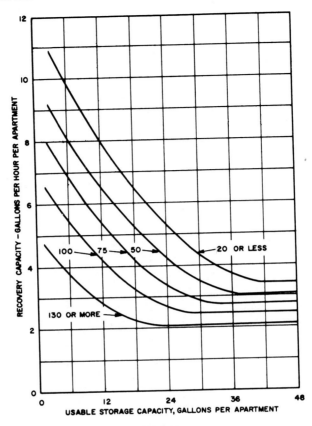

FIGURE 8.41

Apartments

(Courtesy of ASHRAE Handbook & Product Directory)

for various types of buildings if the number and kind of hot-water fixtures are known. The sum of the products of the numbers of the various kinds of fixtures and their demands is the possible maximum demand for hot water. If an instantaneous water heater is to be used, it should have sufficient heating capacity to meet this demand. If a storage water heater is to be used, the capacity of the heating coil should be equal to the probable maximum demand which is obtained by multiplying the possible maximum demand by the applicable demand factor in Table 8.11. The capacity of the storage tank is obtained by multiplying the probable maximum demand by the applicable storage capacity factor in the same table.

EXAMPLE 2:

Find the size of an instantaneous water heater required for an office building having the number of fixtures given below: also to determine the size of a storage water heater for the same building.

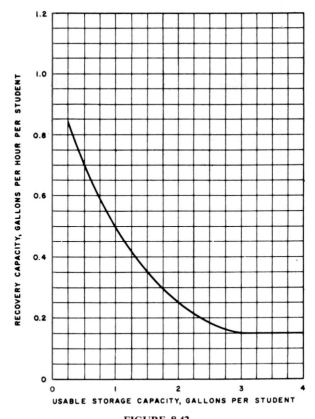

FIGURE 8.42

High Schools

(Courtesy of ASHRAE Handbook & Product Directory)

120 Basins (Public Lavatories)	×	6 = 720 gal per hr
400 Basins (Private Lavatories)	×	2 = 800 gal per hr
22 Slop Sinks	×	20 = 440 gal per hr

Possible Maximum Demand   = 1960 gal per hr
Probable Maximum Demand = 1960 × .30 = 598 gal per hr
Storage tank capacity   = 598 × 2.00 = 1196 gal

Then the capacity of an instantaneous water heater would be 1960 gal/hr.

If a storage water heater were used, the heating coil should have a capacity of 598 gal per hr and the storage tank should hold 1196 gal. Of course, the nearest commercial size would be selected.

Sizing Instantaneous Water Heaters

The recommended method for sizing instantaneous water heaters is based on the Hunter method for sizing hot and cold water piping. A correction factor is applied for hot water and various building types.

The method involves selection of fixture units from Table 8.12 for each fixture using hot water.

TABLE 8.11
HOT WATER DEMAND PER FIXTURE FOR VARIOUS TYPES OF BUILDINGS
[Gallons (litres) of water per hour per fixture, calculated at a final temperature of 140 F (60°C)]

Fixture	Apartment House	Club	Gymnasium	Hospital	Hotel	Industrial Plant	Office Building	Private Residence	School	YMCA
1. Basins, private lavatory	2(7.6)	2(7.6)	2(7.6)	2(7.6)	2(7.6)	2(7.6)	2(7.6)	2(7.6)	2(7.6)	2(7.6)
2. Basins, public lavatory	4(15.2)	6(22.7)	8(30.3)	6(22.7)	8(30.3)	12(45.5)	6(22.7)	—	15(56.8)	8(30.3)
3. Bathtubs	20(75.8)	20(75.8)	30(113.7)	20(75.8)	20(75.8)	—	—	20(75.8)	—	30(113.7)
4. Dishwashers[a]	15(56.8)	50–150	—	50–150	50–200	20–100	—	15(56.8)	20–100	20–100
		(189.5–568.5)		(189.5–568.5)	(189.5–758)	(75.8–379)			(75.8–379)	(75.8–379)
5. Foot basins	3(11.4)	3(11.4)	12(45.5)	3(11.4)	3(11.4)	12(45.5)	—	3(11.4)	3(11.4)	12(45.5)
6. Kitchen sink	10(37.9)	20(75.8)	—	20(75.8)	30(113.7)	20(75.8)	—	10(37.9)	20(75.8)	20(75.8)
7. Laundry, stationary tubs	20(75.8)	28(106.1)	—	28(106.1)	28(106.1)	—	—	20(75.8)	—	28(106.1)
8. Pantry sink	5(18.9)	10(37.9)	—	10(37.9)	10(37.9)	—	—	5(18.9)	10(37.9)	10(37.9)
9. Showers	30(113.7)	150(568.5)	225(852.7)	75(284.2)	75(284.2)	225(852.7)	10(37.9)	30(113.7)	225(852.7)	225(852.7)
10. Slop sink	20(75.8)	20(75.8)	—	20(75.8)	30(113.7)	20(75.8)	20(75.8)	15(56.8)	20(75.8)	20(75.8)
11. Hydrotherapeutic showers				400(1516.0)						
12. Hubbard baths				600(2274.0)						
13. Leg baths				100(379.0)						
14. Arm baths				35(132.6)						
15. Sitz baths				30(113.7)						
16. Continuous-flow baths				165(625.4)						
17. Circular wash sinks				20(75.8)	20(75.8)	30(113.7)	20(75.8)		30(113.7)	
18. Semicircular wash sinks				10(37.9)	10(37.9)	15(56.8)	10(37.9)		15(56.8)	
19. DEMAND FACTOR	0.30	0.30	0.40	0.25	0.25	0.40	0.30	0.30	0.40	0.40
20. STORAGE CAPACITY FACTOR[b]	1.25	0.90	1.00	0.60	0.80	1.00	2.00	0.70	1.00	1.00

[a] Dishwasher requirements should be taken from this table or from manufacturers' data for the model to be used, if this is known.
[b] Ratio of storage tank capacity to probable maximum demand/h. Storage capacity may be reduced where an unlimited supply of steam is available from a central street steam system or large boiler plant.

TABLE 8.12

HOT WATER DEMAND IN FIXTURE UNITS [140 F (60°C) WATER]

Fixture	Apart-ment House	Club	Gym-nasium	Hospi-tal	Hotels and Dormi-tories	Indus-trial Plant	Office Bldg	School	YMCA
Basins, private lavatory	0.75	0.75	0.75	0.75	0.75	0.75	0.75	0.75	0.75
Basins, public lavatory	—	1	1	1	1	1	1	1	1
Bathtubs	1.5	1.5	—	1.5	1.5	—	—	—	—
Dishwashers	1.5	Five (5)Fixture Units per 250 Seating Capacity							
Therapeutic bath	—	—	—	5	—	—	—	—	—
Kitchen sink	0.75	1.5	—	3	1.5	3	—	0.75	3
Pantry sink	—	2.5	—	2.5	2.5	—	—	2.5	2.5
Slop sink	1.5	2.5	—	2.5	2.5	2.5	2.5	2.5	2.5
Showers[a]	1.5	1.5	1.5	1.5	1.5	3.5	—	1.5	1.5
Circular wash fountain	—	2.5	2.5	2.5	—	4	—	2.5	2.5
Semicircular wash fountain .	—	1.5	1.5	1.5	—	3	—	1.5	1.5

[a] In applications where the principal use is showers, as in gymnasiums or at end of shift in industrial plants, use conversion factor of 1.00 to obtain design water flow rate in gpm (1/s).

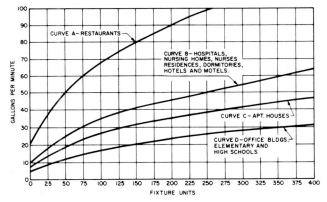

FIGURE 8.43

Modified hunter curve for hot water flow rate (corrected for type of building usage)

(Courtesy of ASHRAE Handbook & Product Directory)

Maximum hot water demand in gpm is obtained from Figure 8.43 or 8.44 by matching total fixture units to the curve for the type of building, and reading gpm. Hot water requirements for fixtures and outlets having constant flows should be added to demand obtained previously.

The heater then is selected with the total demand and temperature rise required. Normal hot water utilization temperatures for some of the services is provided in Table 8.13. For critical applications, such as hospitals, the user of multiple heaters with 100% standby is recommended. Multiple heaters should be considered for building where continuity of service is important.

The minimum recommended size for the semi-instantaneous heater is 10 gpm, except for restaurants, which should be a minimum of 15 gpm. When the flow for a system having equipment for which the flows or diversity are not easily determined, the heater may be sized for the full flow of the piping system. Caution must be used when sizing heaters with very low flows, and careful judgment applied to estimate diversities. Unique hot water requirements in a building should be analyzed by the designer to determine if additional capacity is required. One such example would be a dormitory in a school where all of

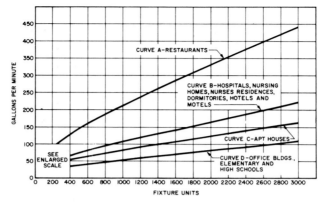

FIGURE 8.44

Enlarged section of modified hunter curve for hot water flow rate (corrected for type of building usage)

(Courtesy of ASHRAE Handbook & Product Directory)

TABLE 8.13

REPRESENTATIVE HOT WATER UTILIZATION TEMPERATURES

Use	Temp. F	(°C)
Lavatory		
Hand washing	105	(40.6)
Shaving	115	(46.1)
Showers and tubs	110	(43.3)
Therapeutic baths	110	(43.3)
Commercial and institutional dishwashing		
Wash	140	(60.0)
Sanitizing rinse	180	(82.2)
Commercial and institutional laundry	180	(82.2)
Residential dishwashing and laundry	140	(60.0)
Surgical scrubbing	110	(43.3)

the showers and lavatories can be used simultaneously when the students return. In such a case, the heater and piping should be sized for the full flow of the system.

EXAMPLE 3:

Determine the hot water flow rate for sizing an instantaneous heater for a high school having the following fixture count: 50 public lavatories, 4 kitchen sinks, 6 showers, 5 slop sinks, and dishwasher at 7 gpm.

SOLUTION:

The calculation using Table 8.13 is as follows:

50 public lavatories	× 1	fixture units =	50 fixture units
4 kitchen sinks	× 0.75	"	3 "
6 showers	× 1.5	"	9 "
5 slop sinks	× 2.5	"	12.5 "
			74.5 "

The flow rate from curve D of Figure 8.43 corresponding to 74.5 fixture units is 14 gpm. To this must be added the dishwasher requirement of 7 gpm. Thus, the total flow is 21 gpm.

Water Distribution System

A well designed water distribution system must consider many of the following system constraints and design factors:
1. flow/draw rate,
2. pressure drops,
3. noise,
4. temperature drop,
5. methods of support,
6. initial investment cost and
7. system operating cost.

Any deficiency in distribution sizing and design may result in improper operation of the system.

The material most commonly used in cold and hot water piping is copper. Table 8.14 contains the physical properties of copper tubing. Of the various classifications, type L is the one most frequently used.

In moderate to large service water heating systems, provision is usually made to recirculate water from the extremities of distribution mains and/or risers back to and through the water heaters.

Such recirculation systems are designed to prevent the water from dropping below the minimum acceptable utilization temperature. Otherwise it would lay dormant in the mains and cool off during periods of little or no hot water use. Most systems employ forced circulation with the thermostatic control of the circulating pump activated by an aquastat located in the return line and set to operate the pump when the sensed temperature reaches a level in the area of 110 F.

The circulating hot water supply may be distributed by either an upfeed or downfeed piping sytem. Three common methods of arranging circulating lines are shown in Figure 8.45. Although the diagrams apply to multi-story buildings, arrangements (a) and (b) are also used in multi-story residential designs.

In circulating systems, consideration should be given to air venting, pressure drops through the heaters and storage tanks, balancing, and line losses. Proper air venting of a circulating system is extremely important, particularly if gravity circulation is used. In Figure 8.45 (a) and (b), venting is accomplished by connecting the circulating line below the top fixture supply. With this arrangement, air is eliminated from the system each time the top fixture is opened.

Where an overhead supply main is located above the highest fixture, as in Figure 8.45 (c), an automatic float-type air vent is installed at the highest point of the system. Alternately, a fixture branch is connected to the top of the main where air venting is desired and then dropped to the fixture outlet.

It is sometimes necessary to make an allowance for pressure drop through the heater when sizing hot water lines, particularly where instantaneous hot water heaters are used and the available pressure is low. Where multiple risers or horizontal loops are used, balancing valves in the return lines are recommended. A check valve should be provided in each return to prevent temporary reversal of flow to reduce heat loss from the piping, particularly during periods of no water demand. To increase the system distribution efficiency and provide satisfactory hot water service, all piping and storage tanks should be insulated.

HUMIDIFICATION BY STEAM

The term "air conditioning" in its broader sense implies control of any and all of the physical and chemical qualities of air. Comfort air conditioning is the process of treating air so as to control simultaneously its distribution, cleanliness, temperature and *humidity*.

Humidity is water vapor or moisture that is always present in the air. By

TABLE 8.14
—PHYSICAL PROPERTIES OF COPPER TUBING

Classification	Nom. Tube Size (in.)	Outside Diam (in.)	Stubbs Gage	Wall Thickness (in.)	Inside Diam (in.)	Transverse Area (sq in.)	Minimum Test Pressure (psi)	Weight of Tube (lb/ft)	Wt. of Water in Tube[a] (lb/ft)	Outside Surface (sq ft/ft)
HARD	1/4	3/8	23	.025	.325	.083	1000	.106	.036	.098
	3/8	1/2	23	.025	.450	.159	1000	.144	.069	.131
	1/2	5/8	22	.028	.569	.254	890	.203	.110	.164
	3/4	7/8	21	.032	.811	.516	710	.328	.224	.229
	1	1 1/8	20	.035	1.055	.874	600	.464	.379	.295
	1 1/4	1 3/8	19	.042	1.291	1.309	590	.681	.566	.360
Govt. Type "M" 250 Lb Working Pressure	1 1/2	1 5/8	18	.049	1.527	1.831	580	.94	.793	.425
	2	2 1/8	17	.058	2.009	3.17	520	1.46	1.372	.556
	2 1/2	2 5/8	16	.065	2.495	4.89	470	2.03	2.120	.687
	3	3 1/8	15	.072	2.981	6.98	440	2.68	3.020	.818
	3 1/2	3 5/8	14	.083	3.459	9.40	430	3.58	4.060	.949
	4	4 1/8	13	.095	3.935	12.16	430	4.66	5.262	1.08
	5	5 1/8	12	.109	4.907	18.91	400	6.66	8.180	1.34
	6	6 1/8		.122	5.881	27.16	375	8.91	11.750	1.60
	8	8 1/8		.170	7.785	47.6	375	16.46	20.60	2.13
HARD	3/8	1/2	19	.035	.430	.146	1000	.198	.063	.131
	1/2	5/8		.040	.545	.233	1000	.284	.101	.164
	3/4	7/8		.045	.785	.484	1000	.454	.209	.229
	1	1 1/8		.050	1.025	.825	880	.653	.358	.295
Govt. Type "L" 250 Lb Working Pressure	1 1/4	1 3/8		.055	1.265	1.256	780	.882	.554	.360
	1 1/2	1 5/8		.060	1.505	1.78	720	1.14	.770	.425
	2	2 1/8		.070	1.985	3.094	640	1.75	1.338	.556
	2 1/2	2 5/8		.080	2.465	4.77	580	2.48	2.070	.687
	3	3 1/8		.090	2.945	6.812	550	3.33	2.975	.818
	3 1/2	3 5/8		.100	3.425	9.213	530	4.29	4.000	.949
	4	4 1/8		.110	3.905	11.97	510	5.38	5.180	1.08
	5	5 1/8		.125	4.875	18.67	460	7.61	8.090	1.34
	6	6 1/8		.140	5.845	26.83	430	10.20	11.610	1.60
HARD	1/4	3/8	21	.032	.311	.076	1000	.133	.033	.098
	3/8	1/2	18	.049	.402	.127	1000	.269	.055	.131
	1/2	5/8	18	.049	.527	.218	1000	.344	.094	.164
	3/4	7/8	16	.065	.745	.436	1000	.641	.189	.229
	1	1 1/8	16	.065	.995	.778	780	.839	.336	.295
Govt. Type "K" 400 Lb Working Pressure	1 1/4	1 3/8	16	.065	1.245	1.217	630	1.04	.526	.360
	1 1/2	1 5/8	15	.072	1.481	1.722	580	1.36	.745	.425
	2	2 1/8	14	.083	1.959	3.014	510	2.06	1.300	.556
	2 1/2	2 5/8	13	.095	2.435	4.656	470	2.92	2.015	.687
	3	3 1/8	12	.109	2.907	6.637	450	4.00	2.870	8.18
	3 1/2	3 5/8	11	.120	3.385	8.999	430	5.12	3.890	.949
	4	4 1/8	10	.134	3.857	11.68	420	6.51	5.05	1.08
	5	5 1/8		.160	4.805	18.13	400	9.67	7.80	1.34
	6	6 1/8		.192	5.741	25.88	400	13.87	11.20	1.60

[a] To change "Wt of Water in Tube (lb/ft)" to "Gallons of Water in Tube (gal/ft)," divide values in table by 8.34.

TABLE 8.14—*Continued*

Classification	Nom. Tube Size (in.)	Outside Diam (in.)	Stubbs Gage	Wall Thickness (in.)	Inside Diam (in.)	Transverse Area (sq in.)	Minimum Test Pressure (psi)	Weight of Tube (lb/ft)	Wt. of Water in Tube[a] (lb/ft)	Outside Surface (sq ft/ft)
SOFT	¼	⅜	21	.032	.311	.076	1000	.133	.033	.098
	⅜	½	18	.049	.402	.127	1000	.269	.055	.131
	½	⅝	18	.049	.527	.218	1000	.344	.094	.164
	¾	⅞	16	.065	.745	.436	1000	.641	.189	.229
	1	1⅛	16	.065	.995	.778	780	.839	.336	.295
Govt. Type "K" 250 Lb Working Pressure	1¼	1⅜	16	.065	1.245	1.217	630	1.04	.526	.360
	1½	1⅝	15	.072	1.481	1.722	580	1.36	.745	.425
	2	2⅛	14	.083	1.959	3.014	510	2.06	1.300	.556
	2½	2⅝	13	.095	2.435	4.656	470	2.92	2.015	.687
	3	3⅛	12	.109	2.907	6.637	450	4.00	2.870	.818
	3½	3⅝	11	.120	3.385	8.999	430	5.12	3.89	.949
	4	4⅛	10	.134	3.857	11.68	420	6.51	5.05	1.08
	5	5⅛		.160	4.805	18.13	400	9.67	7.80	1.34
	6	6⅛		.192	5.741	25.88	400	13.87	11.2	1.60

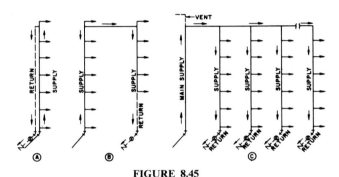

FIGURE 8.45

Methods of arranging hot water circulation lines

(Courtesy of ASHRAE Handbook & Product Directory)

itself the term "humidity" does not indicate the amount of moisture in the air. The most often used measurement of water vapor in the air is "relative humidity." Relative humidity (R.H.) is a statement of the actual amount of water vapor in a unit volume of air compared with the maximum amount of moisture the same volume of air could hold at the existing temperature. Warm air has the capacity to hold more moisture than cold air. For example, 300,000 cubic feet of $-10°F$ air at 45% R.H. will contain .7 gallon of water as a vapor; this same volume of air raised to 74°F would require the addition of 21.2 gallons of water vapor to maintain the relative humidity at 45%.

All the air in a heated building will be exchanged periodically due to infiltration and exfiltration. As the cold outdoor air with low moisture content enters the building, it is heated to become warm dry air. The relative humidity drops to such a low level that it causes trouble in the processing of hygroscopic materials, creates conditions for the accumulation of static electricity, and is less comfortable and healthy for human beings.

Dry air seeks to draw moisture from any source. It will soak up moisture from any hygroscopic material and from the nasal passages and skin of human beings. The only way to solve the dry air problem is to add moisture to the air.

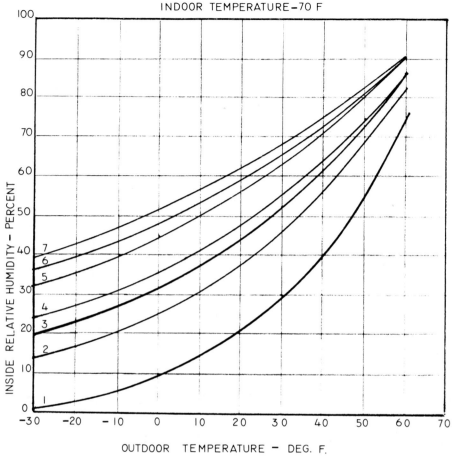

INDOOR TEMPERATURE – 70 F

OUTDOOR TEMPERATURE – DEG. F.

FIGURE 8.46

Condensation on windows, relative humidity conditions at which condensation begins to appear on windows

CURVE 1 SINGLE GLASS.
CURVE 2 WINDOW WITH USUAL STORM SASH. 1½″ AIR SPACE BETWEEN PANES.
CURVE 3 WINDOW WITH TWO GLASS PANES HERMETICALLY SEALED IN SASH. ¼″ BETWEEN PANES.
CURVE 4 WINDOW WITH TWO GLASS PANES HERMETICALLY SEALED IN SASH. ½″ BETWEEN PANES.
CURVE 5 WINDOW WITH VERY TIGHTLY FITTED STORM SASH WITH NO VENTILATOR OPENINGS. 1½″ BETWEEN PANES.
CURVE 6 WINDOW WITH THREE GLASS PANES HERMETICALLY SEALED IN SASH. ¼″ BETWEEN PANES.
CURVE 7 WINDOW WITH THREE GLASS PANES HERMETICALLY SEALED IN SASH. ½″ BETWEEN PANES.

Dry steam is the efficient answer to humidification. All methods of humidification must convert water to vapor and mix the vapor with the air in the space to be humidified. Since water vapor is steam at very low pressure and temperature, the whole process can be simplified by introducing steam directly into the air to be humidified. Advantages of steam for humidification are:

1. steam is immediately absorbed by the air,
2. practically no change in dry bulb temperature,
3. no mineral dust is introduced into the ventilating air,
4. it is easy to control,
5. it creates no sanitation or odor problems,
6. it is economical to operate.

Comparing the psychometric aspects of water spray and steam humidification proves steam to be a superior method of introducing moisture into conditioned air. The water spray method is basically an adiabatic process in which no heat is transferred to or from the working substance. The steam method is essentially an isothermal process in that the temperature of the air remains constant as the moisture is added in vapor form.

Applications

In a simple heating and ventilating system, the humidifier is located downstream from the fan. The space humidostat will modulate the normally closed humidifier valve to maintain the desired humidity level. A valve is wired in parallel with the fan so that the humidifier valve is closed whenever the fan is stopped and prevents damage from any moisture that might be released into the duct when there is no air flow.

The high limit duct humidostat is located six to eight feet downstream from the humidifier. The high limit prevents super saturation and damage from condensation caused by a sudden load or set point change.

In large volume air conditioning systems with provisions for utilizing 100 per cent outdoor air, the humidifier is located downstream from the reheat coil. An insertion type duct humidostat located in the return or exhaust air duct will modulate the normally closed humidifier valve to maintain an average level of humidity in the space.

In industrial plants and areas without air handling systems, area humidifiers are used to discharge dry steam directly into the atmosphere. Installed very much like unit heaters, area humidifiers do not require steam distribution manifolds. Dispersion of the steam is by means of a fan or a jet nozzle. Operation may be electric or pneumatic and is governed by a humidity controller in the area humidified.

Condensation on Windows

A problem associated with humidification, particularly at low outdoor temperatures, is condensation on windows. Figure 8.46 indicates the approximate points where condensation may occur with various window constructions.

CHAPTER 9

The Economic and Financial Analysis of Community Energy Systems

ECONOMICS AND FINANCIAL MANAGEMENT

THE ECONOMICS of district heating include factors affecting the consumer as well as those of interest primarily to the district heating enterprise. There is a close relationship between the two. The district heating services must be available to the consumer at price levels which are both economically acceptable to the consumer and profitable to the supplier. The economic task of the district heating enterprise is to maintain at the same time a price level which makes the service marketable and which provides sufficient earnings to attract investor capital. Thus, the district heating utility as well as the consumer has an interest in the consumer's economic position.

Profitability has many connotations ranging from such basic considerations as the overall conservation of resources through to the monetary reward given for the use of capital in privately financed enterprise. The economic factors of ownership are quite variable, depending upon the nature of the proprietary agency, its financial philosophy, its tax liabilities, and current interest rates and regulatory supervision.

Where the supplier is also the consumer, aspects of both the utility and consumer economic factors are of concern, but to somewhat varying degrees, depending upon the nature of the owning enterprise.

Consumer Considerations

The principal concern of the consumer is that of determining his cost for owning and operating his own facilities to supply his required services as compared to the costs of purchasing the equivalent in district heating and cooling services.

The owning and operating costs of a consumer's own facilities are determined in much the same manner as described hereinafter for the utility. However, values assigned to the several components may be quite different, depending upon the economic philosophy and judgement of each consumer.

The cost of the consumer for services purchased from the utility is a function of the rates and charges of the supplying utility. Such additional costs as may be associated with the use of district heating services, when added thereto, comprise the overall gross cost of purchased service.

Values of intangibles should not be neglected. Either they should be charged to the cost of owning and operating consumer's own facilities or credited against the cost of purchased service.

District Heating Company Considerations

District heating companies, in general, obtain their saleable energy from production plants producing district heating services only (steam, hot water, chilled water, etc.) or from combination heat-electric stations which also produce electric energy.

Combination stations vary as to type, design and concept of operation. The modern heat-electric stations, European style, operate with either extraction and/or back pressure steam turbo generators, heating water for district heating systems via heat exchange in water heating "boilers." In these installations the balance between heat and power requirements is quite good and average annual heat utilization efficiencies of 60 to 70 percent are not uncommon.

In the United States, most of the combined station operations are those where large electric generating stations are geographically located with respect to the district heating distribution system so as to make steam interconnections economically feasible. In such cases, considerable engineering analysis becomes necessary to develop a realistic basis for allocating costs—both owning and operating—between power and heat production.

Among the factors of greater weight in such analyses are:

1. the effect which the supply of steam to the district heating enterprise has upon the electric power production capability of the station, particularly within the period of the electric system's peak loading,
2. owning cost of additional plant auxiliaries (piping, demineralizer, etc.),
3. the production and maintenance costs added by the supply of steam and
4. credits to be allowed for the power available to the electric system in the process of supplying such steam.

Utility Economic Considerations

In all cases, the basic economic factors of capital costs, depreciation, taxes (except where exempt), operating and maintenance costs exert their influences. These factors and their affects upon owning and operating costs are briefly discussed below.

OWNING COSTS

Owning costs may be grouped into two categories; those which are expense items, and those which represent earnings on equity and related income taxes.

The expense items include interest on debt, local taxes, and depreciation. Occasionally insurance costs are also included.

Earnings include the return (or profit) on preferred and common stock and the income taxes payable on gross earnings.

Business and industry have great flexibility in the matter of sources of investment funds. Utilities, however, are often limited by regulation as to the percentage of debt permitted.

Expense items are chiefly interest, taxes, and depreciation. Interest is paid at a rate agreed upon at the time the loans are negotiated. Such rates fluctuate as a function of economic conditions at the time of borrowing.

Local taxes are determined by local laws, assessing policies, and rates established each year.

Depreciation (or amortization as it is sometimes called) is a name applied to the process of apportioning the cost of acquisition over the useful life of the asset.

The amount of plant assets subject to depreciation and its average life, once determined, can be depreciated by one of several methods available to management. Among such methods are:

1. straight line,
2. declining balance,
3. sum of the years digits, and
4. sinking fund.

Straight line depreciation applies a uniform rate (percentage) to the total depreciable plant for each accounting period throughout the estimated service life and the property. The total depreciable plant is usually the original cost less the estimated salvage value. The following is an example of straight-line depreciation:

Estimated plant life	35 years
Original cost	$1,000,000
Estimated salvage value	55,000
Total depreciable plant	$ 945,000

Annual depreciation expense then is $27,000 ($945,000 ÷ 35) or a rate of 2.86% ($27,000 ÷ $945,000).

The double declining balance method takes advantage of regulatory permission to depreciate at a write-off of up to 200% of the straight-line rate. Whatever rate is opted is then applied each year to the then undepreciated balance of the investment. The Tax Code permits a change from the declining balance method to the straight-line method at any time. In addition, the use of accelerated depreciation is permissible for all acquisitions, new construction or reconditioning subsequent to 1954. To offset the effects of the latter on the rate-making process, most regulatory commissions permit "normalization." The latter, in effect, permits the expense of straight-line depreciation to be used in computing the depreciation deduction for tax purposes. The difference is usually credited to a reserve for deferred taxes and thus is not available for dividends, nor subject to income tax.

The sum of the years digits method determines annual depreciation by applying a constantly declining fraction to the original cost less estimated salvage value. *The numerator* of the fraction is equal to the number of years of remaining life, including the current year. The denominator is the numerical sum of the series of years of life (Viz: 1+2+3 ... ÷ 35 for 35-year life.) Examples of depreciation rates for selected years would then be:

1 st Year:	(35–0) ÷ 630 = 5.56%
10th Year:	(35–10) ÷ 630 = 3.97%
20th Year:	(35–20) ÷ 630 = 1.38%
30th Year:	(35–30) ÷ 630 = 0.79%

The sinking-fund method applies a uniform annual depreciation charge which, at compound interest, will result in an accumulated depreciation equal to the original cost of the property less estimated net salvage value over the estimated life of the property. A formula for use with this method is

$$A = R \frac{s^n - 1}{r}$$

where interest is compounded annually and
   A = amount of the principal
   R = payment at regular interval (1 year)
   s = $1 \div r$
   n = number of years
   r = rate of interest (as decimal)
The following is an example of sinking-fund depreciation:

Estimated asset life	35 years
Original cost	$1,000,000
Estimated salvage value	55,000
Total depreciable plant	$ 945,000
Rate of return	6.0%

$$A = R\frac{s^n - 1}{r}$$

$$R = \frac{Ar}{S^n - 1}$$

$\log 1.06 = 0.02531$
$0.02531 \times 35 = 0.08861$

$$= \frac{\$945,000 \times .06}{1.06^{35} - 1}$$

$\log_x .8861 = 7.693$

$$= \frac{56,700}{7,693 - 1}$$

$$R = \$8,470$$

$$\text{Rate} = \$8,470 \div 945,000 = .896\%$$

RETURN ON EQUITY

Equity may be accrued either through preferred or common stock. Preferred stock usually has a fixed dividend rate. In this respect, it is similar to bonded debt. But, it differs from debt in that earnings payable to preferred stockholders are subject to corporate income taxes.

Because of the higher risk involved, common stock is usually rewarded with a higher rate of earnings than preferred stock. It is also a desirable practice to retain some of the current earnings in the business. The latter, to some extent, acts as a hedge against inflation such as escalation of construction costs which would be involved in replacement of plant.

Return on equity may be of interest from two viewpoints:
1. to determine the profitability of operations after the fact and/or
2. to determine the revenues necessary to earn a desired rate of return.

The latter would be of specific interest in the processes of rate-making or in evaluating the economic acceptability of incremental business.

The two methods of depreciation of most interest are:
1. the straight line, and
2. the sinking fund.

These methods have quite different affects upon the cost of capital.

The *straight-line method* accrues a depreciation reserve adequate to recover the investment during the expected life of the equipment. As the reserve accumulates, it is considered to earn a return equivalent to that earned by the business.

This return acts as full support for that portion of the investment represented by the amount of the depreciation reserve at any time and thus, reduces the amount of the capital burden on the business at that time.

Thus, with straight-line depreciation, it is convenient to deal with average investment in determining the capital burden, the average being one-half the original cost-less-estimated-salvage.

The sinking-fund method requires that all earnings of its accumulated reserve be retained in the fund. Thus, the sinking-fund affords no support to the investment as the straight-line method does, and the capital burden is constant throughout the life of the equipment.

OPERATING COSTS

Operating costs include all expense items which are not determined as a function of investment. The main categories of such costs include fuel, maintenance, supplies, labor, fringe benefits, overhead and working capital. All operating costs are deductible from income for tax purposes.

With the exception of working capital, the content of these expense items is quite apparent. Working capital is usually considered to represent about 25 percent of annual operating cost, and the annual cost of such capital is determined at the ongoing rate.

Revenue requirements then become the sum of the owning and operating costs.

The trend in operating costs per unit of sales varies among companies from almost stability to an escalation of up to 3 percent per year. Both load factor and growth are important influences in this respect. For example, the continued growth in sale of steam for air conditioning is making itself evident in annual load factor improvement for those companies promoting it.

INVESTMENT AND OPERATING COST DISTRIBUTION

Investment cost distribution of a typical moderately sized district heating operation in the United States is as follows:

Production facilities	50%
Distribution facilities	47%
Metering facilities	1%
Miscellaneous	2%

Operating cost distribution is in the order of 80 percent for the production plant and 20 percent for distribution and miscellaneous. Within these two major categories the component costs are proportioned as follows, again for the composite typical operation:

Production plant	
Fuel	62%
Labor	17%
Maintenance	13%
Production plant	
Water & Treatment	4%
Supplies & Miscellaneous	4%
Distribution	
Labor	34%
Maintenance	61%
Miscellaneous	5%

Financing Considerations

Development of district heating and cooling is capital intensive. As such, the success of a project depends upon the financial strategy adopted by the developer. While the strategy selected will vary, reflecting the uniqueness of the individual project, it must be based on a careful market study to determine whether there is enough present and potential demand for the system to generate sufficient revenues to meet the financial obligations of the project. Since the price differential between thermal energy and natural gas or fuel oil may not widen over the start-up years of a district heating project, it is advisable that a developer determine whether there is an immediate for thermal energy, particularly from large institutional end-users who will immediately connect up to the district heating system.

TAX EXEMPT OPTIONS

The tax-exempt debt financing of a district heating system is relatively straight-forward. According to financial theory, debt is always conceptually cheaper than equity. An equity holder demands higher yield because the risk involved in being an equity investor is far greater than in being a bond holder. In the case of a tax-exempt bond, the yield demanded by bondholders is far lower than on corporate bonds, because coupons or interest income from municipal bonds are exempt from federal and often state taxes.

A municipally owned entity, a publically owned utility or a not-for-profit corporation may have access to the tax-exempt bond market. The revenue requirements of such public or quasi-public developers would be far less than those of an investor owened utility which would have to raise capital in the corporate bond market as well as show a return on equity investment, and pay taxes. It appears that there have been few, if any, analyses conducted to determine the breakeven interest rate that would render construction of a district heating system economically unfeasible.

REVENUE BONDS

In the short-term, revenue bond issues appear to be the most viable bond financing option for a publically owned district heating system. Despite the fact that district heating is not a well known technology in the United States, there will most likely not be a shortage of revenue bonds investors if the feasibility of a project is demonstrated. In a period of increasing tight credit for developers, a debt instrument that is secured by the revenues of the district heating facility, rather than utilizing the general credit of the municipality, is favored. In addition, potential investors seem to be more encouraged about a project's viability when the project is backed by its own revenues. This is particularly true in the case of new issues or relatively unknown technologies.

Revenue bond financing, however, places pressure on a project to demonstrate the soundness of its revenue projections. To ensure these revenues, a municipality or a developer may want to ask its thermal customers to sign long-term contracts that coincide with the maturity of the bonds. A developer may also wish to request that end-users make available their audited financial statements to lenders to aid investors in assessing the projects financial credit.

ALTERNATIVE FINANCING METHODS

Some privately owned utilities consider district heating a good potential investment. Despite the fact that many investor owned utilities face conventional financing constraints, it is felt that financing techniques such as leverage leasing or split ownership with municipal or European partners could be utilized to make a district heating project a viable one.

There are other financial strategies and mechanisms to be considered in financing district heating systems. States may want to sell general obligation bonds to raise a portion of the capital needed for a district heating system being developed in the state. This would spread the risk of the investment because investors would evaluate the credit risk of the state, and not merely the credit of the municipality or district heating developer. Such an allocation of risk is similar to the concept of project financing that is utilized by corporations for spreading the risk of large scale project development.

A financial mechanism that would reallocate risk, as well as provide part equity in the capital structure, is the leverage lease arrangement. With a leverage lease, a municipality, which cannot take advantage of tax benefits permitted by the government in connection with the purchase and ownership of a capital asset (such as investment tax credits, interest deductions and depreciation allowance), transfers these benefits to a tax paying firm. In such an arrangement, the firm would actually purchase the asset and lease it to the municipality. In return for these tax credits, the firm shares the benefits by substantially lowering the lease payments to the municipality. This method may not provide the municipality with a lower cost of capital than it would have had through tax-exempt debt financing. Such an arrangement, however, may be useful to a municipality that does not desire to raise capital for a district heating project with straight tax-exempt debt, or to a municipality that desires to spread the credit risk.

The problem with leverage leasing is that under the current Energy Tax Credit (ETC), certain elements of district heating construction costs may not be eligible for tax credits, thus providing firms with no incentive to participate in a leverage leasing arrangement. Action on the part of federal government may be needed to change the ETC provisions in order to make leverage leasing a more attractive option for district heating financing in the future.

A municipal developer may also wish to add some public equity to its capital structure in order to reallocate risk. Public equity, funds from a state or the federal government may also help a municipality in the start-up phases of a project.

There are other financial options that a municipality or developer can choose in order to finance its district heating system. "Assessment" or "special bonds" may aid a municipality in circumventing the public purpose aspect of a revenue bond. Utilization of venture capital does not appear to be an attractive option because the high required return on investment would make the cost of capital too high for a municipality.

INVESTORS EVALUATION

It is the responsibility of the public authority or jurisdiction developing a district heating system to create a good investment climate, so that the tax-exempt bond issues will receive excellent ratings. The higher the rate a bond receives, the higher the price of the bond. This, of course, will lower the cost of capital to the developer. In evaluating both revenue and GO bonds, the rating agencies use several general criteria. In addition to a financial analysis, the rating agencies evaluate the economic base, and the management and legal environment. Investors will rely heavily on the district heating feasibility study, both for its technical and economic aspects. Eventually, investors will most likely want to visit the project site.

Due to the fact the bond issues are municipal ones, investors will be very interested in the legal environment, particularly because district heating is a relatively unknown undertaking for public utilities of municipalities. In order to clarify the legal aspects of its proposed municipally owned district heating system for investors, Bellingham, Washington has developed a piece of legislation which the city hopes will be passed by the state legislation. The legislation outlines the general and more specific powers that a municipal district heating facility (either town, city, county, or public utility district) would possess. Powers would include construction, operation, financing and rate setting authority.

Credit risk evaluation involves assessment of the contributing parties to the financing. Investors, however, also evaluate the operating or management risk, particularly when it is a publically owned facility. Therefore, public ownership, but private management by an experienced reputable firm, should be considered.

DEBT RETIREMENT OPTIONS

Although levelized debt service—amortization of debt in equal units until maturity—is the traditional method of tax-exempt debt retirement, there are alternatives which will improve a district heating system's cash flow in the early period of operation. Reduced revenue requirements, due to reduced debt repayments in the initial phase of the system, can ensure that thermal energy is cost competitive. A graduated payment schedule would entail a gradual annual increase in debt service, with full amortization of the bond by maturity.

A balloon debt repayment arrangement is another concept that might be applied to district heating. A balloon arrangement would backload debt service payments so that the bulk of debt service would be repaid in the latter years of a project's life. There are risks to such a strategy, however. A municipality must assess the adoption of an impact of a balloon repayment schedule on the potential investor's evaluation of the project. Utilization of a balloon arrangement by a project may be interpreted by investors as an indication that the project is unsound.

Innovative debt retirement schedules will enable a district heating system to offer lower thermal prices than otherwise would have been possible. In addition, a municipality can carefully develop a rate structure that will also allow the district heating system to offer less expensive thermal energy initially. The Trenton (ICES) project has developed a tripartible rate structure that will include a fixed capital recovery payment component, and variable components for fuel and operating costs. The fuel and operating components of the rate will only be raised as these costs escalate.

Despite efforts to provide competitively priced thermal energy, the financing of end-user retrofits remains a problem. Incentives for individual conversion may have to be created. Payback periods for the investment should be as short as possible. Cities may want to develop an end-user loan program, if it is permitted by state and city charter restrictions. This area is one in which important legislative and charter changes may be useful.

BACKGROUND FOR ECONOMIC ANALYSIS OF COMMUNITY ENERGY SYSTEMS

Attempts to conserve energy generally are aimed at either reducing energy demands or improving the efficiencies of technologies used to meet those demands. Most individual efforts in energy conservation research are limited to examining a single technology or energy use (such as space heating, cooling, or electricity generation). Although this approach has led to significant progress in the development of several energy supply technologies (solar heating is one example), it has not addressed the inefficiencies that result from lack of coordination among the various energy supply systems of a community. For example, only about one-third of the fuel energy input to a conventional fossil-fuel electricity-generating plant reaches consumers as electricity. Meanwhile, power plants eject huge amounts of heat to lakes, rivers, and the atmosphere. Besides being wasteful, this nonproductive discharge of heat from the electricity-generating process can present a serious problem of thermal pollution to the environment. While this heat is being dissipated unproductively, scarce (and increasingly expensive) fuels, such as oil and natural gas, often are used to heat homes, industries, offices, and institutions.

Such overall inefficiencies can be addressed only by viewing energy consumption from a systems perspective at the community level. The term "community energy system" can refers to a wide range of systems that respond to this community-wide view of energy demand and supply. A community energy system is a combination of subsystems that together supply most, or all, of a community's energy-related services. For example, in most community energy systems, electrical and thermal energy are cogenerated. In cogeneration, the thermal energy, normally rejected in the generation of electricity, is recovered and and used for space heating and cooling, water heating, and industrial processes. The common element in each application of a community energy system is that parties with traditionally separate roles in the processes of energy supply and consumption are linked together to improve the community's overall energy utilization. This chapter is intended as an aid in the economic analysis of such systems by providing a consistent means of evaluating individual projects.

EXAMPLES OF COMMUNITY ENERGY SYSTEMS

The central characteristic of any community energy system is the coordination of energy supply services either between separate energy consumers in the community or between various energy types supplied to the community (or, ideally, between both). An example of the first type is a district heating system in which a single energy source, such as hot water or steam, is provided to a group of buildings to meet space heating, domestic water heating, and possibly space cooling and process steam loads. Not all district heating systems are limited to providing thermal services only; generation of electricity and incineration of solid wastes are examples of other kinds of services. Usually these buildings would supply their own space heating requirements in a less efficient manner than would the district heating system.

Alternatively, a community energy system could provide multiple energy services to a single user. Such a system is illustrated by an in-building cogeneration plant. An example of a cogeneration system is the diesel-engine/generator set with heat recovery equipment shown in Figure 9.1. The engine/generator set can supply the electricity needs of the building; heat recovered from the exhaust, cooling, and lubrication systems of the engine can meet the space heating and cooling demands. Another cogeneration system that uses a variable-extraction steam turbine is shown in Figure 9.2.

In its most complete applications, a community energy system coordinates

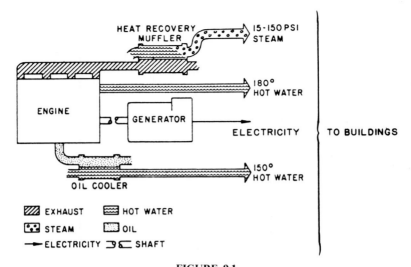

FIGURE 9.1

Reciprocating engine with heat recovery from exhaust gas, jacket coolant, and lube oil

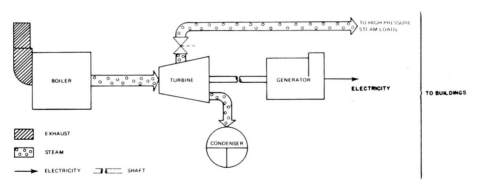

FIGURE 9.2

Variable extraction steam turbine with heat recovery

energy supply among various consumers and different energy types. A system of this sort could meet the requirements for total electricity, space heating and cooling, domestic water heating, process steam, and solid-waste disposal of a mixed-use community. One such system, shown in Figure 9.3, would include a central plant at which heat from coal combustion, supplemented by heat recovered from the incineration of solid wastes, is used to produce steam. The throttling of a steam through variable-extraction turbines would be regulated to match the thermal and electric loads of the community. Absorption chillers, driven by the steam's heat energy, would provide chilled water for space cooling. Both hot and chilled water would be distributed to individual buildings for use in individual building heating, ventilating, and air conditioning (HVAC) systems. Moreover, steam would be distributed for industrial and institutional uses.

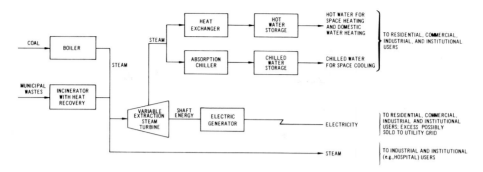

FIGURE 9.3

Varied services produced by a community energy system for a mixed-use community

The previous examples help to illustrate the various types of community energy systems. The kinds of energy services to be provided, as well as the technologies used to provide these services, can be varied. In addition to these design factors, other characteristics that relate to the system's institutional setting vary among systems. One of these considerations is the tie-in method, should one exist, with the conventional electric grid. As long as acceptable energy exchange rates can be negotiated with the electric utility, it is usually advantageous for a community energy system to be tied into the grid. In this way, peak (or backup) power can be purchased from the grid, and excess electricity can be sold. Another nontechnical characteristic with substantial economic impact is the ownership of the system. Both cost of capital and the types of institutional problems to be faced in system implementation are linked to the type of ownership. Typical options include ownership by an investor-owned utility, by a publicly owned utility, by a business corporation, or by some combination of these. Selecting these institutional characteristics is as much a design problem as selecting and sizing the hardware for the energy system.

The term "community energy system" has been used to represent a conceptual approach to energy supply rather than a specific arrangement of hardware. However, most systems that are being examined for near-term applications are cogeneration systems of one sort or another (although some noncogenerating district heating systems and community energy systems using heat pumps have near-term potential). These systems generally use existing technologies and equipment. Typical prime movers include steam turbines, gas turbines, and diesel engines. The fuel usually is coal, oil, or natural gas, possibly supplemented by urban wastes. Use of more exotic fuels and equipment is possible, but applications of these uses are presently limited because of economic and technical constraints.

ECONOMIC FEASIBILITY OF COMMUNITY ENERGY SYSTEMS

The major question facing potential implementors of community energy systems is whether reduced operating costs, primarily from increased fuel utilization, will produce the required return on the initial capital investment. This chapter is intended to help answer that question by comparing the relative economic merits of various energy supply options for a community. The analysis presented here is based on accepted principles of engineering economics applied to a framework designed specifically for the evaluation of community energy systems.

Figure 9.4 illustrates the role of economic analysis of the overall process of a feasibility analysis of community energy systems. As the flow chart indicates, several other tasks must be completed before the economic analysis can proceed. First, the energy demands of the community to be served must be characterized; then a system to meet these demands can be designed. In an initial feasibility assessment, the detail of this design would be limited to determining sufficiently accurate estimates of cost. Cost data are used in the economic analysis to compare the economic attractiveness of the various energy supply options considered for a community. These initial tasks must be completed before the economic analysis described in this chapter can be applied. Specific data

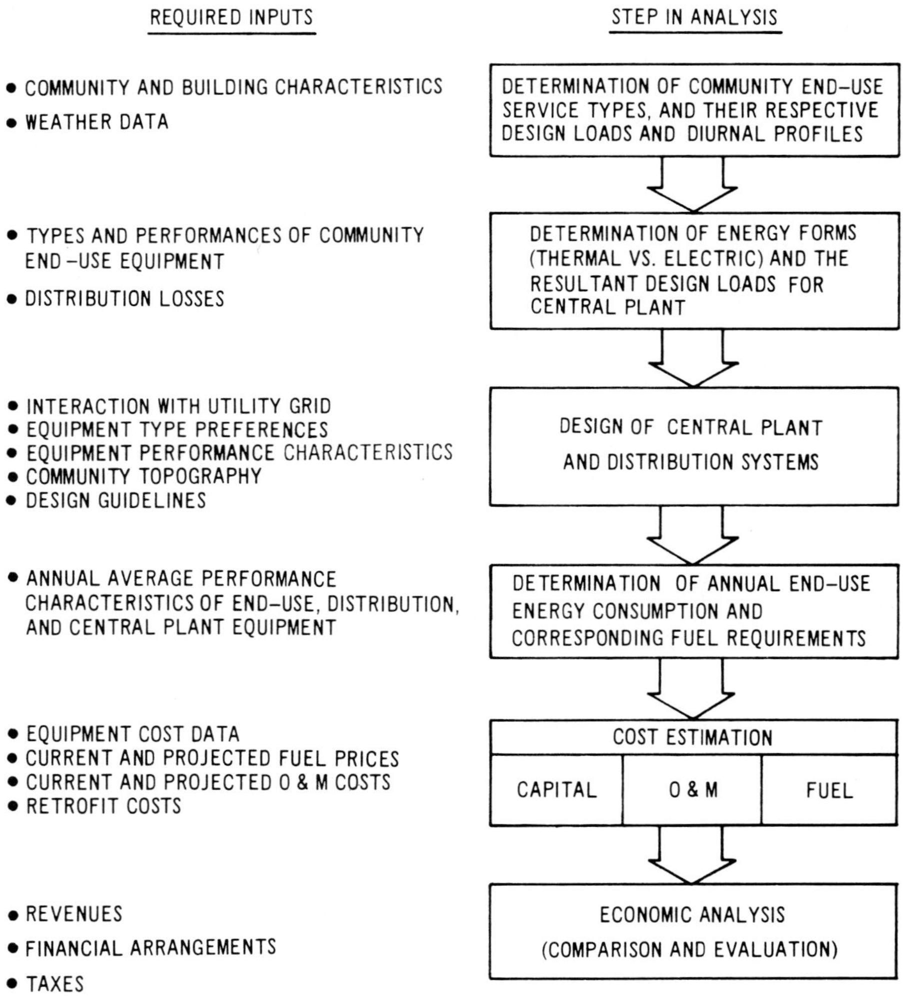

REQUIRED INPUTS	STEP IN ANALYSIS
• COMMUNITY AND BUILDING CHARACTERISTICS • WEATHER DATA	DETERMINATION OF COMMUNITY END–USE SERVICE TYPES, AND THEIR RESPECTIVE DESIGN LOADS AND DIURNAL PROFILES
• TYPES AND PERFORMANCES OF COMMUNITY END –USE EQUIPMENT • DISTRIBUTION LOSSES	DETERMINATION OF ENERGY FORMS (THERMAL VS. ELECTRIC) AND THE RESULTANT DESIGN LOADS FOR CENTRAL PLANT
• INTERACTION WITH UTILITY GRID • EQUIPMENT TYPE PREFERENCES • EQUIPMENT PERFORMANCE CHARACTERISTICS • COMMUNITY TOPOGRAPHY • DESIGN GUIDELINES	DESIGN OF CENTRAL PLANT AND DISTRIBUTION SYSTEMS
• ANNUAL AVERAGE PERFORMANCE CHARACTERISTICS OF END–USE, DISTRIBUTION, AND CENTRAL PLANT EQUIPMENT	DETERMINATION OF ANNUAL END–USE ENERGY CONSUMPTION AND CORRESPONDING FUEL REQUIREMENTS
• EQUIPMENT COST DATA • CURRENT AND PROJECTED FUEL PRICES • CURRENT AND PROJECTED O & M COSTS • RETROFIT COSTS	COST ESTIMATION CAPITAL O & M FUEL
• REVENUES • FINANCIAL ARRANGEMENTS • TAXES	ECONOMIC ANALYSIS (COMPARISON AND EVALUATION)

FIGURE 9.4

Major steps in feasibility analysis of community energy systems

requirements are discussed in the section titled "estimates of costs and revenues."

OVERVIEW OF THE ECONOMIC ANALYSIS OF COMMUNITY ENERGY SYSTEMS

Energy System Cash Flows

In the economic analysis of community energy systems, the various cash flows into and out of a community should be viewed as they result from different energy supply systems. This chapter provides a basis for economic comparison of options of community energy systems and conventional systems. Figure 9.5 compares the energy and cash flows of a conventional energy supply system with those of a community energy system. The circles represent the community limits across which energy and cash flows are measured. The set of energy consumers served by the energy system is bounded by the circle in both cases; however, for the community energy system, the system owners, represented by the community utility, also are included. This community utility may or may not be an actual utility; potential owners, other than investor-owned utilities and municipal utilities, include private and public developers, cooperatives, other nonutility corporations, or numerous other investor groups. The term community utility is synonymous with the group that proposes owning and operating the community energy system.

Cash flows that occur under a conventional energy supply system are straightforward, i.e., consumers purchase equipment such as furnaces and air conditioners, provide for the operation and maintenance (O&M) of that equipment, and purchase fuel to power the equipment. These expenditures are made to equipment suppliers, maintenance personnel, and utilities or other fuel suppliers.

Under a community energy system, both the community utility and the consumers have a set of energy-related expenditures. Consumers would be required to pay for the purchase and O&M of any in-building equipment not

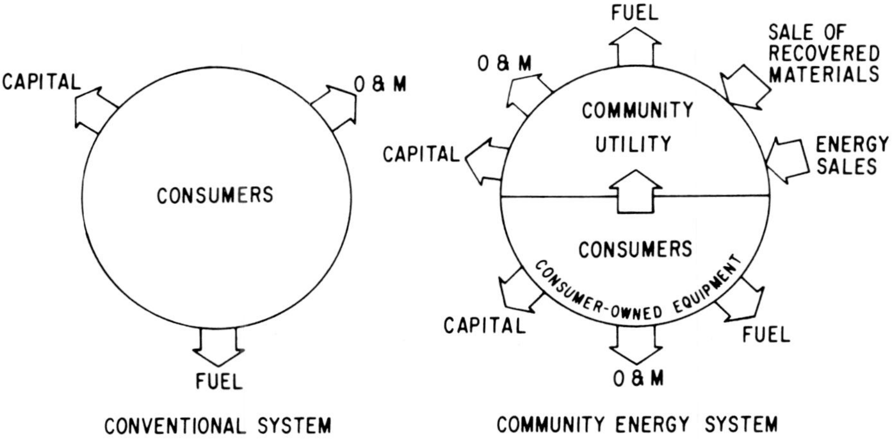

FIGURE 9.5

Comparison of economic options of a community energy system with those of a conventional system

owned by the community utility. Consumers would also pay for fuel required for any supplementary energy services not provided by the community energy system. For example, some customers might require a provision of back-up electrical service from the conventional electric grid. However, most energy expenditures by customers of a community energy system usually would be to the community energy utility itself. These revenues then would be applied to amortization of capital, O&M expenses, and fuel costs. Other revenues to the community utility could be from (1) the sale of energy to parties outside the community, e.g., electricity to the utility grid, sale of fuel produced in a pyrolysis unit, and (2) the sale of recovered materials, such as metal and glass, captured in a solid-waste recovery unit.

Under a community energy system, the allocation of various costs, particularly those relating to in-building equipment, is determined by policy decisions. For example, because of quantity discounts, lower capital costs of in-building HVAC equipment might be possible if portions of the in-building systems are purchased and installed by the community utility. Similarly, the potential exists for lowering O&M costs, if O&M activities are handled by the community utility, which can provide more effective application of maintenance personnel and supplies. Nevertheless, owners of the community utility might want to limit their capital and O&M responsibilities as far as possible, despite potential economic advantages. This would be particularly true if the community utility is to be publicly owned. Such arrangements might also be difficult to negotiate for existing buildings. Because these institutional arrangements usually are not self-evident, various options should be considered in planning a community energy system.

Economic Evaluation and Comparison of Systems

OVERVIEW OF THE ANALYSIS

The question this analysis attempts to answer is whether a particular community energy system would be an economically viable project for its potential investors. To answer this question, the analyst must weigh the costs incurred by the community utility against revenues generated. The evaluation should be based on accepted techniques for life-cycle costing.

By using commonly accepted techniques and a discount rate equal to the minimum acceptable rate of return (MARR) for the community utility, we can compute the present value of all costs (capital, O&M, and fuel) incurred by the community utility. For the community energy system to be an attractive investment, its revenues (also discounted at the MARR) must exceed its costs. Thus, the system's net present value (NPV)—the present value of all revenues minus the present value of all costs—must be positive. In designs of alternative community energy systems, the system with the highest NPV is to be preferred. Use of the NPV and other evaluation criteria is discussed in the section "System Comparison and Selection."

Cost estimation is a routine procedure in system engineering and design studies. Cost estimates for capital, O&M, and fuel are based on past experience and future expectations. However, the estimate of revenues is often more speculative. In particular, estimation of the revenues a community utility can expect to receive from its customers is difficult. The price of electricity offered by the conventional utility defines a competing price for electrical service; usually no such uniform, comparable price exists for thermal service. Where thermal and electric revenues cannot be specified, it is assumed that customers would not be willing to pay more for community energy system services than they would under a conventional energy system (Figure 9.5). Customers of a community energy system have costs other than those paid to the community utility; these costs are shown in the perimeter of the lower half of the circle in Figure 9.5. If these costs are subtracted from the total customer costs under the conventional energy system, the result is the maximum revenue the community utility can hope to collect from its customers. The present value of these revenues over the life of the project must at least equal the present value of all costs to be considered an attractive investment opportunity. The resulting difference is the present value of all savings or benefits that can be either retained by the community utility as profits or passed on to consumers through reduced prices for energy services. The distribution of these benefits would depend on the type of ownership of the community utility.

When revenues from customers are based on their costs under a conventional energy system, the analysis can be viewed also as a cost comparison. If a real estate developer constructs and retains ownership of a commercial complex (e.g., a shopping mall), energy costs under the proposed leases will be borne directly by the developer and will be paid by rent receipts from tenants. Assume that this developer wishes to consider a cogeneration system to reduce energy costs. Unless excess energy will be sold to the utility grid, there will be no actual revenues generated by the community energy system; rather, the system is viewed as a possible cost-reduction measure. In this case the community utility and the consumers are the same entity, namely the developer, and the analysis is simply a comparison of costs under the alternative systems.

Whether the analysis should be viewed as a revenue versus cost analysis or simply as a cost comparison depends on the alternatives offered to the potential investor. In the previous example, the developer had to supply the customer's energy needs, and it was advantageous to find the least expensive way to do so. However, suppose that the energy supply systems will not be owned by the developer, but by individual tenants instead (i.e., HVAC systems will be independently owned and operated, with tenants dealing directly with electric and gas utilities). The developer might view cogeneration as a way to provide the tenants with their required energy services while simultaneously making a profit. In a new business venture of this sort, the cost-revenue interpretation of the analysis is more appropriate. In either case, the analysis is essentially the same and follows the procedures explained here.

For a utility, this analysis addresses itself to the profitability of a particular project rather than to the system-wide economic implications of cogeneration or any other type of community energy system. Thus, use of this analysis will not resolve the optimal extent and locations of community energy systems within a utility's franchise area. Rather, given a potential site application, the analysis will determine whether the generated revenues are sufficient to cover the project's costs.

The savings generated by a community energy system under private ownership are available as profits. However, passing some of these savings along to consumers might become necessary to induce them to become system customers. If the community is part of a larger, regulated utility, these savings will be retained for reinvestment or passed along to stockholders, provided the utility's fair rate of return (RR) does not exceed that allowed by the regulatory body. If the RR it is exceeded, these savings would be passed along to consumers as rate decreases (or smaller increases). If the community energy system is publicly owned, either by a municipal utility or by some other governmental unit, cost savings would be passed on directly to system consumers or to some larger group of taxpayers.

ANALYTICAL PROCEDURES

The application of the concepts discussed in the previous section is outlined in Table 9.1. The analysis begins with the specification of systems to be studied, including the choice of a base case conventional energy system as well as the community energy system options to be considered. The base case conventional energy system is the system that will be built (or, if existing and not requiring replacement, will remain) if a community energy system is not selected. This system might be either known or assumed; sometimes a preceding life-cycle costing analysis will be required to specify the system. The base case conventional system should be specified such that it provides the same services as the community energy systems to be studied. If the various community energy system designs differ in the extent or type of their services, several base case conventional systems should be specified.

Next, costs of the community utility for each community energy system

TABLE 9.1

MAJOR STEPS IN AN ECONOMIC ANALYSIS OF COMMUNITY ENERGY SYSTEMS

Define Systems to Be Studied
  Base-case conventional system
  Options for community energy system
    Technical design
    Institutional parameters
Estimate Community Utility Costs for Community Energy System
  Capital
  O&M (except income taxes)
  Fuel
Estimate Revenues of the Community Utility
  Sales to electric grid
  Sales to customers
    Obvious if electric and thermal rates are known
    Assume customer costs are equal for all systems if rates are not known
  Miscellaneous revenues (sale of recovered materials, dumping fees)
Estimate Income Taxes of the Community Utility
  Specify interest payments
  Specify depreciation schedule
  Compute taxable income
  Compute income taxes
  Adjust for investment tax credit
Compute Values for Criteria for Economic Evaluation
  Net present value, with possible use of discounted payback period suggested
  Rate of return, straight payback period, and savings-to-investment ratio also discussed
Examine Assumptions and Accuracy of Data
  Minimum attractive rate of return
  Fuel prices
  Revenues
  Timing of system construction
  Miscellaneous
Revise Technical or Institutional Parameters and Reanalyze, if Necessary

option must be determined. These include costs for capital, O&M, and fuel. Income taxes will be considered later. Although this chapter discusses costs that must be considered, actual cost data cannot be provided and must be obtained elsewhere.

Revenues collected by the community utility should then be estimated. These revenues are generated from the sale of electricity to the utility grid, from various miscellaneous sources (e.g., sale of recovered materials or dumping fees if a unit for solid waste recovery is included), and from the sale of energy to system customers. If the thermal and electrical energy rates are known, the calculation of revenues is straightforward. If rates are not known, the assumption is made that customers of a community energy system will not pay more than their costs for a conventional energy system. These costs, less any other customer costs under a community energy system, are the maximum revenues customers will supply for the community utility.

After revenues and costs are known, the community utility's income taxes can be estimated. If only a pretax analysis is required or if the community utility is publicly owned, this step can be omitted. The income tax analysis is designed to reflect only major tax effects and will not include subtleties to be considered in the actual preparation of income tax returns. Taxable income is computed by subtracting interest payments, depreciation allowances, and annual expenses from the revenues previously calculated. The income tax rate is applied to the taxable income, and the tax amount is then adjusted for the investment tax credit. To determine the total costs, the income taxes can then be added to the other community utility costs.

Cost and revenue streams must be collapsed into evaluation criteria to facilitate comparison between systems. The choice of criteria for economic evaluation varies widely among organizations. Therefore, although this chapter suggests the use of NPV and possibly the discounted payback period (DPP) to compare energy systems, the application of RR, straight payback period (SPP), and savings-to-investment ratio (SIR) methods also are discussed.

Finally, the values of the evaluation criteria chosen must be supplemented with an inspection of the sensitivity of the results to the various assumptions made. For example, because of the uncertainty over future fuel prices, evaluations of each system should consider several fuel price scenarios. Depending on the results of this sensitivity analysis, the guidebook user might wish to respecify various technical or institutional aspects of the system (e.g., ownership options or various purchase/sell arrangements with the grid) and then reanalyze the system.

The following sections provide details for the application of this analysis, and a sample application of the analysis is presented.

ESTIMATES OF COSTS AND REVENUES

The following section explains the estimation of costs and revenues of a local utility that operates a community energy system. For many of the calculations, worksheets have been provided as aids in organizing data.

Initial Considerations

ASSUMPTIONS AND CONVENTIONS

For estimation of the stream of costs and revenues, the beginning of year 1 corresponds to the beginning of system operation. Each year's costs and revenues are assumed to occur at the end of that particular year. Therefore, capital costs that occur before the system is operational are assumed to occur at the end of year 0.

SELECTION OF THE STUDY PERIOD

The study period for which the costs and revenues of various systems are to be evaluated is the economic life of the community energy system. Usually this period is the same for all competing community energy systems and is assumed to be 20 to 30 years. Most studies have been based on a 30-year life; however, the system and equipment selected and the economic analysis policies of the owners of the potential community utility might call for a different value. All worksheets included here are set up for a maximum 30-year study period.

The system's estimated lifetime usually is applicable to all major system components. Whenever the replacement of major equipment is expected during the study period, the expected replacement dates and costs must be estimated.

Sometimes the expected life of the base case conventional system is less than that of the community energy system. If the difference is substantial (at least 10 years), the selected study period can be the least common multiple of the expected lives of the community energy system and the conventional system. Otherwise, replacement of the conventional energy system can be assumed to occur in the appropriate year.

The salvage value of each system, including the conventional system, should be estimated at the end of the study period. Because salvage value consists of resale value minus removal costs, salvage values often are negative. Furthermore, because of their time separation, salvage values are heavily discounted (e.g., if a 30-year study period and a 20% interest rate are assumed, the present value factor of an end-of-period salvage value is only 0.0042). Therefore, salvage values are generally disregarded. One exception could occur when only a small portion of the useful life of part or all of a system has been realized at the end of the study period. Normally this would occur because of nonequal lifetimes of systems or equipment. If the salvage value is obvious and substantial, it should be estimated and treated as a revenue component in the final year of the study period.

ESTIMATES OF A MINIMUM ACCEPTABLE RATE OF RETURN FOR THE COMMUNITY UTILITY

Energy systems differ not only in the total dollar amounts of revenues and costs they generate but also in the time pattern of those cash flows. Some way of expressing a time preference for many must be established to compare energy system alternatives. The time value of money is a basic tenet of engineering economics. By disregarding tax effects, the receipt of x dollors today is preferable to that of the same total in yearly increments of x/n over the next n years. The x-dollar amount could be placed in a bank savings account where it would accrue interest and could therefore offer annualized proceeds exceeding x/n dollars. The interest rate charged in an exchange of funds represents the time value of money for which the lender is willing to forego the current use of that money in other projects. In evaluating energy systems, as well as other investment opportunities, the return, or interest rate, that a project must earn to be attractive to an investor is the MARR.

The method to be used in selecting a value for the MARR is debated by economic analysts. General agreement prevails that the investor's incremental cost of capital is the lower boundary of a value for the MARR. A firm's incremental cost of capital is expressed by:

$$C = (1 - t)F_d \cdot C_d + F_e \cdot C_e \qquad \text{Eq. 1}$$

where:

C	= cost of capital,
C_d	= cost of debt financing,
C_e	= cost of equity financing,
F_d	= fraction of capital supplied by debt financing,
F_e	= fraction of capital supplied by equity financing,
$F_d + F_e$	= 1.0, and
t	= effective income tax rate (see Federal and State Income Taxes, pp. 437)

Debt financing can come from either direct loans or the sale of bonds, whereas equity funds result from the sale of corporate stock. As Eq. 1 indicates, the after-tax cost of debt capital is less than C_d because debt interest payments can be used as income tax deductions. No such deduction is allowed for dividend payments to stockholders. If a pretax analysis is being conducted, the relevant cost of capital is simply:

$$C = F_d \cdot C_d + F_e \cdot C_e$$

The suggested method for estimating the MARR for a community's energy system depends largely on the type of ownership of the community utility. Municipal governments, publicly owned utilities, and investor-owned utilities are all somewhat restricted in the scope of their activities and in the profits they may earn. The RR these investors may earn is closely tied to the cost of capital, which is an appropriate value for their MARR. Private nonutility corporations are free to invest available funds in a virtually unlimited range of projects, both within and outside the firm. The MARR for such firms is more appropriately determined by a project's opportunity cost.

The most likely vehicle a municipal government can use to finance a community energy system is a municipal utility, whether it exists or is created specifically for the community energy system. A municipal utility has a specific service or set of services to provide, and its investment decisions all capital and operating expenses. Under these circumstances, investment decisions are made on criteria of cost minimization rather than profit maximization. Because revenues must cover costs, and excess revenues will be returned to customers through reduced rates or taxes, the MARR for a public utility is the cost of capital. Generally, revenue bonds will be sold to finance construction, and a rate that reflects the real annual costs (coupon rate + administrative costs) of the bond issue is the MARR.

Like a municipal utility, an investor-owned utility is also limited in its scope or activities. In exchange for its right to be the sole supplier of an energy service within a specified area, an investor-owned utility agrees to furnish services on demand to customers in its service area and to be limited to a fair and reasonable rate of return on its investment. Its motivation, similar to that of the municipal utility, is to provide a service at the utility is C_E, the maximum RR allowed by the state regulatory authority. This specified RR applies to equity funds only; the total allowed RR is specified by Eq. 1. Thus, the cost of capital is the appropriate MARR for a private utility also.

Private nonutility firms typically are not restricted in the nature of their investments and in the returns on those projects. Investment in a community energy system means that funds are diverted from investment in other projects. The value chosen for the MARR should reflect the return that normally can be expected if the funds were invested elsewhere, rather than in the alternatives being considered. This is the opportunity cost of investing in one of the considered alternatives because it reflects the cost of not investing in other opportunities. Selection of a firm's MARR is based on its management's view of the firm's present financial situation and its future investment opportunities.

ESTIMATES OF COMMUNITY MINIMUM ACCEPTABLE RATE OF RETURN

Just as the community utility's MARR expresses its time preference for money, so also is a value needed to express the consumers' time value of money. Various energy systems will require correspondingly different investments in in-building equipment with subsequent effects on annual O&M and fuel costs. A reasonable, although low, estimate for the community's MARR is its average cost of debt capital.

If the community energy system serves only one land-use sector, e.g., industrial, commercial, or residential, an average cost of capital for that sector can be estimated and used as the MARR. If the community to be served is of mixed use, a weighted average cost of capital can be determined. For example, if a community energy system is being proposed for a community that consists of two government office towers (400,000 ft^2 each), a shopping mall (700,000 ft^2), and an apartment complex (500,000 ft^2), an estimate of the community's MARR can be calculated as shown:

Sector	(1) Cost of Debt (%)	(2) Floor Space (ft^2)	(3) Share of Total Floor Space	(4) Weighted MARR (1) × (3)
Public	8	800,000	0.40	3.2
Commercial	15	700,000	0.35	5.3
Residential	10	500,000	0.25	2.5
			Community MARR =	22.0%

INFLATION

In general, inflation can be treated in one of two ways in an engineering economic analysis. The first is to express all cash flow amounts exactly as they are expected to occur, with no adjustment for inflation. Thus, if all costs are expected to escalate at 10% per year, the forecasted annual costs for the system will rise 10% each year. The MARR used in this type of analysis should reflect the decisionmaker's expectations about inflation and the time value of money. Therefore, if a discount rate, based on time only, is 4%, and inflation is assumed to continue at about 10% per year over the study period, the correct MARR to use is:

$$[(1.04)(1.10)]-1 = 0.144 = 14.4\%$$

An alternative treatment of inflation is to express all cash flows in constant dollars adjusted for inflation. In this method, all dollar amounts are expressed in a constant standard, such as 1981 dollars. When cash flows are expressed in this way, the discount rate should not include an adjustment for inflation. Thus, in the above example, if all cash flows are expressed in constant dollars, the correct MARR to use is 4%.

Whether cash flows should be expressed in current dollars or constant dollars depends largely on the way the value of the MARR is specified. The previous section stated that the cost of capital functions is a minimum value for MARR. The cost of capital is determined in the money market by lending institutions, bond purchasers, and stockholders, all of whom have expectations about inflation that can influence the returns they require. Thus, when the MARR is based on the cost of capital, a value determined by the money market, the MARR already has in it an adjustment for inflation, and cash flows should be expressed in current dollars. If desired, the inflation factor could be removed from the MARR, and cash flows could be expressed in constant dollars; however, just what inflation rate the money market is assuming is not precisely clear. This latter procedure also would require that escalation rates for individual items (e.g., fuel) be adjusted for the general inflation rate.

Sometimes a corporation's MARR is specified as a policy decision, apart from considerations of inflation. In this case, the MARR must be adjusted for the expected inflation rate to allow cash flows to be expressed in current dollars.

Based on the above considerations, particularly the inclusion of inflation by the money market in determining the cost of capital, all cash flows to be computed in the following analyses should be expressed in current dollars. Normally the MARR already will have an inflation component. Nevertheless, an adjustment should be made in cases where a firm's MARR has been specified by a policy that does not consider inflation.

Costs Borne by the Community Utility for a Community Energy System

This section reviews the cost data needed to determine the costs the community utility incurs for constructing and operating a community energy system. These costs will include capital expenditures and annual expenses for O&M, fuel, and taxes. Energy consumers within the community also will incur costs, but these costs will not be considered here. The economic viewpoint taken in this analysis is that of the community utility.

Table 9.2 lists capital and annual expenditures that normally should be considered in determining community utility costs. Possible sources of cost data are indicated in Table 9.3. In many cases, the data contained in these sources may not be in the desired format; a different level of aggregation, adjustments for inflation, regional price adjustments, or other adaptations might be required.

Cost categories need not be broken down to the level shown in Table 9.2, the required accuracy of the cost estimates will determine the appropriate degree of cost breakdown. The accuracy with which these costs are estimated is determined largely by the status of the project in the development process. For example, the question facing the investor in the early stages of evaluating a community energy system is whether additional funds and efforts should be directed toward evaluating the system. In this case, substantial estimating errors can be tolerated because only a rough estimate is expected. In this preliminary stage, cost estimates for several types of equipment could be based on rule-of-thumb cost factors. However, as the system design progresses, cost estimates should be refined; final cost estimates should be based on actual price quotations from suppliers. Cost data from any of these levels of detail can be used as input to the economic analysis prescribed here. Nevertheless, the analyst should

TABLE 9.2

COMMUNITY UTILITY COSTS UNDER A COMMUNITY ENERGY SYSTEM

Capital Expenditures

Land
For: central plant, fuel storage, right-of-way for power distribution, residual disposal, if applicable

Building
Central plant

Central plant equipment
Prime movers
Electricity generators
Boilers and accessories
Chillers
Cooling towers
Fuel supply system (e.g., coal handling equipment, oil storage and supply equipment)
Electric switching and control equipment
Chilled water in-plant distribution
In-plant steam and condensate piping
Deaerator, feedwater heater, feed pumps, heat exchangers
Condensate receivers, pumps, wells, transfer system
Water treatment system
Instrumentation
Computer
Boiler and engine exhaust systems
Compressed air system
Thermal (cold and warm) storage facilities

Contingencies

Distribution systems (include installation costs)
Electricity: hookup to utility grid, distribution to customers' meters,
Thermal: steam, hot water, and chilled water distribution lines, pumps, and meters; return lines and pumps

In-building equipment (include installation costs)
Heat exchangers
Air-handling equipment
Fan-coil units
Piping and pumps
Controls
Chillers
Retrofit costs

Engineering services
Conceptual design
Final design
Construction drawings
Inspection and supervision of construction
Operating manuals and operator training

Financial and legal
Financial and legal consultants permit fees
Interest on capital during construction

Annual Expenditures

Operation and maintenance
Salaries and benefits
Parts and supplies
Operating licenses
Insurance
Professional services: auditing, legal, engineering, and data processing makeup water

Taxes
Federal income
State income
Property
Sales and miscellaneous

Fuel
Primary
Secondary
Electricity purchased from grid

---

weigh the results of the economic analysis in the light of the accuracy of the input data. A discussion of each of the major cost categories follows.

CAPITAL COSTS

Capital costs include the cost of all design equipment, and that of installation and administration of the central plant and distribution systems before and during construction. In addition, any in-building equipment costs borne by the community utility also should be estimated. For example, if the owner of the community utility also owns the buildings within the community energy system,

TABLE 9.3

PARTIAL LIST OF SOURCES OF COST DATA

Equipment and Construction Cost Data
Integrated Community Energy Systems Technology Evaluations[1]
Integrated community energy systems case studies[2-4]
Means Construction Cost Data[5]
Means Mechanical and Electrical Cost Data[5]
Equipment catalogues and vendor price quotations
Fuel Prices
U.S. Department of Energy
State energy offices
Data Resources, Inc., and other economic forecasting services
Cost Indexes
Marshall and Stevens Cost Index[6]
Engineering News-Record Construction Index[7]
Handy-Whitman Index[8]
Data Resources, Inc., and other economic forecasting services

capital costs for these buildings should be included under capital costs. In-building equipment costs borne by other building owners or energy consumers within the community need not be considered.

Worksheet, "Community Utility Expenditure Summary" (No. 9.1) all expenditures in the appropriate year under Column 9. Often, all capital costs are assumed to occur just before initial operation of the system, at the beginning (year 0) of the study period. In the worksheet, year 0 corresponds to the beginning of the study period. In other cases, where investment in the system occurs incrementally, this assumption is inadequate. All interest on construction funds should be included in year 0 capital costs.

For the time being, the actual terms under which the project is financed will be kept separate from this analysis, except as far as they affect the MARR. Therefore, capital expenditures in Column 9 should be entered in the actual year of investment.

OPERATION AND MAINTENANCE COSTS

All annual expenses except taxes and fuel are included under O&M costs. Taxes and fuel costs are handled separately to facilitate later computations. The O&M costs estimated here are for the equipment costed above. As with capital costs, the only in-building O&M costs to be considered at this time are those paid for by the community utility. In-building O&M costs could be incurred if the community utility owns the in-building equipment or has a contract for its maintenance.

An annual escalation rate also should be estimated for O&M costs. Typically, this rate will be near the expected regional labor escalation rate. The quantity estimated for total O&M costs will be the first-year O&M cost, and this cost will be increased by the escalation rate for each succeeding year. Both the first-year O&M costs and the annual escalation rate should be entered on the Worksheet. In some situations (e.g., when the complete community energy system is not built at one time), uninflated O&M costs might not be constant over time. In such cases, a constant escalation rate is not appropriate, and O&M costs for each year must be estimated separately. In either case, O&M costs should be computed for each year and entered in Column 10 of the Worksheet.

FUEL COSTS

Fuel costs should be estimated for all raw fuels, as well as for electricity purchased from the uitility grid. The annual consumption of each type of fuel should be an output of the conceptual design for the community energy system. If electricity is purchased from the regional utility grid, total annual charges, including consumption, demand, and service charges, should be included. Worksheet 9.1, Columns 11 and 12, accept cost data for two fuel types; additional estimates may be entered where necessary. An annual cost escalation rate should be entered for each fuel included.

If annual fuel consumption is assumed to be constant over the life of the system, fuel costs will rise according to the assumed fuel cost escalation rates. However, if fuel consumption is not constant, the escalation rates should be applied to the previous year's fuel prices to compute fuel prices for the current year. Then, to compute fuel costs for each year, the estimated consumption of each fuel should be multiplied by the appropriate fuel price for that year. These fuel costs should be entered in Columns 11 and 12 of Worksheet 9.1.

TAXES

Taxes are the only remaining costs to be estimated. Relevant taxes might include local, state, and federal income taxes, property tax, and sales tax on energy sales. Of these, only property taxes can be computed without knowledge of revenues. Therefore, the computation of income taxes and sales tax will be delayed until revenues are estimated. Property taxes are computed by multiplying the taxable value of the investment by the property tax rate. If the total capital investment in the system does not occur in year 0, property taxes will not remain constant throughout the study period.

At this point, all costs except income and sales taxes should have been estimated. The next step is to estimate community utility revenues. Taxes can then be computed, and the economic analysis can be completed, based on total costs and revenues.

Community Utility Revenues

Three primary sources of revenue to the community utility operating the community energy system are:
- Sale of electricity to the electric utility grid;
- Direct sales of thermal and electrical energy to system customers; and
- Sale of recovered materials, e.g., metals and glass, if solid waste recovery is part of the system.

Each of these revenue sources is discussed. The first, electricity sales to the grid, should be disregarded for community energy systems owned by a utility, except in the rare cases where the excess electricity is sold directly to another utilty.

ELECTRICITY SALES TO THE GRID

Generally, it is advantageous from a reliability standpoint for a community energy system to be tied into the regional utility grid to receive backup service for emergency and short, infrequent peak periods. At the same time, selling excess electricity to the utility grid is beneficial for the community utility. Several problems often arise in trying to arrange for electricity sales to a utility. These include:
- Utility's perceptions of cogeneration as market invasion,
- Lack of need for additional capacity by some utilities, and

INPUT DATA

(1) FIRST-YEAR O&M COSTS _____   (5) FIRST-YEAR FUEL B COSTS _____

(2) ANNUAL O&M COST
    ESCALATION RATE _____   (6) ANNUAL FUEL B COST
    ESCALATION RATE _____

(3) FIRST-YEAR FUEL A COSTS _____   (7) PROPERTY TAX RATE _____

(4) ANNUAL FUEL A COST
    ESCALATION RATE _____   (8) TAXABLE PROPERTY VALUE _____

CALCULATIONS

(n) YEAR	(9) CAPITAL	(10) O&M COSTS	(11) FUEL A COSTS	(12) FUEL B COSTS	(13) PROPERTY TAX	(14) INCOME TAXES	(15) TOTAL ANNUAL EXPENSES (10)+(11)+(12) +(13)+(14)
0							
1							
2							
3							
4							
5							
6							
7							
8							
9							
10							
11							
12							
13							
14							
15							
16							
17							
18							
19							
20							
21							
22							
23							
24							
25							
26							
27							
28							
29							
30							

[a] All values are in 10^3 $.

WORKSHEET 9.1
Community Utility Expenditure Summary[a]

- Disparity between the times when the cogenerator has excess power and when that power is required by the utility.

Each of these factors tends to decrease the price that a utility is willing to pay for purchased power. Presently, the exchange rates between cogenerators and utilities are settled primarily by negotiation, based on the conditions surrounding each individual situation. Therefore, anticipating exact rates at which electricity can be sold to a utility is difficult.

In accordance with accepted economic theory, a utility should be willing to pay its marginal cost for the purchase of electricity. The Public Utilities Regulatory Policies Act (PURPA) of 1978, may require that utilities purchase power from cogenerators at the incremental cost to the utility of alternative electrical energy. In the short run, a utility's incremental, or marginal, costs are its variable operating costs. Long-run marginal costs, which account for capacity expansion and replacement, include fixed costs (primarily capital). In those situations in which the cogeneration facility does not permit the utility to reduce or defer its own expansion plans because of utility overcapacity or unavailability of power from the cogenerator at peak periods, the utility would be willing to pay only its short-term marginal costs. However, if the cogenerator's operation would contribute to meeting the utility's peak load and enable the utility to reduce or defer its own construction plans, the utility should be willing to pay its long-term marginal costs to the cogenerator. The rules finally adopted for implementation of PURPA will heavily influence interchange rates between utilities and cogenerators.

Contact with the state utility commission is a good first step in estimating the price a cogenerator could obtain for electricity sold to a utility. However, most states currently have few, if any, regulations specifying how this price is to be determined; implementation of PURPA will change this situation. To obtain an idea of the price that currently can be obtained from a utility, the best sources are contracts obtained by other cogenerators in the utility's franchise area. Because of present scarcity of cogeneration applications, other cogeneration arrangements with the same utility usually do not exist. The utility can be contacted directly for an estimate of what it is willing to pay for electricity from a cogenerator. This price will tend to be on the low side of what the utility might be willing to actually pay because it is trying to establish an advantageous bargaining position. In view of the uncertainty regarding the price that can be obtained from the utility, it is advisable to compute a few revenue estimates, based on various selling prices. The profitability of the community energy system under these various price scenarios then can be investigated.

Total annual revenues from energy sales to the grid will equal the product of the price/unit energy (kWh) and the amount of energy sold per year. If rates vary with the time of day, week, and year in which the electricity is sold, the estimates of energy to be sold must also be disaggregated into these separate price categories. An annual escalation rate for these revenues, based on expected cost increases for the customer utility, also should be estimated. Using this escalation rate and the estimated first-year revenues, the user should estimate revenues for each year of the study period and list them in Column 1 of Worksheet 9.2.

REVENUES FROM DIRECT SALES TO CUSTOMERS

In many community energy systems, most revenues will come from the sale of electricity and thermal energy to consumers within the community. If the

INPUT DATA
    CASE I: COLUMNS 1,4, and 5
    CASE II: COLUMNS 1,2,3, and 5

COMPUTATIONS

(n) YEAR	(1) SALES TO GRID	SKIP COLUMNS 2 & 3 FOR CASE I		(4) MAXIMUM REVENUES FROM CONSUMERS[c]	(5) MISC. REVENUES	(6) TOTAL MAXIMUM REVENUES
		(2) CONVENTIONAL SYSTEM CONSUMER COSTS[a]	(3) COMMUNITY SYSTEM CONSUMER RETAINED COSTS[b]			
1						
2						
3						
4						
5						
6						
7						
8						
9						
10						
11						
12						
13						
14						
15						
16						
17						
18						
19						
20						
21						
22						
23						
24						
25						
26						
27						
28						
29						
30						

[a] Copy from column 17 of Worksheet No. 3.
[b] Copy from Column 14 of Worksheet No. 4.
[c] If Case I, column 4 data are supplied as input.
  If Case II, Column 4 equals Column 2 minus Column 3.

WORKSHEET 9.2
Summary of Community Utility Revenues

prices to be charged for electricity and thermal energy are known in advance, the estimation of revenues for these services is straightforward. Assumed prices usually would be based on the rates charged by existing utilities, because consumers cannot be expected to change systems if a higher cost is incurred. Although electricity rates for service at any location are easy to specify, rates for thermal energy (i.e., hot water or steam) from a central source are not available in most locations. Consequently, the prices that the consumer utility can charge its customers for thermal energy and still be competitive with conventional energy supply options are not known beforehand. The calculation of revenues from direct customer sales when electric and thermal rates are known is discussed below in Case I; the estimation of these revenues when thermal energy prices are not specified in advance is described in Case II.

Case I: Prices for Electricity and Thermal Energy Are Known. If the customers to be served by the community energy system are also served by a district heating system, prices for thermal energy, as well as for electricity, can be specified in advanced. These are the maximum prices the community utility can charge its customers for electrical and thermal energy. Actual revenues probably will be somewhat less because of: (1) a market capture rate less than 100% and (2) the incentive needed to entice consumers from their present or expected use of conventional energy sources. This issue will be considered in the section on Sensitivity Analysis. For now, we shall consider only the maximum revenue amount, because if the system is not economically feasible at these revenues, the same will be true under less optimistic conditions.

The community utility might choose to provide its customers with services (e.g., maintenance of equipment) that were not provided by the electric utility or district heating system. In this case, one would expect a community utility to charge its customers more than if these additional services were not provided. If such a disparity in services to be provided by the conventional system and the community energy system exists, procedures outlined in Case II should be used to compute revenues.

Computations for Case I follow a three-step procedure. First, estimates of the annual consumption of thermal and electrical energy for the community should have been calculated in the engineering analysis that precedes cost estimation. Both steam and electricity rates usually have a wide range of service classifications. The accuracy of the thermal and electricity revenues will depend on the degree to which consumption values can be broken down into the corresponding service classifications. All revenues available from customers in each class are the product of the price of energy in that class and the amount of energy consumed by customers in that class. Second, there might also be demand and service charges that should be considered. Third, annual escalation rates should be estimated for both electrical and thermal energy rates, based on expected increases in utility and district heating rates.

Using the above information, the analyst should compute total maximum electricity and thermal revenues for each year of the study period, sum the revenues, and enter the result in Column 4 of Worksheet 9.2. Worksheets 9.3 and 9.4 can be disregarded for Case-I analyses.

Case II: Thermal Rates Are Not Known Beforehand. Although electricity rates usually can be based on those of the local utility, a supplier of steam or hot water is not available. Therefore, there is no directly comparable market value for thermal energy. The fact that energy consumers will not be willing to pay more for energy services under a community energy system than they pay under a conventional system can be instrumental in estimating the total maximum revenues available to the community utility from its customers. All expenses incurrerd by consumers under a conventional energy system are shown in its circle in Figure 9.5. Consumer expenses under a community energy system are shown emanating from the lower half of the circle. Because the systems are defined such that they both provide the same services, consumers are satisfied by either system if their costs are equal. Therefore, if the consumer costs under the conventional system are estimated and the consumer costs to parties other than the community utility are subtracted, the total maximum customer revenues available to the community utility (the arrow from the lower to the upper half of the circle in Figure 9.5) can be estimated. The details of applying this procedure are described below.

Step 1. Estimate Consumer Costs under the Conventional System.

- Estimate all related capital costs that will be incurred over the study period. Typically, for new construction this would include all equipment used to provide space heating and space cooling, domestic hot water, and any other services provided by the community energy system. For buildings already constructed, the costs of existing systems should be treated as sunk costs and not considered. However, equipment replacement costs incurred during the study period should be considered. Equipment purchased by the consumer and required for the conventional system and all other systems contemplated need not be considered. Enter each capital expenditure in the appropriate year in Column 9 of Worksheet 9.3. Present value factors can be calculated (or obtained from interest tables) using the previously estimated community MARR as the interest rate. Present value factors need to be entered only for years in which capital expenses are incurred. Often, all capital expenses are listed as initial costs (year 0). The present vaue of each capital expense can be computed by multiplying the entry in Column 9 by the corresponding entry in Column 10. The sum of the resulting entries in Column 11 is the total present value of all capital expenses. The total present value, Item 12, should be multiplied by the capital recovery factor, Item 8, to arrive at the amortized capital cost. This value should be entered in Column 13.
- Estimate equipment O&M costs. Estimate annual O&M costs for all HVAC, domestic hot water, and any other relevant systems. Using this first-year O&M cost and an annual escalation rate, compute annual O&M costs for each year of the study period and enter in Column 14 of Worksheet 9.3.
- Estimate fuel costs. Estimate annual expenses for the purchase of electricity, gas, oil, coat, and any other fuels that would otherwise be used by energy consumers to provide the services supplied by the community energy system. Using these first-year fuel costs and annual escalation rates for each fuel, compute fuel costs for each year of the study period and enter in Columns 15 and 16 of Worksheet 9.3. Additional columns will be necessary if more than two fuelds are used.
- Compute total consumer costs. To compute total annual consumer costs to be entered in Column 17, total Columns 13–16 of Worksheet 9.3. These are the total annual costs that are to be borne by energy consumers within the community if the base case conventional energy system is used.

Step 2. Estimate Costs Retained by Consumers under the Community Energy System. The procedure for estimating these costs is essentially identical to that for estimating consumer costs for the conventional energy system described in Step 1. Included here are all costs associated with the provision of the energy

INPUT DATA

(1) FIRST-YEAR O&M COSTS _____

(2) ANNUAL O&M COST
    ESCALATION RATE _____

(3) FIRST-YEAR FUEL
    A COSTS _____

(4) ANNUAL FUEL A COST
    ESCALATION RATE _____

(5) FIRST-YEAR FUEL B COSTS _____

(6) ANNUAL FUEL B COST
    ESCALATION RATE _____

(7) COMMUNITY MARR _____

CALCULATIONS

(8) COMMUNITY CAPITAL RECOVERY FACTOR $= \dfrac{(MARR)(1+MARR)^N}{(1+MARR)^N - 1} =$ _____

(n) YEAR	(9) CAPITAL EXPENSE	(10) PRESENT VALUE FACTOR[b]	(11) PRESENT VALUE OF EXPENSE (9) x (10)	(13) AMORTIZED CAPITAL COSTS (12) x (8)[c]	(14) O&M COSTS	(15) FUEL A COSTS	(16) FUEL B COSTS	(17) TOTAL ANNUAL COSTS (13)+(14) +(15)+(16)
0								
1								
2								
3								
4								
5								
6								
7								
8								
9								
10								
11								
12								
13								
14								
15								
16								
17								
18								
19								
20								
21								
22								
23								
24								
25								
26								
27								
28								
29								
30								
(12) TOTAL PRESENT VALUE =								

[a] All values are in 10^3 $.

[b] Present value factor $= \dfrac{1}{(1+MARR)^n}$

[c] The value should be the same for all years.

WORKSHEET 9.3
Computation of Consumers Costs for Conventional Energy System[a]

INPUT DATA

(1) FIRST—YEAR O & M COSTS _____

(2) ANNUAL O & M COST
     ESCALATION RATE _____

(3) FIRST—YEAR FUEL COSTS _____

(4) ANNUAL FUEL COST _____
     ESCALATION RATE

(5) COMMUNITY MARR· _____

(6) COMMUNITY CAPITAL
     RECOVERY FACTOR[b] _____

CALCULATIONS

(n) YEAR	(7) CAPITAL EXPENSE	(8) PRESENT VALUE FACTOR[c]	(9) PRESENT VALUE OF EXPENSE (7) x (8)	(11) AMORTIZED CAPITAL COSTS[d] (6) x (10)	(12) O & M COSTS	(13) FUEL COSTS	(14) TOTAL ANNUAL COSTS (11)+(12)+(13)
0							
1 2 3 4 5							
6 7 8 9 10							
11 12 13 14 15							
16 17 18 19 20							
21 22 23 24 25							
26 27 28 29 30							
(10) TOTAL PRESENT VALUE =							

[a] All values are in 10^3 $.
[b] Copy from Worksheet No. 3.
[c] Copy from Column 10 of Worksheet No. 3.
[d] The value should be the same for all years.

WORKSHEET 9.4

Computation of Costs Retained by Consumers Under Community Energy System[a]

TABLE 9.4

TYPICAL IN-BUILDING COSTS RETAINED BY CONSUMERS FOR A COMMUNITY
ENERGY SYSTEM

Capital (Fixed Costs)
  Heat exchangers
  Air-handling equipment
  Fan-coil units
  Piping and pumps
  Controls
  Chillers
  Retrofit costs
Annual expenses (Variable Costs)
  Operation and maintenance
  Repair (parts and labor)
  Operator salaries, where appropriate
Fuel
  Any energy purchased from a source other than the community utility e.g., backup
    electricity

services being studied but not paid to the community utility. Typically, these costs would include capital and O&M costs borne directly by energy consumers. An explanation of the procedures for calculating these costs follows. Worksheet 9.4 should be used for these calculations.

- Estimate all capital costs over the life of the study period. These costs would include all new and replacement equipment costs that are to be directly borne by energy consumers. Typical cost items are listed in Table 9.4. Enter the amount of the expenditure in the appropriate year in Column 7 of Worksheet No. 4. To calculate the amortized capital costs, follow the procedures outlined in the first section of Step 1.
- Estimate O&M expenses. Include all O&M costs borne directly by the energy consumer. Use this first-year cost estimate and an assumed O&M cost escalation rate to complete Column 12 of Worksheet 9.4.
- Estimate fuel costs. Usually, all fuel costs are paid to the community energy system, and this value is zero. However, a few rare cases require that this item be considered. For instance, a customer (e.g., a hospital or computer facility) might require direct backup power from the utility grid. The annual costs of this service would be included as fuel costs. Similarly, a community energy system might be a central heat pump system that supplies only heating and cooling. The annual costs of electrical service for backup heating would be included here. Fuel costs should be entered in Column 13 of Worksheet 9.4.
- Compute total consumer costs. Sum Columns 11–13 of Worksheet 9.4. These values are the total annual costs that customers of the community energy system will pay to parties other than the community utility for energy services.

Step 3. Compute Maximum Total Revenues Available to the Community Utility from Its Customers. As explained previously, the maximum amount of revenue that the community utility can collect from its customers and still remain competitive is equal to the total amount it would pay under the base case system minus any other charges the customers pay under the community energy system. For each year of the study period, the maximum total revenues are equal to the amount in Column 17 of Worksheet No. 9.3 minus the amount in Column 14 of Worksheet 9.4. Columns 2, 3, and 4 of Worksheet 9.2 should be used for these calculations.

MISCELLANEOUS REVENUES FROM SOURCES OUTSIDE THE COMMUNITY

Revenues available to the community utility from energy consumers within the community were calculated in Step 1. Some revenues could possibly be collected from sources outside the community (not including electricity sales to grid). Revenues of this type are likely to occur if the community system has a solid- or liquid-waste processing plant that can market recovered metals and glass and derived fuels. Moreover, if the system is privately owned, tipping fees could be collected from local governments or waste disposal contractors. If the system is publicly owned, the capital and O&M costs associated with an alternate waste facility (e.g., a sanitary landfill) would be counted as savings and included under the item. Using first-year estimates and annual escalation rates, the analyst should forecast individual miscellaneous revenues over the study period, and enter this total in column 5 of Worksheet 9.2.

CALCULATION OF TOTAL MAXIMUM REVENUES FOR A COMMUNITY UTILITY

The total maximum revenues available to the community utility from electricity sales to the grid, energy sales to customers, and miscellaneous revenues is the sum of the values in Columns 1, 4, and 5 of Worksheet 9.2. These revenue estimates are used in the following section to compute income taxes, i.e., the final cost yet to be determined. Total revenues, total investment cost, and total annual costs, will be used to determine the economic feasibility of the proposed community energy system.

Estimates of Income Taxes and Miscellaneous Taxes for the Community Utility

After community utility revenues have been estimated, income and miscellaneous taxes can be estimated. Although the procedures outlined here do not incorporate all tax subtleties, they are useful in pointing out the magnitude of the effects of these taxes. If the community utility is publicly owned, taxes are not applicable, and this section can be omitted.

Sales taxes and other miscellaneous local and state taxes might be important in the economic evaluation of a community energy system. Although specific estimating procedures are not provided, these taxes are discussed briefly in "Miscellaneous Taxes".

FEDERAL AND STATE INCOME TAXES

Approximation of the combined effect of federal and state income taxes by an effective income tax rate is often useful. State income taxes usually are deductible from federal income taxes, but the reverse is not usually true:

$$\text{Effective tax rate} = \text{state rate} \\ + (1 - \text{state rate})(\text{federal rate}) \quad \text{(Eq.2)}$$

The following expression specifies the total income taxes for a given year:

$$\text{Income taxes} = (\text{effective tax rate})(\text{revenues} - \text{O\&M} - \text{fuel} \\ - \text{interest payments} - \text{tax depreciation} \quad \text{(Eq.3)} \\ - \text{property taxes}) - \text{investment tax credits}$$

INPUT DATA

(1) FEDERAL INCOME TAX RATE, t_F _____

(2) STATE INCOME TAX RATE, t_S _____

(3) DEPRECIABLE INVESTMENT _____

(4) INVESTMENT TAX CREDIT RATE _____

(5) INTEREST PAYMENT SCHEDULE _____

(6) DEPRECIATION METHOD _____

CALCULATIONS

(7) EFFECTIVE INCOME TAX RATE $= t_S + (1 - t_S)(t_F) =$ _____

(n) YEAR	(8) REVENUES[a]	(9) O&M, FUEL, & PROPERTY TAX[b]	(10) INTEREST PAYMENTS	(11) TAX DEPRECI- ATION	(12) TAXABLE INCOME (8)-(9) -(10)-(11)	(13) UNADJUSTED INCOME TAXES (7)x(12)	(14) INVESTMENT TAX CREDIT	(15) INCOME TAXES (13)-(14)
1								
2								
3								
4								
5								
6								
7								
8								
9								
10								
11								
12								
13								
14								
15								
16								
17								
18								
19								
20								
21								
22								
23								
24								
25								
26								
27								
28								
29								
30								

[a] From Column 6 of Worksheet No. 4.

[b] Sum of Columns 10 through 13 of Worksheet No. 1.

WORKSHEET 9.5
Computation of Community Utility Federal and State Income Taxes

Of the above quantities, only tax depreciation, interest payments, and invest-ment tax credits have not yet been estimated.

Worksheet 9.5 is useful for estimating annual income taxes. Revenues, in Column 8, can be copied from Column 6 of Worksheet 9.2. O&M, Fuel, and Property Tax, in Column 9, is the sum of Columns 10–13 of Worksheet 9.1. Interest payments, to be entered in Column 10, are made on that fraction of the project financed by debt. Annual interest payments are to be based on an assumed debt repayment schedule, the amount of debt, and the cost of debt. If the entire debt principal is to be repaid at one time, such as in the retirement of bonds, interest payments will be constant up to bond retirement. However, if a portion of the principal is repaid each year, annual interest payments will decrease with time.

Depreciation, another tax deduction to be computed, represents the con-sumption of capital needed to produce goods. Nearly all capital for a community energy system, except land, is depreciable for tax purposes. The amount of the depreciable investment should be listed on line 3 of Worksheet 9.5. Next, a method of tax depreciation must be selected. Straightline (SL) depreciation, in which the depreciation charge is constant each year over the tax life of the investment, is the simplest method to use. In contrast to SL depreciation, accelerated depreciation methods shift most of the depreciation charges to the early years of the equipment's lifetime. These methods permit most of the tax benefits from depreciation charges to be gained in the earlier years, and result in an economic benefit caused by the time value of money. Brief descriptions of two popular accelerated depreciation methods, the double-declining-balance (DDB) method and the sum-of-the-years-digit (SYD) method, are provided below.

- Double-Declining-Balance Depreciation. Under the DDB method, the annual depreciation rate is twice the SL depreciation rate. For example, an asset with a tax life of ten years would have a DDB depreciation rate of 20%. Unlike the SL method, the DDB rate is applied to the undepre-ciated balance, rather than to the original investment amount. An asset would never be depreciated fully if the DDB method were continued indefinitely. Therefore, tax laws allow a switch to another depreciation method at some time in the asset's life. That switch is made when the depreciation from another method (usually SYD or SL) exceeds the DDB depreciation charge.

- Sum-of-the-Years-Digit Depreciation. The following expression yields the annual depreciation rate in any year, n, for an asset with a tax life of N years.

$$\text{SYD rate} = (N - n + 1)/(1 + 2 + 3 \ldots + N) \qquad \text{(Eq. 4)}$$

- As in SL depreciation, the depreciation rate is applied to the original depreciable investment amount. The SYD method results in total depre-ciation over the asset's tax life.

Use of SL, DDB, and SYD depreciation methods is illustrated in the example below. When completing Worksheet 3.5, use a depreciation method for tax purposes to calculate depreciation charges and enter the results in Column 11.

Example. An asset worth $1,000 has a tax life of 10 years. Assuming no salvage value, show tax depreciation charges under SL, DDB, and SYD methods. When using the DDB method, switch to SL depreciation when it becomes more advantageous.

1. SL depreciation
   Annual depreciation charge is $1,000/10 = $100
2. DDB depreciation

Year	Undepreciated Balance	Double-Declining-Balance Method[a]	Straight-Line Method on Undepreciated Balance[b]	Selected Depreciation
1	$1,000	$200	$100	$200
2	800	160	89	160
3	640	128	80	128
4	512	102	73	102
5	410	82	68	82
6	328	66	66	66
7	262	—	66	66
8	196	—	66	66
9	130	—	66	66
10	64	—	64[c]	64
				$1,000

[a] (Undepreciated balance) (0.20).
[b] (Undepreciated balance)/(remaining tax life).
[c] Difference caused by rounding error.

In this example the depreciation method switches after the sixth year because after that, the SL depreciation on the undepreciated balance exceeds the DDB depreciation.

3. SYD depreciation
   $1 + 2 + 3 + 4 + 5 + 6 + 7 + 8 + 9 + 10 = 55$

Year	1	2	3	4	5	6	7	8	9	10	Total
Depreciation[a]	$182	164	145	127	109	91	73	55	36	18	$1,000

[a] $(1,000)(11 - n)/55$.

One other potentially important income tax consideration is the investment tax credit. Federal income taxes allow a credit for qualified, depreciable property. The investment tax credit life is based on the asset's depreciation during the eligible life, which is the lesser of the tax life and the useful life period of study. Currently, for an investment with an eligible life greater than 7 years, the investment tax credit rate is 10%. If possible, this total credit can be applied against income taxes due the first year the plant is put into operation. The credit can also be carried back to past income taxes or forward to future income taxes, in accordance with current provision of the Internal Revenue Service. Limits currently are 3 years back and 7 years forward, respectively.

As of January, 1982, the maximum credit that can be claimed in a given year is limited to $25,000 plus 90% of the remaining tax liability. Generally, the community energy system will be only one of many projects in the portfolio of the corporation owning the community utility; therefore, the allowable credit will be based on total corporate tax liability, rather than on just that from the community energy system. An assumption about other corporate tax liabilities must be made to permit distribution of the investment tax credit. For example, if half the credit is assumed to be applied in each of the first two years of operation, 5% of the depreciable investment should be entered in years 1 and 2 of Column 14 of Worksheet 9.5. Investment credits on the state income tax, where they exist, should also be considered.

All data necessary to compute income taxes should now have been entered on Worksheet 9.5. Taxable income, Column 12, is computed by subtracting Columns 9–11 from Column 8. Unadjusted income taxes, Column 13, is the product of the effective income tax rate and taxable income. Investment tax credits, Column 15. Income taxes for each year should be transferred to Column 14 of Worksheet 9.1. Total annual expenses, Column 15, then can be computed by summing Columns 10–14 of Worksheet 9.1.

MISCELLANEOUS TAXES

Depending on the particular situation, a community utility might be subject to other state or local taxes. One of these might be sales taxes on the sale of electrical and thermal energy. Typically sales taxes would apply only when separate charges are made for energy sales. Thus, if energy charges are a nonspecified portion of rent, or if the energy produced is self-consumed, sales taxes would not apply. If sales taxes and other taxes are considered, appropriate deductions should be made to the estimates of taxable income to be used for computing income taxes. Sales taxes and other miscellaneous taxes have not been included on a worksheet because of their wide range of applicability, computation procedures, and their usually minor effect on the analysis.

SYSTEMS COMPARISON AND SELECTION

Criteria for Economic Evaluation

The data generated in the preceeding section can be used in various ways to determine which type of energy system the community utility should select. Criteria most often used in comparing competing alternatives include: NPN, SPP, DPP, RR, and SIR. Each criterion offers advantages and disadvantages in its application. The selection of criteria for economic evaluation varies widely both within and among various industries.

In the remaining paragraphs of this section, each of the above criteria is discussed in terms of its strengths and weaknesses as an aid for economic evaluation. A set of recommended criteria for evaluating community energy systems is then provided. Finally, the computational procedures for computing each of the criteria discussed are outlined.

NET PRESENT VALUE

The MARR indicates a firm's time value of money. Therefore, if a firm's MARR is 20%, it is supposedly equally satisfied by a $1.00 return today or a $120 return 1 year from now. Analysis of present value collapses a time stream of cash flows into one value at some particular point. To compute the present value of a project, future cash flows in year n are translated into present value components by multiplying by the factor,

$$\frac{1}{(1 + MARR)_n}$$

The difference between the initial investment and the present value of net income for all years in the study period is the project's NPV. If this amount exceeds zero, the value of future cash flows exceeds the value of the initial investment based on a discount rate equal to MARR; hence, the project should be undertaken. In the case of mutually exclusive proposals, the project with the greatest NPV should be selected. Use of an NPV comparison will ensure that profits or savings, when discounted at the MARR, are maximized.

The credibility of a project evaluation based on an NPV analysis dependent largely on confidence in the value selected as the MARR. Project rankings will change as the value of the MARR varies, because higher values will increasingly favor projects with more favorable cash flows in the early years of the study period. If future costs, revenues, and inflation could be known accurately, then the MARR would be an exact indication of the acceptable trade-off between present and future receipts. However, investors often place more weight on early-year receipts than is warranted by the value selected as the MARR. Hence, a project that has a high NPV, but does not produce positive returns for several years might be less attractive to some investors than a project with a lower NPV, but with a large portion of its benefits seen early in the project's life. The greater the uncertainty, the less will be the confidence in the NPV as a sole indicator of economic attractiveness.

STRAIGHT AND DISCOUNTED PAYBACK PERIOD

The payback period is defined as the length of time from the initial investment until the difference the initial investment and the cumulative sum of annual savings is zero. By specifying a maximum allowable payback period, an investor recognizes and attempts to compensate for uncertainties in cost and revenue estimates. A firm that requires a short payback period is attempting to limit speculation and to aid its short-term cash flow by selecting only projects with quick profit.

Two types of payback periods generally are recognized. The SPP is calculated on the basis of nondiscounted cash flows. In other words, future savings or profits are not reduced on the basis of an interest rate. The DPP is computed on the basis of discounted cash flows.

Two major flaws become apparent in using the SPP as an economnic criterion. The first is the failure to account for the time value of money. Therefore, a project that costs $1,000 and returns $200 per year has the same SPP, i.e., 5 years, as a project that costs $1,000 and returns $900 the first year, nothing in years 2–4, and $100 in year 5. The second major fault of the SPP is its disregard of cash flows following the payback period. Thus, a project that costs $1,000 and returns $200 per year for five years has the same SPP as a project that costs $1,000 and returns $200 per year for 10 years. Although the DPP removes the objection to the disregard for the time value of money, cash flows beyond the payback period are still not considered.

Despite these flaws in its content, the SPP is one of the most popular economic criteria in American industry. The two principal reasons for this popularity are its computational simplicity (because cash flows are not discounted) and its reflection of capital liquidity. Although each of these advantages is desirable, project selection based only on SPP will not necessarily result in profit maximization, as the examples in the previous paragraph show.

RATE OF RETURN

The RR is another economic yardstick often used to evaluate investments. This criterion is also known as the internal rate of return and the return on investment. The RR is the interest rate that will cause the present value of all capital investments to equal the present value of all returns. Thus, the project's NPV based on a discount rate equal to the RR, is zero.

The RR method of project evaluation has two major advantages. First, the idea that an investment should return an amount in excess of the original investment is readily apparent to investors, so it is somewhat easier for many managers to place an RR value in perspective, as opposed to a present value or equivalent annual value. Second, computation of an RR does not require the previous selection of a MARR, which is usually a subjective decision.

Project ranking based on the RR method usually produces results in close agreement with NPV analyses. Nevertheless, use of the RR in project selection does not guarantee that an investment's NPV, based on a discount rate equal to the MARR, is maximized. For example, assume that one project proposal requires an initial investment of $100 and 1 year later returns $150; a second proposal requires an initial investment of $1,000 and 1 year later returns $1,400. Based on an RR analysis, the first proposal, with an RR of 50%, should be selected over the second proposal that an RR of 40%. Unless the firm's MARR exceeds 38.9%, the second project should be selected if the investment's present value is to be maximized (38.9% is the RR on the incremental investment of $900 and the discount rate that will cause the NPV of both proposals to be equal.)

One of the most serious objections to the RR method of project evaluation is the implicit assumption that returns can be reinvested at the computed RR. Such an assumption often is invalid. As an example of the discrepancies introduced by this assumption, consider the following two projects and their cash flows.

End-of-Year Cash Flow

Project	Year				
	0	1	2	3	4
1	−100	10	35	60	85
2	−100	100	20	20	20

Using a MARR of 10%, the present value of Project 1 is $41.16 and that of Project 2 is $36.13. Therefore, based on a present value comparison, Project 1 is preferable to Project 2. However, when an RR comparison is made, the project rankings switch because the RR of Project 1 can be shown to be 23.4%, while that of Project 2 is 34.5%. This ranking reversal is caused by the reinvestment assumption. Project 2 has higher returns in the first year than Project 1, and these returns are assumed to be reinvested at a 34.5% RR, which may or may not reflect reality.

Another problem with the RR method of project evaluation occurs when an investment could have more than one computed RR. This would be true if the cumulative cash flow changes signs more than once. For example, if a project requires an initial investment and all annual returns are positive, only one RR value can be found. However, if returns in some later years are negative, the project cumulative cash flow could turn negative after it had turned positive, and thereby create the possibility of more than one computed RR. The correct value to use is often not readily apparent and depends on the RR assumed most likely to apply to reinvested returns. Because it concerns community energy systems, the dilemma of multiple solutions would be particularly troublesome if system construction is staged. This could result in negative cash flows from time-distributed capital investments.

SAVINGS-TO-INVESTMENT RATIO

The SIR, also referred to as a profitability index, is defined as the present value of all benefits divided by the present value of the capital investment. The

NPV is the difference between those two quantities, and the SIR is their ratio. An SIR above 1.0 indicates an acceptable project.

Although the SIR indicates projects in which the discounted benefits exceed the present value of the investment, rankings based on this criterion do not insure maximization of profits or savings at the MARR. Discrepancies produced by SIR comparison are similar to those produced by an RR comparison. For example, a low-cost investment with a high RR would be favored over a high-cost investment with lower RR but with a positive NPV. Thus, even though the incremental investment is able to earn the MARR, it is rejected if the projects are mutually exclusive (as they are in the choice of energy systems).

RECOMMENDED CRITERIA

Each of the criteria discussed is valuable as an indicator of some aspect(s) of an investment economic attractiveness. However, to apply any of these criteria properly, the analyst must understand which qualities the criterion measures and the assumptions inherent in the use of that criterion. Therefore, it is not so important to identify a most correct criterion as it is to specify a criterion that is most correct for evaluating a certain aspect of an investment. Consequently, although a set of criteria is recommended below, the flexibility to consider other criteria is retained.

The criteria discussed in the previous sections can be divided into two groups: life-cycle economic measures and project liquidity measures. The first group accounts for the time value of money and provide insight into the balance between costs and revenues over the life of the project. Criteria in this group include NPV, RR, and SIR. These are the criteria usually suggested in engineering economics textbooks for comparing competing alternatives. The second group of criteria accounts for uncertainty about the future and the investor's corresponding desire to avoid big expenditures that generate large, but distant and speculative, incomes. The measures in this second group include SPP and DPP. Although these criteria are more one-dimensional in the view they represent, they can be useful as a supplement to a criterion from the first group by segregating overly speculative projects.

If projects are ranked according to each of the three criteria in the first group, only rankings based on NPV will ensure that profits or savings are maximized at discount rate equal to the MARR. Investment decisions, based on RR and SIR, were discussed. The NPV should be used as the primary criterion for project ranking. Moreover, most firms limit the degree of uncertainty they are willing to accept before proceeding with a project. Elimination of projects that do not return the investment within a specified payback period will reflect this requirement. Because of its consideration of the time value of money, DPP rather than SPP should be used. Although computational procedures for each of the criteria previously discussed are included in the second half of this section, the suggested procedure for project selection is based on NPV and DPP, the suggested evaluation criteria.

Computational Procedures

The following sections describe the use of the data generated in the "Estimates of Costs and Revenues" section to compute the NPV, RR, SIR, SPP, and DPP of a community energy system. These criteria can then be used to select a system from the alternatives studied.

The recommended procedure for system selection is based on NPV and DPP.

INPUT DATA

COLUMNS 1,2, AND 3 (SAME FOR ALL CRITERIA)

UTILITY MARR _____

COMPUTATIONS

COLUMNS AND ITEMS REQUIRED FOR EACH CRITERION:

STRAIGHT PAYBACK PERIOD 4,5   NET PRESENT VALUE 4,6,7,8,9,10

DISCOUNTED PAYBACK PERIOD 4,6,7,8,9,11   SAVINGS—TO—INVESTMENT RATIO 4,6,7,8,9,10

(n) YEAR	(1) CAPITAL[a]	(2) ANNUAL EXPENSES[b]	(3) ANNUAL REVENUES[c]	(4) NET ANNUAL RETURNS (3) – (2)	(5) UNRETURNED INVESTMENT	(6) PV FACTOR[d]	(7) PV OF CAPITAL (6) x (1)	(9) PV OF NET ANNUAL RETURNS (6) x (4)	(11) CUMULATIVE NET PV
0									
1									
2									
3									
4									
5									
6									
7									
8									
9									
10									
11									
12									
13									
14									
15									
16									
17									
18									
19									
20									
21									
22									
23									
24									
25									
26									
27									
28									
29									
30									
					(8) TOTAL PV OF CAPITAL				= (10) TOTAL PV OF NET ANNUAL RETURNS

SUMMARY

STRAIGHT PAYBACK PERIOD = _____ YEARS   NET PRESENT VALUE   = $ _____

DISCOUNTED PAYBACK PERIOD= _____ YEARS   SAVINGS—TO—INVESTMENT RATIO = _____

[a] Copy from Column 9 of Worksheet No. 1.

[b] Copy from Column 15 of Worksheet No. 1.

[c] Copy from Column 6 of Worksheet No. 4.

[d] Present value factor $= \dfrac{1}{(1+\text{MARR})^n}$.

WORKSHEET 9.6

Calculation of Net Present Value, Discounted Payback Period, Straight Payback Period, and Savings-to-Investment Ratio

Worksheets have been provided as aids in computing values for these criteria, as well as for any of the other criteria mentioned above.

In the recommended procedure, systems are ranked according to NPV, although each system must also meet a DPP criterion. To eliminate unnecessary NPV calculations, the analyst can compute the DPP of each community energy system first; systems that do not meet the DPP criterion then can be eliminated from further consideration. Next, compute the NPV of each remaining system and select the system with the highest value. If the NPV of the highest-ranking system is negative, none of the community energy systems considered is economically feasible, and either additional alternatives should be studied or the conventional system should be selected. However, if the NPV is positive, the highest ranking system meets the MARR and is the system among those studied that generates maximum profits for that discount rate.

DATA COLLECTION AND PRELIMINARY CALCULATIONS

Worksheet 9.6 is useful in computing SPP, DPP, NPV, and SIR. Those items and columns of Worksheet 9.6 that must be completed to compute each criterion are listed on the worksheet. Regardless of which of these is to be computed, Column 1, Capital Expenditures; Column 2, Annual Expenses; and Column 3, Annual Revenues, must be completed. These values can be copied from Columns 9 and 15 of Worksheet 9.1 and Column 6 of Worksheet 9.2, respectively. Column 4 of Worksheet 9.6 is computed by subtracting the values in Column 2 from those in Column 3. If the DPP, NPV, or SIR is to be computed, Columns 6, 7, and 9 must also be completed. The present value factors for Column 6 should be computed or copied from interest tables using the MARR as the interest rate. Values in Column 6 multiplied by those in Column 1 will yield values for Column 7 (use negative sign); the product of values in Columns 6 and 4 will provide values for Column 9.

If the RR is to be determined, Worksheet 9.7 should be used. All required input data can be obtained from Worksheet 9.6 Use of Worksheet 9.6 for computing the RR is explained in "Rate of Return" section. All remaining computations for each economic criterion are described in the following sections.

STRAIGHT PAYBACK PERIOD

The SPP should be used only in cases in which the total capital investment is placed at the beginning of the study period. Otherwise, because SPP computations disregard the time value of money, the SPP of a project that has a distributed investment would be the same as that of a project with one equal, initial capital investment and an equivalent stream of returns. This would violate the intent of the criterion to indicate liquidity because the cash flow for the incremental investment is preferable.

The SPP is computed by using the capital investment listed in year 0 of Column 1 on Worksheet 9.6 and the net annual returns contained in Column 4. The capital investment should be entered in year 0 of Column 5. The net annual returns for year 1 then should be subtracted from the value for year 0, and that result entered in year 1 of Column 5. To determine the current year's entry, the net annual returns for each year should be subtracted from the previous year's entry in Column 5. The SPP has been reached when the entry for the current year in Column 5 is less than or equal to zero. Interpolation between years can be used to specify the SPP exactly.

INPUT DATA

COLUMNS 1 AND 2

COMPUTATIONS

(n) YEAR	(1) CAPITAL[a]	(2) NET ANNUAL RETURNS[b]	(3) NET ANNUAL CASH FLOW (2) − (1)	TRIAL 1 (4) ASSUMED RR =		TRIAL 2 (8) ASSUMED RR =		TRIAL 3 (12) ASSUMED RR =	
				(5) PV FACTOR[c]	(6) PV OF NET ANNUAL CASH FLOW (5) x (3)	(9) PV FACTOR[c]	(10) PV OF NET ANNUAL CASH FLOW (9) x (3)	(13) PV FACTOR[c]	(14) PV OF NET ANNUAL CASH FLOW (13) x (3)
0									
1									
2									
3									
4									
5									
6									
7									
8									
9									
10									
11									
12									
13									
14									
15									
16									
17									
18									
19									
20									
21									
22									
23									
24									
25									
26									
27									
28									
29									
30									
				(7) NET PRESENT VALUE =		(11) NET PRESENT VALUE =		(15) NET PRESENT VALUE =	

[a] Copy from Column 1 of Worksheet No. 7.
[b] Copy from Column 4 of Worksheet No. 7.
[c] Present value factor $= \dfrac{1}{(1+RR)^n}$.

WORKSHEET 9.7
Calculation of Rate of Return

DISCOUNTED PAYBACK PERIOD

Unlike the SPP, the DPP can be used for distributed capital investments, as well as for one-time investments. The wider range of applications is caused by the inclusion of a discount rate in the calculation.

Theoretically, the calculation of the DPP is the same as that for the SPP except that discounted cash flows are used instead of actual cash flows. Using

Worksheet 9.6, the analyst must first compute the present value of the capital investment, Item 8, and the present value of each year's net returns, Column 9, before determining the DPP.

The present value of the capital investment (Item 8), is the sum of all entries in Column 7. This sum should be entered in Year 0 of Column 11, the column that indicates the project's cumulative NPV. The entry for year 1 of Column 11 is the year 0 entry minus year 1 entry in Column 9. This procedure should be repeated for each succeeding year until the Column 11 entry is less than or equal to zero. The DPP is reached in the first year for which this condition prevails. Straight-line interpolation between this and the preceding year usually will yield a sufficiently accurate estimate of the DPP.

NET PRESENT VALUE

Using Worksheet 9.6, the user can easily compute a project's NPV if the DPP has been computed. In this case, nearly all input calculations would have been completed. The only remaining piece of input data to be computed is the present value of all net annual returns (Item 10); this value is the sum of the individual items in Column 9. The project's NPV is Item 10 minus Item 8, the present value of the capital investment.

SAVINGS-TO-INVESTMENT RATIO

Computation of the SIR requires the same input data as that for the NPV. The SIR is the ratio of Item 10, the present value of all net annual returns, to Item 8, the present value of the capital investment.

RATE OF RETURN

Many of the available hand-held calculators have programs for calculating RRs that greatly reduce the time required to compute an RR. Data are organized for Worksheet 9.7 for input to RR calculations. The required input data, Columns 1 and 2, can be copied from Columns 1 and 4, respectively, of Worksheet 9.6. On Worksheet 9.7, Column 2 minus Column 1 will yield values for Column 3, the net annual cash flows. These values will be used as the input cash flow stream for the RR computations. The RR that corresponds to this cash flow stream will be provided by the calculation.

If the RR calculations are not available on a computer program, they can be completed manually using the rest of Worksheet 9.7. The basic method for completing RR calculations manually is a trial-and-error approach. The first step is to assume a first-trial RR. Present value factors for the corresponding interest rate should be listed in Column 5. These factors should be multiplied by the values in Column 3, and the products entered in Column 6. The sum of the entries in Column 6 is Item 7, the NPV of the project at the assumed discount rate. At the actual RR, the NPV should be zero. If the NPV is positive, a higher value of RR should be assumed for trial 2. Likewise, a negative NPV requires that a lower RR be assumed for the next trial. The correct value of RR has been bonded when consecutive trials produce NPVs of opposite sign. Additional trials can be used to limit this band. Straight-line interpolation can be used to estimate the correct RR after a sufficiently narrow range has been determined (usually $\leq 10\%$). Worksheet 9.7 has space for three trials; in actual application, more than three trials are often needed.

SENSITIVITY ANALYSIS AND MISCELLANEOUS CONSIDERATIONS

The validity of the results obtained by following the procedures is only as good as the data and assumptions used in the calculations. Certain variables, such as the MARR and the staging of system construction, are influenced by choice. Others, such as cost and revenue estimates, are open to substantial uncertainty. The decision-maker must be aware of the sensitivity of results to the specification of input variables and attempt to influence these conditions advantageously as far as possible, so that the risks of the investment are sufficiently understood. This section discusses several areas in which different policy decisions or unexpected results can substantially change the economic evaluation of a community energy system.

Specification of The Minimum Acceptable Rate of Return

The value chosen as the MARR will have a major effect on the results of the economic analysis. Community energy systems offer reductions in future annual expenses at the cost of increased capital expenditures. Higher values of the MARR will discount future benefits more heavily and will decrease the economic attractiveness of a community energy system.

The MARR is influenced by both the cost of capital and the corporate policy. For public and private utilities, the MARR is the cost of capital. For private, non-utility corporations, although the MARR is influenced by the cost of capital, it is somewhat above it. In each case, a decrease in the cost of capital will cause a decrease in the MARR. Moreover, a publicly owned utility is expected to have the lowest cost of capital, followed by the investor-owned utility, and finally by the private corporation. These observations indicate that decreasing the cost of capital will increase the economic advantage of a community energy system over a conventional, less-efficient system. Although a community energy system might be unattractive to a private developer at a high MARR, a joint venture with a public agency that has a lower cost of capital might reverse the project's economic prospects sufficiently. Many financing schemes would lower the cost of capital to a private corporation.[9] Such arrangements between the private and public sectors include industrial revenue bonds, corporate bonding with municipal guarantees, and state and federal grants, loans, and loan guarantees.

Fuel Cost Escalation

Forecasts of fuel costs for both the community energy system and the conventional energy system will play substantial roles in determining the outcome of the analysis. The life of a community energy system is usually estimated to be about 30 years. Fuel prices are difficult to forecast for 1 year, and almost impossible for 30 years. Uncertainty about fuel costs and availability is the principal reason many firms demand short payback periods for energy-related investments. At the same time, escalating fuel prices are making such short payback periods increasingly possible.

The effects of varying fuel price forecasts depend largely on the type(s) of fuel used by the community energy system, those used by its customers under a conventional energy system for nonelectric energy demands, and those used by the plants supplying the electric grid. The situation in which its fuel prices rise more slowly than those of the conventional system is the most advantageous from the community energy system's perspective. Even if all fuel prices rise at the same rate, the community energy system still offers increased benefits because of its higher fuel efficiency.

To understand the effects that various fuel scenarios can have, the user should perform the economic analysis using a range of assumed values for future fuel prices. A probable range of fuel escalation rates for each fuel can first be identified. A pessimistic scenario that assumes escalation rates detrimental to the community energy system can be considered. Under this scenario, the upper limit of fuel prices for the community energy system would be assumed, and lower prices would be assumed for other fuels that the conventional energy system uses. An optimistic scenario would also be considered. Assumptions under this scenario include a low escalation rate for fuels used by the community energy system fuels and high escalation rates for other fuels used by conventional energy systems. If a community energy system generates a positive NPV under the pessimistic scenario, it is preferable to the conventional energy system(s). The more difficult decision occurs when the sign of the community energy system's NPV changes between the pessimistic and optimistic scenarios. In such a situation, the decision-maker must weigh the probabilities and effects of the occurrence of the optimistic scenario versus that of the pessimistic scenario.

Examination of Revenue Estimates

In the analysis described in "Estimates of Costs and Revenues", when the selling prices of the community utility's electrical and thermal energy are not previously known or the revenues are not prespecified in some other way, estimates of revenues from customers are based on the assumption that the customers would not be willing to pay more for community energy services than they would for the services of a conventional system. These revenues are the maximum that could be collected. In reality, market capture is likely to be less than 100%, and price incentives might be necessary to induce customers to enter into service agreements. Both of these would lower actual revenues. If electricity is to be sold to the utility grid, the uncertainty about the price of electricity to be sold casts further doubt on the amount of estimated revenue.

No clear-cut way exists to account for the uncertainties in project evaluation mentioned above. The investor must be aware of the assumptions used in estimating revenues and know the alternative consequences and their results. Some sort of break-even analysis is often useful for estimating the effects of alternate revenue streams. The manner in which the break-even analysis is performed depends on the parameters that are to be examined and the required detail of the analysis. The general approach is to estimate the revenues required to just cover costs. Various factors that determine the revenues can then be varied to determine the changes to other variables. For example, when all costs for each system have been determined, customer energy prices can be varied to determine the price of electricity that must be obtained from the grid in each case.

In addition to examining the revenue amounts, the analyst must also study the time distribution of revenues. Regardless of whether the community energy system is to serve new construction or retrofit applications, the market will take time to grow. New customers will be added gradually, and the revenue stream should reflect the expected growth rate. Market growth will depend on factors such as expected construction timetables, the rate at which existing HVAC systems are replaced, escalation of grid electric rates, and the market's perception of how well the system's reliability has been demonstrated. Estimating market growth is easier if the community served is owned by the community energy system owners, because construction and replacement schedules can actually be specified, rather than only estimated.

Timing of System Construction

The timing of revenue streams must be accurate to provide a true picture of a system's economic merits. The timing of equipment expenditures should also be examined to verify whether it is realistic. Moreover, time patterns of expenditures should be checked to see if they could be shifted to influence the project more favorably. For example, suppose a community energy system, which will serve a community to be constructed in phases over the next decade, is to be built to total capacity immediately. Equipment not necessary to meet community energy demands in the early years of the project is either not used or is used only minimally; nevertheless it would add to capital recovery costs. However, if the system is not constructed until the community is completely built, the installation of equipment in existing buildings would cause substantial retrofit costs. Therefore, the scheduling of system capacity growth to follow the community's growth in energy demand is desirable. For example, if a diesel cogeneration system is to be built, diesel engines, chillers, and distribution system extensions could be added incrementally as community growth occurs. This phasing of system construction will favorably affect both the NPV and the DPP of the system. Various phasing options should be studied for each type of community energy system considered. In this regard, some types of technologies afford more flexibility than others.

Conclusions

Several conclusions may be drawn:
1. The economic analysis of a community energy system is full of uncertainties.
2. Informed decision-makers must consider a range of possible scenarios, rather than just one set of data and assumptions.
3. Institutional issues must be negotiated and resolved to influence the project favorably.
4. Agreements between public agencies and private investors can be worked out to reduce risk and the cost of capital to the private sector.
5. System design and operation will be influenced by negotiations with the utility.
6. Other nontechnical factors, i.e., market growth, will also alter system design.
7. Redefinition and analysis of a wide range of technical and institutional aspects of a community energy system are necessary to identify the most economically attractive system.

SAMPLE APPLICATION OF THE ECONOMIC ANALYSIS

This sample illustrates how the analysis can be used to analyze the economics of a community energy system. Particular attention is paid to the worksheets in helping to complete the necessary calculations.

1 Define System to be Analyzed

The community energy system to be analyzed is a proposed diesel-engine cogeneration system for an existing mixed-use development. Space heating and

TABLE 9.5

DATA REQUIRED FOR ANALYSIS OF PROPOSED COMMUNITY ENERGY SYSTEM

Proposed Community Energy System

Utility	*Consumer*
Costs ($, 1981)	Costs ($, 1981)
Capital: 22,615,000[a]	Capital (retrofit): 1,000,000
Annual O&M: 750, 000	Annual O&M: 300,000
Annual fuel: 2,400,000	Payments to utility

Revenues ($, 1981)
   Payments from consumers
   Sales to electric grid: 2,000,000

Existing System

Consumer Costs ($, 1981)
   Annual O&M: 500,000
   Annual electric: 5,000,000
   Annual oil and gas: 1,000,000
General Assumptions and Conditions
   Annual escalation rate for O&M: 9%
   Annual escalation rate for electricity prices: 10%
   Annual escalation rate for oil and gas prices: 11%
   Property tax rate for utility: 1%
   Federal income tax rate for utility: 48%
   State income tax rate for utility: 4%
   Investment tax credit: 10% of depreciable investment
   Depreciation method to be used: SYD

[a] $22,415,000 is tax depreciable; $200,000 is for land.

cooling, water heating, and power for lighting and accessories are currently provided by oil, gas, and electricity. The prospective owner and operator of the system is the real estate firm that owns the development. Table 9.5 summarizes the costs to be incurred under the community energy system and those costs presently incurred under the existing system.

2 Compute Community Utility Expenditures (Worksheet 9.1)

Using the data in Table 9.5, the analyst can project capital costs, O&M, fuel, and property tax expenses for the 30-year life of the system. Income taxes can be computed after the utility revenues are estimated. Completed Worksheet 9.1 illustrates this step.

3 Compute Consumer Costs for Conventional Energy System (Worksheet 9.3)

Fuel and O&M costs can be estimated from the data in Table 9.5. The cost of replacing existing equipment with similar equipment must be computed. Two of the buildings are expected to require replacement of their HVAC systems in about 10 years at a total cost of approximately $700,000. This amount is present-valued and then amortized over the study period. Consumers are expected to have a MARR of 20%. Completed Worksheet 9.3 illustrates this step.

INPUT DATA

(1) FIRST-YEAR O&M COSTS __750__

(2) ANNUAL O&M COST ESCALATION RATE __9%__

(3) FIRST-YEAR FUEL A COSTS __2,400__

(4) ANNUAL FUEL A COST ESCALATION RATE __11%__

(5) FIRST-YEAR FUEL B COSTS __NA__

(6) ANNUAL FUEL B COST ESCALATION RATE __NA__

(7) PROPERTY TAX RATE __1%__

(8) TAXABLE PROPERTY VALUE __22,615__

CALCULATIONS

(n) YEAR	(9) CAPITAL	(10) O&M COSTS	(11) FUEL A COSTS	(12) FUEL B COSTS	(13) PROPERTY TAX	(14) INCOME TAXES	(15) TOTAL ANNUAL EXPENSES (10)+(11)+(12) +(13)+(14)
0	22 615	—	—	—	—	—	—
1	0	750	2,400	NA	226	45	3,421
2	0	818	2,664		226	72	3,780
3	0	891	2,957		226	102	4,176
4	0	971	3,282		226	1,155	5,634
5	0	1,059	3,643		226	1,717	6,645
6	0	1,154	4,044		226	2,101	7,525
7	0	1,258	4,489		226	2,523	8,496
8	0	1,371	4,983		226	2,981	9,561
9	0	1,494	5,531		226	3,484	10,735
10	0	1,629	6,139		226	4,032	12,026
11	0	1,776	6,815		226	4,631	13,448
12	0	1,935	7,564		226	5,287	15,012
13	0	2,109	8,396		226	6,005	16,736
14	0	2,299	9,320		226	6,789	18,634
15	0	2,506	10,345		226	7,649	20,726
16	0	2,732	11,483		226	8,588	23,029
17	0	2,978	12,746		226	9,618	25,568
18	0	3,246	14,148		226	10,744	28,364
19	0	3,538	15,704		226	11,980	31,448
20	0	3,856	17,432		226	13,331	34,845
21	0	4,203	19,350		226	14,811	38,590
22	0	4,582	21,478		226	16,431	42,717
23	0	4,994	23,841		226	18,209	47,270
24	0	5,443	26,463		226	20,157	52,289
25	0	5,933	29,374		226	22,290	57,823
26	0	6,467	32,605		226	24,626	63,924
27	0	7,049	36,192		226	27,187	70,654
28	0	7,684	40,173		226	29,992	78,075
29	0	8,375	44,592		226	33,069	86,262
30	0	9,129	49,497		226	36,437	95,289

[a] All values are in 10^3 $.

WORKSHEET 9.1
Community Utility Expenditure Summary[a]

INPUT DATA
CASE I: COLUMNS 1,4, and 5
CASE II: COLUMNS 1,2,3, and 5

COMPUTATIONS

(n) YEAR	(1) SALES TO GRID	(2) CONVENTIONAL SYSTEM CONSUMER COSTS [a]	(3) COMMUNITY SYSTEM CONSUMER RETAINED COSTS [b]	(4) MAXIMUM REVENUES FROM CONSUMERS [c]	(5) MISC. REVENUES	(6) TOTAL MAXIMUM REVENUES
		SKIP COLUMNS 2 & 3 FOR CASE I				
1	2,000	6,523	501	6,022	NA	8,022
2	2,200	7,178	528	6,650		8,850
3	2,420	7,899	557	7,342		9,762
4	2,662	8,694	590	8,104		10,766
5	2,928	9,568	624	8,944		11,872
6	3,221	10,530	663	9,867		13,088
7	3,543	11,590	704	10,886		14,429
8	3,897	12,757	749	12,008		15,905
9	4,287	14,042	799	13,243		17,530
10	4,716	15,457	853	14,604		19,320
11	5,187	17,015	911	16,104		21,291
12	5,706	18,731	975	17,756		23,462
13	6,277	20,619	1,045	19,574		25,851
14	6,905	22,700	1,121	21,579		28,484
15	7,595	24,992	1,204	23,788		31,383
16	8,354	27,515	1,294	26,221		34,575
17	9,190	30,294	1,392	28,902		38,092
18	10,109	33,354	1,499	31,855		41,964
19	11,120	36,726	1,616	35,110		46,230
20	12,232	40,437	1,743	38,694		50,926
21	13,455	44,524	1,882	42,642		56,097
22	14,800	49,027	2,034	46,993		61,793
23	16,281	53,987	2,199	51,788		68,069
24	17,909	59,450	2,378	57,072		74,981
25	19,700	65,467	2,574	62,893		82,593
26	21,670	72,094	2,788	69,306		90,976
27	23,836	79,394	3,021	76,373		100,209
28	26,220	87,435	3,275	84,160		110,380
29	28,842	96,292	3,551	92,741		121,583
30	31,726	106,048	3,853	102,195		133,921

[a] Copy from Column 17 of Worksheet No. 3.
[b] Copy from Column 14 of Worksheet No. 4.
[c] If Case I, Column 4 data are supplied as input.
If Case II, Column 4 equals Column 2 minus Column 3.

WORKSHEET 9.2
Summary of Community Utility Revenues

INPUT DATA

(1) FIRST–YEAR O&M COSTS _500_

(2) ANNUAL O&M COST
ESCALATION RATE _9%_

(3) FIRST–YEAR FUEL
A COSTS _5,000_

(4) ANNUAL FUEL A COST
ESCALATION RATE _10%_

(5) FIRST–YEAR FUEL B COSTS _1,000_

(6) ANNUAL FUEL B COST
ESCALATION RATE _11%_

(7) COMMUNITY MARR _20%_

CALCULATIONS

(8) COMMUNITY CAPITAL RECOVERY FACTOR $= \dfrac{(MARR)(1+MARR)^N}{(1+MARR)^N -1}$ = _0.20085_

(n) YEAR	(9) CAPITAL EXPENSE	(10) PRESENT VALUE FACTOR[b]	(11) PRESENT VALUE OF EXPENSE (9) x (10)	(13) AMORTIZED CAPITAL COSTS (12) x (8)[c]	(14) O&M COSTS	(15) FUEL A COSTS	(16) FUEL B COSTS	(17) TOTAL ANNUAL COSTS (13)+(14) +(15)+(16)
0				—	—	—	—	—
1				23	500	5,000	1,000	6,523
2				23	545	5,500	1,110	7,178
3				23	594	6,050	1,232	7,899
4				23	648	6,655	1,368	8,694
5				23	706	7,321	1,518	9,568
6				23	769	8,053	1,685	10,530
7				23	839	8,858	1,870	11,590
8				23	914	9,744	2,076	12,757
9				23	996	10,718	2,305	14,042
10	700	0.1615	113	23	1,086	11,790	2,558	15,457
11				23	1,184	12,969	2,839	17,015
12				23	1,290	14,266	3,152	18,731
13				23	1,406	15,692	3,498	20,619
14				23	1,533	17,261	3,883	22,700
15				23	1,671	18,988	4,310	24,992
16				23	1,821	20,886	4,785	27,515
17				23	1,985	22,975	5,311	30,294
18				23	2,164	25,272	5,895	33,354
19				23	2,359	27,800	6,544	36,726
20				23	2,571	30,580	7,263	40,437
21				23	2,802	33,637	8,062	44,524
22				23	3,054	37,001	8,949	49,027
23				23	3,329	40,701	9,934	53,987
24				23	3,629	44,772	11,026	59,450
25				23	3,956	49,249	12,239	65,467
26				23	4,312	54,174	13,585	72,094
27				23	4,700	59,591	15,080	79,394
28				23	5,123	65,550	16,739	87,435
29				23	5,584	72,105	18,580	96,292
30				23	6,086	79,315	20,624	106,048
(12) TOTAL PRESENT VALUE =			113					

[a] All values are in 10^3 $.

[b] Present value factor $= \dfrac{1}{(1+MARR)^n}$.

[c] The value should be the same for all years.

WORKSHEET 9.3
Computation of Consumer Costs for Conventional Energy System[a]

INPUT DATA

(1) FIRST-YEAR O & M COSTS _300_

(2) ANNUAL O & M COST
    ESCALATION RATE _9%_

(3) FIRST-YEAR FUEL COSTS _NA_

(4) ANNUAL FUEL COST _NA_
    ESCALATION RATE

(5) COMMUNITY MARR _20%_

(6) COMMUNITY CAPITAL
    RECOVERY FACTOR[b] _0.20085_

CALCULATIONS

(n) YEAR	(7) CAPITAL EXPENSE	(8) PRESENT VALUE FACTOR[c]	(9) PRESENT VALUE OF EXPENSE (7) x (8)	(11) AMORTIZED CAPITAL COSTS[d] (6) x (10)	(12) O & M COSTS	(13) FUEL COSTS	(14) TOTAL ANNUAL COSTS (11)+(12)+(13)
0	1,000	1.0	1,000	—	—	—	—
1				201	300	NA	501
2				201	327		528
3				201	356		557
4				201	389		590
5				201	423		624
6				201	462		663
7				201	503		704
8				201	548		749
9				201	598		799
10				201	652		853
11				201	710		911
12				201	774		975
13				201	844		1,045
14				201	920		1,121
15				201	1,003		1,204
16				201	1,093		1,294
17				201	1,191		1,392
18				201	1,298		1,499
19				201	1,415		1,616
20				201	1,542		1,743
21				201	1,681		1,882
22				201	1,833		2,034
23				201	1,998		2,199
24				201	2,177		2,378
25				201	2,373		2,574
26				201	2,587		2,788
27				201	2,820		3,021
28				201	3,074		3,275
29				201	3,350		3,551
30				201	3,652		3,853
(10) TOTAL PRESENT VALUE =			1,000				

[a] All values are in 10^3 $.

[b] Copy from Worksheet No. 3.

[c] Copy from Column 10 of Worksheet No. 3.

[d] The value should be the same for all years.

WORKSHEET 9.4
Computation of Costs Retained by Consumers under Community Energy System[a]

INPUT DATA

(1) FEDERAL INCOME TAX RATE, t_F 0.48

(4) INVESTMENT TAX CREDIT RATE   10%

(2) STATE INCOME TAX RATE, t_S 0.04

(5) INTEREST PAYMENT SCHEDULE   BONDS TO BE RETIRED IN 30 YEARS

(3) DEPRECIABLE INVESTMENT   22,415

(6) DEPRECIATION METHOD   SUM-OF-THE-YEARS DIGITS

CALCULATIONS

(7) EFFECTIVE INCOME TAX RATE = $t_S + (1 - t_S)(t_F)$ =   0.5008

(n) YEAR	(8) REVENUES[a]	(9) O&M, FUEL, & PROPERTY TAX[b]	(10) INTEREST PAYMENTS	(11) TAX DEPRECI-ATION	(12) TAXABLE INCOME (8) – (9) –(10) – (11)	(13) UNADJUSTED INCOME TAXES (7)×(12)	(14) INVESTMENT TAX CREDIT	(15) INCOME TAXES (13)–(14)
1	8,022	3,376	2,262	1,446	938	470	425	45
2	8,850	3,708	2,262	1,399	1,481	742	670	72
3	9,762	4,074	2,262	1,349	2,077	1,040	938	102
4	10,766	4,479	2,262	1,302	2,723	1,364	209	1,155
5	11,872	4,928	2,262	1,253	3,429	1,717		1,717
6	13,088	5,424	2,262	1,206	4,196	2,101		2,101
7	14,429	5,973	2,262	1,157	5,037	2,523		2,523
8	15,905	6,580	2,262	1,110	5,953	2,981		2,981
9	17,530	7,251	2,262	1,060	6,957	3,484		3,484
10	19,320	7,994	2,262	1,013	8,051	4,032		4,032
11	21,291	8,817	2,262	964	9,248	4,631		4,631
12	23,462	9,725	2,262	917	10,558	5,287		5,287
13	25,851	10,731	2,262	867	11,991	6,005		6,005
14	28,484	11,845	2,262	820	13,557	6,789		6,789
15	31,383	13,077	2,262	771	15,273	7,649		7,649
16	34,575	14,441	2,262	724	17,148	8,588		8,588
17	38,092	15,950	2,262	675	19,205	9,618		9,618
18	41,964	17,620	2,262	628	21,454	10,744		10,744
19	46,230	19,468	2,262	578	23,922	11,980		11,980
20	50,926	21,514	2,262	531	26,619	13,331		13,331
21	56,097	23,779	2,262	482	29,574	14,811		14,811
22	61,793	26,286	2,262	435	32,810	16,431		16,431
23	68,069	29,061	2,262	386	36,360	18,209		18,209
24	74,981	32,132	2,262	338	40,249	20,157		20,157
25	82,593	35,533	2,262	289	44,509	22,290		22,290
26	90,976	39,298	2,262	242	49,174	24,626		24,626
27	100,209	43,467	2,262	193	54,287	27,187		27,187
28	110,380	48,083	2,262	146	59,889	29,992		29,992
29	121,583	53,193	2,262	96	66,032	33,069		33,069
30	133,921	58,852	2,262	49	72,758	36,437		36,437

[a] From Column 6 of Worksheet No. 4.

[b] Sum of Columns 10 through 13 of Worksheet No. 1.

WORKSHEET 9.5

Computation of Community Utility Federal and State Income Taxes

4 Compute Costs Obtained by Consumers Under The Community Energy System (Worksheet 9.4)

The cost of retrofitting existing HVAC equipment to the community energy system is amortized over the life of study period. O&M costs then are taken from Table 9.5. Completed Worksheet 9.4 illustrates this step.

5 Compute Community Utility Revenues (Worksheet 9.2)

Table 9.5 shows the estimated dollar sales of electricity to the local grid, based on the anticipated sales of kWh to the grid and the anticipated sales price per kWh. Utility revenues from consumers are based on calculations from completed Worksheets 9.3 and 9.4. Revenues are summarized on completed Worksheet 9.4.

6 Compute Federal and State Income Taxes for the Community Utility (Worksheet 9.5)

The effective income tax rate for the utility is computed from the applicable state and federal income tax rates in Table 9.3. The utility's revenues and costs for fuel, O&M and property taxes were computed on previous worksheets. Interest payments are 10% of the total capital expenditure. This interest payment schedule corresponds to bond financing, e.g., tax-exempt industrial revenue bonds. Tax depreciation is based on SYD depreciation.

The investment tax credit is 10% of the depreciable investment. Of the $22,615,000 investment, only $200,000 is nondepreciable for tax purposes. In this regard, it was assumed that the computed tax credit would be applied only on income taxes on the investment, i.e., they were not assumed to carry over to taxes on other investments by the utility operators. For each year, the investment tax credit was assumed to be $25,000 plus 90% of the remaining tax credit. Thus, for year 1, the investment tax credit is $25,000 + (0.90) ($110,000 − $25,000). The investment tax credit for succeeding years is computed in the same way until the cumulative investment tax credit is $2,415,000.

After the utility's income taxes have been computed, this figure should be transferred to Worksheet 9.1 to complete the calculation of the utility's costs. Completed Worksheet 9.5 illustrates this step.

7 Compute Net Present Value, Discounted Payback Period, Straight Payback Period, and Savings-to-Investment Ratio (Worksheet 9.6)

Computations of the NPV, DPP, SPP, and SIR are straightforward and are based on procedures explained in the text. A utility MARR of 20% is used for these calculations. The actual rate of return on the investments exceeds 20% because the NPV based on 20% is positive. Completed Worksheet 9.6 illustrates this step.

8 Compute The Rate of Return (Worksheet 9.7)

The completed copy of Worksheet 9.7 illustrates an iterative approach to computing the RR. The initial trial computes the NPV with an assumed RR of 25%. Because the NPV is positive, the actual RR must exceed 25%. Subsequent trials use 26% and 29% as the assumed RR. Interpolation between trials 2 and 3 indicates an actual RR of 26%. Completed Worksheet 9.7 illustrates this step.

9 Other Considerations

In an actual evaluation, this proposed community energy system would be compared with other system configurations. The sensitivity of the results to various assumptions (e.g., escalation rates) would also be tested.

RATE-MAKING PRINCIPLES

The fundamental principles on which rates for district heating should be based are substantially the same as those which are used in the electric and gas

INPUT DATA

COLUMNS 1,2, AND 3 (SAME FOR ALL CRITERIA)
UTILITY MARR   20%

COMPUTATIONS

COLUMNS AND ITEMS REQUIRED FOR EACH CRITERION:

STRAIGHT PAYBACK PERIOD 4,5   NET PRESENT VALUE 4,6,7,8,9,10
DISCOUNTED PAYBACK PERIOD 4,6,7,8,9,11   SAVINGS–TO–INVESTMENT RATIO 4,6,7,8,9,10

(n) YEAR	(1) CAPITAL[a]	(2) ANNUAL EXPENSES[b]	(3) ANNUAL REVENUES[c]	(4) NET ANNUAL RETURNS (3)–(2)	(5) UNRETURNED INVESTMENT	(6) PV FACTOR[d]	(7) PV OF CAPITAL (6)x(1)	(9) PV OF NET ANNUAL RETURNS (6)x(4)	(11) CUMULATIVE NET PV
0	22,615	—	—	—	22,615	1.0000	22,615	—	−22,615
1		3,421	8,022	4,601	18,014	0.8333		3,834	−18,781
2		3,780	8,850	5,070	12,944	0.6944		3,521	−15,260
3		4,176	9,762	5,586	7,358	0.5787		3,233	−12,027
4		5,634	10,766	5,132	2,226	0.4823		2,475	−9,552
5		6,645	11,872	5,227	−3,001	0.4019		2,101	−7,451
6		7,525	13,088	5,563		0.3349		1,863	−5,588
7		8,496	14,429	5,933		0.2791		1,656	−3,932
8		9,561	15,905	6,344		0.2326		1,476	−2,456
9		10,735	17,530	6,795		0.1938		1,317	−1,139
10		12,026	19,320	7,294		0.1615		1,178	39
11		13,448	21,291	7,843		0.1346		1,056	
12		15,012	23,462	8,450		0.1122		948	
13		16,736	25,851	9,115		0.0935		852	
14		18,634	28,484	9,850		0.0779		767	
15		20,726	31,383	10,657		0.0649		692	
16		23,029	34,575	11,546		0.0541		625	
17		25,568	38,092	12,524		0.0451		565	
18		28,364	41,964	13,600		0.0376		511	
19		31,448	46,230	14,782		0.0313		463	
20		34,845	50,926	16,081		0.0261		420	
21		38,590	56,097	17,507		0.0217		380	
22		42,717	61,793	19,076		0.0181		345	
23		47,270	68,069	20,799		0.0151		314	
24		52,289	74,981	22,692		0.0126		286	
25		57,823	82,593	24,770		0.0105		260	
26		63,924	90,976	27,052		0.0087		235	
27		70,654	100,209	29,555		0.0073		216	
28		78,075	110,380	32,305		0.0061		197	
29		86,262	121,583	35,321		0.0051		180	
30		95,289	133,921	38,632		0.0042		162	
					(8) TOTAL PV OF CAPITAL		22,615	32,128	= (10) TOTAL PV OF NET ANNUAL RETURNS

SUMMARY

STRAIGHT PAYBACK PERIOD = 4.7 YEARS   NET PRESENT VALUE   = $ 9,513
DISCOUNTED PAYBACK PERIOD = 10.0 YEARS   SAVINGS–TO–INVESTMENT RATIO = 1.42

[a] Copy from Column 9 of Worksheet No. 1.
[b] Copy from Column 15 of Worksheet No. 1.
[c] Copy from Column 6 of Worksheet No. 4.

[d] Present value factor $= \dfrac{1}{(1+\text{MARR})^n}$

WORKSHEET 9.6

Calculation of Net Present Value, Discounted Payback Period, Straight Payback Period, and Savings-to-Investment Ratio

INPUT DATA

    COLUMNS 1 AND 2

COMPUTATIONS

(n) YEAR	(1) CAPITAL[a]	(2) NET ANNUAL RETURNS[b]	(3) NET ANNUAL CASH FLOW (2) − (1)	TRIAL 1 (4) ASSUMED RR = 25%		TRIAL 2 (8) ASSUMED RR = 26%		TRIAL 3 (12) ASSUMED RR = 27%	
				(5) PV FACTOR[c]	(6) PV OF NET ANNUAL CASH FLOW (5) x (3)	(9) PV FACTOR[c]	(10) PV OF NET ANNUAL CASH FLOW (9) x (3)	(13) PV FACTOR[c]	(14) PV OF NET ANNUAL CASH FLOW (13) x (3)
0	22,615	—	−22,615	1.0000	−22,615	1.0000	−22,615	1.000	−22,615
1		4,601	4,601	0.8000	3,681	0.7937	3,652	0.7874	3,623
2		5,071	5,071	0.6400	3,245	0.6299	3,194	0.6200	3,144
3		5,586	5,586	0.5120	2,860	0.5000	2,793	0.4882	2,727
4		5,132	5,132	0.4096	2,102	0.3968	2,036	0.3344	1,973
5		5,227	5,227	0.3277	1,713	0.3149	1,646	0.3027	1,582
6		5,563	5,563	0.2621	1,458	0.2499	1,390	0.2383	1,326
7		5,933	5,933	0.2097	1,244	0.1983	1,177	0.1877	1,114
8		6,344	6,344	0.1678	1,065	0.1574	999	0.1478	938
9		6,795	6,795	0.1342	912	0.1249	849	0.1164	791
10		7,294	7,294	0.1074	783	0.0992	724	0.0916	668
11		7,843	7,843	0.0859	674	0.0787	617	0.0721	565
12		8,450	8,450	0.0687	581	0.0625	528	0.0568	480
13		9,115	9,115	0.0550	501	0.0496	452	0.0447	407
14		9,850	9,850	0.0440	433	0.0393	387	0.0352	347
15		10,657	10,657	0.0352	375	0.0312	332	0.0277	295
16		11,546	11,546	0.0281	324	0.0248	286	0.0218	252
17		12,524	12,524	0.0225	282	0.0197	247	0.0172	215
18		13,600	13,600	0.0180	245	0.0156	212	0.0135	184
19		14,782	14,782	0.0144	213	0.0124	183	0.0107	158
20		16,081	16,081	0.0115	185	0.0098	158	0.0084	135
21		17,507	17,507	0.0092	161	0.0078	137	0.0066	116
22		19,076	19,076	0.0074	141	0.0062	118	0.0052	99
23		20,799	20,799	0.0059	123	0.0049	102	0.0041	85
24		22,692	22,692	0.0047	107	0.0039	88	0.0032	73
25		24,770	24,770	0.0038	94	0.0031	77	0.0025	62
26		27,052	27,052	0.0030	81	0.0025	68	0.0020	54
27		29,555	29,555	0.0024	71	0.0019	56	0.0016	47
28		32,305	32,305	0.0019	61	0.0015	48	0.0012	39
29		35,321	35,321	0.0015	53	0.0012	42	0.0010	35
30		38,632	38,632	0.0012	46	0.0010	39	0.0008	31
				(7) NET PRESENT VALUE =	1,199	(11) NET PRESENT VALUE =	22	(15) NET PRESENT VALUE =	−1,050

[a] Copy from Column 1 of Worksheet No. 6.
[b] Copy from Column 4 of Worksheet No. 6.
[c] Present value factor $= \dfrac{1}{(1+RR)^{n}}$.

Rate of Return = 26.0%

WORKSHEET 9.7
Calculation of Rate of Return

industries. The rates are based on cost of service, value of service, return and revenue stability requirements, regulatory factors, system load equalization requirements, promotional requirements and historical factors.

Cost of service includes all operating and maintenance expenses, taxes, capital recovery, and a fair return on the investment. The latter should be adequate to attract capital and maintain the financial well being of the enterprise.

Cost analyses, while not the final solution, are often a valuable aid and tool in proper design and application of rates. Generally, such analyses will help to bring the rates for each class of service into a closer relation to the costs of that class, and will indicate the conditions of service which warrant different rate classifications. Each analysis must be based upon the factors and methods developed in, and applicable to, the particular study and problem.

EXAMPLES OF RATE DESIGNS

The intent of this section[10] is to provide two basic rate designs commonly used for steam service; namely, a block rate, and a demand rate. The rates will be designed to follow a cost of service study. An alternative rate will also be presented which departs somewhat from a strict adoption of cost of service, such that it also recognizes the historic rate structure. This section will not attempt to provide all of the various notions of rate design philosophy, but will deal primarily with some of the practical aspects and problems of designing a new rate.

Rate Design Based on Cost of Service

The cost of service that will be used to support the various details of the rate design is that provided in a paper by Russell J. Mayotte[11], entitled "One Approach to Cost of Service for District Heating". Cost details supporting the attached exhibits can be found in this paper.

Figure 9.6 shows that the revenues under the present rates amount to $35 million in total. Specifically, for the rates or classes of service for which rates will be designed in this section, namely the block rate and the demand rate, the present revenues are $4,100,000 and $27,355,000 respectively. The amount of the increase based on the cost of service developed by Mr. Mayotte and shown in Column (d) of Figure 9.6 of this section is $2,315,000 total; and specifically $178,000 for the block rate and $1,985,000 for the demand rate. A new rate will be designed for these two rates to develop the necessary increased revenue so that the resulting revenue is as shown in column (c) of Figure 9.6.

Block Rate

To design a rate, one begins by selecting or developing a rate structure. Figure 9.7, schedule 1, shows that at present the block rate structure provides four commodity blocks in which all revenue is recovered. Schedule 1 shows

FIGURE 9.6

Steam heating department, summary of present and proposed revenue by rate schedule

$(000)

Line No.	(a)	(b) Present Rates	(c) Proposed Rates	(d) Amount of Increase	(e) Percent Increase
1	Block Rate	$ 4,100	$ 4,278	$ 178	4.34%
2	Domestic Rate	900	946	46	5.11%
3	Demand Rate	27,355	29,340	1,985	7.26%
4	Open End Rate	245	281	36	14.69%
5	Industrial Rate	2,400	2,470	70	2.92%
6	Total	$35,000	$37,315	$2,315	6.61%

FIGURE 9.7, SCHEDULE 1

Rate-revenue analysis, block rate "A"

Present Rate

	(a)	(b)	(c)	(d)
Line No.	Blocks	Mlb. in Block	Rate	Revenue
1	1st 50 Mlb.	86,007	$6.75/Mlb.	$ 581,000
2	Next 150 Mlb.	154,222	6.50/Mlb.	1,002,000
3	Next 800 Mlb.	141,288	6.30/Mlb.	890,000
4	Over 1000 Mlb.	113,483	5.83/Mlb.	662,000
5	Fuel Adjustment	495,000	1.93/Mlb.	965,000
6	Total Revenue			$4,100,000

Proposed Rate

7	1st 50 Mlb.	86,007	$9.78/Mlb.	$ 841,000
8	Next 150 Mlb.	154,222	9.06/Mlb.	1,397,000
9	Next 800 Mlb.	141,288	8.41/Mlb.	1,188,000
10	Over 1000 Mlb.	113,483	7.51/Mlb.	852,000
11	Fuel Adjustment	495,000	0.00/Mlb.	
12	Total Revenue			$4,278,000
13	Revenue Increase			$ 178,000
14	Percent Increase			4.16%

FIGURE 9.7, SCHEDULE 2

Development of block rate "A" increments

1st Block Increment

	$(000)
Rate Base	
Plant	
Distribution—Meters	$ 267
Reserve	(186)
Total	$ 81
Expenses	
Meters	$ 51
Return	7
Income Taxes	4
Total Revenue Requirement	$ 62
Sales 1st Block	86,007
Rate $/Mlb.	0.72

2nd Block Increment

	Block
Expenses	
Customer Accounting	$155
Sales Mlb. 86,007	
154,222	
	240,229
Rate $/Mlb.	0.65

FIGURE 9.7, SCHEDULE 2—*continued*

3rd Block Increment

$ (000)

Rate Base

Plant

Street Mains	$1,849
Services	219

Reserve

Street Mains	(827)
Services	(98)
Total	$1,143

Expenses

Street Mains	$ 60
Services	4

Depreciation

Street Mains	44
Services	5
Property Taxes	66
Total	$ 179
Return	103
Income Tax	62
Total Revenue Requirement	$ 344

Sales, Mlb.	86,007	
	154,222	
	141,288	
		381,517
Rate $/Mlb.		0.90

4th Block Increment

$(000)

Total Revenue Requirement		$4,278

Revenue Recovery

1st Block	62	
2nd Block	155	
3rd Block	344	561
Net Revenue Requirement All Sales Mlbs.		$3,717
Total Sales		495,000
Rate $/Mlb.		7.51

FIGURE 9.7, SCHEDULE 3

Comparison of typical monthly bills, block rate "A"

	(a)	(b)	(c)	(d)	(e)
		Present	Proposed	Increase	
Line No.	Monthly Mlb. Use	Monthly Bill	Monthly Bill	Amount	Percent
1	50	$ 434	$ 489	$ 55	12.67
2	200	1,699	1,848	149	8.77
3	500	4,168	4,371	203	4.87
4	1,000	8,283	8,576	293	3.54
5	3,000	23,803	23,596	(207)	(0.90)
6	5,000	39,323	38,616	(707)	(1.80)

The present rates are based on a fuel adjustment of 193.0¢ per thousand pounds of steam. The proposed rates are based on a fuel adjustment of 000.0¢ per thousand pounds of steam.

that the blocks are, namely, the first 50 Mlbs., the next 150 Mlbs., next 800 Mlbs., and all consumption over 1,000 Mlbs. (1 Mlb. = 1,000 lbs. = 453.6 kg). For the ease of this exercise, it will be assumed that no changes will be made in the block structure of this rate; so the existing blocking will remain. From billing information for this class of customers, it is determined that the Mlbs. of sales in each block are as shown in column (b). The total sales for the block rate class is 495,000 Mlbs. The present rates are also shown on schedule 1 in column (c). Note that at present there is a fuel adjustment which is calculated to be $1.93¢/Mlb. The revenue shown in column (d) is the result of the multiplication of columns (b) and (c). The total revenue at present rates is $4,100,000 as indicated earlier and shown on Figure 9.7, Line 1.

At present, this rate has a declining block rate structure. In this type of rate structure, various costs are intended to be recovered by charges in the various blocks. For example, certain costs such as the cost of fuel, the fixed charges on production plant and certain high-pressure mains as well as the maintenance expense for this plant may be recovered from all Mlbs. of sales in the class; other costs such as the cost of service connections and certain local mains may be recovered from a selected block of sales less than the total Mlb. sales for the class. Further, certain other costs, such as the cost for customer accounting and billing and the cost of meters, may be recovered during an initial portion or the first block of sales to that class. The rate to be designed here will follow this format. The development of the rate is shown on Figure 9.7, schedule 2.

Part 1 of Figure 9.7, schedule 2, shows a development of the increment for the initial block of the rate. This increment is the difference between the price of the first block and the second block. As can be seen in the rate structure, the charge for the first block of energy is somewhat higher than the second block. As noted earlier, this is due to the fact that certain costs are expected to be recovered only through the initial block of the rate. The revenue to be produced by the initial block increment intends to recover the expenses for the meters, $51,000, plus a return on the meter rate base, $7,000, as well as the income tax requirement, $4,000. Thus, the total revenue requirement for the metering is $62,000. The sales in the first block, shown on Figure 9.7, schedule 1, column (b), Line 1, is 86,007 Mlbs. Dividing the total revenue requirement for the meters of $62,000 by the sales, results in a rate increment of 72¢ per Mlb. Therefore, the increment between the first and second block should be 72¢ on a cost basis.

The customer accounting expenses will be designed to be recovered by the end of the second block also shown on Schedule 2. The expenses are $155,000. The sales in the first two blocks are 86,007 Mlbs. for the first 50 Mlb. block plus 154,222 Mlbs. for the next block of 150 Mlbs. The total sales in the first two blocks are 240,229 Mlbs. Dividing the expenses by the sales determines that the increment for the recovery of the customer accounting expenses is 65¢ per Mlb. Schedule 2 shows the development of the third block increment and indicates that it is designed to recover the expenses and fixed charges for street mains and services by the end of this block. The calculations are similar to those described above.

The development of the last or fourth block charge is shown next. In order to recover the total revenue requirement for this class of service, this rate, applicable to all Mlbs., must pick up all those costs not already recovered by the increments applicable in the early blocks of the rate. In order to do this, one must take the total revenue requirement less the revenue recovered in the earlier blocks which is shown to be $561,000. Thus the remaining revenue to be

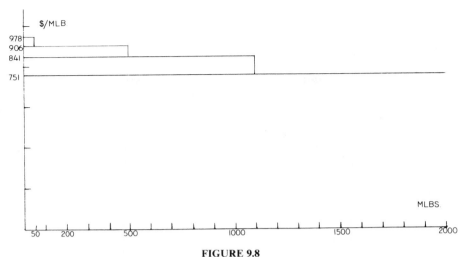

FIGURE 9.8

Rate to consumption at various use levels

recovered is $3,717,000. As the total sales is 495,000 Mlbs., a rate of $7.51 per Mlb. results. The application of the rate to consumption at various use levels is displayed in Figure 9.8.

Returning to Figure 9.7, schedule 1, the net rates as developed in Schedule 2 are shown in schedule 1, column (c), lines 7 through 10. As indicated, the resulting proposed rate is $9.78 per Mlb. for the first block, $9.06 per Mlb. for the second block, $8.41 per Mlb. for the third block and $7.51 for the last block. Note that the fuel adjustment is now $0.00 per Mlb. In developing the proposed rate, the fuel adjustment has been rolled into the rate.

The proposed revenue shown in column (d) is calculated by multiplying Columns (b) and (c). On line 7, the first block develops $841,000; the remaining blocks develop $1,397,000, $1,188,000 and $852,000 respectively. Line 12 of this schedule shows that the total revenue developed is $4,278,000 which is the revenue required. The revenue increase for this class is $178,000 or 4.16%, also shown in Figure 9.7, schedule 1.

Figure 9.7, schedule 3, shows a comparison of typical monthly bills under both the present rate and the proposed rate. You will note that as the consumption rises, the percent increase drops substantially. This would indicate that the present rates did not track the costs as closely as might be desired. If it is desired to more closely track those costs as they relate to consumption levels, the proposed rates designed here would be advisable. Other considerations regarding the final rate proposal for this class will be discussed later.

Demand Rate

In the demand rate, the total revenue requirement is recovered in two pieces, namely, the demand charge and the commodity charge. Generally, the commodity charge attempts to recover all the variable costs to provide service and the demand charge recovers the remaining revenue requirement which is of a more fixed nature. Similar to Figure 9.7, schedule 1, Figure 9.9, schedule 1, provides the development of revenue under the present and proposed rates and shows the billing determinants in column (b) as well as the rates in column (c)

FIGURE 9.9, SCHEDULE 1

Rate-revenue analysis, demand rate "B"

Present Rate

	(a)	(b)	(c)	(d)
Line No.	Demand	Lb./Hr.	Rate	Revenue
1	Revenue—Demand	1,260,254	$4.66/Lb./Hr.	$ 5,874,000
	Commodity	Mlbs.		
2	All Mlbs.	3,956,000	$3.50/Mlb.	$13,846,000
3	Fuel Adjustment	3,956,000	$1.93/Mlb.	7,635,000
4	Revenue—Commodity			$21,481,000
5	Total Revenue—Present			$27,355,000

Proposed Rate

	Demand	Lb./Hr.		
6	Revenue—Demand	1,260,254	$7.90/Lb./Hr.	$ 9,955,000
	Commodity	Mlbs.		
7	All Mlbs.	3,956,000	$4.90/Mlb.	$19,384,000
8	Fuel Adjustment	3,956,000	0.00/Mlb.	$19,384,000
9	Revenue—Commodity			
10	Total Revenue			$29,339,000
11	Revenue Increase			1,985,000
12	Percent Increase			7.25%

FIGURE 9.9, SCHEDULE 2

Development of demand rate "B"

Variable Cost

	$ (000)
Rate Base	
Fuel Inventory	$1,218
O&M	2,268
Total	$3,486
Expenses	
Fuel	$18,514
Other Production	208
Total	$18,722
Return	314
Income Tax	188
Total Revenue Requirement	$19,224
Sales, Mlbs.	3,956,000
Rate $/Mlb.	4.86

and the resulting revenues. The billing determinants are developed based on customer billing information. Normally, to design a demand rate, one first sets the commodity charge to recover variable costs. The variable costs for steam service are primarily fuel related. Schedule 2 shows that there is a total variable cost related investment or rate base of $3,486,000 for the demand rate which would require a return of $314,000 plus income taxes of $188,000. The expenses

FIGURE 9.9, SCHEDULE 3

Comparison of typical monthly bills, demand rate "B"

	(a)	(b)	(c)	(d)	(e)	(f)
			Present	Proposed	Increase	
Line No.	Demand Lb./Hr.	Hours Use	Monthly Bill	Monthly Bill	Amount	Percent
1	1,000	100	$ 931	$ 1,148	$ 217	23.30
2	1,000	200	1,474	1,638	164	11.13
3	1,000	300	2,017	2,128	111	5.50
4	2,000	100	1,862	2,296	434	23.30
5	2,000	200	2,948	3,276	328	11.13
6	2,000	300	4,034	4,256	222	5.50
7	5,000	100	4,655	5,740	1,085	23.30
8	5,000	200	7,370	8,190	820	11.13
9	5,000	300	10,085	10,640	555	5.50

The present rates are based on a fuel adjustment of 193.0¢ per thousand pounds of steam. The proposed rates are based on a fuel adjustment of 000.0¢ per thousand pounds of steam.

which must be recovered are $18,514,000 for fuel and $208,000 for other production expenses which would include primarily fuel handling as well as other miscellaneous variable production expenses. Therefore, the total revenue requirement to be recovered under the commodity charge is $19,224,000. The total sales is 3,956,000 Mlbs. Dividing the revenue requirement by the sales results in a rate of $4.86 per Mlb.

Returning to schedule 1 of Figure 9.9, the commodity charge shown in Column (c) for the proposed rate is $4.90, resulting from rounding up the $4.86 shown on schedule 2. The resulting revenue developed by the commodity charge is $19,384,000. As the total revenue required is $29,339,000, the remainder of $9,955,000 must be provided by the demand charge. Dividing the $9,955,000 by the total demand determinant, 1,260,254 lbs. per hour, results in a demand rate of $7.90 per pound per hour per year. Therefore, the total resulting increase is $1,985,000 which conforms with the desired increase shown on Figure 9.6 for the demand rate in column (d).

Schedule 3 of Figure 9.9 shows a comparison of monthly bills for demand rate "B" for the present and proposed rates. As can be seen in column (f), the proposed rates would increase the charges a greater percentage for the low volume or low hours use consumer. This indicates that the present rates do not closely track the costs incurred as the volume varies with a constant demand. If it is desired to more closely track such costs, proposed rate "B" would be appropriate.

An Alternative Rate Design

When comparing the rate design previously discussed with the present rate design, it may be noticed that customers with certain consumption levels or usage patterns will receive greater increases than others. If it is desired to maintain the present rate relationship for customers of various consumption levels to minimize disruptions, it may be preferable to raise the rates more uniformly. Figures 9.10 and 9.11 provide the rate design which could achieve that goal.

FIGURE 9.10, SCHEDULE 1

Rate-revenue analysis, block rate "A" alternate

Present Rate

	(a)	(b)	(c)	(d)
Line No.	Blocks	Mlb. in Block	Rate	Revenue
1	1st 50 Mlb.	86,007	$6.75/Mlb.	$ 581,000
2	Next 150 Mlb.	154,222	6.50/Mlb.	1,002,000
3	Next 800 Mlb.	141,288	6.30/Mlb.	890,000
4	Over 1000 Mlb.	113,483	5.83/Mlb.	662,000
5	Fuel Adjustment	495,000	1.93/Mlb.	965,000
6	Total Revenue			$4,100,000

Proposed Rate

7	1st 50 Mlb.	86,007	$9.00/Mlb.	$ 774,000
8	Next 150 Mlb.	154,222	8.75/Mlb.	1,349,000
9	Next 800 Mlb.	141,288	8.60/Mlb.	1,215,000
10	Over 1000 Mlb.	113,483	8.28/Mlb.	940,000
11	Fuel Adjustment	495,000	0.00/Mlb.	
12	Total Revenue			$4,278,000
13	Revenue Increase			$ 178,000
14	Percent Increase			4.16%

FIGURE 9.10, SCHEDULE 2

Comparison of typical monthly bills, block rate "A" alternate

	(a)	(b)	(c)	(d)	(e)
Line No.	Monthly Mlb. Use	Present Monthly Bill	Proposed Monthly Bill	Increase Amount	Percent
1	50	$ 434	$ 450	$ 16	3.69
2	200	1,699	1,763	64	3.77
3	500	4,168	4,343	175	4.20
4	1,000	8,283	8,643	360	4.35
5	3,000	23,803	24,843	1,040	4.37
6	5,000	39,323	41,403	2,080	5.29

The present rates are based on a fuel adjustment of 193.0¢ per thousand pounds of steam. The proposed rates are based on a fuel adjustment of 000.0¢ per thousand pounds of steam.

Block Rate

Referring first to Figure 9.10, schedule 1, this shows a rate design for a proposed rate which will provide a more equalized percentage increase for various consumption levels on the block rate. The same billing determinants as in schedule B, schedule 1, are used. To develop the proposed rates shown in column (c), the fuel adjustment amount of $1.93 is added to the present rates for each block. To this amount, a percentage increase which is required for the total revenue increase is added. For example, for the first block, the rate is $6.75 would be added together with the $1.93 for the fuel adjustment; that quantity would be multiplied times 1.0416 which reflects the 4.16% increase required for the total class. The resulting rate is $9.00 per Mlb. which is the resultant figure after rounding. Similarly, the calculations for the second and third block result in proposed rates of $8.75 and $8.60 per Mlb. The rate for the last block is obtained by recovering the remaining revenue requirement from the class. In other words, the amounts recovered from the first three blocks is subtracted from the total revenue requirement of $4,278,000 and divided that figure by 113,483 Mlbs. which are billed in the last block. This calculation results in a rate for the last block of $8.28 Mlb. Schedule 2 of Figure 9.10 shows that the percentage increases for the various consumption levels is much more uniform than the rate design based on the cost of service. The percentage increase under this alternate proposed rate would be more constant at approximately 4% to 5% for the bulk of the customers.

Demand Rate

With regard to the demand rate, an alternative design might be to roll in the increased fuel cost into the commodity portion of the rate and to apply the increased revenue requirement to the demand portion. As noted earlier, the commodity portion of the rate reflects primarily the variable costs which are very largely fuel related. Referring to Figure 9.11, schedule 1, showing the rate-revenue analysis of the demand rate, the billing determinants are obtained from customer billing information and the revenues are developed using existing rates. For the proposed rates, the commodity charge is determined by adding the present commodity charge of $3.50 per Mlb. with the $1.93 Mlb. fuel adjustment charge. The $5.60 proposed rate reflects some increase in return requirement for the increase in cost of fuel resulting in an increased working capital requirement as well as the fuel adjustment roll-in. The demand rate proposed is then determined by subtracting the commodity revenue, resulting at the $5.60 per Mlb. rate from the total revenue requirement from the class and dividing that remaining requirement by the demand billing determinants, namely 1,260,254 pounds per hour. The resulting rate is $5.70 per pound per hour. The proposed rate thus recovers the total revenue requirement of $29,339,000 which has been determined in the cost of service study, which is the same total revenue for the class as the rate design shown in Figure 9.9.

Schedule 2 of Figure 9.11 shows a comparison of typical bills under this alternative rate structure. To some extent the percentage increases are greater for the low hours use customers. This is due to the larger increase in the demand rate relative to the commodity rate. However, comparing the percentage increase variation between this alternative rate and the rate proposed in schedule C, the low use customer percentage increases are approximately half that in the rate proposed in Figure 9.9.

Fuel Adjustment Clause

An important component of a steam rate is the fuel adjustment clause. As fuel costs frequently account for approximately 75% of the revenue requirement, a rate design which does not provide for changes in fuel cost levels quickly and does not satisfactorily track cost to provide service, particularly during inflationary times. A fuel adjustment clause is presently a part of the existing rate, to mitigate such an impact. The text is presented in Figure 9.12.

The two major factors of the clause that should be re-evaluated at the time rates are designed are the base point and adjustment increment. The base point, as indicated in the present clause, is 150.0¢ per million Btu. The unit cost of fuel used in the cost of service on which the new rates are designed is 257.0¢ per million Btu. With the present fuel clause, a fuel adjustment of $1.93 per

FIGURE 9.11, SCHEDULE 1

Rate-revenue analysis demand rate "B" alternate

Present Rate

Line No.	Demand	Lb./Hr.	Rate	Revenue
1	Revenue—Demand	1,260,254	$4.66/Lb./Hr.	$ 5,874,000
	Commodity	Mlbs.		
2	All Mlbs	3,956,000	$3.50/Mlb.	$13,846,000
3	Fuel Adjustment	3,956,000	$1.93/Mlb.	7,635,000
4	Revenue—Commodity			$21,481,000
5	Total Revenue—Present			$27,355,000

Proposed Rate

	Demand	Lb./Hr.		
6	Revenue—Demand	1,260,254	$5.70/Lb./Hr.	$ 7,184,000
	Commodity	Mlbs.		
7	All Mlbs.	3,956,000	$5.60/Mlb.	$22,155,000
8	Fuel Adjustment	3,956,000	0.00/Mlb.	
9	Revenue—Commodity			$22,155,000
10	Total Revenue			$29,339,000
11	Revenue Increase			$ 1,985,000
12	Percent Increase			7.25%

FIGURE 9.11, SCHEDULE 2

Comparison of typical monthly bills, demand rate "B" alternative

	(a)	(b)	(c)	(d)	(e)	(f)
			Present	Proposed	Increase	
Line No.	Demand Lb./Hr.	Hours Use	Monthly Bill	Monthly Bill	Amount	Percent
1	1,000	100	$ 931	$ 1,035	$104	11.17
2	1,000	200	1,474	1,595	121	8.21
3	1,000	300	2,017	2,155	138	6.84
4	2,000	100	1,862	2,070	208	11.17
5	2,000	200	2,948	3,190	242	8.21
6	2,000	300	4,034	4,310	276	6.84
7	5,000	100	4,655	5,175	520	11.17
8	5,000	200	7,370	7,975	605	8.21
9	5,000	300	10,085	10,775	690	6.84

The present rates are based on a fuel adjustment of 193.0¢ per thousand pounds of steam. The proposed rates are based on a fuel adjustment of 000.0¢ per thousand pounds of steam.

Mlb. results. This calculation is shown in Figure 9.12. As the proposed rate is designed to roll in the present fuel adjustment, in effect, the rate is designed at the 257.0¢ per million Btu fuel cost level. Therefore, the fuel adjustment clause for the new rate should provide an adjustment for fuel cost above or below the 257.0¢ level. Thus, the base point for the proposed rate is 257.0¢ per million Btu.

FIGURE 9.12

Present fuel adjustment clause

The fuel adjustment shall consist of an increase or decrease of .18¢ per thousand pounds of steam consumed for each full .1¢ increase or decrease in the cost of fuel above or below 150.0¢ per million Btu. The price per million Btu during any month shall be the average cost of one million Btu of fuel burned during the preceding month at the Central Heating Plants, figured to the nearest one-thousandth of a cent. The cost of fuel shall include the cost of transportation to the Central Heating Plants for such fuel, plus any excise or taxes placed upon the purchase or transportation of fuel, excluding cost of unloading, trucking, reloading and storage, and overhead charges.

Proposed fuel adjustment clause

The fuel adjustment shall consist of an increase or decrease of .18¢ per thousand pounds of steam consumed for each full .1¢ increase or decrease in the cost of fuel above or below 257.0¢ per million Btu. The price per million Btu during any month shall be the average cost of one million Btu of fuel burned during the preceding month at the Central Heating Plants, figured to the nearest one-thousandth of a cent. The cost of fuel shall include the cost of transportation to the Central Heating Plants for such fuel, plus any excise or taxes placed upon the purchase or transportation of fuel, excluding cost of unloading, trucking, reloading and storage, and overhead charges.

Determination of fuel adjustment factor at present rate

$$\text{FUEL ADJUSTMENT} = \left(\frac{\text{Unit Cost} - \text{Base Cost}}{.001} \right) \times .0018$$

$$= \left(\frac{2.57 - 1.50}{.001} \right) \times .0018$$

$$= \$1.93/\text{MLB}.$$

Determination of fuel adjustment increment

Heat in Fuel Consumed Steam Sales (M lbs)

$$\text{Average Heat Rate} = \frac{9,000,000 \text{ MBTU}}{5,000,000 \text{ Mlbs}} = 0.0018 \text{ MBTU/lb}.$$

The second factor that should be re-evaluated is the adjustment increment. The increment in the present clause is 0.18¢ per thousand pounds for each full 0.1¢ change in fuel cost per million Btu. This increment, in effect, translates the change in cost of fuel to a change in price per thousand pounds of steam. Thus, the increment is an expression of the average heat rate used in the test period cost of service. In the particular case at hand, the average heat rate calculated on Figure 9.12, is 9,000,000 Btu, the total heat provided by the fuel burned divided by 5,000,000 Mlbs., the total steam sales. The result is 0.0018 million Btu per pound of steam. The proper adjustment increment thus should remain at 0.18¢ per thousand pounds of steam for each full 0.1¢ change in fuel cost per million Btu. Therefore, the fuel clause appropriate with the proposed rates is as shown in Figure 9.12. As the same fuel cost level is designed into rates A and B, as well as their alternates, the proposed fuel clause is equally applicable.

When performing a rate design task, other criteria must also be weighed in addition to the cost and historical relationships. These would include: simplicity, fairness, and revenue stability.

REFERENCES

1. Various authors, *Integrated Community Energy Systems Technology Evaluations*, published by Argonne National Laboratory, Argonne, Ill. (1977–1979).

2. Kennedy, A. S., and C. Lee, *Integrated Community Energy System Commercialization Case Studies. Vol. I: Direct Economic and Energy Analysis of ICES Concepts*, Argonne National Laboratory Report ANL/ICES-TM-4 (Jan. 1978).
3. Kron, N. F., Jr., A. A. Davis, and H. A. Davis, *Energy Supply Options for Soldiers Grove, Wisconsin: A Summary of Recommendations*, Argonne National Laboratory Report ANL/ICES-TM-32 (Feb. 1979).
4. Lee, C. A., A. Davis, and N. F. Kron, Jr., *Philadelphia's Gallery II Shopping Center Complex: An Analysis for the Application of an Integrated Community Energy System, Vol 1: Executive Summary, Vol 2: Complete Data Report*, Argonne National Laboratory Report ANL/CNSV-TM-19, Vols. 1 & 2 (Nov. 1979).
5. *Means Construction Cost Data and Means Mechanical and Electrical Cost Data*, published anually by R. S. Means Co., Inc., Kingston, Mass.
6. *Chemical Engineering*, published bi-weekly by McGraw-Hill, Inc., New York, N.Y.
7. *Engineering News Record*, published weekly by McGraw-Hill, Inc., New York, N.Y.
8. *Handy-Whitman Index of Public Utility Costs*, published semiannually by Whitman, Requandt, and Associates, Baltimore, Md.
9. Croke, K., J. Baum, and R. Rosenberg, *Municipal Financing of Integrated Community Energy Systems*, Argonne National Laboratory Report ANL/ICES-TM-3 (Nov. 1977).
10. Based on IDHA Paper, Steam Heating Rate Design, 1981, Donald W. Okon, Detroit Edison Co.
11. Proceedings of IDHA, 1980. Russell J. Mayotte, The Detroit Edison Co., Section 18, 34 pp.

Supplemental References

Thorsen, H. G., W. V. Fabmycky, and G. J. Thorsen, *Engineering Economy*, Prentice-Hall, Inc., Englewood, N.J. (1977).
Park, W. R., *Cost Engineering Analysis: A Guide to the Economic Evaluation of Engineering Projects*, Wiley and Sons, Inc., New York, N.Y. (1973).
Riggs, J. L., *Engineering Economics*, McGraw-Hill, Inc., New York, N.Y. (1977).

APPENDIX

Length Equivalents

To Obtain by / Multiply Number of	Meters	Inches	Feet	Millimeters	Miles	Kilometers
Meters	1	39.37	3.2808	1000	0.0006214	0.001
Inches	0.0254	1	0.0833	25.4	0.00001578	0.0000254
Feet	0.3048	12	1	304.8	0.0001894	0.0003048
Millimeters	0.001	0.03937	0.0032808	1	0.0000006214	0.000001
Miles	1609.35	63,360	5,280	1,609,350	1	1.60935
Kilometers	1,000	39,370	3280.83	1,000,000	0.62137	1

1 meter = 100 centimeters = 1000 millimeters = 0.001 kilometers = 1,000,000 micrometers
To convert metric units, merely adjust the decimal point.
1 millimeter = 1000 microns = 0.03937 inches = 39.37 mils.

Whole Inch-Millimeter Equivalents

In.	0	1	2	3	4	5	6	7	8	9
	mm									
0	0.0	25.4	50.8	76.2	101.6	127.0	152.4	177.8	203.2	228.6
10	254.0	279.4	304.8	330.2	355.6	381.0	406.4	431.8	457.2	482.6
20	508.0	533.4	558.8	584.2	609.6	635.0	660.4	685.8	711.2	736.6
30	762.0	787.4	812.8	838.2	863.6	889.0	914.4	939.8	965.2	990.6
40	1016.0	1041.4	1066.8	1092.2	1117.6	1143.0	1168.4	1193.8	1219.2	1244.6
50	1270.0	1295.4	1320.8	1346.2	1371.6	1397.0	1422.4	1447.8	1473.2	1498.6
60	1524.0	1549.4	1574.8	1600.2	1625.6	1651.0	1676.4	1701.8	1727.2	1752.6
70	1778.0	1803.4	1828.8	1854.2	1879.6	1905.0	1930.4	1955.8	1981.2	2006.6
80	2032.0	2057.4	2082.8	2108.2	2133.6	2159.0	2184.4	2209.8	2235.2	2260.6
90	2286.0	2311.4	2336.8	2362.2	2387.6	2413.0	2438.4	2463.8	2489.2	2514.6
100	2540.0	2565.4	2590.8	2616.2	2641.6	2667.0	2692.4	2717.8	2743.2	2768.6

Note: All values in this table are exact, based on the relation 1 in = 25.4 mm. By manipulation of the decimal point any decimal value or multiple of an inch may be converted to its exact equivalent in millimeters.

Fractional Inches To Millimeters
(1 Inch = 25.4 Millimeters)

mm

In.	0	1/16	1/8	3/16	1/4	5/16	3/8	7/16	1/2	9/16	5/8	11/16	3/4	13/16	7/8	15/16
0	0.0	1.6	3.2	4.8	6.4	7.9	9.5	11.1	12.7	14.3	15.9	17.5	19.1	20.6	22.2	23.8
1	25.4	27.0	28.6	30.2	31.8	33.3	34.9	36.5	38.1	39.7	41.3	42.9	44.5	46.0	47.6	49.2
2	50.8	52.4	54.0	55.6	57.2	58.7	60.3	61.9	63.5	65.1	66.7	68.3	69.9	71.4	73.0	74.6
3	76.2	77.8	79.4	81.0	82.6	84.1	85.7	87.3	88.9	90.5	92.1	93.7	95.3	96.8	98.4	100.0
4	101.6	103.2	104.8	106.4	108.0	109.5	111.1	112.7	114.3	115.9	117.5	119.1	120.7	122.2	123.8	125.4
5	127.0	128.6	130.2	131.8	133.4	134.9	136.5	138.1	139.7	141.3	142.9	144.5	146.1	147.6	149.2	150.8
6	152.4	154.0	155.6	157.2	158.8	160.3	161.9	163.5	165.1	166.7	168.3	169.9	171.5	173.0	174.6	176.2
7	177.8	179.4	181.0	182.6	184.2	185.7	187.3	188.9	190.5	192.1	193.7	195.3	196.9	198.4	200.0	201.6
8	203.2	204.8	206.4	208.0	209.6	211.1	212.7	214.3	215.9	217.5	219.1	220.7	222.3	223.8	225.4	227.0
9	228.6	230.2	231.8	233.4	235.0	236.5	238.1	239.7	241.3	242.9	244.5	246.1	247.7	249.2	250.8	252.4
10	254.0	255.6	257.2	258.8	260.4	261.9	263.5	265.1	266.7	268.3	269.9	271.5	273.1	274.6	276.2	277.8

Area Equivalents

To Obtain / Multiply Number of by	Square Meters	Square Inches	Square Feet	Square Miles	Square Kilometers
Square Meters	1	1549.99	10.7639	3.861×10^{-7}	1×10^{-6}
Square Inches	0.0006452	1	6.944×10^{-3}	2.491×10^{-10}	6.452×10^{-10}
Square Feet	0.0929	144	1	3.587×10^{-8}	9.29×10^{-8}
Square Miles	2,589,999	. . .	27,878,400	1	2.59
Square Kilometers	1,000,000	. . .	10,763,867	0.3861	1

1 square meter = 10,000 square centimeters.
1 square millimeter = 0.01 square centimeter = 0.00155 square inches.

Volume Equivalents

To Obtain / Multiply Number of by	Cubic Decimeters (Liters)	Cubic Inches	Cubic Feet	U.S. Quart	U.S. Gallon	Imperial Gallon	U.S. Barrel (Petroleum)
Cubic Decimeters (Liters)	1	61.0234	0.03531	1.05668	0.264178	0.220083	0.00629
Cubic Inches	0.01639	1	5.787×10^{-4}	0.01732	0.004329	0.003606	0.000103
Cubic Feet	28.317	1728	1	29.9221	7.48055	6.22888	0.1781
U.S. Quart	0.94636	57.75	0.03342	1	0.25	0.2082	0.00595
U.S. Gallon	3.78543	231	0.13368	4	1	0.833	0.02381
Imperial Gallon	4.54374	277.274	0.16054	4.80128	1.20032	1	0.02877
U.S. Barrel (Petroleum)	158.98	9702	5.6146	168	42	34.973	1

1 cubic meter = 1,000,000 cubic centimeters.
1 liter = 1000 milliliters = 1000 cubic centimeters.

Volume Rate Equivalents

To Obtain / Multiply Number of by	Liters Per Minute	Cubic Meters Per Hour	Cubic Feet Per Hour	Liters Per Hour	U.S. Gallon Per Minute	U.S. Barrel Per Day
Liters Minute	1	0.06	2.1189	60	0.264178	9.057
Cubic Meters Per Hour	16.667	1	35.314	1000	4.403	151
Cubic Feet Per Hour	0.4719	0.028317	1	28.317	0.1247	4.2746
Liters Per Hour	0.016667	0.001	0.035314	1	0.004403	0.151
U.S. Gallon Per Minute	3.785	0.2273	8.0208	227.3	1	34.28
U.S. Barrel Per Day	0.1104	0.006624	0.23394	6.624	0.02917	1

Pressure Equivalents

To Obtain → by Multiply Number of	Kg. Per Sq. Cm.	Lb. Per Sq. In.	Atm.	Bar	In. of Hg.	Kilopascals	In. of Water	Ft. of Water
Kg. Per Sq. Cm.	1	14.22	0.9678	0.98067	28.96	98.067	394.05	32.84
Lb. Per Sq. In.	0.07031	1	0.06804	0.06895	2.036	6.895	27.7	2.309
Atm.	1.0332	14.696	1	1.01325	29.92	101.325	407.14	33.93
Bar	1.01972	14.5038	0.98692	1	29.53	100	402.156	33.513
In. of Hg.	0.03453	0.4912	0.03342	0.033864	1	3.3864	13.61	1.134
Kilopascals	0.0101972	0.145038	0.0098696	0.01	0.2953	1	4.02156	0.33513
In. of Water	0.002538	0.0361	0.002456	0.00249	0.07349	0.249	1	0.0833
Ft. of Water	0.03045	0.4332	0.02947	0.029839	0.8819	2.9839	12	1

1 ounce/sq. inch = 0.0625 lbs./sq. inch.

Mass Conversion—Pounds to Kilograms
(1 pound = 0.4536 kilogram)

Pounds	0	1	2	3	4	5	6	7	8	9
					Kilograms					
0	0.00	0.45	0.91	1.36	1.81	2.27	2.72	3.18	3.63	4.08
10	4.54	4.99	5.44	5.90	6.35	6.80	7.26	7.71	8.16	8.62
20	9.07	9.53	9.98	10.43	10.89	11.34	11.79	12.25	12.70	13.15
30	13.61	14.06	14.52	14.97	15.42	15.88	16.33	16.78	17.24	17.69
40	18.14	18.60	19.05	19.50	19.96	20.41	20.87	21.32	21.77	22.23
50	22.68	23.13	23.59	24.04	24.49	24.95	25.40	25.86	26.31	26.76
60	27.22	27.67	28.12	28.58	29.03	29.48	29.94	30.39	30.84	31.30
70	31.75	32.21	32.66	33.11	33.57	34.02	34.47	34.93	35.38	35.83
80	36.29	36.74	37.20	37.65	38.10	38.56	39.01	39.46	39.92	40.37
90	40.82	41.28	41.73	42.18	42.64	43.09	43.55	44.00	44.45	44.91

Pressure Conversion—Pounds per Square Inch to Bar*

Pounds Per Square Inch	Bar									
	0	1	2	3	4	5	6	7	8	9
0	0.000000	0.068948	0.137895	0.206843	0.275790	0.344738	0.413685	0.482633	0.551581	0.620528
10	0.689476	0.758423	0.827371	0.896318	0.965266	1.034214	1.103161	1.172109	1.241056	1.310004
20	1.378951	1.447899	1.516847	1.585794	1.654742	1.723689	1.792637	1.861584	1.930532	1.999480
30	2.068427	2.137375	2.206322	2.275270	2.344217	2.413165	2.482113	2.551060	2.620008	2.688955
40	2.757903	2.826850	2.895798	2.964746	3.033693	3.102641	3.171588	3.240536	3.309484	3.378431
50	3.447379	3.516326	3.585274	3.654221	3.723169	3.792117	3.861064	3.930012	3.998959	4.067907
60	4.136854	4.205802	4.274750	4.343697	4.412645	4.481592	4.550540	4.619487	4.688435	4.757383
70	4.826330	4.895278	4.964225	5.033173	5.102120	5.171068	5.240016	5.308963	5.377911	5.446858
80	5.515806	5.584753	5.653701	5.722649	5.791596	5.860544	5.929491	5.998439	6.067386	6.136334
90	6.205282	6.274229	6.343177	6.412124	6.481072	6.550019	6.618967	6.687915	6.756862	6.825810
100	6.894757	6.963705	7.032652	7.101600	7.170548	7.239495	7.308443	7.377390	7.446338	7.515285

*To convert to kilopascals, move decimal point two positions to right; to convert to Megapascals, move decimal point one position to left. For example, 30 psi = 2.068427 bar = 206.8427 kPa = 0.2068427 MPa.

Note: Round off decimal points to provide no more than the desired degree of accuracy.

Temperature Conversion Tables

Temperature Conversion Formulas

To Convert From	To	Substitute in Formula
Degrees Celsius	Degrees Fahrenheit	$(°C \times 9/5) + 32$
Degrees Celsius	Kelvin	$(°C + 273.16)$
Degrees Fahrenheit	Degrees Celsius	$(°F - 32) \times 5/9$
Degrees Fahrenheit	Degrees Rankin	$(°F + 459.69)$

Temperature Conversions

°C	Temp. in °C or °F to be Converted	°F	°C	Temp. in °C or °F to be Converted	°F	°C	Temp. in °C or °F to be Converted	°F
−273.16	−459.69		−90.00	−130	−202.0	−17.8	0	32.0
−267.78	−450		−84.44	−120	−184.0	−16.7	2	35.6
−262.22	−440		−78.89	−110	−166.0	−15.6	4	39.2
−256.67	−430		−73.33	−100	−148.0	−14.4	6	42.8
−251.11	−420		−70.56	−95	−139.0	−13.3	8	46.4
−245.56	−410		−67.78	−90	−130.0	−12.2	10	50.0
−240.00	−400		−65.00	−85	−121.0	−11.1	12	53.6
−234.44	−390		−62.22	−80	−112.0	−10.0	14	57.2
−228.89	−380		−59.45	−75	−103.0	−8.89	16	60.8
−223.33	−370		−56.67	−70	−94.0	−7.78	18	64.4
−217.78	−360		−53.89	−65	−85.0	−6.67	20	68.0
−212.22	−350		−51.11	−60	−76.0	−5.56	22	71.6
−206.67	−340		−48.34	−55	−67.0	−4.44	24	75.2
−201.11	−330		−45.56	−50	−58.0	−3.33	26	78.8
−195.56	−320		−42.78	−45	−49.0	−2.22	28	82.4
−190.00	−310		−40.00	−40	−40.0	−1.11	30	86.0
−184.44	−300		−38.89	−38	−36.4	0	32	89.6
−178.89	−290		−37.78	−36	−32.8	1.11	34	93.2
−173.33	−280		−36.67	−34	−29.2	2.22	36	96.8
−169.53	−273.16	−459.69	−35.56	−32	−25.6	3.33	38	100.4
−168.89	−272	−457.6	−34.44	−30	−22.0	4.44	40	104.0
−167.78	−270	−454.0	−33.33	−28	−18.4	5.56	42	107.6
−162.22	−260	−436.0	−32.22	−26	−14.8	6.67	44	111.2
−156.67	−250	−418.0	−31.11	−24	−11.2	7.78	46	114.8
−151.11	−240	−400.0	−30.00	−22	−7.6	8.89	48	118.4
−145.56	−230	−382.0	−28.89	−20	−4.0	10.0	50	122.0
−140.00	−220	−364.0	−27.78	−18	−0.4	11.1	52	125.6
−134.44	−210	−346.0	−26.67	−16	3.2	12.2	54	129.2
−128.89	−200	−328.0	−25.56	−14	6.8	13.3	56	132.8
−123.33	−190	−310.0	−24.44	−12	10.4	14.4	58	136.4
−117.78	−180	−292.0	−23.33	−10	14.0	15.6	60	140.0
−112.22	−170	−274.0	−22.22	−8	17.6	16.7	62	143.6
−106.67	−160	−256.0	−21.11	−6	21.2	17.8	64	147.2
−101.11	−150	−238.0	−20.00	−4	24.8	18.9	66	150.8
−95.56	−140	−220.0	−18.89	−2	28.4	20.0	68	154.4

- Continued -

Temperature Conversions (Continued)

°C	Temp. in °C or °F to be Converted	°F	°C	Temp. in °C or °F to be Converted	°F	°C	Temp. in °C or °F to be Converted	°F
21.1	70	158.0	204.4	400	752.0	454.4	850	1562.0
22.2	72	161.6	210.0	410	770.0	460.0	860	1580.0
23.3	74	165.2	215.6	420	788.0	465.6	870	1598.0
24.4	76	168.8	221.1	430	806.0	471.1	880	1616.0
25.6	78	172.4	226.7	440	824.0	476.7	890	1634.0
26.7	80	176.0	232.2	450	842.0	482.2	900	1652.0
27.8	82	179.6	237.8	460	860.0	487.8	910	1670.0
28.9	84	183.2	243.3	470	878.0	493.3	920	1688.0
30.0	86	186.8	248.9	480	896.0	498.9	930	1706.0
31.1	88	190.4	254.4	490	914.0	504.4	940	1724.0
32.2	90	194.0	260.0	500	932.0	510.0	950	1742.0
33.3	92	197.6	265.6	510	950.0	515.6	960	1760.0
34.4	94	201.2	271.1	520	968.0	521.1	970	1778.0
35.6	96	204.8	276.7	530	986.0	526.7	980	1796.0
36.7	98	208.4	282.2	540	1004.0	532.2	990	1814.0
37.8	100	212.0	287.8	550	1022.0	537.8	1000	1832.0
43.3	110	230.0	293.3	560	1040.0	543.3	1010	1850.0
48.9	120	248.0	298.9	570	1058.0	548.9	1020	1868.0
54.4	130	266.0	304.4	580	1076.0	554.4	1030	1886.0
60.0	140	284.0	310.0	590	1094.0	560.0	1040	1904.0
65.6	150	302.0	315.6	600	1112.0	565.6	1050	1922.0
71.1	160	320.0	321.1	610	1130.0	571.1	1060	1940.0
76.7	170	338.0	326.7	620	1148.0	576.7	1070	1958.0
82.2	180	356.0	332.2	630	1166.0	582.2	1080	1976.0
87.8	190	374.0	337.8	640	1184.0	587.8	1090	1994.0
93.3	200	392.0	343.3	650	1202.0	593.3	1100	2012.0
98.9	210	410.0	348.9	660	1220.0	598.9	1110	2030.0
104.4	220	428.0	354.4	670	1238.0	604.4	1120	2048.0
110.0	230	446.0	360.0	680	1256.0	610.0	1130	2066.0
115.6	240	464.0	365.6	690	1274.0	615.6	1140	2084.0
121.1	250	482.0	371.1	700	1292.0	621.1	1150	2102.0
126.7	260	500.0	376.7	710	1310.0	626.7	1160	2120.0
132.2	270	518.0	382.2	720	1328.0	632.2	1170	2138.0
137.8	280	536.0	387.8	730	1346.0	637.8	1180	2156.0
143.3	290	554.0	393.3	740	1364.0	643.3	1190	2174.0
148.9	300	572.0	398.9	750	1382.0	648.9	1200	2192.0
154.4	310	590.0	404.4	760	1400.0	654.4	1210	2210.0
160.0	320	608.0	410.0	770	1418.0	660.0	1220	2228.0
165.6	330	626.0	415.6	780	1436.0	665.6	1230	2246.0
171.1	340	644.0	421.1	790	1454.0	671.1	1240	2264.0
176.7	350	662.0	426.7	800	1472.0	676.7	1250	2282.0
182.2	360	680.0	432.2	810	1490.0	682.2	1260	2300.0
187.8	370	698.0	437.8	820	1508.0	687.8	1270	2318.0
193.3	380	716.0	443.3	830	1526.0	693.3	1280	2336.0
198.9	390	734.0	448.9	840	1544.0	698.9	1290	2354.0

A.P.I. and Baumé Gravity Tables and Weight Factors

A.P.I. Gravity	Baumé Gravity	Specific Gravity	Lb/ U.S. Gal	U.S. Gal/ Lb	A.P.I. Gravity	Baumé Gravity	Specific Gravity	Lb/ U.S. Gal	U.S. Gal/ Lb
0	10.247	1.0760	8.962	0.1116	51	50.57	0.7753	6.455	0.1549
1	9.223	1.0679	8.895	0.1124	52	51.55	0.7711	6.420	0.1558
2	8.198	1.0599	8.828	0.1133	53	52.54	0.7669	6.385	0.1566
3	7.173	1.0520	8.762	0.1141	54	53.53	0.7628	6.350	0.1575
4	6.148	1.0443	8.698	0.1150	55	54.52	0.7587	6.316	0.1583
5	5.124	1.0366	8.634	0.1158					
6	4.099	1.0291	8.571	0.1167	56	55.51	0.7547	6.283	0.1592
7	3.074	1.0217	8.509	0.1175	57	56.50	0.7507	6.249	0.1600
8	2.049	1.0143	8.448	0.1184	58	57.49	0.7467	6.216	0.1609
9	1.025	1.0071	8.388	0.1192	59	58.48	0.7428	6.184	0.1617
10	10.00	1.0000	8.328	0.1201	60	59.47	0.7389	6.151	0.1626
11	10.99	0.9930	8.270	0.1209	61	60.46	0.7351	6.119	0.1634
12	11.98	0.9861	8.212	0.1218	62	61.45	0.7313	6.087	0.1643
13	12.97	0.9792	8.155	0.1226	63	62.44	0.7275	6.056	0.1651
14	13.96	0.9725	8.099	0.1235	64	63.43	0.7238	6.025	0.1660
15	14.95	0.9659	8.044	0.1243	65	64.42	0.7201	6.994	0.1668
16	15.94	0.9593	7.989	0.1252	66	65.41	0.7165	5.964	0.1677
17	16.93	0.9529	7.935	0.1260	67	66.40	0.7128	5.934	0.1685
18	17.92	0.9465	7.882	0.1269	68	67.39	0.7093	5.904	0.1694
19	18.90	0.9402	7.830	0.1277	69	68.37	0.7057	5.874	0.1702
20	19.89	0.9340	7.778	0.1286	70	69.36	0.7022	5.845	0.1711
21	20.88	0.9279	7.727	0.1294	71	70.35	0.6988	5.817	0.1719
22	21.87	0.9218	7.676	0.1303	72	71.34	0.6953	5.788	0.1728
23	22.86	0.9159	7.627	0.1311	73	72.33	0.6919	5.759	0.1736
24	23.85	0.9100	7.578	0.1320	74	73.32	0.6886	5.731	0.1745
25	24.84	0.9042	7.529	0.1328	75	74.31	0.6852	5.703	0.1753
26	25.83	0.8984	7.481	0.1337	76	75.30	0.6819	5.676	0.1762
27	26.82	0.8927	7.434	0.1345	77	76.29	0.6787	5.649	0.1770
28	27.81	0.8871	7.387	0.1354	78	77.28	0.6754	5.622	0.1779
29	28.80	0.8816	7.341	0.1362	79	78.27	0.6722	5.595	0.1787
30	29.79	0.8762	7.296	0.1371	80	79.26	0.6690	5.568	0.1796
31	30.78	0.8708	7.251	0.1379	81	80.25	0.6659	5.542	0.1804
32	31.77	0.8654	7.206	0.1388	82	81.24	0.6628	5.516	0.1813
33	32.76	0.8602	7.163	0.1396	83	82.23	0.6597	5.491	0.1821
34	33.75	0.8550	7.119	0.1405	84	83.22	0.6566	5.465	0.1830
35	34.73	0.8498	7.076	0.1413	85	84.20	0.6536	5.440	0.1838
36	35.72	0.8448	7.034	0.1422	86	85.19	0.6506	5.415	0.1847
37	36.71	0.8398	6.993	0.1430	87	86.18	0.6476	5.390	0.1855
38	37.70	0.8348	6.951	0.1439	88	87.17	0.6446	5.365	0.1864
39	38.69	0.8299	6.910	0.1447	89	88.16	0.6417	5.341	0.1872
40	39.68	0.8251	6.870	0.1456	90	89.15	0.6388	5.316	0.1881
41	40.67	0.8203	6.830	0.1464	91	90.14	0.6360	5.293	0.1889
42	41.66	0.8155	6.790	0.1473	92	91.13	0.6331	5.269	0.1898
43	42.65	0.8109	6.752	0.1481	93	92.12	0.6303	5.246	0.1906
44	43.64	0.8063	6.713	0.1490	94	93.11	0.6275	5.222	0.1915
45	44.63	0.8017	6.675	0.1498	95	94.10	0.6247	5.199	0.1924
46	45.62	0.7972	6.637	0.1507	96	95.09	0.6220	5.176	0.1932
47	50.61	0.7927	6.600	0.1515	97	96.08	0.6193	5.154	0.1940
48	50.60	0.7883	6.563	0.1524	98	97.07	0.6166	5.131	0.1949
49	50.59	0.7839	6.526	0.1532	99	98.06	0.6139	5.109	0.1957
50	50.58	0.7796	6.490	0.1541	100	99.05	0.6112	5.086	0.1966

Viscosity Conversion Nomograph

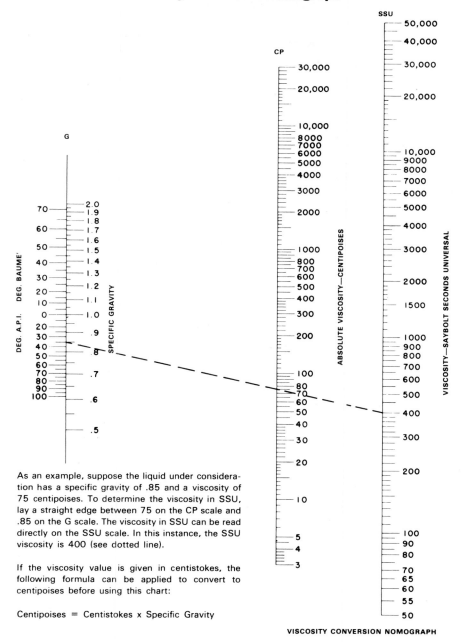

As an example, suppose the liquid under consideration has a specific gravity of .85 and a viscosity of 75 centipoises. To determine the viscosity in SSU, lay a straight edge between 75 on the CP scale and .85 on the G scale. The viscosity in SSU can be read directly on the SSU scale. In this instance, the SSU viscosity is 400 (see dotted line).

If the viscosity value is given in centistokes, the following formula can be applied to convert to centipoises before using this chart:

Centipoises = Centistokes x Specific Gravity

VISCOSITY CONVERSION NOMOGRAPH

Equivalent Volume and Weight
Flow Rates of Compressible Fluids

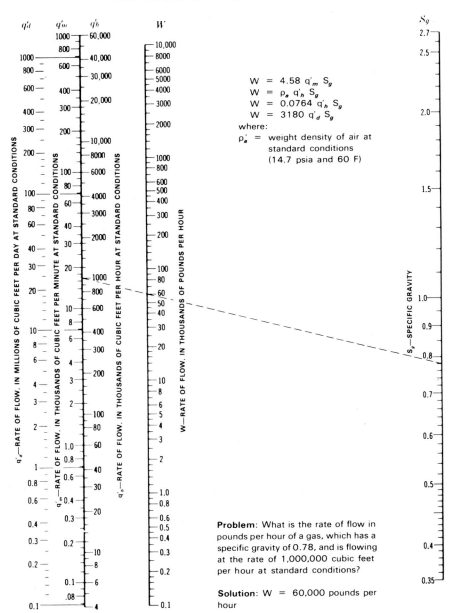

$$W = 4.58 \; q'_m \; S_g$$
$$W = \rho_a \; q'_h \; S_g$$
$$W = 0.0764 \; q'_h \; S_g$$
$$W = 3180 \; q'_d \; S_g$$

where:

ρ_a = weight density of air at standard conditions (14.7 psia and 60 F)

Problem: What is the rate of flow in pounds per hour of a gas, which has a specific gravity of 0.78, and is flowing at the rate of 1,000,000 cubic feet per hour at standard conditions?

Solution: W = 60,000 pounds per hour

Properties of Water

Temperature of Water (°F)	Saturation Pressure (Pounds Per Square Inch Absolute)	Weight (Pounds Per Gallon)	Specific Gravity 60/60 F	Conversion Factor, * lbs./hr. to GPM
32	.0885	8.345	1.0013	.00199
40	.1217	8.345	1.0013	.00199
50	.1781	8.340	1.0007	.00199
60	.2653	8.334	1.0000	.00199
70	.3631	8.325	.9989	.00200
80	.5069	8.314	.9976	.00200
90	.6982	8.303	.9963	.00200
100	.9492	8.289	.9946	.00201
110	1.2748	8.267	.9919	.00201
120	1.6924	8.253	.9901	.00201
130	2.2225	8.227	.9872	.00202
140	2.8886	8.207	.9848	.00203
150	3.718	8.182	.9818	.00203
160	4.741	8.156	.9786	.00204
170	5.992	8.127	.9752	.00205
180	7.510	8.098	.9717	.00205
190	9.339	8.068	.9681	.00206
200	11.526	8.039	.9646	.00207
210	14.123	8.005	.9605	.00208
212	14.696	7.996	.9594	.00208
220	17.186	7.972	.9566	.00209
240	24.969	7.901	.9480	.00210
260	35.429	7.822	.9386	.00211
280	49.203	7.746	.9294	.00215
300	67.013	7.662	.9194	.00217
350	134.63	7.432	.8918	.00224
400	247.31	7.172	.8606	.00232
450	422.6	6.892	.8270	.00241
500	680.8	6.553	.7863	.00254
550	1045.2	6.132	.7358	.00271
600	1542.9	5.664	.6796	.00294
700	3093.7	3.623	.4347	.00460

*Multiply flow in pounds per hour by the factor to get equivalent flow in gallons per minute.   Weight per gallon is based on 7.48 gallons per cubic foot.

Metric Prefixes and Symbols

Multiplication Factor	Prefix	Symbol
1 000 000 000 000 000 000 = 10^{18}	exa	E
1 000 000 000 000 000 = 10^{15}	peta	P
1 000 000 000 000 = 10^{12}	tera	T
1 000 000 000 = 10^{9}	giga	G
1 000 000 = 10^{6}	mega	M
1 000 = 10^{3}	kilo	k
100 = 10^{2}	hecto*	h
10 = 10^{1}	deka*	da
0.1 = 10^{-1}	deci*	d
0.01 = 10^{-2}	centi*	c
0.001 = 10^{-3}	milli	m
0.000 001 = 10^{-6}	micro	μ
0.000 000 001 = 10^{-9}	nano	n
0.000 000 000 001 = 10^{-12}	pico	p
0.000 000 000 000 001 = 10^{-15}	femto	f
0.000 000 000 000 000 001 = 10^{-18}	atto	a

* Avoid usage, if possible.

Greek Alphabet

Caps	Lower Case	Greek Name	Caps	Lower Case	Greek Name	Caps	Lower Case	Greek Name
A	α	Alpha	I	ι	Iota	P	ρ	Rho
B	β	Beta	K	κ	Kappa	Σ	σ	Sigma
Γ	γ	Gamma	Λ	λ	Lambda	T	τ	Tau
Δ	δ	Delta	M	μ	Mu	Y	υ	Upsilon
E	ε	Epsilon	N	ν	Nu	Φ	φ φ	Phi
Z	ζ	Zeta	Ξ	ξ	Xi	X	χ	Chi
H	η	Eta	O	o	Omicron	Ψ	ψ	Psi
θ	θ	Theta	Π	π	Pi	Ω	ω	Omega

Other Useful Conversions

To Convert From	To	Multiply By
Cu Ft (Methane)	B.T.U.	1000 (approx.)
Cu Ft of Water	Lbs of Water	62.4
Degrees	Radians	0.01745
Gals	Lbs of Water	8.336
Grams	Ounces	0.0352
Horsepower (mech.)	Ft Lbs per Min	33,000
Horsepower (elec.)	Watts	746
Kg	Lbs	2.205
Kg per Cu Meter	Lbs per Cu Ft	0.06243
Kilowatts	Horsepower	1.341
Lbs	Kg	0.4536
Lbs of Air (14.7 psia and 60°F)	Cu Ft of Air	13.1
Lbs per Cu Ft	Kg per Cu Meter	16.0184
		13.1
Lbs per Hr (Water)	Gals per Min	0.002

COMMENTARY: "C" = 140 FLOW CHART AND SIZING TABLE

By Dr. Alfred Steele, P.E.

Design engineers are well aware that water flowing in a pipe is always subject to frictional losses. They may not, however, be aware that the present critieria for calculating friction head losses are out of date and lead to increased costs and wasted energy.

Analysis of fluid flow and experiments in the early 1900s indicated that friction head loss varied directly with the relative length of the pipe (L/D) and velocity head (V²/2g). Among many formulas proposed for the calculation of friction head loss, the Hazen-Williams formula has become the most widely used by engineers.

The value of "C" = 140 for new black steel pipe was originally proposed by Williams and Hazen more than fifty years ago, based upon the prevalent roughness of interior pipe surfaces of that era.

There have been significant improvements in manufacturing during the past half-century. American Iron and Steel Institute (AISI) decided to sponsor a research study at the National Bureau of Standards (NBS) to determine whether the value of "C" = 140 for new steel pipe was valid. The NBS report* confirmed that modern, domestic black steel pipe is much smoother and offers less resistance to flow.

The test set-up at the NBS comprised a pump, an open-topped weighing tank, the test pipe, and precision instrumentation. Tests were performed on ten pipes ranging in size from one to three inches and twenty feet long. Sixty to seventy test runs were made on each pipe.

Negligible corrosion occurs in typical closed-loop systems, such as air conditioning chilled water and hydronic systems, because additional fresh oxygen is not introduced into the circulated water. The water in the NBS test, however, became highly oxygenated from circulating in and out of the open-topped weighing tank. Further corrosion occurred due to a time lapse (as much as one day) between test runs on each pipe, which exposed the wetted pipe interior to air.

Despite these adverse test conditions, the C value frequently exceeded 150 and, in one test run, peaked at "C" = 165. The average value of "C" was found to be 148.3.

The correct value of "C" for new black steel pipe

*"Fluid Friction Losses in Two Sets of Black Steel Pipe of Recent Manufacture." NBSIR 80-2041.

is the first step toward a rational value of "C" for system design. Note that, when using the Hazen-Williams formula, the "C" value is the design value, not the value for new pipe. For design it becomes necessary to decrease the "C" value of new pipe to allow for aging, manufacturing tolerances and other conditions that could cause variations in the interior pipe surfaces. Due to the high aeration of the water and repeated exposure of the pipe to air for extended periods in the NBS tests, it is reasonable to conclude that the NBS average value of "C" = 148.3 could be used for the piping design of closed-loop systems such as chilled water and hydronic systems. To be conservative, AISI has recommended a design value of "C" = 140.

The practical implications of the NBS research study are truly surprising. When the AISI recommended "C" = 140 is used instead of the old arbitrarily selected value of "C" = 100, calculated friction head losses are decreased by more than 60 percent!

Lower friction head losses will permit smaller size pipe to convey the required quantities of flow. Of equal if not more importance, a 60 percent reduction in friction head loss means a pump of lower horsepower could be selected, resulting in significant savings of energy.

Horsepower (energy) of a pump is determined by the following formula:

$$HP = \frac{\text{Head (ft)} \times \text{GPM}}{3960 \times \text{Efficiency}}$$

In a closed-loop system the only head on the pump is the friction head. The formula shows that any reduction in the friction head will automatically result in a reduction of horsepower.

COMMITTEE OF STEEL PIPE PRODUCERS,
AMERICAN IRON AND STEEL INSTITUTE
1000 16TH STREET, N.W.
WASHINGTON, D.C. 20036

Note: The information presented was prepared in keeping with generally accepted engineering principles as a design aid. AISI does not warrant its applicability to the design of any specific piping system, which must be the responsibility of a qualified professional engineer.

SCHEDULE 40 BLACK STEEL PIPE
BASED ON HAZEN-WILLIAMS FORMULA

Flow gpm	Velocity fps	Head Loss psi/100'	Velocity fps	Head Loss psi/100'	Velocity fps	Head Loss psi/100'	Velocity fps	Head Loss psi/100'	Velocity fps	Head Loss psi/100'	Head Loss psi/100'	Head Loss psi/100'	Flow gpm
	½"		¾"		1"		1¼"		1½"		2"		
2	2.11	1.77	1.20	0.45	—	—	—						2
4	4.23	6.38	2.41	1.62	1.49	0.50	—	—	—				4
6	6.34	13.50	3.61	3.44	2.23	1.06	—	—	—				6
8	8.45	23.00	4.82	5.83	2.97	1.84	1.72	0.49	—	—			8
10	10.6	34.83	6.02	8.86	3.71	2.75	2.15	0.70	—	—			10
12			7.22	12.37	4.46	3.83	2.57	1.03	—	—			12
14			8.43	16.47	5.20	5.08	3.00	1.34	—	—			14
16			9.63	21.11	5.49	6.53	3.43	1.72	2.52	0.81	—		16
18					6.68	8.10	3.86	2.13	2.84	1.01	—		18
20					7.43	9.83	4.29	2.59	3.15	1.24	—		20
25					9.28	14.90	5.36	3.94	3.94	1.84	2.39	0.54	25
30					11.1	20.84	6.43	5.51	4.73	2.59	2.87	0.76	30
35	2½"						7.51	7.29	5.51	2.92	3.35	1.03	35
40	2.68	0.54					8.58	9.34	6.30	4.43	3.82	1.30	40
45	3.02	0.70					9.16	11.72	7.09	5.51	4.30	1.62	45
50	3.35	0.81	3"				10.7	14.15	7.88	6.70	4.78	2.00	50
60	4.02	1.20							9.46	9.34	5.74	2.81	60
70	4.69	1.57	3.04	0.54					11.0	12.42	6.69	3.67	70
80	5.36	2.00	3.47	0.70							7.65	4.75	80
90	6.03	2.48	3.91	0.86							8.61	5.90	90
100	6.70	2.97	4.34	1.03							9.56	7.13	100
110	7.37	3.56	4.77	1.24							10.5	8.35	110
120	8.04	4.21	5.21	1.46									120
130	8.71	4.91	5.64	1.67	4"								130
140	9.38	5.62	6.08	1.94	3.53	0.54							140
160	10.7	7.18	6.94	2.48	4.03	0.65							160
180			8.24	3.40	4.54	0.81							180
200			8.68	3.78	5.05	1.03							200
220			9.55	4.48	5.55	1.19							220
240			10.4	5.29	6.05	1.40	5"						240
260					6.55	1.62	4.17	0.54					260
280					7.06	1.89	4.49	0.65					280
300					7.57	2.11	4.81	0.70					300
350					8.83	2.81	5.61	0.92	6"				350
400					10.1	3.62	6.41	1.19	4.44	0.49			400
450							7.22	1.51	5.00	0.59			450
500							8.02	1.84	5.56	0.76			500
600							9.62	2.54	6.66	0.92			600
700									7.78	1.40	8"		700
800									8.90	1.78	5.13	0.49	800
900									10.0	2.21	5.77	0.59	900
1000											6.41	0.70	1000
1100											7.05	0.86	1100
1200											7.69	0.97	1200
1300											8.33	1.13	1300
1400											8.97	1.30	1400
1500											9.61	1.51	1500
1600											10.3	1.67	1600

Pipe Data
Carbon and Alloy Steel—Stainless Steel

Identification, wall thickness and weights are extracted from ANSI B36.10 and B39.19. The notations STD, XS, and XXS indicate Standard, Extra Strong, and Double Extra Strong pipe respectively.

Transverse internal area values listed in "square feet" also represent volume in cubic feet per foot of pipe length.

NOMINAL PIPE SIZE (INCHES)	OUTSIDE DIAM. (INCHES)	Steel Iron Pipe Size	Steel Sched. No.	Stainless Steel Sched. No.	WALL THICKNESS (t) (INCHES)	INSIDE DIAMETER (d) (INCHES)	AREA OF METAL (SQUARE INCHES)	(a) (Square Inches)	(A) (Square Feet)	WEIGHT PIPE (POUNDS PER FOOT)	WEIGHT WATER (POUNDS PER FOOT OF PIPE)
1/8	0.405	...	...	10S	0.049	0.307	0.0548	0.0740	0.00051	0.19	0.032
		STD	40	40S	0.068	0.269	0.0720	0.0568	0.00040	0.24	0.025
		XS	80	80S	0.095	0.215	0.0925	0.0364	0.00025	0.31	0.016
1/4	0.540	...	...	10S	0.065	0.410	0.0970	0.1320	0.00091	0.33	0.057
		STD	40	40S	0.088	0.364	0.1250	0.1041	0.00072	0.42	0.045
		XS	80	80S	0.119	0.302	0.1574	0.0716	0.00050	0.54	0.031
3/8	0.675	...	...	10S	0.065	0.545	0.1246	0.2333	0.00162	0.42	0.101
		STD	40	40S	0.091	0.493	0.1670	0.1910	0.00133	0.57	0.083
		XS	80	80S	0.126	0.423	0.2173	0.1405	0.00098	0.74	0.061
1/2	0.840	...	...	5S	0.065	0.710	0.1583	0.3959	0.00275	0.54	0.172
		...	...	10S	0.083	0.674	0.1974	0.3568	0.00248	0.67	0.155
		STD	40	40S	0.109	0.622	0.2503	0.3040	0.00211	0.85	0.132
		XS	80	80S	0.147	0.546	0.3200	0.2340	0.00163	1.09	0.102
		...	160	...	0.187	0.466	0.3836	0.1706	0.00118	1.31	0.074
		XXS	...	...	0.294	0.252	0.5043	0.050	0.00035	1.71	0.022

Nominal Pipe Size	Outside Diameter	Schedule	Schedule	Schedule							
3/4	1.050	5S	...	...	0.065	0.920	0.2011	0.6648	0.00462	0.69	0.288
		10S	...	...	0.083	0.884	0.2521	0.6138	0.00426	0.86	0.266
		40S	STD	40	0.113	0.824	0.3326	0.5330	0.00371	1.13	0.231
		80S	XS	80	0.154	0.742	0.4335	0.4330	0.00300	1.47	0.188
		...	...	160	0.219	0.612	0.5698	0.2961	0.00206	1.94	0.128
		...	XXS	...	0.308	0.434	0.7180	0.148	0.00103	2.44	0.064
1	1.315	5S	...	...	0.065	1.185	0.2553	1.1029	0.00766	0.87	0.478
		10S	...	...	0.109	1.097	0.4130	0.9452	0.00656	1.40	0.409
		40S	STD	40	0.133	1.049	0.4939	0.8640	0.00600	1.68	0.375
		80S	XS	80	0.179	0.957	0.6388	0.7190	0.00499	2.17	0.312
		...	...	160	0.250	0.815	0.8365	0.5217	0.00362	2.84	0.230
		...	XXS	...	0.358	0.599	1.0760	0.282	0.00196	3.66	0.122
1-1/4	1.660	5S	...	...	0.065	1.530	0.3257	1.839	0.01277	1.11	0.797
		10S	...	...	0.109	1.442	0.4717	1.633	0.01134	1.81	0.708
		40S	STD	40	0.140	1.380	0.6685	1.495	0.01040	2.27	0.649
		80S	XS	80	0.191	1.278	0.8815	1.283	0.00891	3.00	0.555
		...	...	160	0.250	1.160	1.1070	1.057	0.00734	3.76	0.458
		...	XXS	...	0.382	0.896	1.534	0.630	0.00438	5.21	0.273
1-1/2	1.900	5S	...	...	0.065	1.770	0.3747	2.461	0.01709	1.28	1.066
		10S	...	...	0.109	1.682	0.6133	2.222	0.01543	2.09	0.963
		40S	STD	40	0.145	1.610	0.7995	2.036	0.01414	2.72	0.882
		80S	XS	80	0.200	1.500	1.068	1.767	0.01225	3.63	0.765
		...	...	160	0.281	1.338	1.429	1.406	0.00976	4.86	0.608
		...	XXS	...	0.400	1.100	1.885	0.950	0.00660	6.41	0.42
2	2.375	5S	...	...	0.065	2.245	0.4717	3.958	0.02749	1.61	1.72
		10S	...	...	0.109	2.157	0.7760	3.654	0.02538	2.64	1.58
		40S	STD	40	0.154	2.067	1.075	3.355	0.02330	3.65	1.45
		80S	XS	80	0.218	1.939	1.477	2.953	0.02050	5.02	1.28
		...	...	160	0.344	1.687	2.190	2.241	0.01556	7.46	0.97
		...	XXS	...	0.436	1.503	2.656	1.774	0.01232	9.03	0.77

Pipe Data
Carbon and Alloy Steel—Stainless Steel

NOMINAL PIPE SIZE (INCHES)	OUTSIDE DIAM. (INCHES)	IDENTIFICATION			WALL THICK-NESS (t) (INCHES)	INSIDE DIAM-ETER (d) (INCHES)	AREA OF METAL (SQUARE INCHES)	TRANSVERSE INTERNAL AREA		WEIGHT PIPE (POUNDS PER FOOT)	WEIGHT WATER (POUNDS PER FOOT OF PIPE)
		Iron Pipe Size	Sched. No.	Stainless Steel Sched. No.				(a) (Square Inches)	(A) (Square Feet)		
2-1/2	2.875	...	...	5S	0.083	2.709	0.7280	5.764	0.04002	2.48	2.50
		...	...	10S	0.120	2.635	1.039	5.453	0.03787	3.53	2.36
		STD	40	40S	0.203	2.469	1.704	4.788	0.03322	5.79	2.07
		XS	80	80S	0.276	2.323	2.254	4.238	0.02942	7.66	1.87
		...	160	...	0.375	2.125	2.945	3.546	0.02463	10.01	1.54
		XXS	...	...	0.552	1.771	4.028	2.464	0.01710	13.69	1.07
3	3.500	...	...	5S	0.083	3.334	0.8910	8.730	0.06063	3.03	3.78
		...	...	10S	0.120	3.260	1.274	8.347	0.05796	4.33	3.62
		STD	40	40S	0.216	3.068	2.228	7.393	0.05130	7.58	3.20
		XS	80	80S	0.300	2.900	3.016	6.605	0.04587	10.25	2.86
		...	160	...	0.438	2.624	4.205	5.408	0.03755	14.32	2.35
		XXS	...	...	0.600	2.300	5.466	4.155	0.02885	18.58	1.80
3-1/2	4.000	...	...	5S	0.083	3.834	1.021	11.545	0.08017	3.48	5.00
		...	...	10S	0.120	3.760	1.463	11.104	0.07711	4.97	4.81
		STD	40	40S	0.226	3.548	2.680	9.886	0.06870	9.11	4.29
		XS	80	80S	0.318	3.364	3.678	8.888	0.06170	12.50	3.84
4	4.500	...	...	5S	0.083	4.334	1.152	14.75	0.10245	3.92	6.39
		...	...	10S	0.120	4.260	1.651	14.25	0.09898	5.61	6.18
		STD	40	40S	0.237	4.026	3.174	12.73	0.08840	10.79	5.50
		XS	80	80S	0.337	3.826	4.407	11.50	0.07986	14.98	4.98
		...	120	...	0.438	3.624	5.595	10.31	0.0716	19.00	4.47
		...	160	...	0.531	3.438	6.621	9.28	0.0645	22.51	4.02
		XXS	...	...	0.674	3.152	8.101	7.80	0.0542	27.54	3.38

5	5.563			5S	0.109	5.345	1.868	22.44	0.1558	6.36	9.72
				10S	0.134	5.295	2.285	22.02	0.1529	7.77	9.54
		STD	40	40S	0.258	5.047	4.300	20.01	0.1390	14.62	8.67
		XS	80	80S	0.375	4.813	6.112	18.19	0.1263	20.78	7.88
		...	120	...	0.500	4.563	7.953	16.35	0.1136	27.04	7.09
		...	160	...	0.625	4.313	9.696	14.61	0.1015	32.96	6.33
		XXS	...	...	0.750	4.063	11.340	12.97	0.0901	38.55	5.61
6	6.625			5S	0.109	6.407	2.231	32.24	0.2239	7.60	13.97
				10S	0.134	6.357	2.733	31.74	0.2204	9.29	13.75
		STD	40	40S	0.280	6.065	5.581	28.89	0.2006	18.97	12.51
		XS	80	80S	0.432	5.761	8.405	26.07	0.1850	28.57	11.29
		...	120	...	0.562	5.501	10.70	23.77	0.1650	36.39	10.30
		XXS	160	...	0.719	5.187	13.32	21.15	0.1469	45.35	9.16
		...	...	40S	0.864	4.897	15.64	18.84	0.1308	53.16	8.16
8	8.625			5S	0.109	8.407	2.916	55.51	0.3855	9.93	24.06
				10S	0.148	8.329	3.941	54.48	0.3784	13.40	23.61
		...	20	...	0.250	8.125	6.57	51.85	0.3601	22.36	22.47
		...	30	...	0.277	8.071	7.26	51.16	0.3553	24.70	22.17
		STD	40	40S	0.322	7.981	8.40	50.03	0.3474	28.55	21.70
		...	60	...	0.406	7.813	10.48	47.94	0.3329	35.64	20.77
		XS	80	80S	0.500	7.625	12.76	45.66	0.3171	43.39	19.78
		...	100	...	0.594	7.437	14.96	43.46	0.3018	50.95	18.83
		...	120	...	0.719	7.187	17.84	40.59	0.2819	60.71	17.59
		...	140	...	0.812	7.001	19.93	38.50	0.2673	67.76	16.68
		XXS	...	...	0.875	6.875	21.30	37.12	0.2578	72.42	16.10
		...	160	40S	0.906	6.813	21.97	36.46	0.2532	74.69	15.80
10 (Cont.)	10.750			5S	0.134	10.482	4.36	86.29	0.5992	15.19	37.39
				10S	0.165	10.420	5.49	85.28	0.5922	18.65	36.95
		...	20	...	0.250	10.250	8.24	82.52	0.5731	28.04	35.76
		...	30	...	0.307	10.136	10.07	80.69	0.5603	34.24	34.96
		STD	40	40S	0.365	10.020	11.90	78.86	0.5475	40.48	34.20

Pipe Data
Carbon and Alloy Steel—Stainless Steel

NOMINAL PIPE SIZE (INCHES)	OUTSIDE DIAM. (INCHES)	IDENTIFICATION			WALL THICK-NESS (t) (INCHES)	INSIDE DIAM-ETER (d) (INCHES)	AREA OF METAL (SQUARE INCHES)	TRANSVERSE INTERNAL AREA		WEIGHT PIPE (POUNDS PER FOOT)	WEIGHT WATER (POUNDS PER FOOT OF PIPE)
		Steel		Stainless Steel Sched. No.				(a) (Square Inches)	(A) (Square Feet)		
		Iron Pipe Size	Sched. No.								
10 (Cont.)	10.750	XS	60	80S	0.500	9.750	16.10	74.66	0.5185	54.74	32.35
			80		0.594	9.562	18.92	71.84	0.4989	64.43	31.13
			100		0.719	9.312	22.63	68.13	0.4732	77.03	29.53
			120		0.844	9.062	26.24	64.53	0.4481	89.29	27.96
		XXS	140		1.000	8.750	30.63	60.13	0.4176	104.13	26.06
			160		1.125	8.500	34.02	56.75	0.3941	115.64	24.59
12	12.75			5S	0.156	12.438	6.17	121.50	0.8438	20.98	52.65
				10S	0.180	12.390	7.11	120.57	0.8373	24.17	52.25
			20		0.250	12.250	9.82	117.86	0.8185	33.38	51.07
			30		0.330	12.090	12.87	114.80	0.7972	43.77	49.74
		STD		40S	0.375	12.000	14.58	113.10	0.7854	49.56	49.00
			40		0.406	11.938	15.77	111.93	0.7773	53.52	48.50
	12.75	XS		80S	0.500	11.750	19.24	108.43	0.7528	65.42	46.92
			60		0.562	11.626	21.52	106.16	0.7372	73.15	46.00
			80		0.688	11.374	26.03	101.64	0.7058	88.63	44.04
			100		0.844	11.062	31.53	96.14	0.6677	107.32	41.66
		XXS	120		1.000	10.750	36.91	90.76	0.6303	125.49	39.33
			140		1.125	10.500	41.08	86.59	0.6013	139.67	37.52
			160		1.312	10.126	47.14	80.53	0.5592	160.27	34.89
14 (Cont.)	14.00			5S	0.156	13.688	6.78	147.15	1.0219	23.07	63.77
				10S	0.188	13.624	8.16	145.78	1.0124	27.73	63.17
			10		0.250	13.500	10.80	143.14	0.9940	36.71	62.03
			20		0.312	13.376	13.42	140.52	0.9758	45.61	60.89
		STD	30		0.375	13.250	16.05	137.88	0.9575	54.57	59.75
			40		0.438	13.124	18.66	135.28	0.9394	63.44	58.64

Nom.	OD	Desig.		Sched.	Wall	ID					
14 (Cont.)	14.00	XS	...	...	0.500	13.000	21.21	132.73	0.9217	72.09	57.46
		...	...	60	0.594	12.812	24.98	128.96	0.8956	85.05	55.86
		...	...	80	0.750	12.500	31.22	122.72	0.8522	106.13	53.18
		...	...	100	0.938	12.124	38.45	115.49	0.8020	130.85	50.04
		...	...	120	1.094	11.812	44.32	109.62	0.7612	150.79	47.45
		...	...	140	1.250	11.500	50.07	103.87	0.7213	170.28	45.01
		...	...	160	1.406	11.188	55.63	98.31	0.6827	189.11	42.60
16	16.00	...	5S	...	0.165	15.670	8.21	192.85	1.3393	27.90	83.57
		...	10S	...	0.188	15.624	9.34	191.72	1.3314	31.75	83.08
		...	...	10	0.250	15.500	12.37	188.69	1.3103	42.05	81.74
		...	...	20	0.312	15.376	15.38	185.69	1.2895	52.27	80.50
		STD	...	30	0.375	15.250	18.41	182.65	1.2684	62.58	79.12
		XS	...	40	0.500	15.000	24.35	176.72	1.2272	82.77	76.58
		...	...	60	0.656	14.688	31.62	169.44	1.1766	107.50	73.42
		...	...	80	0.844	14.312	40.14	160.92	1.1175	136.61	69.73
		...	...	100	1.031	13.938	48.48	152.58	1.0596	164.82	66.12
		...	...	120	1.219	13.562	56.56	144.50	1.0035	192.43	62.62
		...	...	140	1.438	13.124	65.78	135.28	0.9394	223.64	58.64
		...	...	160	1.594	12.812	72.10	128.96	0.8956	245.25	55.83
18	18.00	...	5S	...	0.165	17.670	9.25	245.22	1.7029	31.43	106.26
		...	10S	...	0.188	17.624	10.52	243.95	1.6941	35.76	105.71
		...	...	10	0.250	17.500	13.94	240.53	1.6703	47.39	104.21
		...	...	20	0.312	17.376	17.34	237.13	1.6467	58.94	102.77
		STD	...	...	0.375	17.250	20.76	233.71	1.6230	70.59	101.18
		...	...	30	0.438	17.124	24.17	230.30	1.5990	82.15	99.84
		XS	...	...	0.500	17.000	27.49	226.98	1.5763	93.45	98.27
		...	...	40	0.562	16.876	30.79	223.68	1.5533	104.67	96.93
		...	...	60	0.750	16.500	40.64	213.83	1.4849	138.17	92.57
		...	...	80	0.938	16.124	50.23	204.24	1.4183	170.92	88.50
		...	...	100	1.156	15.688	61.17	193.30	1.3423	207.96	83.76
		...	...	120	1.375	15.250	71.81	182.66	1.2684	244.14	79.07
		...	...	140	1.562	14.876	80.66	173.80	1.2070	274.22	75.32
		...	...	160	1.781	14.438	90.75	163.72	1.1369	308.50	70.88

Pipe Data
Carbon and Alloy Steel—Stainless Steel

NOMINAL PIPE SIZE (INCHES)	OUTSIDE DIAM. (INCHES)	IDENTIFICATION			WALL THICK-NESS (t) (INCHES)	INSIDE DIAM-ETER (d) (INCHES)	AREA OF METAL (SQUARE INCHES)	TRANSVERSE INTERNAL AREA		WEIGHT PIPE (POUNDS PER FOOT)	WEIGHT WATER (POUNDS PER FOOT OF PIPE)
		Steel		Stainless Steel Sched. No.				(a) (Square Inches)	(A) (Square Feet)		
		Iron Pipe Size	Sched. No.								
20	20.00	...	...	5S	0.188	19.624	11.70	302.46	2.1004	39.78	131.06
		...	...	10S	0.218	19.564	13.55	300.61	2.0876	46.06	130.27
		...	10	...	0.250	19.500	15.51	298.65	2.0740	52.73	129.42
		...	20	...	0.375	19.250	23.12	290.04	2.0142	78.60	125.67
		STD	30	...	0.500	19.000	30.63	283.53	1.9690	104.13	122.87
		XS	40	...	0.594	18.812	36.15	278.00	1.9305	123.11	120.46
		...	60	...	0.812	18.376	48.95	265.21	1.8417	166.40	114.92
		...	80	...	1.031	17.938	61.44	252.72	1.7550	208.87	109.51
		...	100	...	1.281	17.438	75.33	238.83	1.6585	256.10	103.39
		...	120	...	1.500	17.000	87.18	226.98	1.5762	296.37	98.35
		...	140	...	1.750	16.500	100.33	213.82	1.4849	341.09	92.66
		...	160	...	1.969	16.062	111.49	202.67	1.4074	379.17	87.74
22	22.00	...	...	5S	0.188	21.624	12.88	367.25	2.5503	43.80	159.14
		...	...	10S	0.218	21.564	14.92	365.21	2.5362	50.71	158.26
		...	10	...	0.250	21.500	17.08	363.05	2.5212	58.07	157.32
		STD	20	...	0.375	21.250	25.48	354.66	2.4629	86.61	153.68
		XS	30	...	0.500	21.000	33.77	346.36	2.4053	114.81	150.09
		...	60	...	0.875	20.250	58.07	322.06	2.2365	197.41	139.56
		...	80	...	1.125	19.75	73.78	306.35	2.1275	250.81	132.76
		...	100	...	1.375	19.25	89.09	291.04	2.0211	302.88	126.12
		...	120	...	1.625	18.75	104.02	276.12	1.9175	353.61	119.65
		...	140	...	1.875	18.25	118.55	261.59	1.8166	403.00	113.36
		...	160	...	2.125	17.75	132.68	247.45	1.7184	451.06	107.23

Nom.	O.D.			Wall	I.D.					
24	24.00	5S	...	0.218	23.564	16.29	436.10	3.0285	55.37	188.98
		10S	10	0.250	23.500	18.65	433.74	3.0121	63.41	187.95
		...	20	0.375	23.250	27.83	424.56	2.9483	94.62	183.95
		STD	...	0.500	23.000	36.91	415.48	2.8853	125.49	179.87
		XS	30	0.562	22.876	41.39	411.00	2.8542	140.68	178.09
		...	40	0.688	22.624	50.31	402.07	2.7921	171.29	174.23
		...	60	0.969	22.062	70.04	382.35	2.6552	238.35	165.52
		...	80	1.219	21.562	87.17	365.22	2.5362	296.58	158.26
		...	100	1.531	20.938	108.07	344.32	2.3911	367.39	149.06
		...	120	1.812	20.376	126.31	326.08	2.2645	429.39	141.17
		...	140	2.062	19.876	142.11	310.28	2.1547	483.12	134.45
		...	160	2.344	19.312	159.41	292.98	2.0346	542.13	126.84
26	26.00	...	10	0.312	25.376	25.18	505.75	3.5122	85.60	219.16
		STD	...	0.375	25.250	30.19	500.74	3.4774	102.63	216.99
		XS	20	0.500	25.000	40.06	490.87	3.4088	136.17	212.71
28	28.00	...	10	0.312	27.376	27.14	588.61	4.0876	92.26	255.07
		STD	...	0.375	27.250	32.54	583.21	4.0501	110.64	252.73
		XS	20	0.500	27.000	43.20	572.56	3.9761	146.85	248.11
		...	30	0.625	26.750	53.75	562.00	3.9028	182.73	243.53
30	30.00	5S	...	0.250	29.500	23.37	683.49	4.7465	79.43	296.18
		10S	10	0.312	29.376	29.10	677.76	4.7067	98.93	293.70
		STD	...	0.375	29.250	34.90	671.96	4.6664	118.65	291.18
		XS	20	0.500	29.000	46.34	660.52	4.5869	157.53	286.22
		...	30	0.625	28.750	57.68	649.18	4.5082	196.08	281.31
32	32.00	...	10	0.312	31.376	31.06	773.19	5.3694	105.59	335.05
		STD	...	0.375	31.250	37.26	766.99	5.3263	126.66	332.36
		XS	20	0.500	31.000	49.48	754.77	5.2414	168.21	327.06
		...	30	0.625	30.750	61.60	742.64	5.1572	209.43	321.81
		...	40	0.688	30.624	67.68	736.57	5.1151	230.08	319.18

Pipe Data
Carbon and Alloy Steel—Stainless Steel

NOMINAL PIPE SIZE (INCHES)	OUTSIDE DIAM. (INCHES)	IDENTIFICATION			WALL THICK-NESS (t) (INCHES)	INSIDE DIAM-ETER (d) (INCHES)	AREA OF METAL (SQUARE INCHES)	TRANSVERSE INTERNAL AREA		WEIGHT PIPE (POUNDS PER FOOT)	WEIGHT WATER (POUNDS PER FOOT OF PIPE)
		Steel		Stainless Steel Sched. No.				(a) (Square Inches)	(A) (Square Feet)		
		Iron Pipe Size	Sched. No.								
34	34.00	...	10	...	0.344	33.312	36.37	871.55	6.0524	123.65	377.67
		STD	...	...	0.375	33.250	39.61	868.31	6.0299	134.67	376.27
		XS	20	...	0.500	33.000	52.62	855.30	5.9396	178.89	370.63
		...	30	...	0.625	32.750	65.53	842.39	5.8499	222.78	365.03
		...	40	...	0.688	32.624	72.00	835.92	5.8050	244.77	362.23
36	36.00	...	10	...	0.312	35.376	34.98	982.90	6.8257	118.92	425.92
		STD	...	...	0.375	35.250	41.97	975.91	6.7771	142.68	422.89
		XS	20	...	0.500	35.000	55.76	962.11	6.6813	189.57	416.91
		...	30	...	0.625	34.750	69.46	948.42	6.5862	236.13	417.22
		...	40	...	0.750	34.500	83.06	934.82	6.4918	282.35	405.09

American Pipe Flange Dimensions
Number of Stud Bolts and Diameter in Inches
Per ANSI B16.1, B16.5, and B16.24

NOMINAL PIPE SIZE (INCHES)	ANSI CLASS* 125 (CAST IRON) OR CLASS 150 (STEEL)		ANSI CLASS† 250 (CAST IRON) OR CLASS 300 (STEEL)		ANSI CLASS 600		ANSI CLASS 900		ANSI CLASS 1500		ANSI CLASS 2500	
	No.	Dia.	No.	Dia.	No.	Dia.	No.	Dia.	No.	Dia.	No.	Dia.
1	4	0.50	4	0.62	4	0.62	4	0.88	4	0.88	4	0.88
1-1/4	4	0.50	4	0.62	4	0.62	4	0.88	4	0.88	4	1.00
1-1/2	4	0.50	4	0.75	4	0.75	4	1.00	4	1.00	4	1.12
2	4	0.62	8	0.62	8	0.62	8	0.88	8	0.88	8	1.00
2-1/2	4	0.62	8	0.75	8	0.75	8	1.00	8	1.00	8	1.12
3	4	0.62	8	0.75	8	0.75	8	0.88	8	1.12	8	1.25
4	8	0.62	8	0.75	8	0.75	8	1.12	8	1.25	8	1.50
5	8	0.75	8	0.75	8	1.00	8	1.25	8	1.50	8	1.75
6	8	0.75	12	0.75	12	1.00	12	1.12	12	1.38	8	2.00
8	8	0.75	12	0.88	12	1.12	12	1.38	12	1.62	12	2.00
10	12	0.88	16	1.00	16	1.25	16	1.38	12	1.88	12	2.50
12	12	0.88	16	1.12	20	1.25	20	1.38	16	2.00	12	2.75
14	12	1.00	20	1.12	20	1.38	20	1.50	16	2.25	...	...
16	16	1.00	20	1.25	20	1.50	20	1.62	16	2.50	...	...
18	16	1.12	24	1.25	20	1.62	20	1.88	16	2.75	...	...
20	20	1.12	24	1.25	24	1.62	20	2.00	16	3.00	...	...
24	20	1.25	24	1.50	24	1.88	20	2.50	16	3.50	...	...
30	28	1.25	28	1.75	...	...	...	...	...	...	...	...
36	32	1.50	32	2.00	...	...	...	...	...	...	...	...
42	36	1.50	36	2.00	...	...	...	...	...	...	...	...
48	44	1.50	40	2.00	...	...	...	...	...	...	...	...

* Sizes 1-inch through 12-inch also apply to ANSI Class 150 bronze flanges.
† Sizes 1-inch through 8-inch also apply to ANSI Class 300 bronze flanges.

Properties of Saturated Steam

ABSOLUTE PRESSURE		VACUUM (INCHES OF Hg)	TEMPER-ATURE t (°F)	HEAT OF THE LIQUID (BTU/LB)	LATENT HEAT OF EVAPORATION (BTU/LB)	TOTAL HEAT OF STEAM H_g (BTU/LB)	SPECIFIC VOLUME $\overline{V}$ (CU FT PER LB)
Lbs Per Sq In. P'	Inches of Hg						
0.20	0.41	29.51	53.14	21.21	1063.8	1085.0	1526.0
0.25	0.51	29.41	59.30	27.36	1060.3	1087.7	1235.3
0.30	0.61	29.31	64.47	32.52	1057.4	1090.0	1039.5
0.35	0.71	29.21	68.93	36.97	1054.9	1091.9	898.5
0.40	0.81	29.11	72.86	40.89	1052.7	1093.6	791.9
0.45	0.92	29.00	76.38	44.41	1050.7	1095.1	708.5
0.50	1.02	28.90	79.58	47.60	1048.8	1096.4	641.4
0.60	1.22	28.70	85.21	53.21	1045.7	1098.9	540.0
0.70	1.43	28.49	90.08	58.07	1042.9	1101.0	466.9
0.80	1.63	28.29	94.38	62.36	1040.4	1102.8	411.7
0.90	1.83	28.09	98.24	66.21	1038.3	1104.5	368.4
1.0	2.04	27.88	101.74	69.70	1036.3	1106.0	333.6
1.2	2.44	27.48	107.92	75.87	1032.7	1108.6	280.9
1.4	2.85	27.07	113.26	81.20	1029.6	1110.8	243.0
1.6	3.26	26.66	117.99	85.91	1026.9	1112.8	214.3
1.8	3.66	26.26	122.23	90.14	1024.5	1114.6	191.8
2.0	4.07	25.85	126.08	93.99	1022.2	1116.2	173.73
2.2	4.48	25.44	129.62	97.52	1020.2	1117.7	158.85
2.4	4.89	25.03	132.89	100.79	1018.3	1119.1	146.38
2.6	5.29	24.63	135.94	103.83	1016.5	1120.3	135.78
2.8	5.70	24.22	138.79	106.68	1014.8	1121.5	126.65
3.0	6.11	23.81	141.48	109.37	1013.2	1122.6	118.71
3.5	7.13	22.79	147.57	115.46	1009.6	1125.1	102.72
4.0	8.14	21.78	152.97	120.86	1006.4	1127.3	90.63
4.5	9.16	20.76	157.83	125.71	1003.6	1129.3	81.16
5.0	10.18	19.74	162.24	130.13	1001.0	1131.1	73.52
5.5	11.20	18.72	166.30	134.19	998.5	1132.7	67.24
6.0	12.22	17.70	170.06	137.96	996.2	1134.2	61.98
6.5	13.23	16.69	173.56	141.47	994.1	1135.6	57.50
7.0	14.25	15.67	176.85	144.76	992.1	1136.9	53.64
7.5	15.27	14.65	179.94	147.86	990.2	1138.1	50.29
8.0	16.29	13.63	182.86	150.79	988.5	1139.3	47.34
8.5	17.31	12.61	185.64	153.57	986.8	1140.4	44.73
9.0	18.32	11.60	188.28	156.22	985.2	1141.4	42.40
9.5	19.34	10.58	190.80	158.75	983.6	1142.3	40.31
10.0	20.36	9.56	193.21	161.17	982.1	1143.3	38.42
11.0	22.40	7.52	197.75	165.73	979.3	1145.0	35.14
12.0	24.43	5.49	201.96	169.96	976.6	1146.6	32.40
13.0	26.47	3.45	205.88	173.91	974.2·	1148.1	30.06
14.0	28.50	1.42	209.56	177.61	971.9	1149.5	28.04

Properties of Saturated Steam

PRESSURE (LBS PER SQ IN.)		TEMPER-ATURE t (°F)	HEAT OF THE LIQUID (BTU/LB)	LATENT HEAT OF EVAPORATION (BTU/LB)	TOTAL HEAT OF STEAM H_g (BTU/LB)	SPECIFIC VOLUME $\overline{V}$ (CU FT PER LB)
Absolute P'	Gauge P					
14.696	0.0	212.00	180.07	970.3	1150.4	26.80
15.0	0.3	213.03	181.11	969.7	1150.8	26.29
16.0	1.3	216.32	184.42	967.6	1152.0	24.75
17.0	2.3	219.44	187.56	965.5	1153.1	23.39
18.0	3.3	222.41	190.56	963.6	1154.2	22.17
19.0	4.3	225.24	193.42	961.9	1155.3	21.08
20.0	5.3	227.96	196.16	960.1	1156.3	20.089
21.0	6.3	230.57	198.79	958.4	1157.2	19.192
22.0	7.3	233.07	201.33	956.8	1158.1	18.375
23.0	8.3	235.49	203.78	955.2	1159.0	17.627
24.0	9.3	237.82	206.14	953.7	1159.8	16.938
25.0	10.3	240.07	208.42	952.1	1160.6	16.303
26.0	11.3	242.25	210.62	950.7	1161.3	15.715
27.0	12.3	244.36	212.75	949.3	1162.0	15.170
28.0	13.3	246.41	214.83	947.9	1162.7	14.663
29.0	14.3	248.40	216.86	946.5	1163.4	14.189
30.0	15.3	250.33	218.82	945.3	1164.1	13.746
31.0	16.3	252.22	220.73	944.0	1164.7	13.330
32.0	17.3	254.05	222.59	942.8	1165.4	12.940
33.0	18.3	255.84	224.41	941.6	1166.0	12.572
34.0	19.3	257.58	226.18	940.3	1166.5	12.226
35.0	20.3	259.28	227.91	939.2	1167.1	11.898
36.0	21.3	260.95	229.60	938.0	1167.6	11.588
37.0	22.3	262.57	231.26	936.9	1168.2	11.294
38.0	23.3	264.16	232.89	935.8	1168.7	11.015
39.0	24.3	265.72	234.48	934.7	1169.2	10.750
40.0	25.3	267.25	236.03	933.7	1169.7	10.498
41.0	26.3	268.74	237.55	932.6	1170.2	10.258
42.0	27.3	270.21	239.04	931.6	1170.7	10.029
43.0	28.3	271.64	240.51	930.6	1171.1	9.810
44.0	29.3	273.05	241.95	929.6	1171.6	9.601
45.0	30.3	274.44	243.36	928.6	1172.0	9.401
46.0	31.3	275.80	244.75	927.7	1172.4	9.209
47.0	32.3	277.13	246.12	926.7	1172.9	9.025
48.0	33.3	278.45	247.47	925.8	1173.3	8.848
49.0	34.3	279.74	248.79	924.9	1173.7	8.678
50.0	35.3	281.01	250.09	924.0	1174.1	8.515
51.0	36.3	282.26	251.37	923.0	1174.4	8.359
52.0	37.3	283.49	252.63	922.2	1174.8	8.208
53.0	38.3	284.70	253.87	921.3	1175.2	8.062
54.0	39.3	285.90	255.09	920.5	1175.6	7.922

- Continued -

Properties of Saturated Steam (Continued)

PRESSURE (LBS PER SQ IN.)		TEMPER-ATURE t (°F)	HEAT OF THE LIQUID (BTU/LB)	LATENT HEAT OF EVAPORATION (BTU/LB)	TOTAL HEAT OF STEAM H$_g$ (BTU/LB)	SPECIFIC VOLUME $\overline{V}$ (CU FT PER LB)
Absolute P′	Gauge P					
55.0	40.3	287.07	256.30	919.6	1175.9	7.787
56.0	41.3	288.23	257.50	918.8	1176.3	7.656
57.0	42.3	289.37	258.67	917.9	1176.6	7.529
58.0	43.3	290.50	259.82	917.1	1176.9	7.407
59.0	44.3	291.61	260.96	916.3	1177.3	7.289
60.0	45.3	292.71	262.09	915.5	1177.6	7.175
61.0	46.3	293.79	263.20	914.7	1177.9	7.064
62.0	47.3	294.85	264.30	913.9	1178.2	6.957
63.0	48.3	295.90	265.38	913.1	1178.5	6.853
64.0	49.3	296.94	266.45	912.3	1178.8	6.752
65.0	50.3	297.97	267.50	911.6	1179.1	6.655
66.0	51.3	298.99	268.55	910.8	1179.4	6.560
67.0	52.3	299.99	269.58	910.1	1179.7	6.468
68.0	53.3	300.98	270.60	909.4	1180.0	6.378
69.0	54.3	301.96	291.61	908.7	1180.3	6.291
70.0	55.3	302.92	272.61	907.9	1180.6	6.206
71.0	56.3	303.88	273.60	907.2	1180.8	6.124
72.0	57.3	304.83	274.57	906.5	1181.1	6.044
73.0	58.3	305.76	275.54	905.8	1181.3	5.966
74.0	59.3	306.68	276.49	905.1	1181.6	5.890
75.0	60.3	307.60	277.43	904.5	1181.9	5.816
76.0	61.3	308.50	278.37	903.7	1182.1	5.743
77.0	62.3	309.40	279.30	903.1	1182.4	5.673
78.0	63.3	310.29	280.21	902.4	1182.6	5.604
79.0	64.3	311.16	281.12	901.7	1182.8	5.537
80.0	65.3	312.03	282.02	901.1	1183.1	5.472
81.0	66.3	312.89	282.91	900.4	1183.3	5.408
82.0	67.3	313.74	283.79	899.7	1183.5	5.346
83.0	68.3	314.59	284.66	899.1	1183.8	5.285
84.0	69.3	315.42	285.53	898.5	1184.0	5.226
85.0	70.3	316.25	286.39	897.8	1184.2	5.168
86.0	71.3	317.07	287.24	897.2	1184.4	5.111
87.0	72.3	317.88	288.08	896.5	1184.6	5.055
88.0	73.3	318.68	288.91	895.9	1184.8	5.001
89.0	74.3	319.48	289.74	895.3	1185.1	4.948
90.0	75.3	320.27	290.56	894.7	1185.3	4.896
91.0	76.3	321.06	291.38	894.1	1185.5	4.845
92.0	77.3	321.83	292.18	893.5	1185.7	4.796
93.0	78.3	322.60	292.98	892.9	1185.9	4.747
94.0	79.3	323.36	293.78	892.3	1186.1	4.699
95.0	80.3	324.12	294.56	891.7	1186.2	4.652
96.0	81.3	324.87	295.34	891.1	1186.4	4.606
97.0	82.3	325.61	296.12	890.5	1186.6	4.561
98.0	83.3	326.35	296.89	889.9	1186.8	4.517
99.0	84.3	327.08	297.65	889.4	1187.0	4.474

- Continued -

Properties of Saturated Steam (Continued)

PRESSURE (LBS PER SQ IN.)		TEMPER- ATURE t (°F)	HEAT OF THE LIQUID (BTU/LB)	LATENT HEAT OF EVAPORATION (BTU/LB)	TOTAL HEAT OF STEAM H_g (BTU/LB)	SPECIFIC VOLUME V (CU FT PER LB)
Absolute P'	Gauge P					
100.0	85.3	327.81	298.40	888.8	1187.2	4.432
101.0	86.3	328.53	299.15	888.2	1187.4	4.391
102.0	87.3	329.25	299.90	887.6	1187.5	4.350
103.0	88.3	329.96	300.64	887.1	1187.7	4.310
104.0	89.3	330.66	301.37	886.5	1187.9	4.271
105.0	90.3	331.36	302.10	886.0	1188.1	4.232
106.0	91.3	332.05	302.82	885.4	1188.2	4.194
107.0	92.3	332.74	303.54	884.9	1188.4	4.157
108.0	93.3	333.42	304.26	884.3	1188.6	4.120
109.0	94.3	334.10	304.97	883.7	1188.7	4.084
110.0	95.3	334.77	305.66	883.2	1188.9	4.049
111.0	96.3	335.44	306.37	882.6	1189.0	4.015
112.0	97.3	336.11	307.06	882.1	1189.2	3.981
113.0	98.3	336.77	307.75	881.6	1189.4	3.947
114.0	99.3	337.42	308.43	881.1	1189.5	3.914
115.0	100.3	338.07	309.11	880.6	1189.7	3.882
116.0	101.3	338.72	309.79	880.0	1189.8	3.850
117.0	102.3	339.36	310.46	879.5	1190.0	3.819
118.0	103.3	339.99	311.12	879.0	1190.1	3.788
119.0	104.3	340.62	311.78	878.4	1190.2	3.758
120.0	105.3	341.25	312.44	877.9	1190.4	3.728
121.0	106.3	341.88	313.10	877.4	1190.5	3.699
122.0	107.3	342.50	313.75	876.9	1190.7	3.670
123.0	108.3	343.11	314.40	876.4	1190.8	3.642
124.0	109.3	343.72	315.04	875.9	1190.9	3.614
125.0	110.3	344.33	315.68	875.4	1191.1	3.587
126.0	111.3	344.94	316.31	874.9	1191.2	3.560
127.0	112.3	345.54	316.94	874.4	1191.3	3.533
128.0	113.3	346.13	317.57	873.9	1191.5	3.507
129.0	114.3	346.73	318.19	873.4	1191.6	3.481
130.0	115.3	347.32	318.81	872.9	1191.7	3.455
131.0	116.3	347.90	319.43	872.5	1191.9	3.430
132.0	117.3	348.48	320.04	872.0	1192.0	3.405
133.0	118.3	349.06	320.65	871.5	1192.1	3.381
134.0	119.3	349.64	321.25	871.0	1192.2	3.357
135.0	120.3	350.21	321.85	870.6	1192.4	3.333
136.0	121.3	350.78	322.45	870.1	1192.5	3.310
137.0	122.3	351.35	323.05	869.6	1192.6	3.287
138.0	123.3	351.91	323.64	869.1	1192.7	3.264
139.0	124.3	352.47	324.23	868.7	1192.9	3.242
140.0	125.3	353.02	324.82	868.2	1193.0	3.220
141.0	126.3	353.57	325.40	867.7	1193.1	3.198
142.0	127.3	354.12	325.98	867.2	1193.2	3.177
143.0	128.3	354.67	326.56	866.7	1193.3	3.155
144.0	129.3	355.21	327.13	866.3	1193.4	3.134

- Continued -

Properties of Saturated Steam (Continued)

PRESSURE (LBS PER SQ IN.)		TEMPER-ATURE t (°F)	HEAT OF THE LIQUID (BTU/LB)	LATENT HEAT OF EVAPORATION (BTU/LB)	TOTAL HEAT OF STEAM H_g (BTU/LB)	SPECIFIC VOLUME V (CU FT PER LB)
Absolute P'	Gauge P					
145.0	130.3	355.76	327.70	865.8	1193.5	3.114
146.0	131.3	356.29	328.27	865.3	1193.6	3.094
147.0	132.3	356.83	328.83	864.9	1193.8	3.074
148.0	133.3	357.36	329.39	864.5	1193.9	3.054
149.0	134.3	357.89	329.95	864.0	1194.0	3.034
150.0	135.3	358.42	330.51	863.6	1194.1	3.015
152.0	137.3	359.46	331.61	862.7	1194.3	2.977
154.0	139.3	360.49	332.70	861.8	1194.5	2.940
156.0	141.3	361.52	333.79	860.9	1194.7	2.904
158.0	143.3	362.53	334.86	860.0	1194.9	2.869
160.0	145.3	363.53	335.93	859.2	1195.1	2.834
162.0	147.3	364.53	336.98	858.3	1195.3	2.801
164.0	149.3	365.51	338.02	857.5	1195.5	2.768
166.0	151.3	366.48	339.05	856.6	1195.7	2.736
168.0	153.3	367.45	340.07	855.7	1195.8	2.705
170.0	155.3	368.41	341.09	854.9	1196.0	2.675
172.0	157.3	369.35	342.10	854.1	1196.2	2.645
174.0	159.3	370.29	343.10	853.3	1196.4	2.616
176.0	161.3	371.22	344.09	852.4	1196.5	2.587
178.0	163.3	372.14	345.06	851.6	1196.7	2.559
180.0	165.3	373.06	346.03	850.8	1196.9	2.532
182.0	167.3	373.96	347.00	850.0	1197.0	2.505
184.0	169.3	374.86	347.96	849.2	1197.2	2.479
186.0	171.3	375.75	348.92	848.4	1197.3	2.454
188.0	173.3	376.64	349.86	847.6	1197.5	2.429
190.0	175.3	377.51	350.79	846.8	1197.6	2.404
192.0	177.3	378.38	351.72	846.1	1197.8	2.380
194.0	179.3	379.24	352.64	845.3	1197.9	2.356
196.0	181.3	380.10	353.55	844.5	1198.1	2.333
198.0	183.3	380.95	354.46	843.7	1198.2	2.310
200.0	185.3	381.79	355.36	843.0	1198.4	2.288
205.0	190.3	383.86	357.58	841.1	1198.7	2.234
210.0	195.3	385.90	359.77	839.2	1199.0	2.183
215.0	200.3	387.89	361.91	837.4	1199.3	2.134
220.0	205.3	389.86	364.02	835.6	1199.6	2.087
225.0	210.3	391.79	366.09	833.8	1199.9	2.0422
230.0	215.3	393.68	368.13	832.0	1200.1	1.9992
235.0	220.3	395.54	370.14	830.3	1200.4	1.9579
240.0	225.3	397.37	372.12	828.5	1200.6	1.9183
245.0	230.3	399.18	374.08	826.8	1200.9	1.8803
250.0	235.3	400.95	376.00	825.1	1201.1	1.8438
255.0	240.3	402.70	377.89	823.4	1201.3	1.8086
260.0	245.3	404.42	379.76	821.8	1201.5	1.7748
265.0	250.3	406.11	381.60	820.1	1201.7	1.7422
270.0	255.3	407.78	383.42	818.5	1201.9	1.7107

- Continued -

Properties of Saturated Steam (Continued)

PRESSURE (LBS PER SQ IN.)		TEMPER-ATURE t (°F)	HEAT OF THE LIQUID (BTU/LB)	LATENT HEAT OF EVAPORATION (BTU/LB)	TOTAL HEAT OF STEAM H_g (BTU/LB)	SPECIFIC VOLUME ∇ (CU FT PER LB)
Absolute P'	Gauge P					
275.0	260.3	409.43	385.21	816.9	1202.1	1.6804
280.0	265.3	411.05	386.98	815.3	1202.3	1.6511
285.0	270.3	412.65	388.73	813.7	1202.4	1.6228
290.0	275.3	414.23	390.46	812.1	1202.6	1.5954
295.0	280.3	415.79	392.16	810.5	1202.7	1.5689
300.0	285.3	417.33	393.84	809.0	1202.8	1.5433
320.0	305.3	423.29	400.39	803.0	1203.4	1.4485
340.0	325.3	428.97	406.66	797.1	1203.7	1.3645
360.0	345.3	434.40	412.67	791.4	1204.1	1.2895
380.0	365.3	439.60	418.45	785.8	1204.3	1.2222
400.0	385.3	444.59	424.0	780.5	1204.5	1.1613
420.0	405.3	449.39	429.4	775.2	1204.6	1.1061
440.0	425.3	454.02	434.6	770.0	1204.6	1.0556
460.0	445.3	458.50	439.7	764.9	1204.6	1.0094
480.0	465.3	462.82	444.6	759.9	1204.5	0.9670
500.0	485.3	467.01	449.4	755.0	1204.4	0.9278
520.0	505.3	471.07	454.1	750.1	1204.2	0.8915
540.0	525.3	475.01	458.6	745.4	1204.0	0.8578
560.0	545.3	478.85	463.0	740.8	1203.8	0.8265
580.0	565.3	482.58	467.4	736.1	1203.5	0.7973
600.0	585.3	486.21	471.6	731.6	1203.2	0.7698
620.0	605.3	489.75	475.7	727.2	1202.9	0.7440
640.0	625.3	493.21	479.8	722.7	1202.5	0.7198
660.0	645.3	496.58	483.8	718.3	1202.1	0.6971
680.0	665.3	499.88	487.7	714.0	1201.7	0.6757
700.0	685.3	503.10	491.5	709.7	1201.2	0.6554
720.0	705.3	506.25	495.3	705.4	1200.7	0.6362
740.0	725.3	509.34	499.0	701.2	1200.2	0.6180
760.0	745.3	512.36	502.6	697.1	1199.7	0.6007
780.0	765.3	515.33	506.2	692.9	1199.1	0.5843
800.0	785.3	518.23	509.7	688.9	1198.6	0.5687
820.0	805.3	521.08	513.2	684.8	1198.0	0.5538
840.0	825.3	523.88	516.6	680.8	1197.4	0.5396
860.0	845.3	526.63	520.0	676.8	1196.8	0.5260
880.0	865.3	529.33	523.3	672.8	1196.1	0.5130
900.0	885.3	531.98	526.6	668.8	1195.4	0.5006
920.0	905.3	534.59	529.8	664.9	1194.7	0.4886
940.0	925.3	537.16	533.0	661.0	1194.0	0.4772
960.0	945.3	539.68	536.2	657.1	1193.3	0.4663
980.0	965.3	542.17	539.3	653.3	1192.6	0.4557
1000.0	985.3	544.61	542.4	649.4	1191.8	0.4456
1050.0	1035.3	550.57	550.0	639.9	1189.9	0.4218
1100.0	1085.3	556.31	557.4	630.4	1187.8	0.4001
1150.0	1135.3	561.86	564.6	621.0	1185.6	0.3802
1200.0	1185.3	567.22	571.7	611.7	1183.4	0.3619

- Continued -

Properties of Saturated Steam (Continued)

PRESSURE (LBS PER SQ IN.)		TEMPER-ATURE t (°F)	HEAT OF THE LIQUID (BTU/LB)	LATENT HEAT OF EVAPORATION (BTU/LB)	TOTAL HEAT OF STEAM H_g (BTU/LB)	SPECIFIC VOLUME $\bar{V}$ (CU FT PER LB)
Absolute P′	Gauge P					
1250.0	1235.3	572.42	578.6	602.4	1181.0	0.3450
1300.0	1285.3	577.46	585.4	593.2	1178.6	0.3293
1350.0	1335.3	582.35	592.1	584.0	1176.1	0.3148
1400.0	1385.3	587.10	598.7	574.7	1173.4	0.3012
1450.0	1435.3	591.73	605.2	565.5	1170.7	0.2884
1500.0	1485.3	596.23	611.6	556.3	1167.9	0.2765
1600.0	1585.3	604.90	624.1	538.0	1162.1	0.2548
1700.0	1685.3	613.15	636.3	519.6	1155.9	0.2354
1800.0	1785.3	621.03	648.3	501.1	1149.4	0.2179
1900.0	1885.3	628.58	660.1	482.4	1142.4	0.2021
2000.0	1985.3	635.82	671.7	463.4	1135.1	0.1878
2100.0	2085.3	642.77	683.3	444.1	1127.4	0.1746
2200.0	2185.3	649.46	694.8	424.4	1119.2	0.1625
2300.0	2285.3	655.91	706.5	403.9	1110.4	0.1513
2400.0	2385.3	662.12	718.4	382.7	1101.1	0.1407
2500.0	2485.3	668.13	730.6	360.5	1091.1	0.1307
2600.0	2585.3	673.94	743.0	337.2	1080.2	0.1213
2700.0	2685.3	679.55	756.2	312.1	1068.3	0.1123
2800.0	2785.3	684.99	770.1	284.7	1054.8	0.1035
2900.0	2885.3	690.26	785.4	253.6	1039.0	0.0947
3000.0	2985.3	695.36	802.5	217.8	1020.3	0.0858
3100.0	3085.3	700.31	825.0	168.1	993.1	0.0753
3200.0	3185.3	705.11	872.4	62.0	934.4	0.0580
3206.2	3191.5	705.40	902.7	0.0	902.7	0.0503

Properties of Superheated Steam

$\bar{V}$ = specific volume, cubic feet per pound
h_g = total heat of steam, Btu per pound

PRESSURE (LBS PER SQ IN.) Absolute P'	Gauge P	SAT. TEMP. t		TOTAL TEMPERATURE—DEGREES FAHRENHEIT (t)										
				360°	400°	440°	480°	500°	600°	700°	800°	900°	1000°	1200°
14.696	0.0	212.00	$\bar{V}$	33.03	34.68	36.32	37.96	38.78	42.86	46.94	51.00	55.07	59.13	67.25
			h_g	1221.1	1239.9	1258.8	1277.6	1287.1	1334.8	1383.2	1432.3	1482.3	1533.1	1637.5
20.0	5.3	227.96	$\bar{V}$	24.21	25.43	26.65	27.86	28.46	31.47	34.47	37.46	40.45	43.44	49.41
			h_g	1220.3	1239.2	1258.2	1277.1	1286.6	1334.4	1382.9	1432.1	1482.1	1533.0	1637.4
30.0	15.3	250.33	$\bar{V}$	16.072	16.897	17.714	18.528	18.933	20.95	22.96	24.96	26.95	28.95	32.93
			h_g	1218.6	1237.9	1257.0	1276.2	1285.7	1333.8	1382.4	1431.7	1481.8	1532.7	1637.2
40.0	25.3	267.25	$\bar{V}$	12.001	12.628	13.247	13.862	14.168	15.688	17.198	18.702	20.20	21.70	24.69
			h_g	1216.9	1236.5	1255.9	1275.2	1284.8	1333.1	1381.9	1431.3	1481.4	1532.4	1637.0
50.0	35.3	281.01	$\bar{V}$	9.557	10.065	10.567	11.062	11.309	12.532	13.744	14.950	16.152	17.352	19.747
			h_g	1215.2	1235.1	1254.7	1274.2	1283.9	1332.5	1381.4	1430.9	1481.1	1532.1	1636.8
60.0	45.3	292.71	$\bar{V}$	7.927	8.357	8.779	9.196	9.403	10.427	11.441	12.449	13.452	14.454	16.451
			h_g	1213.4	1233.6	1253.5	1273.2	1283.0	1331.8	1380.9	1430.5	1480.8	1531.9	1636.6
70.0	55.3	302.92	$\bar{V}$	6.762	7.136	7.502	7.863	8.041	8.924	9.796	10.662	11.524	12.383	14.097
			h_g	1211.5	1232.1	1252.3	1272.2	1282.0	1331.1	1380.4	1430.1	1480.5	1531.6	1636.3
80.0	65.3	312.03	$\bar{V}$	5.888	6.220	6.544	6.862	7.020	7.797	8.562	9.322	10.077	10.830	12.332
			h_g	1209.7	1230.7	1251.1	1271.1	1281.1	1330.5	1379.9	1429.7	1480.1	1531.3	1636.2
90.0	75.3	320.27	$\bar{V}$	5.208	5.508	5.799	6.084	6.225	6.920	7.603	8.279	8.952	9.623	10.959
			h_g	1207.7	1229.1	1249.8	1270.1	1280.1	1329.8	1379.4	1429.3	1479.8	1531.0	1635.9
100.0	85.3	327.81	$\bar{V}$	4.663	4.937	5.202	5.462	5.589	6.218	6.835	7.446	8.052	8.656	9.860
			h_g	1205.7	1227.6	1248.6	1269.0	1279.1	1329.1	1378.9	1428.9	1479.5	1530.8	1635.7
120.0	105.3	341.25	$\bar{V}$	3.844	4.081	4.307	4.527	4.636	5.165	5.683	6.195	6.702	7.207	8.212
			h_g	1201.6	1224.4	1246.0	1266.9	1277.2	1327.7	1377.8	1428.1	1478.8	1530.2	1635.3

- Continued -

p (psia)	p (psig)	t												
140.0	125.3	353.02	$\bar{v}$	3.258	3.468	3.667	3.860	3.954	4.413	4.861	5.301	5.738	6.172	7.035
			h_g	1197.3	1221.1	1243.3	1264.7	1275.2	1326.4	1376.8	1427.3	1478.2	1529.7	1634.9
160.0	145.3	363.53	$\bar{v}$	...	3.008	3.187	3.359	3.443	3.849	4.244	4.631	5.015	5.396	6.152
			h_g	...	1217.6	1240.6	1262.4	1273.1	1325.0	1375.7	1426.4	1477.5	1529.1	1634.5
180.0	165.3	373.06	$\bar{v}$	...	2.649	2.813	2.969	3.044	3.411	3.764	4.110	4.452	4.792	5.466
			h_g	...	1214.0	1237.8	1260.2	1271.0	1323.5	1374.7	1425.6	1476.8	1528.6	1634.1
200.0	185.3	381.79	$\bar{v}$	...	2.361	2.513	2.656	2.726	3.060	3.380	3.693	4.002	4.309	4.917
			h_g	...	1210.3	1234.9	1257.8	1268.9	1322.1	1373.6	1424.8	1476.2	1528.0	1633.7
220.0	205.3	389.86	$\bar{v}$	...	2.125	2.267	2.400	2.465	2.772	3.066	3.352	3.634	3.913	4.467
			h_g	...	1206.5	1231.9	1255.4	1266.7	1320.7	1372.6	1424.0	1475.5	1527.5	1633.3
240.0	225.3	397.37	$\bar{v}$	...	1.9276	2.062	2.187	2.247	2.533	2.804	3.068	3.327	3.584	4.093
			h_g	...	1202.5	1228.8	1253.0	1264.5	1319.2	1371.5	1423.2	1474.8	1526.9	1632.9
260.0	245.3	404.42	$\bar{v}$	...	...	1.8882	2.006	2.063	2.330	2.582	2.827	3.067	3.305	3.776
			h_g	...	...	1225.7	1250.5	1262.3	1317.7	1370.4	1422.3	1474.2	1526.3	1632.5
280.0	265.3	411.05	$\bar{v}$	...	...	1.7388	1.8512	1.9047	2.156	2.392	2.621	2.845	3.066	3.504
			h_g	...	...	1222.4	1247.9	1260.0	1316.2	1369.4	1421.5	1473.5	1525.8	1632.1
300.0	285.3	417.33	$\bar{v}$	...	...	1.6090	1.7165	1.7675	2.005	2.227	2.442	2.652	2.859	3.269
			h_g	...	...	1219.1	1245.3	1257.6	1314.7	1368.3	1420.6	1472.8	1525.2	1631.7
320.0	305.3	423.29	$\bar{v}$	...	...	1.4950	1.5985	1.6472	1.8734	2.083	2.285	2.483	2.678	3.063
			h_g	...	...	1215.6	1242.6	1255.2	1313.2	1367.2	1419.8	1472.1	1524.7	1631.3
340.0	325.3	428.97	$\bar{v}$	...	...	1.3941	1.4941	1.5410	1.7569	1.9562	2.147	2.334	2.518	2.881
			h_g	...	...	1212.1	1239.9	1252.8	1311.6	1366.1	1419.0	1471.5	1524.1	1630.9
360.0	345.3	434.40	$\bar{v}$	...	...	1.3041	1.4012	1.4464	1.6533	1.8431	2.025	2.202	2.376	2.719
			h_g	...	...	1208.4	1237.1	1250.3	1310.1	1365.0	1418.1	1470.8	1523.5	1630.5

- Continued -

Properties of Superheated Steam (Continued)

$\overline{V}$ = specific volume, cubic feet per pound
h_g = total heat of steam, Btu per pound

| PRESSURE (LBS PER SQ IN.) | | SAT. TEMP. | | TOTAL TEMPERATURE—DEGREES FAHRENHEIT (t) | | | | | | | | | | |
Absolute P'	Gauge P	t		500°	540°	600°	640°	660°	700°	740°	800°	900°	1000°	1200°
380.0	365.3	439.60	$\overline{V}$	1.3616	1.4444	1.5605	1.6345	1.6707	1.7419	1.8118	1.9149	2.083	2.249	2.575
			h_g	1247.7	1273.1	1308.5	1331.0	1342.0	1363.8	1385.3	1417.3	1470.1	1523.0	1630.0
400.0	385.3	444.59	$\overline{V}$	1.2851	1.3652	1.4770	1.5480	1.5827	1.6508	1.7177	1.8161	1.9767	2.134	2.445
			h_g	1245.1	1271.0	1306.9	1329.6	1340.8	1362.7	1384.3	1416.4	1469.4	1522.4	1629.6
420.0	405.3	449.39	$\overline{V}$	1.2158	1.2935	1.4014	1.4697	1.5030	1.5684	1.6324	1.7267	1.8802	2.031	2.327
			h_g	1242.5	1268.9	1305.3	1328.3	1339.5	1361.6	1383.3	1415.5	1468.7	1521.9	1629.2
440.0	425.3	454.02	$\overline{V}$	1.1526	1.2282	1.3327	1.3984	1.4306	1.4934	1.5549	1.6454	1.7925	1.9368	2.220
			h_g	1239.8	1266.7	1303.6	1326.9	1338.2	1360.4	1382.3	1414.7	1468.1	1521.3	1628.8
460.0	445.3	458.50	$\overline{V}$	1.0948	1.1685	1.2698	1.3334	1.3644	1.4250	1.4842	1.5711	1.7124	1.8508	2.122
			h_g	1237.0	1264.5	1302.0	1325.4	1336.9	1359.3	1381.3	1413.8	1467.4	1520.7	1628.4
480.0	465.3	462.82	$\overline{V}$	1.0417	1.1138	1.2122	1.2737	1.3038	1.3622	1.4193	1.5031	1.6390	1.7720	2.033
			h_g	1234.2	1262.3	1300.3	1324.0	1335.6	1358.2	1380.3	1412.9	1466.7	1520.2	1628.0
500.0	485.3	467.01	$\overline{V}$	0.9927	1.0633	1.1591	1.2188	1.2478	1.3044	1.3596	1.4405	1.5715	1.6996	1.9504
			h_g	1231.3	1260.0	1298.6	1322.6	1334.2	1357.0	1379.3	1412.1	1466.0	1519.6	1627.6
520.0	505.3	471.07	$\overline{V}$	0.9473	1.0166	1.1101	1.1681	1.1962	1.2511	1.3045	1.3826	1.5091	1.6326	1.8743
			h_g	1228.3	1257.7	1296.9	1321.1	1332.9	1355.8	1378.2	1411.2	1465.3	1519.0	1627.2
540.0	525.3	475.01	$\overline{V}$	0.9052	0.9733	1.0646	1.1211	1.1485	1.2017	1.2535	1.3291	1.4514	1.5707	1.8039
			h_g	1225.3	1255.4	1295.2	1319.7	1331.5	1354.6	1377.2	1410.3	1464.6	1518.5	1626.8
560.0	545.3	478.85	$\overline{V}$	0.8659	0.9330	1.0224	1.0775	1.1041	1.1558	1.2060	1.2794	1.3978	1.5132	1.7385
			h_g	1222.2	1253.0	1293.4	1318.2	1330.2	1353.5	1376.1	1409.4	1463.9	1517.9	1626.4
580.0	565.3	482.58	$\overline{V}$	0.8291	0.8954	0.9830	1.0368	1.0627	1.1131	1.1619	1.2331	1.3479	1.4596	1.6776
			h_g	1219.0	1250.5	1291.7	1316.7	1328.8	1352.3	1375.1	1408.6	1463.2	1517.3	1626.0

- Continued -

600.0	585.3	486.21	$\bar{v}$	0.7947	0.8602	0.9463	0.9988	1.0241	1.0732	1.1207	1.1899	1.3013	1.4096	1.6208
			h_g	1215.7	1248.1	1289.9	1315.2	1327.4	1351.1	1374.0	1407.7	1462.5	1516.7	1625.5
620.0	605.3	489.75	$\bar{v}$	0.7624	0.8272	0.9118	0.9633	0.9880	1.0358	1.0821	1.1494	1.2577	1.3628	1.5676
			h_g	1212.4	1245.5	1288.1	1313.7	1326.0	1349.9	1373.0	1406.8	1461.8	1516.2	1625.1
640.0	625.3	493.21	$\bar{v}$	0.7319	0.7963	0.8795	0.9299	0.9541	1.0008	1.0459	1.1115	1.2168	1.3190	1.5178
			h_g	1209.0	1243.0	1286.2	1312.2	1324.6	1348.6	1371.9	1405.9	1461.1	1515.6	1624.7
660.0	645.3	496.58	$\bar{v}$	0.7032	0.7670	0.8491	0.8985	0.9222	0.9679	1.0119	1.0759	1.1784	1.2778	1.4709
			h_g	1205.4	1240.4	1284.4	1310.6	1323.2	1347.4	1370.8	1405.0	1460.4	1515.0	1624.3
680.0	665.3	499.88	$\bar{v}$	0.6759	0.7395	0.8205	0.8690	0.8922	0.9369	0.9800	1.0424	1.1423	1.2390	1.4269
			h_g	1201.8	1237.7	1282.5	1309.1	1321.7	1346.2	1369.8	1404.1	1459.7	1514.5	1623.9
700.0	685.3	503.10	$\bar{v}$	. . .	0.7134	0.7934	0.8411	0.8639	0.9077	0.9498	1.0108	1.1082	1.2024	1.3853
			h_g	. . .	1235.0	1280.6	1307.5	1320.3	1345.0	1368.7	1403.2	1459.0	1513.9	1623.5
750.0	735.3	510.86	$\bar{v}$	. . .	0.6540	0.7319	0.7778	0.7996	0.8414	0.8813	0.9391	1.0310	1.1196	1.2912
			h_g	. . .	1227.9	1275.7	1303.5	1316.6	1341.8	1366.0	1400.9	1457.2	1512.4	1622.4
800.0	785.3	518.23	$\bar{v}$	. . .	0.6015	0.6779	0.7223	0.7433	0.7833	0.8215	0.8763	0.9633	1.0470	1.2088
			h_g	. . .	1220.5	1270.7	1299.4	1312.9	1338.6	1363.2	1398.6	1455.4	1511.0	1621.4
850.0	835.3	525.26	$\bar{v}$	. . .	0.5546	0.6301	0.6732	0.6934	0.7320	0.7685	0.8209	0.9037	0.9830	1.1360
			h_g	. . .	1212.7	1265.5	1295.2	1309.0	1335.4	1360.4	1396.3	1453.6	1509.5	1620.4
900.0	885.3	531.98	$\bar{v}$	. . .	0.5124	0.5873	0.6294	0.6491	0.6863	0.7215	0.7716	0.8506	0.9262	1.0714
			h_g	. . .	1204.4	1260.1	1290.9	1305.1	1332.1	1357.5	1393.9	1451.8	1508.1	1619.3
950.0	935.3	538.42	$\bar{v}$	. . .	0.4740	0.5489	0.5901	0.6092	0.6453	0.6793	0.7275	0.8031	0.8753	1.0136
			h_g	. . .	1195.5	1254.6	1286.4	1301.1	1328.7	1354.7	1391.6	1450.0	1506.6	1618.3
1000.0	985.3	544.61	$\bar{v}$	. . .	. . .	0.5140	0.5546	0.5733	0.6084	0.6413	0.6878	0.7604	0.8294	0.9615
			h_g	. . .	. . .	1248.8	1281.9	1297.0	1325.3	1351.7	1389.2	1448.2	1505.1	1617.3

- Continued -

Properties of Superheated Steam (Continued)

$\overline{V}$ = specific volume, cubic feet per pound

h_g = total heat of steam, Btu per pound

PRESSURE (LBS PER SQ IN.)		SAT. TEMP.		TOTAL TEMPERATURE—DEGREES FAHRENHEIT (t)										
Absolute P'	Gauge P	t		660°	700°	740°	760°	780°	800°	860°	900°	1000°	1100°	1200°
1100.0	1085.3	556.31	$\overline{V}$	0.5110	0.5445	0.5755	0.5904	0.6049	0.6191	0.6601	0.6866	0.7503	0.8117	0.8716
			h_g	1288.5	1318.5	1345.8	1358.9	1371.7	1384.3	1420.8	1444.5	1502.2	1558.8	1615.2
1200.0	1185.3	567.22	$\overline{V}$	0.4586	0.4909	0.5206	0.5347	0.5484	0.5617	0.6003	0.6250	0.6843	0.7412	0.7967
			h_g	1279.6	1311.0	1339.6	1353.2	1366.4	1379.3	1416.7	1440.7	1499.2	1556.4	1613.1
1300.0	1285.3	577.46	$\overline{V}$	0.4139	0.4454	0.4739	0.4874	0.5004	0.5131	0.5496	0.5728	0.6284	0.6816	0.7333
			h_g	1270.2	1303.4	1333.3	1347.3	1361.0	1374.3	1412.5	1437.0	1496.2	1553.9	1611.0
1400.0	1385.3	587.10	$\overline{V}$	0.3753	0.4062	0.4338	0.4468	0.4593	0.4714	0.5061	0.5281	0.5805	0.6305	0.6789
			h_g	1260.3	1295.5	1326.7	1341.3	1355.4	1369.1	1408.2	1433.1	1493.2	1551.4	1608.9
1500.0	1485.3	596.23	$\overline{V}$	0.3413	0.3719	0.3989	0.4114	0.4235	0.4352	0.4684	0.4893	0.5390	0.5862	0.6318
			h_g	1249.8	1287.2	1320.0	1335.2	1349.7	1363.8	1403.9	1429.3	1490.1	1548.9	1606.8
1600.0	1585.3	604.90	$\overline{V}$	0.3112	0.3417	0.3682	0.3804	0.3921	0.4034	0.4353	0.4553	0.5027	0.5474	0.5906
			h_g	1238.7	1278.7	1313.0	1328.8	1343.9	1358.4	1399.5	1425.3	1487.0	1546.4	1604.6
1700.0	1685.3	613.15	$\overline{V}$	0.2842	0.3148	0.3410	0.3529	0.3643	0.3753	0.4061	0.4253	0.4706	0.5132	0.5542
			h_g	1226.8	1269.7	1305.8	1322.3	1337.9	1352.9	1395.0	1421.4	1484.0	1543.8	1602.5
1800.0	1785.3	621.03	$\overline{V}$	0.2597	0.2907	0.3166	0.3284	0.3395	0.3502	0.3801	0.3986	0.4421	0.4828	0.5218
			h_g	1214.0	1260.3	1298.4	1315.5	1331.8	1347.2	1390.4	1417.4	1480.8	1541.3	1600.4
1900.0	1885.3	628.58	$\overline{V}$	0.2371	0.2688	0.2947	0.3063	0.3173	0.3277	0.3568	0.3747	0.4165	0.4556	0.4929
			h_g	1200.2	1250.4	1290.6	1308.6	1325.4	1341.5	1385.8	1413.3	1477.7	1538.8	1598.2
2000.0	1985.3	635.82	$\overline{V}$	0.2161	0.2489	0.2748	0.2863	0.2972	0.3074	0.3358	0.3532	0.3935	0.4311	0.4668
			h_g	1184.9	1240.0	1282.6	1301.4	1319.0	1335.5	1381.2	1409.2	1474.5	1536.2	1596.1
2100.0	2085.3	642.77	$\overline{V}$	0.1962	0.2306	0.2567	0.2682	0.2789	0.2890	0.3167	0.3337	0.3727	0.4089	0.4433
			h_g	1167.7	1229.0	1274.3	1294.0	1312.3	1329.5	1376.4	1405.0	1471.4	1533.6	1593.9

- Continued -

Pressure														
2200.0	2185.3	649.46	∇	0.1768	0.2135	0.2400	0.2514	0.2621	0.2721	0.2994	0.3159	0.3538	0.3887	0.4218
			h_g	1147.8	1217.4	1265.7	1286.3	1305.4	1323.3	1371.5	1400.8	1468.2	1531.1	1591.8
2300.0	2285.3	655.91	∇	0.1575	0.1978	0.2247	0.2362	0.2468	0.2567	0.2835	0.2997	0.3365	0.3703	0.4023
			h_g	1123.8	1204.9	1256.7	1278.4	1298.4	1316.9	1366.6	1396.5	1464.9	1528.5	1589.6
2400.0	2385.3	662.12	∇	...	0.1828	0.2105	0.2221	0.2327	0.2425	0.2689	0.2848	0.3207	0.3534	0.3843
			h_g	...	1191.5	1247.3	1270.2	1291.1	1310.3	1361.6	1392.2	1461.7	1525.9	1587.4
2500.0	2485.3	668.13	∇	...	0.1686	0.1973	0.2090	0.2196	0.2294	0.2555	0.2710	0.3061	0.3379	0.3678
			h_g	...	1176.8	12-7.6	1261.8	1283.6	1303.6	1356.5	1387.8	1458.4	1523.2	1585.3
2600.0	2585.3	673.94	∇	...	0.1549	0.1849	0.1967	0.2074	0.2172	0.2431	0.2584	0.2926	0.3236	0.3526
			h_g	...	1160.6	1227.3	1252.9	1275.8	1296.8	1351.4	1383.4	1455.1	1520.6	1583.1
2700.0	2685.3	679.55	∇	...	0.1415	0.1732	0.1853	0.1960	0.2059	0.2315	0.2466	0.2801	0.3103	0.3385
			h_g	...	1142.5	1216.5	1243.8	1267.9	1289.7	1346.1	1378.9	1451.8	1518.0	1580.9
2800.0	2785.3	684.99	∇	...	0.1281	0.1622	0.1745	0.1854	0.1953	0.2208	0.2356	0.2685	0.2979	0.3254
			h_g	...	1121.4	1205.1	1234.2	1259.6	1282.4	1340.8	1374.3	1448.5	1515.4	1578.7
2900.0	2885.3	690.26	∇	...	0.1143	0.1517	0.1644	0.1754	0.1853	0.2108	0.2254	0.2577	0.2864	0.3132
			h_g	...	1095.9	1193.0	1224.3	1251.1	1274.9	1335.3	1369.7	1445.1	1512.7	1576.5
3000.0	2985.3	695.36	∇	...	0.0984	0.1416	0.1548	0.1660	0.1760	0.2014	0.2159	0.2476	0.2757	0.3018
			h_g	...	1060.7	1180.1	1213.8	1242.2	1267.2	1329.7	1365.0	1441.8	1510.0	1574.3
3100.0	3085.3	700.31	∇	...	...	0.1320	0.1456	0.1571	0.1672	0.1926	0.2070	0.2382	0.2657	0.2911
			h_g	...	...	1166.2	1202.9	1233.0	1259.3	1324.1	1360.3	1438.4	1507.4	1572.1
3200.0	3185.3	705.11	∇	...	...	0.1226	0.1369	0.1486	0.1589	0.1843	0.1986	0.2293	0.2563	0.2811
			h_g	...	...	1151.1	1191.4	1223.5	1251.1	1318.3	1355.5	1434.9	1504.7	1569.9
3206.2	3191.5	705.40	∇	...	...	0.1220	0.1363	0.1480	0.1583	0.1838	0.1981	0.2288	0.2557	0.2806
			h_g	...	...	1150.2	1190.6	1222.9	1250.5	1317.9	1355.2	1434.7	1504.5	1569.8

Index

A

Absorption chiller, 219
Acid rain, 57
Air, gas mixing, 83
Air- and water-systems, 348
Air conditioning, 215, 371
    steam turbine-driven equipment, 379
Air pollution, 36
Air preheaters, 153, 165, 169
    corrosion, 156, 162, 166, 169
Air systems, 340
Air-to-air heat exchangers, 358
All-water systems, 351
American Boiler Manufacturers Association,
    The (ABMA), 146
American Gas Association, The (AGA), 146
Anchors, steam-line, 262
Asbestos cement pipe, 127
Ash, 162, 169
ASME codes, 141, 147
Averaging Pitot, 305

B

Baffles, 172
Baghouse, 58
Birdsill Holly, 2
Block rate, community energy systems, 461,
    468
Boiler, 141
    auxiliary, geothermal district heating, 115
    blowdown, 200
    chemical cleaning, 161
    codes and standards, 146
    construction materials, 142
    controls, 148, 186
    corrosion, 205, 211
    efficiency, 158
    losses, 158
    fuel for, 3
    operation and maintenance procedures, 156
    outage maintenance, 160
    pressure drop, 160
    sizing of, 147
    start-up, 164
    water supply system, 159
Boiler stack economizer, 361
    tube, 104, 140, 171
        failure, 103
Bottoming systems, 91
BTU meters, 312

C

Calculated heat-loss method, 323
Capacity control method, 374
Carryover, 205
Caustic embrittlement, 205
Centrifugal chiller drives, 218, 225
Centrifugal refrigeration machines, 229
Chemical softeners, 206
Chilled water systems, 15, 17
    layout, 283
    load, 216, 222
    piping system cost, 216
    sales, 215
    supply and return piping, 283, 284
Chillers
    absorption, 219
    centrifugal, 218, 225
    screw compressor, 226
    water, 216
Coal, 51
    burning, equipment for, 58–69
    characteristics, 54, 55
    classifications, 51–53
    commercial sizes, 56
    environmental concerns, 56
    fluidized bed combustion, 58
    pulverized, 62
    washing, 58
Codes and standards, boiler, 146
Cogeneration, 15, 90
    retrofit to, 19
Combined heat and power (CHP), 15
Combustion, 139
    control, 190
    measuring devices, 184
    stoichiometric, 140
Community energy systems
    capital costs, 426
    cash flows, 417
    cost data for construction and operation,
        425
    depreciation, 439
    direct sales to customers, 430
    economic feasibility, 415
    estimates of costs and revenues, 421, 428
    examples of, 413
    fuel costs, 428
        escalation, 449
    income taxes, 437
    inflation, 424

investment tax credit, 440
operation and maintenance costs, 427
payback period, 442, 446, 447
project evaluation, 443
rate-making principles, 458, 461
rate of return, 422–424, 442
    minimum acceptable, 449
sale of energy, 418
sensitivity analysis, 449
taxes, 428, 437
timing of construction, 451
Compressed air systems, 170, 197
Computer, steam flow, 309
Computer analysis method, space heating, 335
Condensate, 151, 213, 299, 301
removal and return, 238
Condensate meters, 301
testing and calibration of, 302
Condensation, 403
Construction planning, 178
performance specifications, 178
Consumer considerations, 405
Cooling, absorption, 128
Cooling system
electrically driven, 224
gas engine-driven, 227
gas turbine-driven, 228
steam turbine-driven, 229
Cooling towers, 383
performance, 385
Copper tubing, 399
Corrosion, 120
Corrosion inhibitors, 223
Cyclone separators, 170

D

Degree-day method, 320
Degree-hours method, 319
Demand forecasts, 173
prediction of, 176
Demand rate, 465, 469
Denmark, district heating in, 5
Depreciation (amortization), 407
Design temperature, 30
Desuperheater, 250
Direct radiation, 336
Displacement meter, 312
Distribution loop installation
construction procedures, 290
investigation, 289
public nuisance, 291
safety, 291
soil characteristics, 289
standards, 289
testing procedures, 291
Distribution systems, 34
design, 231

hot water, 16
planning for, 231
District heating
barriers, 10
benefits, 10
boilers, fuel for, 3
classification by service area, 8
commercial applications, 1
companies, 406
consumer considerations, 405
depreciation (amortization), 407
economic analysis, 405
    background, 412
    steps in, 420
economics of, 31
energy conservation, 41
environmental impact, 36
equity, 408
feasibility of, 34
feasibility study, 42
financial analysis, 405
financing
    alternative, 410
    revenue bonds, 410
    tax-exempt debt, 410
growth of, 4
history, 1
issues and barriers, 46
operating costs, 409
other countries, 4
overall considerations, 13
service to users, 319
social impacts, 39
sources of energy, 51
supplies, 18
Draft, 191
Draft fans, 169
Drip legs, 238
Drums, corrosion, 171
Dual-duct system, 346
Dual energy use (DEUS), 15

E

Economic analysis, 405
background, 412
steps in, 420
Economic feasibility, community energy systems, 415
Economizers, 153
corrosion, 168, 205
maintenance of, 168
Electrical generators, 145
Electricity sales, community energy systems, 428
End-user retrofits, financing of, 412
Energy conservation, district heating, 41
Energy recovery equipment, cost savings, 370

Energy Tax Credit, 411
England, district heating in, 7
Environment
  coal effects, 56
  district heating and, 36
  nuclear power impact, 133
Europe, district heating in, 4
Evaporators, 200
Expansion joints
  bellows type, 260
  slip type, 260
Expansion loops, 260

F

Fans, 165, 194
Feasibility, 34, 42
Feed heaters, corrosion, 205
Feedwater conditioning, 167
Feedwater controls, 189
Feedwater deaeration, corrosion and, 209
Feedwater heaters, 198
Financial analysis, 405
Finland, district heating in, 6
Fittings, 268
Flow measuring devices, 183
Flow meters, 299
  head type, 300
  insertion turbine, 300
  measurement, 302
  shunt, 307
    testing, 308
  shunted flow, 300
Flow nozzle, 305
Fluidized bed combustion, 58
Fuel costs
  community energy systems, 428
  escalation, 449
  refuse-derived, 21
  synthetic, 137
Fuel adjustment clause, community energy
    systems, 469
Fuel use method, space heating, 335
Furnace, waterwall, 98

G

Gas, temperature, 157
Gas turbine-driven cooling system, 228
Geopressured resources, 110
Geothermal district heating
  agricultural applications, 109
  auxiliary boiler, 115
  capital costs, 113
  equipment, 120
  feasibility factors, 112
  industrial uses, 109
  load size, 115

temperature drop, 115
  well drilling, 113
Geothermal energy, 108
Geothermal sources, 16

H

Head-type meter, 314
Heat density, 116
Heat exchanger, 16, 123–126, 219, 357, 358,
    362, 366
Heat loss, insulated buried steam lines, 259
Heat pipe, 359
Heat pumps, 228
  systems, 355
Heat recovery, 228
High density clusters, 9
Hot dry rock resources, 111
Hot water systems, 14
  design features, 279
  distribution, 16
  pipe materials, 279
  piping installation, 280
Humidification, 400
Hydronics Institute, The, 146
Hydrostatic tests, 163
Hydrothermal deposits, 109

I

Incineration, 21, 34, 366
  exhaust gases, 21
Industrial complexes, 9
Institutional issues, district heating, 46
Insulation
  thermal, 251
  types of, 253
Integrated community energy systems (ICES),
    97
Ion exchange softening, 206
Italy, district heating in, 7

J

Jet mixers, 83

L

Land, use by district heating, 37
Leak detection systems, 281
  location, 293
Load factor, 24, 117
Load size, geothermal district heating, 115
Loop systems, 233

M

Maintenance schedules, 173
Manholes, 272
  corrosion in, 274
  prefabricated, 274

Manometers, 182
Market areas, identification, 23
Mass burning, 101
Mechanical compressor systems, 223
Metal, temperature, 157
Metering, 276, 295
    condensate, 301, 302
    equipment, 127
    water, 312
        accuracy, 316
        start-up procedure, 315
Meters
    condensate, 301, 302
    head type, 300, 314
    insertion turbine, 300
    measurement, 302
    shunt, 307
        testing, 308
Modular combustors, 103
Multi-zone system, 346
Municipal solid waste (MSW), 98

N

National District Heating Association, 2
Natural gas, 110
    air mixing, 83
    burning
        equipment for, 82
        maintenance on equipment, 87
    reserves, 81
Noise, 37
Nuclear power, 129
    environmental impact, 133

O

Oil
    atomizing, 78
    burning, equipment for, 78
    types and properties of, 69
Oil burner, 78
Oil shale, 135
Orifice plates, 183, 304
Oxidation, 140
Oxygen, dissolved, 210

P

Pascal's law, 297
pH, control, 211
Physical properties, 295
Pilots, 86
Pipe, 266
    expansion, 288
    failure, 282
    materials, 285
    sizing, 245, 284
Piping, 127

asbestos, 127
code, 266
corrosion, 165, 205
    electrochemical reaction, 243
    from gases, 242
expansion and contraction, 260
installation, hot water systems, 280
plastic, 127
steel, 127
supply and return, 283, 284
system cost, chilled water, 216, 217
Pollution
    air, 36
    water, 36
Polyurethane foam, insulation, 281
Power yield, 92
Pressure
    absolute, 299
    liquid, 297
Pressure differential measurements, 157
Pressure gage, 182, 299
Pressure gages, 299
Propeller-type meter, 312
Public Utilities Regulatory Policies Act, 430
Pump, 121, 165, 218
Pyrolysis, 137

R

Radial systems, 233
Rate-making principles, 458, 461
Rate of return, 422–424, 442, 449
Rates
    block, 461, 468
    cost of service, 460, 461
    demand, 465, 469
    fuel adjustment clause, 469
Reciprocating chillers, 224
Refractory walls, 172
Refrigeration
    absorption, 372
        components of, 373
        controls, 377
        selection of, 375
    applications, 371
    steam turbine-driven equipment, 379
Refrigeration equipment, 364
Refuse-derived energy, 98
Refuse-derived fuel (RDF), 21, 135
Relative humidity, 401
Residential areas, low density, 9
Retrofit, 19, 31, 34, 98
Revenue bonds, district heating, 410
Rotary heat exchanger, 357
Run-around system, 360

S

Sales
 chilled water systems, 215
 energy, 418
 electricity, 428
Saturated steam, 151, 245
Scale, 161, 205, 212
Scaling, 120
Screw compressor chiller, 226
Separators, 203
Service water heating, 387
Shell and tube heat exchanger, 362
Single-zone systems, 342
Sludge, 57
Solar electrical generation, 134
Solar energy, 134
Solid waste, 21, 38
 municipal, 98
Sonic velocity, 244
Sootblower operation, 162
Space heating
 computer analysis method, 335
 fuel use method, 335
 steam requirements for, 319
Spreader stoker, 106
Stack economizer, 361
Stacks, 192
 corrosion, 170
 maintenance, 170
Steam
 condensate, 15
 flow rate, 244
 heat-only operations, 15
 low pressure, 15
 saturated, 151, 245
 temperature, 157
 water content of, 245
Steam-jet refrigeration, equipment, 383
Steam-line
 anchors, 264
 guides, 264
Steam refrigeration, 371
Steam requirements
 commercial and industrial processes, 336
 estimating, 319
 for air conditioning, 336
Steam separators, 150
Steam system, 14
 building, 336
 cause of condensation, 276
 controls for, 275
 design, 235
 efficiency, 276
 maintenance, 277
 metering, 276
 turn-on procedures, 277

Steam traps, 201, 238
 mechanical, 239
 thermodynamic, 241
 thermostatic, 241
Steam tunnels, 233
Steam turbine-driven equipment,
 air conditioning and refrigeration, 379
 cooling system, 229
Steam turbines, 91
 back-pressure, 91
 extraction, 91
Steel pipe, 127
Stoichiometric combustion, 140
Stokers, 58–62
 spreader, 106
Storage, 118
Strainers, 203
Super heat, 250
Superheaters, 151
 corrosion in, 106
 maintenance of, 167
Supplies, district heat, 18
Suspension burning, 107
Suspension firing, 104
Sweden, district heating in, 6
Switzerland, district heating in, 7
Synthetic fuels, 137

T

Taxes, community energy systems, 428, 437
Tax-exempt debt financing, district heating, 410
Temperature
 absolute, 299
 design, 30
 drop, geothermal district heating, 115
 gas, 157
 metal, 157
 steam and water, 157
Terminal reheat system, 342
Thermal expansion, 281
Thermal load
 analysis, 27
 densities, 23
Thermocouples, 180
Thermometers, 180
Topping systems, 91
Total energy demand, in United States, 3
Tunnels, 268
Turbines, 379
Twin-tower sprays, 360

U

Underground conduits, 268
United States, district heating in, 2
Urban areas, densely populated, 8
U.S.S.R., district heating in, 5, 7

V

Vacuum, 299
Valves, 165, 266
    gate, 265
    pressure-reducing, 264
Variable volume system, 345
Venturi, 85, 183, 305

W

Waste-heat boilers, 367
Waste heat reclamation systems, 356
Water
    softening, 206
    temperature, 157

    treatment, 205, 212
Water chillers, 216
Water conditioners, 199
Water distribution system, 399
Water hammer, 238, 249, 277
Water heaters
    instantaneous, 395
    storage, 388
    types, 387
Water pollution, 37
Waterwall furnaces, 98
Waterwall incineration, 21
West Germany, district heating in, 5, 7
Wood, 135